CULTURAL

GEOGRAPHY:

Selected Readings

DATE DUE

CULTURAL

GEOGRAPHY:

Selected Readings

edited by FRED E. DOHRS
Wayne State University

and LAWRENCE M. SOMMERS
Michigan State University

THOMAS Y. CROWELL COMPANY
New York
Established 1834

LIBRARY OF CONGRESS CATALOG CARD NUMBER: 67-26837
Designed by Judith Woracek Barry. Manufactured in the United States of America.

PREFACE

In compiling this as well as the previous two volumes of readings in the series, we have sought materials from the wide variety of literature available that would be especially suitable for introductory geography courses. We have endeavored to cover each of the main topics discussed in the majority of introductory texts, and although our organization is systematic, we have included articles pertaining to most of the major regions of the earth, thus making the collection suitable for courses of the regional type.

Introductory college and university geography courses have become increasingly man-oriented in recent years. *Cultural Geography: Selected Readings* emphasizes the significance of man, culture, and the cultural process in the organization of space on the earth's surface. The literature on the geography of man from which the readings were obtained is rich and rapidly growing.

The first section deals with historical geography or reconstruction of the geographies of the past; the following, with man's perception of his environment and its concern to the geographer. Next are sections on how people have organized their rural and urban settlements and examples of the role of the social, economic, and political processes upon areas. The book closes with articles demonstrating the development of cultural regions and Stuart Chase's thought-provoking warnings for the future of the earth as the home of man.

Selections in this volume were made to provide (1) examples of the various approaches to cultural geography, (2) illustrations of important ideas and concepts of geography, (3) methods of approaching some challenging spatial problems, and (4) coverage or at least a sampling of writings on diverse world regions with varying cultures, and political, economic, and social processes and conditions. In geography it is often impossible to separate the natural and cultural environment; thus, some of the articles do contribute to an earlier volume in this set, *Physical Geography: Selected Readings*, and, likewise, parts of that volume supplement this one. It should be emphasized that separation into physical- and man-oriented volumes is for convenience only. The impact of man and his cultures on the character of the earth's surface needs to be studied along with, as well as in relation to, the natural environment.

To make this volume as useful as possible for teacher and student alike, several distinctive features have been included. Each section is preceded by a brief introduction that suggests the breadth and scope of the subject covered within the section, and its place within the field of geography as a whole. In addition, preceding each selection there are headnotes that place each article in relation to the topic being covered, as well as to the other articles in that section. We have also provided brief bibliographical notes on the opening page of each selection, which serve to identify the author and the source from which the selection was taken. Finally, to aid the instructor in making assignments, a table has been included that correlates chapters in selected introductory geography texts with the articles in this book.

Footnotes, graphs, photographs, and tables that originally appeared in the articles, as a rule, have been omitted or reduced in number; only when deemed vital to the meaning have they been retained.

Cultural Geography: Selected Readings is the last of three volumes in the series. The first volume, *Introduction to Geography: Selected Readings* and the second, *Physical Geography: Selected Readings,* will, when used with this collection, provide instructors of basic courses with an abundance of materials from which to choose, thus adding depth and interest to introductory geography. It is hoped that the inherent flexibility of the three volumes, as well as the coverage of the series as a whole, will allow the teacher to select articles or volumes consistent with his own emphasis and his own notions of how the course should be taught.

Deep appreciation is expressed to the authors and publishers of the articles included, and to colleagues and others who gave valuable suggestions and assistance.

F.E.D.

L.M.S.

CONTENTS

I. INTRODUCTION

Man's effect on the surface of the earth is increasing as his numbers multiply. The projected increase in the human population is phenomenal; when compared to available resources in given areas of the world, it is frightening. The total population of nearly three billion is growing at a rate of 125 thousand per day and nearly fifty million per year. This annual increment is approximately equivalent to the population of France or one-fourth the population of the United States. The net increase is more than one person per second. The gain is distributed unevenly throughout the world, and such countries as India and China are experiencing severe problems from intense population pressure.

The total numbers of people and their distribution is but one of the variables that concerns the geographer in his attempt to analyze the "variable character of the earth's surface as the home of man." Equally important are the activities of man over time that have altered the face of the earth. These changes vary according to the history and culture of the people—their social, political, and economic processes, their attitudes, values, and objectives. The rate of change is affected by the level of education and technology, which in turn is reflected by the stage of economic and cultural development. Change is also related to the nature of the physical environment, the available usable resources, and the ability or inability of man to control disease, fire, flood, war, and other disasters.

Thus the total impact of man on a given space of the earth's surface is very difficult to ascertain. As man has raised his educational level and technology, his ability to change and utilize the natural environment has increased. Early man's livelihood was much more attuned to the restrictions of his immediate environment than is true of modern man. Yet we can find today such peoples as the pygmies of Africa and the bushmen of interior Australia that are very much controlled by their environment. In most instances, Western civilization has had considerable impact upon such isolated peoples. For example, rapid change took place in the way of life of the Eskimo after contact with other societies—the incidence of various diseases such as tuberculosis increased, and the place and nature of his residence and work was often altered.

Modern urban and industrial areas evidence man's ability to change the original landforms, vegetation, and other natural attributes of places. The political process has an impact upon spatial distributions; we see distinct differences between urban and rural landscapes in communist,

socialist, and democratic nations. The agricultural patterns of a collective farm system vary from that of private enterprise or the cooperative system. At the local and state levels, the impact upon environment
of laws and political decisions is discernible.

Thus the physical and cultural environment as altered by man is the
major concern of the geographer. The myriad factors that have affected
an area and the interrelationships between them is complex indeed.
The significant cultural processes of man are examined in this volume.
These processes differ in the various parts of the world due to the diverse cultures and environments in which they take place.

The tone for the volume is set by Sauer, "Agency of Man on Earth,"
who writes of the "historically cumulative effects, with the physical and
biologic processes that man sets in motion, inhibits, or deflects, and with
the differences in cultural conduct that distinguish one human group
from another."

1. Agency of Man on Earth
Carl O. Sauer

The impact of man's civilizing process is of signal
importance to the nature of the earth's surface at any given
time. Sauer has been a pioneer in American geography in
research, publication, and teaching about the relationships
among anthropology, history, archeology, and geography.
His major concern has been to look at how the earth's
surface has been modified by the origin and spread of culture.
His publications such as "Aboriginal Population of
Northwestern Mexico," "Colima of New Spain in the
Sixteenth Century," "Agricultural Origins and Dispersals,"
"The End of the Ice Age and Its Witnesses," and "Fire and
Early Man" illustrate his approach. The following reading
indicates the role of natural change such as climate
upon man, as well as the dynamic role of man on
earth.

Every human population, at all times, has needed to evaluate the
economic potential of its inhabited area, to organize its life about its

SOURCE: William L. Thomas, Jr., ed., *Man's Role in Changing the Face of the
Earth* (Chicago: University of Chicago Press, 1956), pp. 49–60. Copyright 1956
by the University of Chicago. The author is professor emeritus of geography, University of California, Berkeley.

natural environment in terms of the skills available to it and the values which it accepted. In the cultural *mise en valeur* of the environment, a deformation of the pristine, or prehuman, landscape has been initiated that has increased with length of occupation, growth in population, and addition of skills. Wherever men live, they have operated to alter the aspect of the earth, both animate and inanimate, be it to their boon or bane.

The general theme may be described, therefore, in its first outline, as an attempt to set forth the geographic effects, that is, the appropriation of habitat by habit, resulting from the spread of differing cultures to all the *oikoumene* throughout all we know of human time. We need to understand better how man has disturbed and displaced more and more of the organic world, has become in more and more regions the ecologic dominant, and has affected the course of organic evolution. Also how he has worked surficial changes as to terrain, soil, and the waters on the land and how he has drawn upon its minerals. Latterly, at least, his urban activities and concentrations have effected local alterations of the atmosphere. We are trying to examine the processes of terrestrial change he has entrained or originated, and we are attempting to ask, from our several interests and experiences, relevant questions as to cultural behaviors and effects. Thus we come properly also to consider the qualities of his actions as they seem to affect his future wellbeing. In this proper study of mankind, living out the destiny ascribed in Genesis—"to have dominion over all the earth"—the concern is valid as to whether his organized energies (social behavior) have or should have a quality of concern with regard to his posterity.

On the Nature of Man

The primordial condition of man setting our kind apart from other primates involved more than hands, brain, and walking upright. Man owes his success in part to his digestive apparatus, which is equaled by none of his near-kin or by few other similarly omnivorous animals as to the range of potential food which can sustain him on a mixed, vegetarian, or flesh diet. The long, helpless infancy and the dependence through the years of childhood have forged, it would seem, *ab origine* a maternal bond that expresses itself in persistence of family and in formal recognition of kinship, system of kinship being perhaps the first basis of social organization. When humans lost the oestrous cycle is unknown; its weakening and loss is probably a feature of domestication, and it may have occurred early in the history of man, eldest of the domesticated creatures.

Built into the biologic nature of man therefore appear to be qualities tending to maximize geographic expansiveness, vigorous reproduction, and a bent toward social development. His extreme food range favored numerical increase; I question, for instance, any assumptions of sporadic or very sparse populations of Paleolithic man in any lands he had occupied. The dominant and continuous role of woman in caring for the family suggests further inferences. Maternal duties prescribed as sedentary a life as possible. Her collecting of food and other primary materials was on the short tether of her dependent offspring. Hers also was the care of what had been collected in excess of immediate need, the problem of storage, hers the direction toward homemaking and furnishing. To the "nature" of woman we may perhaps ascribe an original social grouping, a cluster of kindred households, in which some stayed home to watch over bairns and baggage while others ranged afield. Baby-sitting may be one of the most ancient of human institutions.

Implicit in this interpretation of the nature of man and primordial society, as based on his trend to sedentary life and clustering, are territoriality, the provision of stores against season of lack, and probably a tendency to monogamy. These traits are familiar enough among numerous animals, and there is no reason for denying them to primitive man. Shifts of population imposed by seasons do not mean wandering, homeless habits; nomadism is an advanced and specialized mode of life. Folk who stuffed or starved, who took no heed of the morrow, could not have possessed the earth or laid the foundations of human culture. To the ancestral folk we may rather ascribe practical-minded economy of effort. Their success in survival and in dispersal into greatly differing habitats tells of ability to derive and communicate sensible judgments from changing circumstances.

The culture of man is considered in the main a continuum from the beginning; such is its treatment by archeology. The record of artifacts is much greater, more continuous, and begins earlier than do his recovered skeletal remains. Thereby hangs the still-argued question of human evolution, about which divergent views are unreconciled. If culture was transmitted and advanced in time and space as the archeologic record indicates, there would appear to be a linked history of a mankind that includes all the specific and generic hominid classifications of physical anthropology. Man, *sensu latiore,* therefore may conceivably be one large species complex, from archaic to modern forms, always capable of interbreeding and intercommunication. Variation occurred by long geographic isolation, blending usually when different stocks met. The former is accepted; the latter seems assured to some and is rejected by others, the Mount Carmel series of skulls being thus notoriously in dispute.

Neanderthal man, poor fellow, has had a rough time of it. He invented the Mousterian culture, a major advance which appears to have been derived from two anterior culture lines. The Abbé Breuil has credited him with ceremonial cults that show a developed religious belief and spiritual ceremonial. Boyd, in his serologic classification of mankind, the only system available on a genetic basis, has surmised that Neanderthal is ancestral to a Paleo-European race. There is no basis for holding Neanderthal man as mentally inferior or as unable to cope with the late Pleistocene changes of European climate. Yet there remains aversion to admitting him to our ancestry. The sad confusion of physical anthropology is partly the result of its meager knowledge of hereditary factors, but also to *Homo's* readiness to crossbreed, a trait of his domestication and a break with the conservatism of the in-stinctive.

We are groping in the obscurity of a dim past; it may be better to consider cultural growth throughout human time as proceeding by invention, borrowing, and blending of learning, rather than by evolu-tion of the human brain, until we know more of biological evolution in man. The little that we have of skeletal remains is subject to unrecon-ciled evaluations; the record of his work is less equivocal. The question is not, could Peking man have left the artifacts attributed to him, as has been the subject of debate, but did he, that is, do the bones belong with the tools?

When primordial man began to spread over the earth, he knew little, but what he had learned was by tested and transmitted experience; he cannot have been fear-ridden but rather, at least in his successful kinds, was venturesome, ready to try out his abilities in new surroundings. More and more he imposed himself on his animal competitors and impressed his mark on the lands he inhabited. Wherever he settled, he came to stay unless the climate changed too adversely or the spreading sea drove him back.

Climatic Changes and Their Effects on Man

The age of man is also the Ice Age. Man may have witnessed its begin-ning; we perhaps are still living in an interglacial phase. His growth of learning and his expansion over the earth have taken place during a geologic period of extreme instability of climates and also of extreme simultaneous climatic contrast. His span has been cast within a period of high environmental tensions. Spreading icecaps caused the ocean to shrink back from the shallow continental margins, their waning to spread the seas over coastal plains. With lowered sea levels, rivers trenched their valley floors below coastal lowlands; as sea level rose, streams flooded and aggraded their valleys. Glacial and recent time have been governed by some sort of climatic pendulum, varying in amplitude of swing, but affecting land and sea in all latitudes, and life in most areas. The effects have been most felt in the Northern Hemisphere, with its large continental masses, wide plains, high mountain ranges, and broad plateaus. Millions of square miles of land were alternately buried under ice and exposed; here, also, the shallow seas upon the continental shelf spread and shrank most broadly.

This time of recurrent changes of atmosphere, land, and sea gave advantage to plastic, mobile, and prolific organisms, to plants and animals that could colonize newly available bodies of land, that had progeny some of which withstood the stresses of climatic change. The time was favorable for biologic evolution, for mutants suited to a changed environment, for hybrids formed by mingling, as on ecologic frontiers. To this period has been assigned the origin of many annual plant species dependent on heavy seed production for success. Adaptive variations in human stocks, aided by sufficiently isolating episodes of earth history, have also been inferred.

The duration of the Ice Age and of its stages has not been determined. The old guess of a million years over all is still convenient. The four glacial and three interglacial stages may have general validity; there are doubts that they were strictly in phase in all continents. In North America the relations of the several continental icecaps to the phases of Rocky Mountain glaciation, and of the latter to the Pacific mountains, are only inferred, as is the tie-in of pluvial stages in our Southwest. That great lakes and permanent streams existed in many of the present dry lands of the world is certain, that these pluvial phases of intermediate latitudes correspond to glacial ones in high latitudes and altitudes is in considerable part certain, but only in a few cases has a pluvial state been securely tied to a contemporaneous glacial stage. The promising long-range correlation of Pleistocene events by eustatic marine terraces and their dependent alluvial terraces is as yet only well started. Except for northwestern Europe, the calendar of the later geologic past is still very uncertain. The student of further human time, anxious for an absolute chronology, is at the moment relying widely on the ingenious astronomical calendar of Milankovitch and Zeuner as an acceptable span for the Ice Age as a whole and for its divisions. It is not acceptable, however, to meteorology and climatology. Slowly and bit by bit only are we likely to see the pieces fall into their proper order; nothing is gained by assurance as to what is insecure.

The newer meteorology is interesting itself in the dynamics of climatic change. Changes in the general circulation pattern have been inferred as conveying, in times of glacial advance, more and more frequent masses of moist, relatively warm air into high latitudes and thereby also increasing the amount of cloud cover. The importance now attached to condensation nuclei has directed attention again to the possible significance of volcanic dust. Synoptic climatological data are being examined for partial models in contemporary conditions as conducive to glaciation and deglaciation. To the student of the human past, reserve is again indicated in making large climatic reconstructions. Such cautions I should suggest, with reserve also as to my competence to offer them, with regard to the following:

It is misleading to generalize glacial stages as cold and interglacial ones as warm. The developing phases of glaciation probably required relatively warm moist air, and decline may have been by the dominance of cold dry air over the ice margins. The times of climatic change may thus not coincide with the change from glacial advance to deglaciation. We may hazard the inference that developing glaciation is associated with low contrast of regional climates; regression of ice and beginning of an interglacial phase probably are connected (although not in each case) with accentuated contrast or "continentality" of climates. One interglacial did not repeat necessarily the features of another; nor must one glacial phase duplicate another. We need only note the difference in centers of continental glaciation, of direction of growth of ice lobes, of terminal moraine-building, of structure of till and of fluvioglacial components to see the individuality of climates of glacial stages. In North America, in contrast to Europe, there is very little indication of a periglacial cold zone of tundra and of permafrost in front of the continental icecaps. Questionable also is the loess thesis of dust as whipped up from bare ground and deposited in beds by wind, these surfaces somehow becoming vegetated by a cold steppe plant cover.

The events of the last deglaciation and of the "postglacial" are intelligible as yet only in part. A priori it is reasonable to consider that the contemporary pattern of climates had become more or less established before the last ice retreat began. Later, lesser local climatic oscillations were found but have been improperly extended and exaggerated, however, in archeological literature. In the pollen studies of bogs of northwestern Europe, the term "climatic optimum" was introduced innocently to note a poleward and mountainward extension of moderate proportions for certain plants not occurring at the same time over the entire area. Possibly this expansion of range means that there were sunnier summers and fall seasons, permitting the setting and maturing of seed for such plants somewhat beyond their prior and present range, that is, under more "continental" and less "maritime" weather conditions. This modest and expectable variation of a local climate in the high latitudes and at the changing sea borders of North Atlantic Europe has been construed by some students of prehistory into a sort of climatic golden age, existent at more or less the same time in distant parts of the world, without regard to dynamics or patterns of climates. We might well be spared such naïvely nominal climatic constructions as have been running riot through interpretations of prehistory and even of historic time.

The appearance or disappearance, increase or decrease, of particular plants and animals may not spell out obligatory climatic change, as has been so freely inferred. Plants differ greatly in rate of dispersal, in pioneering ability, in having routes available for their spread, and in other ways that may enter into an unstable ecologic association, as on the oft-shifted stage of Pleistocene and recent physiography. The intervention of man and animals has also occurred to disturb the balance. The appearance and fading of pines in an area, characteristic in many bog pollen columns, may tell nothing of climatic change: pines are notorious early colonizers, establishing themselves freely in mineral soils and open situations and yielding to other trees as shading and organic cover of ground increase. Deer thrive on browse; they increase wherever palatable twigs become abundant, in brush lands and with young tree growth; ecologic factors of disturbance other than climate may determine the food available to them and the numbers found in archeologic remains.

The penetration of man to the New World is involved in the question of past and present climates. The origin and growth of the dominant doctrine of a first peopling of the Western Hemisphere in postglacial time is beyond our present objective, but it was not based on valid knowledge of climatic history. The postglacial and present climatic pattern is one of extremes rarely reached or exceeded in the past of the earth. Passage by land within this time across Siberia, Alaska, and Canada demanded specialized advanced skills in survival under great and long cold comparable to those known to Eskimo and Athabascan, an excessive postulate for many of the primitive peoples of the New World. Relatively mild climates did prevail in high latitudes at times during the Pleistocene. At such times in both directions between Old and New World, massive migrations took place of animals incapable of living on tundras, animals that are attractive game for man. If man was then living in eastern Asia, nothing hindered him from migrating along with such non-boreal mammals. The question is of fundamental interest, because it asks whether man in the New World, within a very few thousand years, achieved independently a culture growth comparable and curiously parallel to that of the Old, which required a much greater span. There is thus also the inference that our more primitive aborigines passed the high latitudes during more genial climes rather than that they lost subsequently numerous useful skills.

Fire

Speech, tools, and fire are the tripod of culture and have been so, we think, from the beginning. About the hearth, the home and workshop are centered. Space heating under shelter, as a rock overhang, made living possible in inclement climates; cooking made palatable many plant products; industrial innovators experimented with heat treatment of wood, bone, and minerals. About the fireplace, social life took form, and the exchange of ideas was fostered. The availability of fuel has been one of the main factors determining the location of clustered habitation.

Even to Paleolithic man, occupant of the earth for all but the last 1 or 2 per cent of human time, must be conceded gradual deformation of vegetation by fire. His fuel needs were supplied by dead wood, drifted or fallen, and also by the stripping of bark and bast that caused trees to die and become available as fuel supply. The setting or escape of fire about camp sites cleared away small and young growth, stimulated annual plants, aided in collecting, and became elaborated in time into the fire drive, a formally organized procedure among the cultures of the Upper Paleolithic *grande chasse* and of their New World counterpart.

Inferentially, modern primitive peoples illustrate the ancient practices in all parts of the world. Burning, as a practice facilitating collecting and hunting, by insensible stages became a device to improve the yield of desired animals and plants. Deliberate management of their range by burning to increase food supply is apparent among hunting and collecting peoples, in widely separated areas, but has had little study. Mature woody growth provides less food for man and ground animals than do fire-disturbed sites, with protein-rich young growth and stimulated seed production, accessible at ground levels. Game yields are usually greatest where the vegetation is kept in an immediate state of ecologic succession. With agricultural and pastoral peoples, burning in preparation for planting and for the increase of pasture has been nearly universal until lately.

The gradually cumulative modifications of vegetation may become large as to selection of kind and as to aspect of the plant cover. Pyrophytes include woody monocotyledons, such as palms, which do not depend on a vulnerable cambium tissue, trees insulated by thick corky bark, trees and shrubs able to reproduce by sprouting, and plants with thick, hard-shelled seeds aided in germination by heat. Loss of organic matter on and in the soil may shift advantage to forms that germinate well in mineral soils, as the numerous conifers. Precocity is advantageous. The assemblages consequent upon fires are usually characterized by a reduced number of species, even by the dominance of few and single species. Recurrent burning has offered minor elements in a natural flora, originally mainly confined to accidentally disturbed and exposed situations, such as windfalls and eroding slopes, the chance to spread and multiply. In most cases the shift is from mesophytic to less exacting, more xeric, forms, to those that do not require ample soil moisture and can tolerate at all times full exposure to sun. In the long run the scales are tipped against the great, slowly maturing plants —the trees (a park land of mature trees may be the last stand of what was a complete woodland). Our eastern woodlands, at the time of white settlement, seem largely to have been in process of change to park lands. Early accounts stress the open stands of trees, as indicated by the comment that one could drive a coach from seaboard to the Mississippi River over almost any favoring terrain. The "forest primeval" is exceptional. In the end the success in a land occupied by man of whatever cultural level goes to the annuals and short-lived perennials, able to seed heavily or to reproduce by rhizome and tuber. This grossly drawn sketch may introduce the matter of processes resulting in what is called ecologically a secondary fire association, or subclimax, if it has historical persistence.

The climatic origin of grasslands rests on a poorly founded hypothesis. In the first place, the individual great grasslands extend over long climatic gradients from wet to dry and grade on their driest margins into brush and scrub. Woody growth occurs in them where there are breaks in the general surface, as in the Cross Timbers of our Southwest. Woody plants establish themselves freely in grasslands if fire protection is given: the prairies and steppes are suited to the growth of the trees and shrubs native to adjacent lands but may lack them. An individual grassland may extend across varied parent-materials. Their most common quality is that they are upland plains, having periods of dry weather long enough to dry out the surface of the ground, which accumulate a sufficient amount of burnable matter to feed and spread a fire. Their position and limits are determined by relief; nor do they extend into arid lands or those having a continuously wet ground surface. Fires may sweep indefinitely across a surface of low relief but are checked shortly at barriers of broken terrain, the checking being more abrupt if the barrier is sunk below the general surface. The inference is that origin and preservation of grasslands are due, in the main, to burning and that they are in fact great and, in some cases, ancient cultural features.

In other instances simplified woodlands, such as the pine woods of our Southeast, *palmares* in tropical savannas, are pyrophytic deformations; there are numerous vegetational alternatives other than the formation of grassland by recurrent burning. Wherever primitive man has had the opportunity to turn fire loose on a land, he seems to have done so, from time immemorial; it is only civilized societies that have undertaken to stop fires.

In areas controlled by customary burning, a near-ecologic equilibrium may have been attained, a biotic recombination maintained by similarly repeated human intervention. This is not destructive exploitation. The surface of the ground remains protected by growing cover, the absorption of rain and snow is undiminished, and loss of moisture from ground to atmosphere possibly is reduced. Microclimatic differences between woodland and grassland are established as effect if not as cause, and some are implicit in the Shelter Belt Project.

Our modern civilization demands fire control for the protection of its property. American forestry was begun as a remedy for the devastation by careless lumbering at a time when dreadful holocausts almost automatically followed logging, as in the Great Lakes states. Foresters have made a first principle of fire suppression. Complete protection, however, accumulates tinder year by year; the longer the accumulation, the greater is the fire hazard and the more severe the fire when it results. Stockmen are vociferous about the loss of grazing areas to brush under such protection of the public lands. Here and there, carefully controlled light burning is beginning to find acceptance in range and forest management. It is being applied to long-leaf pine reproduction in southeastern states and to some extent for grazing in western range management. In effect, the question is now being raised whether well-regulated fires may not have an ecologic role beneficent to modern man, as they did in older days.

Peasant and Pastoral Ways

The next revolutionary intervention of man in the natural order came as he selected certain plants and animals to be taken under his care, to be reproduced, and to be bred into domesticated forms increasingly dependent on him for survival. Their adaptation to serve human wants runs counter, as a rule, to the processes of natural selection. New lines and processes of organic evolution were entrained, widening the gap between wild and domestic forms. The natural land became deformed, as to biota, surface, and soil, into unstable cultural landscapes.

Conventionally, agricultural origins are placed at the beginning of Neolithic time, but it is obvious that the earliest archeologic record of the Neolithic presents a picture of an accomplished domestication of plants and animals, of peasant and pastoral life resembling basic conditions that may still be met in some parts of the Near East.

Three premises as to the origin of agriculture seem to me to be necessary: (1) That this new mode of life was sedentary and that it arose out of an earlier sedentary society. Under most conditions, and especially among primitive agriculturists, the planted land must be watched over continuously against plant predators. (2) That planting and domestication did not start from hunger but from surplus and leisure. Famine-haunted folk lack the opportunity and incentive for the slow and continuing selection of domesticated forms. Village communities in comfortable circumstances are indicated for such progressive steps. (3) Primitive agriculture is located in woodlands. Even the pioneer American farmer hardly invaded the grasslands until the second quarter of the past century. His fields were clearings won by deadening, usually by girdling, the trees. The larger the trees, the easier the task; brush required grubbing and cutting; sod stopped his advance until he had plows capable of ripping through the matted grass roots. The forest litter he cleaned up by occasional burning; the dead trunks hardly interfered with his planting. The American pioneer learned and followed Indian practices. It is curious that scholars, because they carried into their thinking the tidy fields of the European plowman and the felling of trees by ax, have so often thought that forests repelled agriculture and that open lands invited it.

The oldest form of tillage is by digging, often but usually improperly called "hoe culture." This was the only mode known in the New World, in Negro Africa, and in the Pacific islands. It gave rise, at an advanced level, to the gardens and horticulture of Monsoon Asia and perhaps of the Mediterranean. Its modern tools are spade, fork, and hoe, all derived from ancient forms. In tropical America this form of tillage is known as the *conuco*, in Mexico as the milpa, in the latter case a planting of seeds of maize, squash, beans, and perhaps other annuals. The *conuco* is stocked mainly by root and stem cuttings, a perennial garden plot. Recently, the revival of the Old Norse term *swithe,* or *swidden,* has been proposed.

Such a plot begins by deadening tree growth, followed toward the end of a dry period by burning, the ashes serving as quick fertilizer. The cleared space then is well stocked with a diverse assemblage of useful plants, grown as tiers of vegetation if moisture and fertility are adequate. In the maize-beans-squash complex the squash vines spread over the ground, the cornstalks grow tall, and the beans climb up the cornstalks. Thus the ground is well protected by plant cover, with good interception of the falling rain. In each *conuco* a high diversity of plants may be cared for, ranging from low herbs to shrubs, such as cotton and manioc, to trees entangled with cultivated climbers. The seeming disorder is actually a very full use of light and moisture, an admirable ecologic substitution by man, perhaps equivalent to the natural cover also in the protection given to the surface of the ground. In the tropical *conuco* an irregular patch is dug into at convenient spots and at almost any time to set out or collect different plants, the planted surface at no time being wholly dug over. Digging roots and replanting may be going on at the same time. Our notions of a harvest season when the whole crop is taken off the field are inapplicable. In the *conucos* something may be gathered on almost any day through the year. The same plant may yield pot and salad greens, pollen-rich flowers, immature fruit, and ripened fruit; garden and field are one, and numerous domestic uses may be served by each plant. Such multiple population of the tilled space makes possible the highest yields per unit of surface, to which may be added the comments that this system has developed plants of highest productivity, such as bananas, yams, and manioc, and that food production is by no means the only utility of many such plants.

The planting systems really do not deserve the invidious terms given them, such as "slash and burn" or "shifting agriculture." The abandonment of the planting after a time to the resprouting and reseeding wild woody growth is a form of rotation by which the soil is replenished by nutriments carried up from deep-rooted trees and shrubs, to be spread over the ground as litter. Such use of the land is freed from the limitations imposed on the plowed field by terrain. That it may give good yields on steep and broken slopes is not an argument against the method, which gives much better protection against soil erosion than does any plowing. It is also in these cultures that we find that systems of terracing of slopes have been established.

Some of the faults charged against the system derive from the late impact from our own culture, such as providing axes and machetes by which sprouts and brush may be kept whacked out instead of letting the land rest under regrowth, the replacement of subsistence crops by money crops, the world-wide spurt in population, and the demand for manufactured goods which is designated as rising standard of living. Nor do I claim that under this primitive planting man could go on forever growing his necessities without depleting the soil; but rather that, in its basic procedure and crop assemblages, this system has been most conservative of fertility at high levels of yield; that, being protective and intensive, we might consider it as being fully suited to the physical and cultural conditions of the areas where it exists. Our Western know-how is directed to land use over a short run of years and is not the wisdom of the primitive peasant rooted to his ancestral lands.

Our attitudes toward farming stem from the other ancient trunk whence spring the sowers, reapers, and mowers; the plowmen, dairymen, shepherds, and herdsmen. This is the complex already well represented in the earliest Neolithic sites of the Near East. The interest of this culture is directed especially toward seed production of annuals, cereal grasses in particular. The seedbed is carefully prepared beforehand to minimize weed growth and provide a light cover of well-worked soil in which the small seeds germinate. An evenly worked and smooth surface contrasts with the hit-or-miss piling of earth mounds, "hills" in the American farm vernacular, characteristic of *conuco* and milpa. Instead of a diversity of plants, the prepared ground receives the seed of one kind. (Western India is a significant exception.) The crop is not further cultivated and stands to maturity, when it is reaped at one time.

After the harvest the field may lie fallow until the next season. The tillage implement is the plow, in second place, the harrow, both used to get the field ready for sowing. Seeding traditionally is by broadcasting, harvesting by cutting blades.

Herd animals, meat cattle, sheep, goats, horses, asses, camels, are either original or very early in this system. The keeping of grazing and browsing animals is basic. All of them are milked or have been so in the past. In my estimation milking is an original practice and quality of their domestication and continued to be in many cases their first economic utility; meat and hides, the product of surplus animals only.

The over-all picture is in great contrast to that of the planting cultures: regular, elongated fields minimize turning the animals that pull the plow; fields are cultivated in the off season, in part to keep them free of volunteer growth; fields are fallowed but not abandoned, the harvest season is crowded into the end of the annual growth period; thereafter, stock is pastured on stubble and fallow; land unsuited or not needed for the plow is used as range on which the stock grazes and browses under watch of herdboys or herdsmen.

This complex spread from its Near Eastern cradle mainly in three directions, changing its character under changed environments and by increase of population.

1. Spreading into the steppes of Eurasia, the culture lost its tillage and became completely pastoral, with true nomadism. This is controversial, but the evidence seems to me to show that all domestication of the herd animals (except for reindeer) was effected by sedentary agriculturists living between India and the Mediterranean and also that the great, single, continuous area in which milking was practiced includes all the nomadic peoples, mainly as a fringe about the milking seed-farmers. It has also been pointed out that nomadic cultures depend on agricultural peoples for some of their needs and, thus lacking a self-contained economy, can hardly have originated independently.

2. The drift of the Celtic, Germanic, and Slavic peoples westward (out of southwestern and western Asia?) through the northern European plain appears to have brought them to their historic seats predominantly as cattle- and horse-raisers. Their movement was into lands of cooler and shorter summers and of higher humidity, in which wheat and barley did poorly. An acceptable thesis is that in southwestern Asia, rye and probably oats were weed grasses growing in fields of barley and wheat. They were harvested together and not separated by winnowing. In the westward movement of seed farmers across Europe, the weed grains did better and the noble grain less well. The cooler and wetter the summers, the less wheat and barley did the sower reap and the more of rye and oat seeds, which gradually became domesticated by succeeding where the originally planted kinds failed.

Northwestern and central Europe appear to be the home of our principal hay and pasture grasses and clovers. As the stockraising colonists deadened and burned over tracts of woodland, native grasses and clovers spontaneously took possession of the openings. These were held and enlarged by repetition of burning and cutting. Meadow and pasture, from the agricultural beginnings, were more important here than plowland. Even the latter, by pasturing the rye fields and the feeding of oat straw and grain, were part of animal husbandry. Here, as nowhere else, did the common farmer concern himself with producing feed for his stock. He was first a husbandman; he cut hay to store for winter feed and cured it at considerable trouble; he stabled his animals over the inclement season, or stall-fed them through the year; the dung-hill provided dressing for field and meadow. House, barn, and stable were fused into one structure. The prosperity of farmstead and village was measured by its livestock rather than by arable land.

The resultant pattern of land use, which carries through from the earliest times, as recovered by archeology in Denmark and northern Germany, was highly conservative of soil fertility. The animal husbandry maintained so effective a ground cover that northern Europe has known very little soil erosion. Animal manure and compost provided adequate return of fertility to the soil. Man pretty well established a closed ecologic cycle. It was probably here that man first undertook to till the heavy soils. Clayey soils, rich in plant food but deficient in drainage, are widespread in the lowlands, partly because of climatic conditions, partly a legacy of the Ice Age. The modern plow with share, moldboard, and colter had either its origin or a major development here for turning real furrows to secure better aeration and drainage. Beneficial in northwestern and central Europe, it was later to become an instrument of serious loss elsewhere.

3. The spread of sowing and herding cultures westward along both sides of the Mediterranean required no major climatic readjustment. Wheat and barley continued to be the staple grains; sheep and goats were of greater economic importance than cattle and horses. Qualities of the environment that characterized the Near East were accentuated to the west: valleys lie imbedded in mountainous terrain, the uplands are underlain by and developed out of limestone, and, to the south of the Mediterranean, aridity becomes prevalent. The hazard of drought lay ever upon the Near Eastern homeland and on the colonial regions to the west and south. No break between farmer and herdsman is discernible at any time; as the village Arab of today is related to the Bedouin, the environmental specialization may have been present from the beginning: flocks on the mountains and dry lands, fields where moisture sufficed and soil was adequate.

That the lands about the Mediterranean have become worn and

frayed by the usage to which they have been subjected has long been recognized, though not much is known as to when and how. The eastern and southern Mediterranean uplands especially are largely of limestone, fertile but, by their nature, without deep original mantle of soil or showing the usual gradation of subsoil into bedrock and thus are very vulnerable to erosion. The less suited the land was or became to plow cultivation, the greater the shift to pastoral economy. Thus a downslope migration of tillage characterized, in time, the retreating limits of the fields, and more and more land became range for goats, sheep, and asses. Repeatedly prolonged droughts must have speeded the downslope shift, hillside fields suffering most, and with failing vegetation cover becoming more subject to washing when rains came.

Thus we come again to the question of climatic change as against attrition of surface and increased xerophytism of vegetation by human disturbance and, in particular, to what is called the "desertification" of North Africa and the expansion of the Sahara. A case for directional change in the pattern of atmospheric circulation has been inferred from archeology and faunal changes. I am doubtful that it is a good case within the time of agricultural and pastoral occupation. Another view is that the progressive reduction of plant cover by man has affected soil and ground-surface climate unfavorably. Largely, and possibly wholly, the deterioration of the borders of the dry lands may have been caused by adverse, cumulative effects of man's activities. From archeologic work we need much more information as to whether human occupation has been failing in such areas over a long time, or whether it has happened at defined intervals, and also whether, if such intervals are noted, they may have a cultural rather than an environmental (climatic) basis.

No protective herbaceous flora became established around the shores of the Mediterranean on pastures and meadows as was the case in the north. Flocks and herds grazed during the short season of soft, new grass but most of the year browsed on woody growth. The more palatable feed was eaten first and increasingly eliminated; goats and asses got along on range that had dropped below the support levels required by more exacting livestock. As is presently true in the western United States, each prolonged drought must have left the range depleted, its carrying capacity reduced, and recovery of cover less likely. Natural balance between plants and animals is rarely reestablished under such exploitation, since man will try to save his herd rather than their range. A large and long deterioration of the range may therefore fully account for the poor and xerophytic flora and fauna without postulating progressive climatic desiccation, for the kinds of life that survive under overuse of the land are the most undemanding inhabitants.

Comparative studies of North Africa and of the American Southwest and northern Mexico are needed to throw light on the supposed "desiccation" of the Old World. We know the dates of introduction of cattle and sheep to the American ranges and can determine rate and kind of change of vegetation and surface. The present desolate shifting-sand area that lies between the Hopi villages and the Colorado River was such good pasture land late in the eighteenth century that Father Escalante, returning from his canyon exploration, rested his travel-worn animals there to regain flesh. The effects of Navaho sheep-herding in little more than a century and mainly in the last sixty years are well documented. Lower California and Sonora are climatic homologues of the western Sahara. Against the desolation of the latter, the lands about the Gulf of California are a riot of bloom in spring and green through summer. Their diversity, in kind and form, of plant and of animal life is high, and the numbers are large. When Leo Waibel came from his African studies to Sonora and Arizona, he remarked: "But your deserts are not plant deserts." Nor do we have hammadas or *ergs*, though geologic and meteorologic conditions may be similar. The principal difference may be that we have had no millennial, or even centuries-long, overstocking of our arid, semiarid, and subhumid lands. The scant life and even the rock and sand surfaces of the Old World deserts may record long attrition by man in climatic tension zones.

Impact of Civilization in Antiquity and the Middle Ages

Have the elder civilizations fallen because their lands deteriorated? Ellsworth Huntington read adverse climatic change into each such failure; at the other extreme, political loss of competence has been asserted as sufficient. Intimate knowledge of historical sources, archeologic sites, biogeography and ecology, and the processes of geomorphology must be fused in patient field studies, so that we may read the changes in habitability through human time for the lands in which civilization first took form.

The rise of civilizations has been accomplished and sustained by the development of powerful and elaborately organized states with a drive to territorial expansion, by commerce in bulk and to distant parts, by monetary economy, and by the growth of cities. Capital cities, port cities by sea and river, and garrison towns drew to themselves population and products from near and far. The ways of the country became subordinated to the demands of the cities, the *citizen* distinct from the *miserabilis plebs*. The containment of community by locally available resources gave way to the introduction of goods, especially foodstuffs, regulated by purchasing, distributing, or taxing power.

Thereby removal of resource from place of origin to place of demand tended to set up growing disturbance of whatever ecologic equilibrium had been maintained by the older rural communities sustained directly within their metes. The economic history of antiquity shows repeated shifts in the area of supply of raw materials that are not explained by political events but raise unanswered questions as to decline of fertility, destruction of plant cover, and incidence of soil erosion. What, for instance, happened to Arabia Felix, Numidia, Mauretania, to the interior Lusitania that has become the frayed Spanish Extremadura of today? When and at whose hands did the forest disappear that furnished ship and house timbers, wood for burning lime, the charcoal for smelting ores, and urban fuel needs? Are political disasters sufficient to account for the failure of the civilizations that depended on irrigation and drainage engineering? How much of the wide deterioration of Mediterranean and Near Eastern lands came during or after the time of strong political and commercial organization? For ancient and medieval history our knowledge as to what happened to the land remains too largely blank, except for the central and northern European periphery. The written documents, the testimony of the archeologic sites, have not often been interpreted by observation of the physical condition of the locality as it is and comparison with what it was.

The aspect of the Mediterranean landscapes was greatly changed by classical civilization through the introduction of plants out of the East. Victor Hehn first described Italy as wearing a dress of an alien vegetation, and, though he carried the theme of plant introduction out of the East too far, his study of the Mediterranean lands through antiquity is not only memorable but retains much validity. The westward dispersal of vine, olive, fig, the stone fruits, bread wheat, rice, and many ornamentals and some shade trees was due in part or in whole to the spread of Greco-Roman civilization, to which the Arabs added sugar cane, date palm, cotton, some of the citrus fruits, and other items.

European Overseas Colonization

When European nations ventured forth across the Atlantic, it was to trade or raid, the distinction often determined by the opportunity. In Africa and Asia the European posts and factories pretty well continued in this tradition through the eighteenth century. In the New World the same initial activities soon turned into permanent settlement of Old World forms and stocks. Columbus, searching only for a trade route, started the first overseas empire. Spain stumbled into colonization, and the other nations acquired stakes they hoped might equal the Spanish terrritorial claim. The Casa de Contratación, or House of Trade, at Seville, the main Atlantic port, became the Spanish colonial office. The conquistadores came not to settle but to make their fortunes and return home, and much the same was true for the earlier adventurers from

other nations. Soldiers and adventurers rather than peasants and artisans made up the first arrivals, and few brought their women. Only in
New England did settlement begin with a representative assortment
of people, and only here were the new communities transplanted from
the homeland without great alteration.

The first colony, Santo Domingo, set in large measure the pattern of
colonization. It began with trade, including ornaments of gold. The
quest for gold brought forced labor and the dying-off of the natives,
and this, in turn, slave-hunting and importation of black slaves. Decline
of natives brought food shortages and wide abandonment of *conucos*.
Cattle and hogs were pastured on the lately tilled surfaces; and Spaniards, lacking labor to do gold-placering, became stock ranchers. Some
turned to cutting dyewoods. Of the numerous European plants introduced to supply accustomed wants, a few, sugar cane, cassia, and gin-
ger, proved moderately profitable for export, and some of the hesitant
beginnings became the first tropical plantations. One hope of fortune
failing, another was tried; the stumbling into empire was under way
by men who had scarcely any vision of founding a new homeland.

What then happened to the lands of the New World in the three
colonial centuries? In the first place, the aboriginal populations in contact with Europeans nearly everywhere declined greatly or were extinguished. Especially in the tropical lowlands, with the most notable
exception of Yucatán, the natives faded away, and in many cases the
land was quickly repossessed by forest growth. The once heavily populous lands of eastern Panama and northwestern Colombia, much of the
lowland country of Mexico, both on the Pacific and Gulf sides, became
emptied in a very few years, was retaken by jungle and forest, and in
considerable part remains such to the present. The highlands of Mexico,
of Central America, and of the Andean lands declined in population
greatly through the sixteenth and perhaps well through the seventeenth
century, with slow, gradual recovery in the eighteenth. The total population, white and other, of the areas under European control was, I
think, less at the end of the eighteenth century than at the time of discovery. Only in British and French West Indian islands were dense
rural populations built up.

It is hardly an exaggeration to say that the early Europeans supported
themselves on Indian fields. An attractive place to live for a European
would ordinarily have been such for an Indian. In the Spanish colonies,
unlike the English and French, the earlier grants were not of land titles
but of Indian communities to serve colonist and crown. In crops and
their tillage the colonists of all nations largely used the Indian ways,
with the diversion of part of the field crop to animal feed. Only in the
Northeast, most of all in our Middle Colonies, were native and European crops fused into a conservative plow-and-animal husbandry, with

field rotation, manuring, and marl dressing. The Middle Colonies of the eighteenth century appear to have compared favorably with the best farming practices of Western Europe.

Sugar cane, first and foremost of the tropical plantations, as a closely planted giant grass, gave satisfactory protection to the surface of the land. The removal of cane from the land did reduce fertility unless the waste was properly returned to the canefields. The most conservative practices known are from the British islands, where cane waste was fed to cattle kept in pens, and manuring was customary and heavy. Bagasse was of little value as fuel in this period because of the light crushing rollers used for extracting cane juice; thus the colonial sugar mills were heavy wood users, especially for boiling sugar. The exhaustion of wood supply became a serious problem in the island of Haiti within the sixteenth century.

Other plantation crops—tobacco, indigo, cotton, and coffee—held more serious erosion hazards, partly because they were planted in rows and given clean cultivation, partly because they made use of steeper slopes and thinner soils. The worst offender was tobacco, grown on land that was kept bared to the rains and nourished by the wood ashes of burned clearings. Its cultivation met with greatest success in our upper South, resulted in rapidly shifting clearings because of soil depletion, and caused the first serious soil erosion in our country. Virginia, Maryland, and North Carolina show to the present the damages of tobacco culture of colonial and early post-colonial times. Southern Ohio and eastern Missouri repeated the story before the middle of the nineteenth century.

As had happened in Haiti, sharp decline of native populations brought elsewhere abandonment of cleared and tilled land and thereby opportunity to the stockman. The plants that pioneer in former fields which are left untilled for reasons other than because of decline of fertility include forms, especially annuals, of high palatability, grasses, amaranths, chenopods, and legumes. Such is the main explanation for the quick appearance of stock ranches, of *ganado mayor* and *menor*, in the former Indian agricultural lands all over Spanish America. Cattle, horses, and hogs thrived in tropical lowland as well as in highland areas. Sheep-raising flourished most in early years in the highlands of New Spain and Peru, where Indian population had shrunk. Spanish stock, trespassing upon Indian plantings, both in lowland and in highland, afflicted the natives and depressed their chances of recovery. In the wide savannas stockmen took over the native habits of burning.

The Spaniards passed in a few years from the trading and looting of metals to successful prospecting, at which they became so adept that it is still said that the good mines of today are the *antiguas* of colonial working. When mines were abandoned, it was less often due to the working-out of the ore bodies than to inability to cope with water in shafts and to the exhaustion of the necessary fuel and timber. A good illustration has been worked out for Parral in Mexico. Zacatecas, today in the midst of a high sparse grassland, was in colonial times a wood-land of oak and pine and, at lower levels, of mesquite. About Andean mines the scant wood was soon exhausted, necessitating recourse to cutting mats of *tola* heath and even the clumps of coarse *ichu* (stipa) grass. Quite commonly the old mining *reales* of North and South America are surrounded by a broad zone of reduced and impoverished vegetation. The effects were increased by the concentration of pack and work animals in the mines, with resultant overpasturing. Similar attrition took place about towns and cities, through timber-cutting, charcoal- and lime-burning, and overpasturing. The first viceroy of New Spain warned his successor in 1546 of the depletion of wood about the city of Mexico.

I have used mainly examples from Spanish America for the colonial times, partly because I am most familiar with this record. However, attrition was more sensible here because of mines and urban concen-trations and because, for cultural and climatic reasons, the vegetation cover was less.

Last Frontiers of Settlement

The surges of migration of the nineteenth century are family history for many of us. Never before did, and never again may, the white man expand his settlements as in that brief span that began in the later eighteenth century and ended with the First World War. The prelude was in the eighteenth century, not only as a result of the industrial revolution as begun in England, but also in a less heralded agricultural revolution over western and central Europe. The spread of potato-growing, the development of beets and turnips as field crops, rotation of fields with clover, innovations in tillage, improved livestock breeds— all joined to raise agricultural production to new levels in western Europe. The new agriculture was brought to our middle colonies by a massive immigration of capable European farmers and here further transformed by adding maize to the small grains-clover rotation. Thus was built on both sides of the North Atlantic a balanced animal hus-bandry of increased yield of human and animal foods. Urban and rural growth alike went into vigorous upswing around the turn of the eigh-teenth century. The youth of the countryside poured into the rising industrial cities but also emigrated, especially from central Europe into Pennsylvania, into Hungarian and Moldavian lands repossessed from the Turks and into South Russia gained from the Tartars. The last *Völkerwanderung* was under way and soon edging onto the grasslands.

The year 1800 brought a new cotton to the world market, previously an obscure annual variant known to us as Mexican Upland cotton; still uncertainly understood is how it got into our South. Cleaned by the new gin, its profitable production rocketed. The rapidly advancing frontier of cotton-planting was moved westward from Georgia to Texas within the first half of the century. This movement was a more southerly and even greater parallel to the earlier westward drive of the tobacco frontier. Both swept away the woodlands and the Indians, including the farming tribes. The new cotton, like tobacco, a clean cultivated row crop and a cash crop, bared the fields to surface wash, especially in winter. The southern uplands soils gradually lost their organic horizons, color, and protection; gullies began to be noted even before the Civil War. Guano and Chilean nitrate and soon southern rock phosphate were applied increasingly to the wasting soils. Eugene Hilgard told the history of cotton in our South tersely and well in the United States Census of 1880. As I write, across from my window stands the building bearing his name and the inscription: TO RESCUE FOR HUMAN SOCIETY THE NATIVE VALUES OF RURAL LIFE. It was in wasting cotton fields that Hilgard learned soil science and thought about a rural society that had become hitched wholly to world commerce. Meantime the mill towns of England, the Continent, and New England grew lustily; with them, machine industries, transport facilities, and the overseas shipment of food.

The next great American frontier may be conveniently and reasonably dated by the opening of the Erie Canal in 1825, providing the cities with grain and meat on both sides of the North Atlantic, first by canal and river, soon followed by the railroad. The earlier frontiers had been pushed from the Atlantic seaboard to and beyond the Mississippi by the cultivation of tropical plants in extratropical lands, were dominantly monocultural, preferred woodlands, and relied mainly on hand labor. For them the term "plantation culture" was not inapt. The last thrust, from the Mohawk Valley to the Mississippi, was west European as to agricultural system, rural values, settlers, and largely as to crops.

By the time of the Civil War, the first great phase of the northern westward movement had crossed the Missouri River into Kansas and Nebraska. New England spilled over by way of the Great Lakes, especially along the northern fringe of prairies against the North Woods. New York and Baltimore were gateways for the masses of continental emigrants hurrying to seek new homes beyond the Alleghenies. The migrant streams mingled as they overspread the Mississippi Valley, land of promise unequaled in the history of our kind. These settlers were fit to the task: they were good husbandmen and artisans. They came to put down their roots, and the gracious country towns, farmsteads, and rural churches still bear witness to the homemaking way of life they brought and kept. At last they had land of their own, and it was good. They took care of their land, and it did well by them; surplus rather than substance of the soil provided the foodstuffs that moved to eastern markets. Steel plows that cut through the sod, east-west railroads, and cheap lumber from the white-pine forests of the Great Lakes unlocked the fertility of the prairies; the first great plowing-up of the grasslands was under way.

Many prairie counties reached their maximum population in less than a generation, many of them before the beginning of the Civil War. The surplus, another youthful generation, moved on farther west or sought fortune in the growing cities. Thus, toward the end of the century the trans-Missouri grassy plains had been plowed up to and into the lands of drought hazard. Here the Corn Belt husbandry broke down, especially because of the great drought of the early nineties, and the Wheat Belt took form, a monocultural and unbalanced derivative. I well remember parties of land-lookers going out from my native Missouri county, first to central Kansas and Nebraska, then to the Red River Valley, and finally even to the Panhandle of Texas and the prairies of Manitoba. The local newspapers "back home" still carry news today from these daughter-colonies, and still those who long ago moved west are returned "home" at the last to lie in native soil.

The development of the Middle West did exact its price of natural resources. The white-pine stands of the Great Lakes were destroyed to build the farms and towns of the Corn Belt; the logged-over lands suffered dreadful burning. As husbandry gave way westward to wheat-growing, the land was looked on less as homestead and more as speculation, to be cropped heavily and continuously for grain, without benefit of rotation and manuring, and to be sold at an advantageous price, perhaps to reinvest in new and undepleted land.

The history of the extratropical grasslands elsewhere in the world is much like our own and differs little in period and pace. Southern Russia, the Pampas, Australia, and South Africa repeat largely the history of the American West. The industrial revolution was made possible by the plowing-up of the great non-tropical grasslands of the world. So also was the intensification of agriculture in western Europe, benefiting from the importation of cheap overseas feedstuffs, grains, their by-products of milling (note the term "shipstuff"), oil-seed meals. Food and feed were cheap in and about the centers of industry, partly because the fertility of the new lands of the world was exported to them without reckoning the maintenance of resource.

At the turn of the century serious concern developed about the adequacy of resources for industrial civilization. The conservation movement was born. It originated in the United States, where the depletion of lately virgin lands gave warning that we were drawing recklessly on a diminishing natural capital. It is to be remembered that this awareness came, not to men living in the midst of the industrial and commercial centers of the older country-sides, but to foresters who witnessed devastation about the Great Lakes, to geologists who had worked in the iron and copper ranges of the Great Lakes and prospected the West in pioneer days, to naturalists who lived through the winning of the West.

The Ever Dynamic Economy

As a native of the nineteenth century, I have been an amazed and bewildered witness of the change of tempo that started with the First World War, was given an additional whirl on the Second, and still continues to accelerate. The worry of the earlier part of the century was that we might not use our natural resources thriftily; it has given way to easy confidence in the capacities of technologic advance without limit. The natural scientists were and still may be conservation-minded; the physical scientists and engineers today are often of the lineage of Daedalus, inventing even more daring reorganizations of matter and, in consequence, whether they desire it or not, of social institutions. Social science eyes the attainments of physical science enviously and hopes for similar competence and authority in reordering the world. Progress is the common watchword of our age, its motor-innovating techniques, its objective the ever expanding "dynamic economy," with ever increasing input of energy. Capacity to produce and capacity to consume are the twin spirals of the new age which is to have no end, if war can be eliminated. The measure of progress is "standard of living," a term that the English language has contributed to the vernaculars of the world. An American industrialist says, roundly, that our principal problem now is to accelerate obsolescence, which remark was anticipated at the end of the past century by Eduard Hahn when he thought that industrialization depended on the production of junk.

Need we ask ourselves whether there still is the problem of limited resources, of an ecologic balance that we disturb or disregard at the peril of the future? Was Wordsworth of the early industrial age far-sighted when he said that "getting and spending we lay waste our powers"? Are our newly found powers to transform the world, so successful in the short run of the last years, proper and wise beyond the tenure of those now living? To what end are we committing the world to increasing momentum of change?

The steeply increasing production of late years is due only in part to better recovery, more efficient use of energy, and substitution of abundant for scarce materials. Mainly we have been learning how to deplete more rapidly the resources known to be accessible to us. Must we not admit that very much of what we call production is extraction?

Even the so-called "renewable resources" are not being renewed. Despite better utilization and substitution, timber growth is falling farther behind use and loss, inferior stands and kinds are being exploited, and woodland deterioration is spreading. Much of the world is in a state of wood famine, without known means of remedy or substitution.

Commercial agriculture requires ample working capital and depends in high degree on mechanization and fertilization. A late estimate assigns a fourth of the net income of our farms to the purchase of durable farm equipment. The more farming becomes industry and business, the less remains of the older husbandry in which man lived in balance with his land. We speak with satisfaction of releasing rural population from farm to urban living and count the savings of man-hours in units of farm product and of acres. In some areas the farmer is becoming a town dweller, moving his equipment to the land for brief periods of planting, cultivating, and harvest. Farm garden, orchard, stable, barn, barnyards, and woodlots are disappearing in many parts, the farm families as dependent as their city cousins on grocer, butcher, baker, milkman, and fuel services. Where the farm is in fact capital in land and improvements, requiring bookkeeping on current assets and liabilities, the agriculturist becomes an operator of an outdoor factory of specialized products and is concerned with maximizing the profits of the current year and the next. Increasing need of working capital requires increased monetary returns; this is perhaps all we mean by "intensive" or "scientific" farming, which is in greater and greater degree extractive.

The current agricultural surpluses are not proof that food production has ceased to be a problem or will cease to be the major problem of the world. Our output has been secured at unconsidered costs and risks by the objective of immediate profit, which has replaced the older attitudes of living with the land. The change got under way especially as motors replaced draft animals. Land formerly used for oats and other feed crops became available to grow more corn, soybeans, cotton, and other crops largely sold and shipped. The traditional corn-oats-clover rotation, protective of the surface and maintaining nitrogen balance, began to break down. Soybeans, moderately planted in the twenties and then largely for hay, developed into a major seed crop, aided by heavy governmental benefit payments as soil-building, which they are not. Soil-depleting and soil-exposing crops were given strong impetus in the shift to mechanized farming; less of the better land is used for pasture and hay; less animal and green manure is returned to fields. The fixation of nitrogen by clover has come to be considered too slow; it "pays better" to put the land into corn, beans, and cotton and to apply nitrogen from bag or tank. Dressing the soil with commercial nitrogen makes it possible to plant more closely, thus doubling the number of corn and other plants to the acre at nearly the same tillage cost. Stimulation of plant growth by nitrogen brings increased need of additional phosphorus and potash. In the last ten years the Corn Belt has more or less caught up with the Cotton Belt in the purchase of commercial fertilizer. The more valuable the land, the greater the investment in farm machinery, the more profitable the application of more and more commercial fertilizers.

The so-called row crops, which are the principal cash crops, demand cultivation during much of their period of growth. They give therefore indifferent protection to the surface while growing and almost none after they are harvested. They are ill suited to being followed by a winter cover crop. The organic color is fading from much of our best-grade farm lands. Rains and melting snow float away more and more of the top soil. There is little concern as long as we can plow more deeply and buy more fertilizer. Governmental restriction of acreage for individual crops has been an inducement to apply more fertilizer to the permitted acreage and to plant the rest in uncontrolled but usually also cash crops. Our commercial agriculture, except what remains in animal husbandry such as dairying, is kept expanding by increasing overdraft on the fertility of our soils. Its limits are set by the economically available sources of purchased nitrogen, phosphorus, potassium, and sulfur.

Since Columbus, the spread of European culture has been continuous and cumulative, borne by immediate self-interest, as in mercantilist economy, but sustained also by a sense of civilizing mission redefined from time to time. In the spirit of the present, this mission is to "develop the underdeveloped" parts of the world, material good and spiritual good now having become one. It is our current faith that the ways of the West are the ways that are best for the rest of the world. Our own ever growing needs for raw materials have driven the search for metals and petroleum to the ends of the earth in order to move them into the stream of world commerce. Some beneficial measure of industry and transport facility thereby accrues to distant places of origin. We also wish to be benefactors by increasing food supply where food is inadequate and by diverting people from rural to industrial life, because such is our way, to which we should like to bring others.

The road we are laying out for the world is paved with good intentions, but do we know where it leads? On the material side we are hastening the depletion of resources. Our programs of agricultural aid pay little attention to native ways and products. Instead of going out to learn what their experiences and preferences are, we go forth to introduce our ways and consider backward what is not according to our pattern. Spade and hoe and mixed plantings are an affront to our faith in progress. We promote mechanization. At the least, we hold, others should be taught to use steel plows that turn neat furrows, though we have no idea how long the soil will stay on well-plowed slopes planted to annuals. We want more fields of maize, rice, beans of kinds familiar to us, products amenable to statistical determination and available for commercial distribution. To increase production, we prescribe dressing with commercial fertilizers. In unnoticed contrast to our own experience these are to be applied in large measure to lands of low productivity and perhaps of low effectiveness of fertilizers. Industrialization is recommended to take care of the surplus populations. We present and recommend to the world a blueprint of what works well with us at the moment, heedless that we may be destroying wise and durable native systems of living with the land. The modern industrial mood (I hesitate to add intellectual mood) is insensitive to other ways and values.

For the present, living beyond one's means has become civic virtue, increase of "output" the goal of society. The prophets of a new world by material progress may be stopped by economic limits of physical matter. They may fail because people grow tired of getting and spending as measure and mode of living. They may be checked because men come to fear the requisite growing power of government over the individual and the community. The high moments of history have come not when man was most concerned with the comforts and displays of the flesh but when his spirit was moved to grow in grace. What we need more perhaps is an ethic and aesthetic under which man, practicing the qualities of prudence and moderation, may indeed pass on to posterity a good earth.

II. HISTORICAL GEOGRAPHY

Historical geography is the study and reconstruction of the record of man and his activities; thus, history and geography complement one another in many ways. Any geographical or spatial analysis must take into account historical events. The decisions and actions of men significantly change the cultural and physical landscape; conversely, the natural and cultural environments often have a distinct bearing on the course of history.

The methodological problems of geography and history are similar. Neither has a body of subject matter they can call their own exclusively, but both deal with all pertinent phenomena—history in a temporal sense, geography in a spatial sense. Immanuel Kant, the German philosopher, identified three approaches to knowledge: the *systematic* such as chemistry and sociology which are identified by their distinct subject matter, the *chronological* such as history, and the *chorological* such as geography. Both the latter approaches are important in contributing to the solution of problems or the understanding of areas or cultures at a given time.

The study of the past often reveals significant information helping us to understand the present. All areas of the world have evolved over time. Thus an important segment of the broader field of cultural geography is historical geography, of which Carl Sauer, the author of the previous article, was an early leader in its development. The two articles that follow indicate the relationship between geography and history and the lasting impact on the land of General Sherman's march through Georgia during the Civil War.

2. On the Relations of Geography and History

H. C. Darby

Geography as a university discipline in the United States often started in combination with geology and in rarer instances with history. The lack of a more frequent combination with history is somewhat difficult to explain, as the two disciplines have similar methodologies. Neither has a distinct body of subject matter but rather depends upon organizing approaches to deal with all pertinent phenomena—time in the case of history and space in the case of geography. Darby, a world renowned expert in historical geography, indicates it is "difficult to delimit the frontier between the two studies" and that "all geography is historical geography, either actual or potential." There is no question that the two fields complement one another and are essential to understanding the nature and problems of an area or region and the diverse cultures created by man.

The theme of the relations of geography and history is a well-worn one. It has engaged the attention of man since he first began to examine the nature of human society upon the face of the earth. The classical philosophers speculated upon the connection between peoples and their environments, and the Histories of Herodotus and Thucydides are impregnated with geographical descriptions and considerations. Throughout the Middle Ages, this speculation fell somewhat into abeyance, but, with the revival of the Rennaissance, it sprang to life once more. There is a much quoted sentence from Peter Heylyn's *Microcosmus* which runs: 'Historie without Geographie like a dead carkasse hath neither life nor motion at all'; but what we do not so often hear is the beginning of the quotation: 'Geographie without Historie hath life and motion but at randome, and unstable.' [1]

Since 1621, when Peter Heylyn wrote, a vast literature has accumulated about the relations of the two studies, and many have made forays into the debatable land that lies between them. I am not going

SOURCE: *Journal of the Institute of British Geographers*, No. 19 (1954), pp. 1–11. The author is professor of geography at University College, London.

[1] Peter Heylyn, *Microcosmus, or a little description of the great world* (1621), 11.

to attempt to map with any precision the features of this debatable land. All I can say is that here is a borderland with many trails and many different types of country. In particular, I would like to offer some remarks about the geography behind history, about the geographies of the past, and about the history behind geography, and then to conclude with some comment about the bearing of these matters upon the study of geography as we conceive it today.

The Geography behind History

The closing years of the eighteenth century witnessed what amounted almost to a new beginning in men's way of thinking. It was a revolution as profound, in its different way, as that of the sixteenth century. The change can be seen in the contrast between Goldsmith and Crabbe. Oliver Goldsmith, in *The Deserted Village* of 1770, viewed the scene through the spectacles of a sentimental convention. His was a village 'where health and plenty cheer'd the labouring swain'. The challenge came in 1783 when George Crabbe published his *Village*, harsh and sombre, and full of a desire to give what he called 'the real picture' without the 'tinsel trappings'. It was Byron who described Crabbe as 'Nature's sternest painter, yet her best', and Crabbe's poetry is full of the countryside of eastern Suffolk which he knew so well. This new attitude has been called 'realism', and, although the term is not above reproach, it is probably as good a label as any. Whatever it be called, it was rooted, like the earlier Renaissance, in contemporary change, and it had effects upon all ways of thinking. Nor was it restricted to one country.

Hitherto, the pre-occupation of historical study had been with political relations and incidents. But now its vision was extended until it came to include almost every aspect of human endeavour, social and economic. And, as the study of history became more realistic, it also became more geographical. One of the main, and most influential, products of the new outlook was Michelet's *Histoire de France* (1833). Other writers had reduced the history of France to a long struggle for monarchical centralization and to a tale of domestic politics. It is true that some had thought of the ground as a stage upon which the players acted, but to Michelet the soil was not an inert plank of a theatre. He proclaimed that history was, in the first place, all geographical; and, in order to equip himself for his task, he made long wanderings through various parts of France to gain a first-hand impression of its varying countrysides. Reviewing his work, later in life, he wrote:

Without a geographical basis, the people, the makers of history, seem to be walking on air, as in those Chinese pictures where the ground is wanting. The soil too must not be looked on only as the scene of action. Its influence appears in a hundred ways, such as food, climate, etc. As the nest, so is the bird. As the country, so are the men.[2]

So powerful was his example that it became customary for French historians to preface their studies with a geographical introduction; and we must not forget that Vidal de la Blache's *Tableau de la géographie de la France* appeared in 1911 as an introductory volume to Lavisse's great history of France.

I have taken Michelet as the type of the new spirit in historical writing, but there were others, and not only in France. A long list of professions of the new faith could be made, longer than one might think at first. In 1851, in Germany, appeared an account of the history and geography of the Pelopónnisos by Ernst Curtius.[3] To him, the aged Humboldt wrote: 'I have read your first volume line by line. Your survey of the country is a masterpiece of nature painting.' Similar manifestations were evident in England, and one English example must stand for the rest—A. P. Stanley's *Sinai and Palestine in connection with their history* which appeared in 1856. This was an attempt to illustrate geography and history and, as Stanley said, 'the relation in which each stands to the other'. It is of special interest to us because Stanley, as he confessed, owed something to Carl Ritter.

Not all historians have adopted a geographical approach, and indeed there is no reason why many should have, but this does not prevent me from saying that the *Cambridge Modern History* would have been a better history had Lord Acton been something of a geographer. On the other hand, the heady wine of environmentalism led many to attempt to explain history by geography, and to produce such statements as: 'History is governed by geography'; 'History is geography set into motion'; 'History is geography accumulating at compound interest.'

While the geographical explanation of history features in many studies and permeates others, there are three full-length studies that especially call for comment, if only because the inclusion of the word 'geography' in their titles has led to their appearance in our libraries. The first is George Adam Smith's *Historical geography of the Holy Land*, which was published in 1894 and which has run into twenty-five editions. His object was, he tells us, 'to discover from "the lie of the land" why the history took certain lines', but his treatment is far less deterministic than these words might suggest. The more austere puritans among us might object to his use of the term 'historical geography', but, whatever we think, the fact is that this Scottish divine had a power of description that mere geographers find it easier to envy than to emulate. The two other

[2] Jules Michelet, *Histoire de France*, preface to the edition of 1869.
[3] Ernst Curtius, *Peloponnesos: eine historisch-geographische Beschreibung der Halbinsel*, 2 vols. (Gotha, 1851–2).

books are E. C. Semple's *American history and its geographic conditions* and A. P. Brigham's *Geographic influences in American history*. They invite comparison, not only because of their theme, but because both were written by professional geographers, and both appeared in 1903. Miss Semple's study interprets the different phases of the history of the United States in the light of its geography. It is a great work that must command our affection, if not our allegiance. Brigham's book is different. It is organized upon a geographical basis, and is concerned not so much with geographical influences upon history as with the history that has entered into areal differences. As he said: 'One must invent a method as he can, for models in this field can scarcely be said to exist.' It is possible that Miss Semple's book is the more well known among us, but I am sure that Brigham's book is the more relevant to us.

All these books that, in some sense, find a spiritual ancestor in Michelet are not studies in geography. It is not for us, as geographers, to imitate them. Just because a geographical spirit ought to, and does, inspire certain studies, it does not follow that such studies should be incorporated within even the broad embrace of geography. On the other hand, we cannot fail to be interested in this work, partly out of curiosity, and partly because the recognition of geographical study in other fields is not irrelevant to our own progress.

Past Geographies

The term 'historical geography' has come to be increasingly identified with an approach in which the data are historical but in which the method is geographical. The purpose of the historical geographer, according to this view, is to reconstruct the geography of past times. While geography itself cuts through time at the present period, historical geography cuts through it at some preceding period. In this sense we can speak of the geography of France in 1500, or that of Tierra del Fuego in 1837. Some historians have found it necessary to attempt such reconstructions as part of a particular task before them. Macaulay in his *History of England* (1848) stated clearly the necessity for this: 'If we would study with profit the history of our ancestors, we . . . must never forget that the country of which we read was a very different country from that in which we live.' Accordingly, in his famous third chapter he set out to describe the landscape of England in 1685 as a prelude to the political history of post-Restoration times. Let a few lines of his prose speak for themselves:

Could the England of 1685 be, by some magical process, set before our eyes, we should not know one landscape in a hundred, or one building in ten thousand. The country gentleman would not recognize his own fields. The inhabitant of the town would not recognize his own street. Everything has been changed, but the great features of nature, and a few massive and durable works of human art.

And so he set the stage upon which his figures were to move and act. It was with similar intent that, almost a century later, Macaulay's kinsman, G. M. Trevelyan, prefaced his trilogy, *England under Queen Anne* (1930-33) with what he described as 'a survey' of 'Queen Anne's island', based largely upon Daniel Defoe's account of it. And about this time also, J. H. Clapham in his trilogy, *An economic history of modern Britain* (1926-38), gave two accounts of what he called 'the face of the country', in 1820 and again in 1886.

These three stand out as classic examples of the practice of historical geography by historians. To a greater or less extent, other historians have attempted analogous reconstructions. Nor has their effort been limited to prose. C. H. Pearson's *Historical maps of England* (1869) was an outstanding pioneer attempt to portray the main features of the medieval scene; its preface speaks of 'reconstructions of early geography'. By its side can be placed the maps that accompanied J. R. Green's *The making of England* (1885). Green found that he could give an adequate account of the Anglo-Saxon settlement only by reconstructing the disposition of marsh and wood and open country. It was in the preface to this book that he delivered the famous dictum: 'the ground itself, where we can read the information it affords, is, whether in the account of the Conquest or in that of the Settlement of Britain, the fullest and most certain of documents'.

All these studies, and others too, are most illuminating, and they command our respect on geographical grounds, quite apart from their other excellencies. But they all must be considered in their contexts, and it is possible that none of them would satisfy the specifications, so to speak, that a historical geographer of today might set out in an outline scheme.

Let me, therefore, turn to the practice of historical geography by geographers themselves. One of the most outstanding reconstructions yet achieved is Ralph Brown's *Mirror for Americans* (1943), what he called a 'likeness of the Eastern Seaboard' in 1810. Brown invented an imaginary author, T. P. Keystone, and then he wrote the book that Keystone might have written in 1810, based upon the sources that would have been available at that time. The idiosyncrasy of this treatment makes for great charm, but it also has a limiting effect in the sense that the reconstruction does not avail itself of our modern knowledge of the relief and soils and climate of the eastern seaboard. These are only discussed in so far as they were understood in 1810, and the method of presentation and illustrations are also those of the period. The mythical Keystone was obviously a man who not only had something to say, but who could say it well. Yet, a study by Ralph Brown himself might possibly have given us, in some respects, an even clearer view of the geography of the area in 1810.

Other period reconstructions usually do use later points of view to interpret their period material, but they sometimes lay themselves open to the criticism that they do not use sources *earlier* than those of their period. By this I mean that an account of, say, England in 1550, based only on sixteenth-century material, would lack a genetic approach. It would be an empirical account without depth. Just as an account of the twentieth century should consider the relevant circumstances of past centuries, so should an account of the sixteenth, or of any other century. Paradoxically, therefore, some essays in historical geography can be criticized, on methodological grounds, because they lack a historical approach.

One way of meeting this criticism is to provide successive cross-sections in which each can assume what has gone before; and a number of attempts have been made along these lines. One is a valuable study, by Alfred H. Meyer in 1935, of the Kankakee Marsh in northern Indiana and Illinois.[4] In this study, four reconstructions correspond to the four main phases of land utilization:

(i) The period of the Indian hunter and French trader (before 1840)
(ii) The period of the pioneer trapper and frontier farmer (1840–80)
(iii) The period of the stock farmer and the sportsman fowler (1880–1910)
(iv) The period of the Corn Belt farmer and the river resorter (since 1910).

This method of successive cross-sections was adopted by some of us in the early 1930s when we set out to prepare *An historical geography of England before A.D. 1800* that appeared in 1936. It was, as the preface says, an experiment, and it is interesting to look back and consider the method it applied.

A succession of cross-sections does provide treatment in depth, but it also creates certain practical difficulties in that the different elements that make up a landscape do not change at the same rate nor at the same time. Thus while the marshes are being drained, the heaths are not being reclaimed. Some information has to be repeated in cross-section after cross-section, and, even when change takes place, repetition is unavoidable. It might be said that these are not theoretical difficulties, and that the problems they present can be solved by practical common sense. But only too often they involve uneasy compromise, and it may well be that any cross-section in a series fails adequately to reflect reality. In spite of these difficulties, I still think that the method of successive cross-sections has much to be said for it, especially if the cross-sections are so chosen as to coincide with marked changes in an area as a whole.

[4] Alfred H. Meyer, 'The Kankakee Marsh of northern Indiana and Illinois', *Papers of the Michigan Academy of Science, Arts and Letters,* 21 (1935), 359–96.

The History behind Geography

Having spoken of the geography behind history, and of past geographies, let me turn to the history behind geography. Speaking strictly
as a geographer, I find it difficult to delimit the frontier between the
two studies, and for two reasons. In the first place, the geography of
the present-day is but a thin layer that even at this moment is becoming
history. The Land Utilisation Survey, directed by L. Dudley Stamp in
the early thirties, is the most important achievement of British geographical study. Yet it is becoming almost as much a document of history as,
say, the surveys of the Board of Agriculture round about 1800. When
did it, or lot of it, cease to be geography and become historical geography? Can we fix a date? Can we draw a line between geography
and history? The answer is 'no', for the process of becoming is one
process. All geography is historical geography, either actual or potential.

In the second place, the characteristics of different landscapes are the
result not only of relief and soil and climate, but also of the utilization of
these by successive generations of inhabitants. It was Vidal de la
Blache who called geography 'the science of places', but he meant
places as modified by man and not as they were upon the first morning
of creation. On another page he wrote: 'A geographical individuality
does not result simply from geological and climatic conditions. It is not
something delivered complete from the hand of Nature.' We might continue the train of his thought by adding that it is something that
emerges when men wrest their livelihood from the soil. Art as well
as Nature has gone into the making of most landscapes. The English
poet William Cowper once said that 'God made the country and man
made the town'. Nothing could be more misleading, and Cowper should
have known better. He wrote that line in 1783 at the village of Olney, in
Buckinghamshire, where he had settled in 1767. In 1768, the open fields
of Olney were enclosed, and Cowper must have watched, with his
own eyes, the new landscape of field and hedgerow take form. The landscape of Olney, like the English countryside in general, is as artificial as
any urban scene.

Let me for a moment take an example, modest but concrete, of the
time element in geography. The East Anglian Breckland was once
thought to be a natural heathland. But recent work has shown that even
its light soils were not devoid of wood when farming first began, and
that the so-called 'natural heath' had its origin in the clearing of the
wood by Neolithic farmers. The continued existence of the heathland
has depended upon some factors that have prevented the re-estab-
lishment and growth of trees. The more obvious factors are grazing by
sheep or rabbits, recurrent fires which destroy tree seedlings, and, lastly,
the direct action of man.

But while a certain amount of grazing maintains heathland, too much destroys it. Heavy and continuous pasturing by sheep or rabbits converts it into grassland. The reason is that the animals nibble down to about half an inch above the ground, and that shrubs cannot endure this, while grass can. In the competition between heather and grass, the grass therefore survives and spreads. When rabbits enter a heathland with some existing trees, the trees are trimmed in a spectacular fashion up to a height of about 20 inches—that is the height to which a rabbit can reach with its mouth when standing on its hind legs; young seedlings do not survive the experience. If the rabbits depart or are excluded from a heathland, the heather rapidly recolonizes the ground at the expense of the grass. The story does not end there, for the ultimate effect of rabbit-grazing may be to destroy the vegetation completely in some localities. Entrances to rabbit burrows, and a general thinning of vegetation, may give the wind a purchase on the sand so that it blows away; grass-heath fades out locally into bare sand. A further complication is that rabbits do not like bracken fern which in places thus flourishes triumphantly amid the savage battle for life raging around.

The net result of these struggles is that an expanse of heathland usually presents a variety of surface, and a variety that is never still. Stretches of *calluna* and *erica* merge into a light wood cover or into bracken, or grass or bare soil. A heathland is, therefore, not only a geographical fact, but a most delicate compromise between the forces promoting it and those destroying it. The scene that confronts us represents a momentary balance of power, an equipoise, sensitive, as we have seen, to short-term changes, responsive also to long-term changes—to the introduction in the eighteenth century, of turnips and clover which completely altered the appearance of vast areas, and to afforestation which likewise has had great effect. Even so, many tracts of heathland still remain as inliers of an older and wilder landscape surrounded by improvement.

In the light of these facts, can anyone be satisfied with an empirical descriptive approach to the geography of heathlands, or to the geography of any other area? The landscape we see is not a static arrangement of objects. It has become what it is, and it is usually in the process of becoming something different. A close analogy is to regard our momentary glimpse of it as a 'still' taken out of a long film. Let us then not study a static picture, but a process that is continuing and, seemingly, never-ending.

The main instrument of historic change is, of course, Man himself, and there is an enormous literature dealing with his works and influence upon the face of the earth. Topics such as draining, stream-regulation, irrigation and surface-subsidence are discussed in the various engineering journals; while changes in agriculture are described in the journals of economic history. Such themes have also made their appearance in our geographical literature, and the phrase 'Man and his conquest of Nature' is no new one to us.

Curiously enough, there was a promising beginning of investigation along these lines in the middle of the nineteenth century. It was the publication of G. P. Marsh's *Man and nature* (1864). Marsh was a farmer, a business-man, and a Congressman from the state of Vermont. He was a follower of Humboldt, and he described geography as 'both a poetry and a philosophy'. One of his main themes was the rapid clearing of forests in the United States, and his work has been hailed as the fountain-head of the American conservation movement. But, as far as I can see, the main line of his thought has not often been pursued to its logical conclusion, and there are relatively few studies explicitly devoted to the investigation of the consequences of man as an agent of change in the landscape. When R. L. Sherlock published his book, *Man as a geological agent*, in 1922, he had to state that he had been 'unable to discover any comprehensive account of the effect of Man on geographical or geological conditions'. He would not need to make such a sweeping statement today. One recent book, for example, which does deal with this problem is A. H. Clark's *The invasion of New Zealand by people, plants and animals* (1949). It is described in the preface as 'a report on a revolutionary change in the character of a region, which occurred in a period of less than two centuries'. The result of the report is a clearer understanding of the geography of the South Island of New Zealand as it appears today.

With this line of thought in mind, it is impossible to envisage a treatment of the historical element in the English landscape different from that of the experiment of 1936. The data can be organized in terms not of horizontal cross-sections but of vertical themes—the clearing of the wood, the draining of the marsh, the reclamation of the heathlands, changes in settlement, and so on. This was the approach that I had the opportunity of developing two years ago.[5] I am not going to set one method against the other for both, it seems to me, are permissible, and maybe desirable.

This vertical method can, however, be criticized. In the first place, in thus analysing a landscape into its changing elements, a picture of the whole developing as one is lost. That is a just criticism, but against it two considerations can be urged: (*a*) Even a horizontal treatment, whether historical or present-day, has to some extent to present its material analytically; we cannot apprehend reality in one flash. (*b*) In practice, it is possible to mitigate the division into separate

[5] H. G. Darby, 'The changing English landscape', *Geographical Journal*, 117 (1951), 377–98.

themes by taking a broad view of each of them, e.g. to make reference to, say, settlement while discussing the clearing of the wood or the reclamation of heathlands. But there is a second criticism. The form of the presentation is that of successive narratives, and we are inevitably faced with the question as to what is economic history and what is historical geography. This is a question that has troubled many an honest mind. The answer is clear. If economic change is part of historical study, as it must be, then such a treatment is historical. If an understanding of landscape is part of geographical study, as it must be, then such a treatment is geographical. Let us confess that such treatments lie in an intellectual borderland. To set tariff frontiers around our different academic subjects, and so hinder the flow of ideas, is as unnecessary as it is unprofitable.

The Historical Element in Geography

What of geography itself? Granted that without history it is but 'at randome, and unstable', how are we to secure, in a purely geographical description, the appropriate historical approach? When we cease to be historical geographers, and graduate to become complete geographers of the present, how are we to conduct ourselves? If it is the purpose of a geographer to explain the landscape, it is clear that he is unable to rely only on what he sees. The visible scene cannot give us the whole sum of the factors affecting it. Field work provides us with the data, and, on occasions, takes us some way towards the elucidation of those data. It is an article of faith among us that field work is the essential basis of geographical study. When R. H. Tawney said that what economic historians needed was stouter boots, many of us paused to consider the condition of our own shoe leather, and the cry among us has quite properly been 'field work and more field work'. To many, the field has been a welcome relief from the methodological babble to which I am adding today. I can well imagine a geographer thinking as Tennyson did when he wrote:

> And forth into the fields I went,
> And Nature's living motion lent
> The pulse of hope to discontent.

Yet I suggest that the new cry might well be 'Field work is not enough'. The map, to use F. W. Maitland's familiar phrase, is a 'marvellous palimpsest'.[6] Not all the ancient writing is legible through what has been written since, but much of it is, and still more of it is for those who have eyes to see. When, as geographers, we gaze around, one question forces itself upon our attention; it takes a variety of form: 'Why does

[6] F. W. Maitland, *Domesday Book and beyond* (1897), 15.

this countryside look as it does? What has given this landscape its present character?' The moment we ask this question, that moment are we committed to historical geography in one form or another.

But difficulties lie in ambush, not so much theoretical ones as practical ones. As Derwent Whittlesey asked in 1945: 'Is there a solution for the puzzle of writing incontestable geography that also incorporates the chains of event necessary to understand fully the geography of the present day?'[7] Theoretically there are two possible solutions. One is to be concerned not with the reconstruction of past geographies or with the analysis of the changing elements in a scene, but only with those past phases of occupation that have left vestiges of themselves, and so continue to exist in the present. This is the basic idea behind the American term 'sequent occupance', invented by Whittlesey in 1929.[8] In this same year, Preston James laid the basis for his description and interpretation of the Blackstone Valley in southern New England by discussing what he called 'the development of the landscapes':

Into this not too hospitable land came man, and with man came these modifications of the original terrain which it is our special task to analyze. Three distinct periods in the modification of the original terrain can be discerned. First the native Indians with their primitive methods of land occupation created landscape forms characteristic of their culture. Then came the European settlers, first interested in farming, and these people developed out of the earlier landscape, largely obliterating it, a new set of forms reflecting a more advanced agricultural economy. Finally, industrial cities with an entirely new set of cultural forms were imposed upon the rural landscape, not by any means obliterating it, but rather forming patches scattered especially in the valley, and forming vivid contrasts with the earlier landscapes in which they are embedded.[9]

After discussing each of these phases, Preston James proceeded, in the light of what he had already said, to an analysis of the landscapes that confronted him. Other American geographers have also adopted this approach and so enriched their regional studies to our advantage. The practical difficulty of the method lies in the fact that it is not always easy to separate the surviving elements of a past phase from associated phenomena that have disappeared. The danger is that the treatment might easily lead to a full-scale reconstruction of some past-geography. According to one's point of view, one might regard that as falling down the slippery slope or as scaling the heights.

There is, as I have said, a second way of providing a historical ap-

[7] Derwent Whittlesey, 'The horizon of geography', Annals of the Association of American Geographers, 35 (1945), 32.
[8] Derwent Whittlesey, 'Sequent occupance', Annals of the Association of American Geographers, 19 (1929), 162–5.
[9] Preston E. James, 'The Blackstone valley', Annals of the Association of American Geographers, 19 (1929), 72.

proach in geographical description. It is to start not at the beginning but with the present-day—to describe an existing landscape, and look back only when, and in so far as, this or that element cannot be explained in contemporary terms; to restrict historical comment severely to relict landscape features. One would naturally need to look farther back for some origins than for others. Theoretically there is much to be said for this approach, except that some would prefer to put first things first, and that frequently a past phase of occupation has influenced the present arrangement in ways other than by leaving souvenirs of itself. In practice, however, it is not easy to achieve a completely satisfying presentation along these lines. To keep looking back over one shoulder is always uncomfortable and sometimes perilous. The appropriate asides and parentheses in any descriptive writing have to be many, that is unless one adopts an elaborate system of footnotes. The combination of a running geographical text with historical footnotes would be a form of cheating.

As far as I know, there is no full-bodied treatment along the lines of this second approach, but it is far from being a theoretical abstraction. Something of it can be seen in many studies—in John Bygott's *Eastern England* (1923), for example; in many of the French regional monographs; and in some chapters of the volumes of the *Géographie Universelle*. A representative list would be a long one. I can only conclude that the complete success of this interwoven geography and history depends partly upon the nature of the region described and partly upon literary skill.

Whatever be the relations of geography and history, in a methodological sense, I must end by affirming that a fourth dimension is a necessary ingredient in geographical study. An analogy with geomorphology naturally suggests itself. To understand the physical landscape it is necessary to do more than take photographs and make measurements. The sequence of events in Tertiary and Quaternary times, at least, is often necessary to an understanding, as opposed to a description, of the present scene; an empirical sight of meandering streams or erosion surfaces does not take us far along the way of comprehension. There are, of course, limits beyond which we need not advance into the subject matter of geology and history. But I venture to say that those limits are not to be defined by nice methodological argument or by jugglery with words and definitions. The limits are best set by the nature of a particular problem we are attempting to unravel, or by the character of a particular landscape we are trying to describe. Some problems and some landscapes tak us farther into geology and history than others. Whatever the limits be, the fact remains that the landscape we see today is a collection of legacies from the past, some from geological, some from historical, times. And I am sometimes inclined to think that the foundations of geographical study lie in geomorphology and in historical geography. Here are the basic elements of our discipline. Do not misunderstand me. I am not saying that geomorphology and historical geography are the most important parts of geography. For, after all, foundations are meant for greater things to be built on them.

3. Where Sherman Passed By

D. J. de Laubenfels

War has wrought change in the various parts of the world over time. Unfortunately, much of that change is a product of death and destruction from military campaigns; but, as well, new ideas, forms of government, social reforms, and economies have also resulted from war. German cities such as Hamburg have a markedly different appearance today as a result of rebuilding after the destruction from Allied bombing during the Second World War. North Norway and Finland have been rebuilt because of the "scorched earth" policy of the retreating Nazi German army. More recently, many Korean and Vietnamese cities and villages have been destroyed in battle. An example in our own country is the infamous march of Sherman to the sea during the Civil War and its impact upon Georgia, which de Laubenfels reconstructs in this selection. With the massive increase in destructive power of thermonuclear weapons, man possesses the ability for even more widespread damage and consequently change.

Thus human conflict is an important agent of change with which the geographer must deal. Hopefully it is one that will be eliminated in the future, but even then the historical geographer must continue to evaluate the significance of vast conflicts on world regions.

The stated purpose of Sherman's march through Georgia was to "cripple their military resources." Primarily this meant railroads and factories, but food supplies were also important. Sherman himself claimed to have "consumed stores and provisions that were essential to Lee's and Hood's armies"; indeed, Georgia was the main source of food supplies for the

SOURCE: *Geographical Review*, (October, 1957), 380–95. The author is associate professor of geography at Syracuse University.

FIGURE 1: Location map, showing Captain Rziha's traverse. Bracket indicates section covered in Figure 2.

Confederate army in Virginia. Central Georgia, in particular, was a rich agricultural region. How it has changed since that time!

Fortunately, much of the landscape where Sherman passed by can be described. Detailed field maps drawn by one of his officers give an intimate view—houses, fields, roads, and terrain. When compared with the present-day landscape, they prove surprisingly accurate. Here then is an unusual opportunity to compare the various landscape features of central Georgia over a span of nearly a century.

The Civil War maps are part of a journal kept by Captain John Rziha, chief topographical engineer of the XIV Corps; General Sherman himself accompanied this corps from Atlanta to Milledgeville (Fig. 1). Captain Rziha had among his duties the location of suitable routes for the march and the construction of bridges where necessary. His maps constitute a traverse about half a mile wide across the lower Georgia Piedmont from a point five miles west of Covington to Milledgeville, a distance of about 60 miles not counting a gap of six miles near Eatonton.

The present writer made field observations along the route during the summer of 1955.

Sherman's famous march is perhaps the best-known event that has taken place in central Georgia, but it is by no means the only important one. In fact, three far-reaching invasions mark the recent history of the region. Each invasion has been followed by sweeping changes in the settlement pattern.

Agriculture before 1864

The rising tide of agricultural settlement moved slowly in Georgia during the colonial period. But in 1802 and 1804 the land was released from Indian title. It was quickly surveyed and divided into plots of 202½ acres, ownership to which was acquired by lottery. Agricultural settlers, predominantly Scotch-Irish, swarmed into the forests of central Georgia in the first of the three invasions. Population densities that prevailed for half a century were reached in little more than a decade.

Two hundred and two and a half acres is not exactly a plantation. Nevertheless, the new settlers called their properties "plantations" and set about changing their environment into the familiar patterns that prevailed farther east along the coast. Negro slaves were brought in to do the work. At first the white population was twice the colored, but as the years passed, the situation was reversed. Many of the earliest settlers left, no doubt to settle farther west. Because of this, some property owners were able to increase their holdings, and a few "honest-to-goodness" plantations were created. Nonetheless, the usual property remained more a farm than a plantation.

A period of growth followed the invasion. Land had to be cleared of woods; roads were needed. These things progressed slowly and at different rates on different farms, but progress they did. And there were houses to be built. The first houses were rough cabins, some of which continued in use. Sooner or later, however, the usual farm boasted a substantial house.

This was a young and vigorous region. It was also self-reliant. Crops and livestock were adequate to meet nearly all local needs. With the increase in farmland came an increase in livestock, and in the years before the Civil War cattle—milch cows, beef cattle, oxen—became nearly as numerous as people. Hogs rooted about the farms in numbers more than twice the human population. Horses, as many as two per capita, were more numerous than the rapidly increasing mules. There were even sheep. The principal grain was corn, and other grains and garden vegetables helped to provide food. The one big cash crop was cotton. Profits from the sale of cotton made landowners rich. When the Civil War came, most cottonland was diverted to food crops, and Georgia became the breadbasket of the Confederacy.

Towns grew but little. The economy was one of individually centralized large farms and plantations. There were two kinds of towns: county seats and hamlets. The county seats, although larger, counted their populations only by hundreds. Here the more prosperous planters had their residences, and more elegant houses would have been hard to find; indeed, in central Georgia one must look in the towns for the ante bellum mansions. Hamlets were few. Their reason for existence might originally have been the presence of a tavern or a post station for changing horses. Schools, churches, and mills likely as not stood by themselves. Farm headquarters were not uncommonly larger than the neighboring hamlet.

Before the second invasion ushered in another period of settlement, two new landscape factors entered the rural scene, one advantageous to the economy, the other not. Georgia early became a supporter of railroads. In the 1840's a rail network took shape in the state, and two main lines with several branches crossed the fertile farmland of central Georgia. Half a century of farming, however, had modified that fertile farmland. Severe erosion began to be seen. As early as 1849, George White noted: "The soil has been impoverished by a bad system of cultivation." Further, he warned, "the lands generally are much worn, but susceptible of improvement." But such deterioration of land is not to be wondered at among farmers used to finding new lands to clear when the old ones wore out.

The Landscape of 1864

The year 1864 marked the end of a period. Because the change began abruptly, a description of the landscape as it was in the last hours of the period is typical. The way of life prevailing when Sherman's troops spread over the land was meant to continue indefinitely. What the soldiers saw was a civilization taken by surprise, its ordinary affairs sharply disrupted.

It was a healthy picture. As one writer described it: "The country between Madison, Covington, and Milledgeville, is a perfect garden; . . . farmyards well stocked with hogs and poultry, stacks of corn fodder, corn-houses, and bins filled with corn and grain." And he mentions the abundance of sweet potatoes, sheep, and cattle.

The land was about evenly divided between fields and woods. If Captain Rziha's traverse is separated into sections of about four miles, variation between extremes of one-third and two-thirds cleared is found. Yet there was no grouping or regionalization of cleared or wooded land. Fields generally were fairly large and were indiscriminately scattered, seemingly in almost complete disregard of variations in the land surface. Low, wet places, steep slopes, gullies—all appeared within the field boundaries. A roughly rectangular shape of 80 to 100 acres was typical.

One or two large fields near the house accounted for the bulk of the cleared land, but a few small fields and a few houses associated with only a small nonforested area did occur. No evidence is available to indicate to what degree, if any, the woods included second-growth stands. The chances are that abandonment of fields was not important here before 1864, though in longer-settled parts of the state it was widespread.

A cluster of buildings formed the center of activity for the farm—or "plantation," as the local people were pleased to call them. A few plantation headquarters, it is true, consisted of a solitary cabin or house. Some, if not all, of these solitary houses represented rudimentary farms, and small fields and large wooded areas tended to be associated with them. But the usual plantation house was accompanied by as many as eight other buildings, or even more. Some of the buildings were barns, according to Captain Rziha, though he labeled fewer barns than farmhouses; other unlabeled buildings could also have been barns. Most of the buildings were clustered about the house or about an adjoining yard, often in neat rows; these latter were probably the slave quarters. There were not many such plantation headquarters: only 72 appear in the some 30 square miles mapped by Captain Rziha. A quick calculation will show how little the average farm had increased in size from the original land grant. The farmhouses were rather evenly spaced along the road, generally half a mile from one to the next, with occasional gaps of more than a mile.

Because many of the houses seen by Captain Rziha are still standing, the typical ante bellum house can be described further. It was a one- or two-story rectangular building of huge hewn logs to which cross pieces were fastened by slots and pegs; the exterior was made of overlapping slats. A chimney was placed at each end, and the house rested on short pillars, without a cellar. Generally there were porches and wings.

Roads were streaks of red mud or dust across the landscape. "Considering the nature of the roads," said Sherman, "fifteen miles per day was deemed the limit" for the wagons traveling from dawn until soon after noon. Nor were the roads numerous: slaves would not be traveling around often. Farms were largely self-sufficient, and most county seats were by then connected by rail lines. Primarily roads served wagons carrying cotton to town.

Captain Rziha passed through several towns. He did not map Covington or Milledgeville, but he did map three villages or hamlets, at least partly. Sandtown, later called Newborn by the Post Office, was the first —a tavern at the crossroads, a church, a repair shop, and six other buildings. Fifteen years earlier about a dozen families had been living there. Nine miles down the road was Shady Dale. Captain Rziha's map shows a church, a cluster of six buildings, and the neighboring farm headquarters of Squire Whitfield. In 1849 there had been in Shady Dale two churches, a tavern, a store, and an "academy." The third hamlet was on the downgrade. Clopton's Mills, which "used to be Post Office," consisted of a church, a sawmill some distance away, and a farmhouse in between.

Along the traverse and standing alone were several nonfarm buildings. Three miles west of Covington near the Yellow River were a mill and a church. A town could perhaps have grown here but for the Civil War. Between Sandtown and Shady Dale was a schoolhouse, and beyond Shady Dale an isolated church.

The Second Invasion and Its Aftermath

Local history dates from the visit of General Sherman. And well it may because life began anew when the last stragglers and lawless "bummers" disappeared from sight. An account of the great march is not necessary here; many books have been written on the subject. The important thing is what happened to the landscape.

Sherman's soldiers conducted a thorough invasion across central Georgia. They carried off all the food they could lay their hands on. Temporarily this meant hunger or even starvation for the Georgians. But food included also seed and livestock, the bases for future production. Slaves, the human-labor factor, were set free—many to wander about aimlessly for a time. Disruption of the former way of life was nearly complete.

Loss of work animals and dispersal of the labor supply caused the temporary abandonment of most of the agricultural land. Some whites and more colored people left the state. More than anything else, however, the great reduction in horses, mules, and oxen limited the amount of land that could be cultivated. Where the livestock had escaped the depredations of the invading army, the attitude of the freedmen was the dominant factor: the plantation owner simply could not get laborers to do the work. Five years after Sherman's march less than half of the formerly improved land was in use.

A decade passed before an equilibrium became established. It was not a return to ante bellum conditions except for the crops planted. Attempts to hire Negroes as laborers where before they had worked as slaves were partly successful for a time. Soon, however, an entirely new way of life emerged.

The Post-Civil War Landscape

Information about the landscape associated with the postwar way of life is scattered. Census statistics that become more and more detailed; a map showing houses and roads in 1894; the evidence left in the landscape—all these are prime sources.

Cleared land had never returned to its prewar condition. After 1880 improved land became stabilized at about one-third of the total area; the census of that year reported abandoned or "old fields," which when added to improved acreage about equaled the prewar total of improved land. However, recent inspection reveals that at least 80 per cent of the land has been cleared at one time or another. At first, recovery from the aftereffects of the war included cleaning up abandoned fields, but soon worn-out fields covered with a tangle of valueless second growth ceased to be attractive. New land had to come from woods. Furthermore, erosion was taking its inexorable toll. Thus clearing of land little more than balanced the loss due to abandonment of worn-out land.

Thirty years after Yankee troops had scoured the countryside, part of the area of the traverse was included on a United States Geological Survey topographic map. Houses had increased threefold. Study of these houses in the present landscape quickly reveals that the increase was due entirely to construction of cabins or tenant houses. Freedmen had spread out over the former plantations to take up farming as tenants, and the rural population became dispersed. As a result, farm units were much smaller: where farms of less than 200 acres had been rare, now more than half were smaller than 50 acres, and the average size had dropped below 100 acres.

Fields also were necessarily smaller, even though the kinds of crops had changed little. Ten of the fields around a cabin equaled one field formerly cared for by slaves. To counterbalance a shortage of labor, land use grew more intensive, and fertilizers came into use for the first time. Corn and cotton were the main crops; all other crops together did not occupy as large an area as either of these two. Cotton continued to be the product that brought in cash.

Freedom and dispersal of farm labor produced other changes. More roads were needed as shopping and social activities increased. Roads on the 1894 map are nearly double in number those shown by Captain Rziha. New railroads were built after the old ones had been rebuilt; the Middle Georgia and Atlanta Railroad ran beside the Covington-Eatonton road for at least half of the traverse. The larger towns grew even larger, and hamlets spread over the countryside almost like a rash. Along major roads hamlets, consisting of a few houses and perhaps a store at a crossroads or at a railroad stop, appeared about every two miles except near the larger towns; nine or more grew along the traverse in addition to the places previously mentioned. With a head start, Shady Dale and Newborn became fair-sized villages of several hundred citizens.

Even the character of the livestock changed. Sheep and oxen eventually became rarities. Hogs and horses never regained their former importance, though considerable numbers were still kept. Cattle were used primarily for milk, and only incidentally for meat. Mules rapidly exceeded their former numbers and were unquestionably the dominant traction animal. In those days the colored man aspired to his "forty acres and a mule."

Colored population increased everywhere. Urban white population also increased, though the numbers of rural whites remained little changed. More colored farmers meant more fields planted to cotton, which became steadily more dominant in the landscape, even though corn did not decline. Slight increases in the area of cultivated land and the number of cows were recorded. Unseen perhaps, but not unfelt, was the gradual loss of soil fertility through erosion. The streams ran red-brown with Georgia clay.

The settlement period of tenant farmers lasted for more than half a century. Earlier, when slaves had been regarded as capital investment, the average farmer had appeared prosperous. Now, with crude cabins and tenant farms everywhere, the wealth per farmer amounted to much less. The agricultural frontier had long gone by, and the lower Georgia Piedmont was no longer a superior farm region. It was a region of humble farmers plodding behind mules in their cotton fields. The large number of Negroes earned it the name "Black Belt," and the dependence on cotton let it be included in the "Cotton Belt." Then, just before the 1920's, a third invasion disrupted this state of affairs.

King Cotton Dethroned

The twenties were not gay in Georgia. No violence marked the third invasion, but it might just as well have done so, for the damage was easily as severe as that of 60 years before. Cotton, as usual, was the source of all wealth. Without cotton, what was there? This question rapidly became urgent; for across the borders of the state advanced an army of boll weevils, which made quick work of the cotton in the growing boll.

Despair followed in the wake of the boll weevil. Whole communities disappeared, their members going off to cities near or far. Almost half of the Negro population left, and mules, horses, and hogs decreased in proportion. Half the cropland was abandoned. Cotton was no longer king, and many of those who had paid it allegiance left its former domain. Corn was now the leading crop, even though its acreage had diminished.

The decrease in agricultural crops, animals, and workers was precipitous; there is therefore a tendency to lay all the blame on the boll weevil alone. Investigation, however, hints that all was not well even before the boll weevil invasion. Rural villages such as Newborn and Shady Dale were already in decline. Rural Negro population had ceased to grow, though there was an increase among Negroes in general. Why

were so many people leaving the rural areas? The answer is obvious
There was no longer any new land available, and the soil was wearing
out; yields of cotton and corn were maintained only by use of more
and more fertilizer. Better opportunities for making a living were being
found in factories in northern cities. The road to the city had already
been explored; it rapidly became a highway.

The kind of land abandoned during the 1920's is revealing. Recent
maps and aerial photographs provide abundant information. Steep and
rough areas were abandoned wholesale, level places continued in
cultivation. This was a time when differences in the quality of land
were thrown into bold relief. Good land continued to be farmed, poor
land was left to grow up in woods. Poverty areas of the "Tobacco Road"
variety must have been relatively common.

Not that attempts at conservation were unknown. In order to combat
soil erosion and make farming on steep slopes profitable again, contour
plowing and terracing were tried. They helped, but it was too late in
most areas, and many a contoured hill today helps retain soil moisture
for second-growth woods. The boll weevil invasion was really the final
blow that brought down an already weakened structure.

The Present Landscape

Remnants of the tenant period are still to be seen. These serve to
emphasize the changes that are becoming fixed into yet another settlement pattern.

Regional differences in woodland and cleared land are striking
(Fig. 2). Some areas have little or no cleared land; some more than
a square mile in extent may be 80 per cent cleared. Because Captain
Rziha's traverse follows an old road, it is not absolutely representative
of general conditions. The road sought out favorable areas, and about
half of the traverse is thus not wooded. Averages put forests today at
two-thirds to three-quarters of the total. Before the reader reflects that
this is not much of a change, there is more to say.

During the last 15 years woods have increased consistently everywhere, though the increase has generally been small except in areas already mostly in forest; only small fields or irregular and poorly accessible parts of larger fields have been surrendered to trees. Trees have
been cleared from some spots, but the cleared places add up to only
one-quarter as much area as that claimed by woodland. Large-scale
clearing of fields has not been important recently.

But a fundamental change in fields is again taking place. The large
field is returning: the present-day field typically covers some 50 acres.
Frequently, irregular clumps of woods somehow became established
between fields. Thus, by eliminating a few trees and combining small

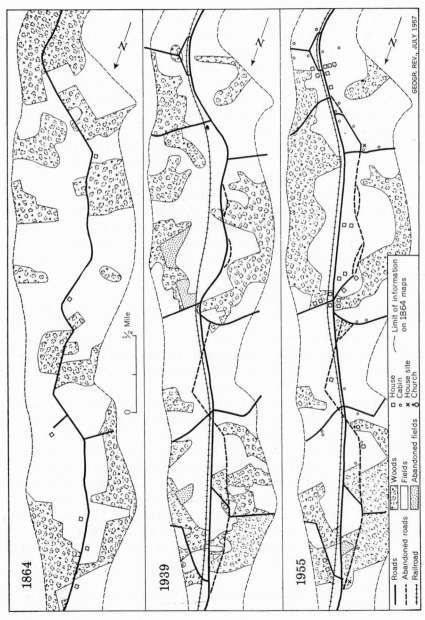

FIGURE 2: Section of Captain Rziha's 1864 traverse remapped in 1939 and 1955, showing changes in pattern of woods and fields. This area lies between Shady Dale and Newborn (See Figure 1).

1864

1939

1955

N

½ Mile

0

GEOGR. REV., JULY 1957

Roads
Abandoned roads
Railroad

Woods
Fields
Abandoned fields

□ House
○ Cabin
× House site
⚲ Church

—— Limit of information
on 1864 maps

plots, it was possible to obtain a larger field. Tiny fields are making their last stands in the undesirable regions where forest is rapidly capturing all the land. Furthermore, the shape of fields is no longer regular. All sorts of irregular forms are represented, depending a great deal on the terrain.

It is interesting to compare present-day fields with those of 1864. In general pattern, no correlation is evident. However, the land more attractive in drainage and slope that was clear of woods in 1864 remains clear today. Such fields are associated with houses whose sites, or occasionally even the identical house, have continued to be occupied. This fact, together with the comments of local residents, indicates a retention of superior fields in regular use for more than a century. Other fields have obviously been abandoned or cleared since 1864. The size of trees on the bulk of abandoned land precludes the possibility of fluctuation between fields and woods. There has, however, been a decided adjustment of fields to the terrain, especially in recent years.

Two notable exceptions to land abandonment were encountered in the recent traverse: two farms were being established from forest. In both, marketable pine standing on favorable terrain had been bought and cut, and the cutover land was being cleaned up for cultivation. Much of these pine stands had already been cleared in 1864. The evidence indicates that they all represent land formerly cultivated and since abandoned. Pure stands of pine along the traverse frequently identify abandoned fields. In contrast, mixed woods represent the natural vegetation.

Census statistics confirm what the visitor observes about land-use practices. A beef economy is emerging and eclipsing the cotton-tenant economy. Beef is the big new crop. Where cropland formerly occupied nearly all cleared land, it now occupies less than half, and pastures have become important. Herds of beef cattle are seen everywhere. Corn and cotton, wheat and oats, still grow in some fields, but beside them are farms newly fenced and embarked on a program of meat production. Significant in this connection is the recent appearance of farm ponds. Thirteen were located along the 1955 traverse where aerial photographs taken 15 years ago before showed none. These ponds serve primarily for the watering of livestock and only incidentally for erosion control.

Rural population has decreased, and farm size has increased. The average farm size has risen rapidly to more than 200 acres. This larger size is the result of the near disappearance of small tenant farms and a corresponding growth of the "neoplantation" boasting more than 500 acres.

The rural colored population has decreased markedly, but, surprisingly, the rural white population has remained fairly constant. There are now almost as many white people in rural areas as there are colored.

The explanation is the appearance of a rural nonfarm element. This change in farm population is reflected by rural housing. True, many farmhouses stand empty, yet the number of houses is tending to increase. But the new houses are rural nonfarm dwellings, a status that some former farmhouses now also enjoy. There are regional differences, however. Where good roads are not near, the number of houses is decreasing.

A few old houses and cabins are still in use. But those sturdy ante bellum houses which somehow escaped destruction by Sherman's army and have withstood the erosion of years are disappearing. Dry rot is taking its inevitable toll, and the demand for better homes is having its effect. The once-common cabin is going down the same road. Some are used to store hay. Others are in all stages of decay. Present housebuilding and replacement, following no dominant architectural style, are going on at a rate that must amaze old residents.

Unusual concentrations of rural nonfarm populations are to be found in a part of the traverse—a rural-urban phenomenon of the automobile age. Covington lies only 35 miles from the center of metropolitan Atlanta, and parts of the traverse to the west are even closer; people make their home in this zone and commute to Atlanta to work.

The road pattern of today is essentially the road pattern of 1894. Nevertheless, there have been significant changes. Sections of a mile or so have been abandoned here and there, and more than twice as many new stretches have appeared. Until recently, "primitive" was the only word to describe the transportation routes. After the advent of the automobile hard-surfaced roads appeared slowly, restricted to major through routes. As late as 1940 the Covington-Eatonton road was a winding axle breaker. It crossed the parallel rail line 10 times in 25 miles. Then during World War II road building finally moved into high gear. The Covington-Eatonton road was rebuilt as a highway with three rail crossings instead of ten, and other routes have been or are being relocated and rebuilt.

Not much traffic is seen these days on the once proud rail lines. With increased automobile travel, passenger service on the lesser lines has been discontinued. Significantly, little bus transportation is available to replace the trains.

The little towns have also lost out. One by one the hamlets are disappearing. Only a few have remained vigorous. Along the highway and remote from shopping centers such as Covington two hamlets in the area of the traverse are still present and even growing; elsewhere three can boast a group of houses or a store. In contrast, one hamlet has grown in recent years to a population of well over 100: Almon, west of Covington, enjoys a position in the expanding shadow of Atlanta. Shady Dale and Newborn are in a state of suspended animation. On the other hand, the county seats along the traverse are growing rapidly and have populations numbering several thousands. Industries are coming their way. Developments in the cities outside the traverse are teaming up with rural change to make an entirely new South.

The Future

By World War II the machine age had reached rural Georgia. The war drew more farm laborers to the cities and factories. For them, new horizons were opened, and many did not intend to go back to following a mule. This drain on the already diminished labor supply reduced the rural population still further, and the resultant labor shortages stimulated the development of mechanization. For those who could be induced to stay, better conditions had to be offered. Menial labor is now rapidly disappearing. More and more of the farm work is being done by tractor, which is also another factor in the increase in field size. A greater yield per man-hour is becoming necessary if the South is to compete for the ever more expensive worker.

Only the best lands are now being used in the lower Georgia Piedmont. A new prosperity is appearing here and there in the forest, and crops will no doubt continue to be grown on those scattered openings of good land (Fig. 2). One suspects that cotton persists, even in reduced amount, through the forces of tradition and subsidy. The accusation has even been heard that beef production can pay only for those with outside sources of capital. Be that as it may, a better life is possible than that of the old tenant farmer, but to provide it, large farms are necessary, whether pastured or cultivated. The steep, worn-out land will have to rest for many years and, incidentally, yield a valuable crop of forest products.

III. MAN'S PERCEPTION OF HIS ENVIRONMENT

Cultural background, time, and place are important variables in man's perception of his environment. The varying nature of this perception influences how physical and human resources are utilized as well as the human attitude toward liabilities and amenities of diverse regions. Thus, in order to describe and analyze areal differences from place to place, geographers must take these variables into consideration.

This approach has considerable affinity to human ecology or the linkages of man to the plants, animals, and his physical environment in general. In the early 1920's Harlan Barrows proposed that human ecology receive the main emphasis in geography. He recommended that the geographer abandon pure research on the physical environment and urged that he concern himself only with the physical environment in relation to man. This advice was not followed, and a new approach to ecology, man's perception of his relation to his natural surroundings, has developed in the period after the Second World War. This approach examines how man views such things as flood hazards along a hurricane coast or a river valley. Man's settlement pattern, particularly his persistence in staying in danger areas, can be related to the attitude of the occupant toward the area. Such an attitude is often based in the cultural background of the person.

The selections in this section exemplify the geographic view of man's perception of the environment. The article by Morgan and Moss is a recent interpretation of the value of the ecological approach to geography and is followed by Lowenthal's philosophical article on perception. Flannery summarizes the evolution of food ecology in Mesopotamia and Gould illustrates a quantitative and model-building approach to the topic of "Man against His Environment."

4. Geography and Ecology: The Concept of the Community and Its Relation to Environment

W. B. Morgan and R. P. Moss

Harlan Barrows made a plea for the development of geography as "human ecology" in the early 1920's. His advice to abandon the study of the physical environment was fortunately not accepted at that time. Since then, the discipline of geography has evolved in its thinking about the concept, and Morgan and Ross present here a recent interpretation. They suggest that developments in ecological studies, particularly community ecology and biogeography, would place "stress on relationships such as energy balance, biogeochemical cycles, limiting factors, and population dynamics, [and result in] a geography of communities [which] would be closely linked with other expanding fields of knowledge." This statement brings up to date the geographical approach toward ecology—the linkages between man, plants, and animals with their environments. Of particular interest is the significance they place on this approach to teaching and research.

Geography has to deal with such a wide variety of phenomena that it contains many specialists with divergent interests, and several attempts have been made to narrow the field. Concern with the "causal relationships existing in the complex of heterogenous phenomena at one place and the causal connections among phenomena at different places" provides so vast a task that, as Hartshorne confesses, there must be "some principle of selection." It is not our intention to follow the arguments which lead to the conclusion that geography is the study of "the earth as the home of man," but rather to seek another principle of selection, to discover within the field a form of enquiry which may provide a coherent theme for teaching and research for some of those geographers dissatified with the present situation. No claim will be made that any principle discovered should be the

SOURCE: *Annals of the Association of American Geographers,* LV (June, 1965), 339–50. The authors are members of the Department of Geography, University of Birmingham, England.

sole guide in future geographic studies, although the authors naturally are concerned to seek a principle which will fit current trends and provide a starting point for profitable and possibly new lines of enquiry. The search for such a unifying principle has characterized geography throughout its development, with, in many cases, important results. For example, Davis, although concerned with providing a disciplinary fiber for geography from methods evolved within a systematic branch, instead developed a distinct science, whereas the cultural landscape concept of Sauer has provided, and still provides, for many geographers a unifying principle giving a distinctive field of study.

The Geography of Living Things

The distinction between natural and human phenomena is not easy to make. Indeed it has been argued that one of the peculiar features of geography is that it makes no such distinction; consequently, it bridges the gap between the physical and the social sciences. The best available summary of these views is contained in chapter VI of Hartshorne's *Perspective on the Nature of Geography*. Nevertheless, despite perhaps the lesser importance of the distinction in geography than in other related sciences, classification of phenomena by headings such as human and natural serves a useful purpose, even though the distinction between human and biological may be very difficult to make, perhaps more difficult than between either and physical phenomena. It is with the problem of distinguishing human from biological phenomena that we are concerned, or rather with its artificiality as a device which has set human geography apart from the other branches of study.

Our second concern is with the neglect by many geographers of the biological sciences and even of the social sciences; as a result methods developed in closely related fields which might usefully be applied in geography are frequently ignored. The greater neglect of the two has been of the biological sciences, which is surprising in view of the importance of soils, plants, and animals to man, and the importance, too, of considering man himself as a biological phenomenon and an agent. In a study which claims to attach so much importance to the relationships between man and physical environment, the neglect of soil, human nutrition, and disease is extraordinary. Only recently have soil studies begun to play a major part in geographical research and has the importance of food production in calorific terms been stressed. Despite assertions, early in the history of the subject, that the soil was the basis of the state and that ecology was an organizing principle of geography, until recently, soils and ecology have

played only a minor role in the curricula of most university geography departments. Although these early assertions may now seem extravagant, it might have been supposed that the rapid expansion of
knowledge and ideas in these two important branches of knowledge
would have led to some earlier reappraisals of the situation by geographers.

It is the authors' view that there is a geography of living things
which, whatever the relationships between biological phenomena on
the one hand and the so-called physical basis on the other, has its
own peculiar problems common to its various branches. Such a geography is more than ecology and it is directly concerned with problems
of relationship such as those between man and environment which so
many geographers have claimed to be their chief interest. Whereas
such a geography may comprehend the various forms of human geography, it can hardly contain geomorphology and climatology as they
are mainly taught and studied, since these subjects are concerned
with inanimate nature and with the classification and origins of certain
earth phenomena rather than with their relationship, and they have
their own distinctive methods. Geomorphology and climatology might
together be properly considered a distinct physical geography. A
geography of living things is concerned not with certain forms of
relationship as ecology but with all forms of relationship affecting the
distribution, location, and space organization of living things as they
appear on the surface of the earth. The study is concerned with reality
and not with phenomena in isolation or even in part isolation. Yet, it
is contended that study must proceed by analysis, that is by the distinction of given phenomena or groups of phenomena, one from another, and the study of these as central features within a perceived
system of relationships. The notion that either synthesis or integration can be attempted by geographers is rejected. Both were dismissed by Stevens as semantic errors: "You cannot integrate man and
his environment. Those who believe so have been carried away with
a word and imagined it a thought." In any case if either synthesis
or integration were possible both would already exist in nature and
have to be observed and analyzed by geographers, not created by
them.

The concept of a regional geography distinct from systematic geography should, therefore, also be rejected. This does not mean that
the entire content of work hitherto labeled regional is not useful
in the new context. The point is that all geographic study is concerned
with relationships considered areally. The distinction lies not between
systematic and regional divisions, but between studies concerned with
individual features or species, and studies concerned with groups of
different features or species. For the most part studies of individual

features or species will require considering these in groups, since geographers are not often concerned with single individuals. Such groups of like individuals may be termed societies. The areas they occupy on the surface of the earth may be regarded as formal regions. Studies concerned with groups of different although related individuals will be concerned with "communities." The areas they occupy may be regarded as functional regions. Thus regional and systematic concepts will be useful alike within both of the major divisions of study and would serve equally to provide understanding of the features studied as earth phenomena. There would be no place for the scissors-and-paste synthesis rightly criticized by Wooldridge.

Development of the Concept of the Community

The concept of the community is one of special interest to us and we regard it as important in the development of future teaching and research. The study of societies in a geographical context may simply continue the methods already developed in systematic geography and in the nearest related sciences. The study of communities in geography, however, offers an approach akin to that of regional geography and yet fundamentally different in that the method must still proceed by analysis. The patterns of relationship to be understood and appreciated are more complex than those affecting societies. Yet the task of discerning the region, that is, the area occupied by the community, will be easier than that of distinguishing some of the more nebulous regions hitherto recommended for geographical appreciation, and its distinction may provide useful information. Therefore, something indicating the aims and the problems of community study within the field of geography, its relations to ecology and sociology, and its development as a geographical concept must now be provided.

In part the authors' notions have been developed from the ideas of Stevens. These ideas were largely ignored when published, as they were in one sense before and in another sense after their time, for Stevens proposed a revolution in geographical thinking, based not on the views of contemporaries, but on those of a previous generation of geographers, notably Herbertson. The core of Stevens' thinking is contained in the following quotation:

Man must be looked at objectively by the geographer and even his significant antics must be taken to be as natural as the physical environment. The natural geographical region is a result of what, for want of a better word, we may agree to call synthesis proceeding in nature, under our eyes, but not by our voluntary action. There are two aspects of this synthetic product: the environmental aspect, essential to which is man himself, and the human aspect, using the language of ecology. Dissociation of these had led geographers to attempts for which they are not qualified and certain unqualified students to call themselves geographers. . . .

For these two aspects of the same thing there are convenient names, but it is essential to remember that coherent geography must regard them as indicating mere aspects of the same thing. The one is *region*, and it focuses attention on the environment as space. The other is *community*, and it indicates that special attention is to be paid to the functioning, or dynamic, aspect of the case. The natural geographical region must be defined by reference to both. Otherwise it is necessary to drop the *geographical*. The physical region of 'uniform' or 'dominating' physical characteristic may interest the topographer (in the survey sense), the climatologist, the pedologist. It is an irrelevance in geography.

Some may consider the last sentence rather sweeping and dogmatic, and it is no part of the present thesis to argue in its favor. The significant point to be drawn from the quotation is that here is the notion of community linked with that of region to provide a concept of basic significance in geography. It is not without interest that Stevens had planned in outline a course of geographical instruction at university level in which the main theme was the study of human and animal communities and in which a recommended basic text was to have been Wallace's *Island Life*.

A second major influence on us has been the environment of west Africa. Geographers who have worked in tropical Africa have had experience not only of environments differing greatly from those of Europe and North America, but have lived within a region of enormous cultural variety. Balandier has drawn attention, for example, to the richness and diversity of political experience in Africa, likening the continent to a great laboratory containing varied political forms. This variety of political and social institutions emphasizes the differences between communities in Africa in a way which is more readily apparent than in Europe. African communities provide distinctive elements in the population distribution map, and their different cultures provide different responses to and use of environment. Their agricultural practices and their economies are frequently profoundly influenced by social practices and structure. This viewpoint has already been expressed in a paper with limited circulation in which it was suggested that there should be a definition of regions on the basis of a community rather than on a physical basis and that this would lead to the following differences of outlook:

1. The region would be regarded as a changing area according to the expansion, contraction, or migration of the people concerned.

2. Study of the physical environment would be from the viewpoint of the community and would thus be integrated with human studies.

3. The old order of approach (to regional studies) would be in-

verted, for one would begin with man and his problems of adaptation and end with the physical conditions.

This does not mean that in human geography the idea of a community region belongs mainly to African studies, although clearly it may serve a useful purpose there. There are many different kinds of community and ranks or hierarchies of communities. In Europe, for example, one may recognize the areas occupied by nation states as forms of community region, just as they also are in Africa, but forming larger units than the tribal regions and sometimes even cutting across them. Europe's tribal regions may have disappeared, but there are other forms of smaller community units in, for example, villages, towns, and cities. Political geography, as the study of nation states, may in this context form a very important part of geographical studies oriented around the theme of communities. Political geography might assume once more some of the importance which was attached to it at the end of the last century before Herbertson sought to turn attention away from political to his natural regions.

A third influence upon our thinking results from attempting to solve practical problems of agricultural planning in Nigeria. Studies of soils by reconnaissance methods for the rapid assessment of agricultural potential served to emphasize the unity of the community in which an individual soil series existed. Detailed and involved studies of the soil itself would almost always provide the information required concerning the effect of vegetation and of farming, as well as of other soil properties, but it was far simpler to consider the soil-plant community as a unit, introducing animals also where they played a major part in community relationships, as in the case of insects in plantations. No distinction needed to be made between communities in which human influence was profound and those in which it was not. Such composite observation is the basic technique of soil survey work both in Ghana and Nigeria, and is only validly interpreted if particular associations of plants, soils, and animals, including man, express in some considerable measure community functions, and interrelationships between unlike phenomena; that is to say, it is validly interpreted if functional interdependence finds formal expression as areal units.

Causation and the Unity of Nature

The search for natural laws or natural regions illustrates that concern with causes and with the assumed close relationship of man and the natural environment which governed late nineteenth century geographical thinking. Unfortunately the search for laws was abandoned by many geographers, some of whom undertook a somewhat sterile descriptive form of geography in which the concepts of land-scape and of the formal region played the chief roles. The exponents of late nineteenth century determinism, particularly Ratzel, and his later successors, were severely criticized and their views brought into disrepute. Determinist arguments, unfortunately, had all too often been based on limited or even flimsy evidence. Despite tremendous progress in the natural sciences in the nineteenth century, particularly in geology, botany, and zoology, and the importance of geographical thinking in the evolutionary theories of Darwin and Wallace, at least one sector of geographic science still lacked material and had to await the ecological and pedological research which has been such an im-portant feature of twentieth century field science. If Ratzel were right in maintaining that the soil was the basis of the state, then his political geography had to await another half century of research before his theories could be applied.

The Relationship of Biocenosis with Biotope

The early Russian pedologists were also very conscious of the wider significance of soil study, and of the relationship of the soil to nature as a whole. Dokuchaev in the late nineteenth century advocated the development of a new natural science which would emphasize the unity of nature. He wrote:

In studying these factors (the individual aspects of natural phenomena) espe-cially in trying to control them, one has to keep in mind as far as possible the unity, the completeness and the individuality of nature, and not its individual parts.

and also

Until now special bodies have been studies, . . . These studies have not con-sidered the correlation between the elements, nor the genetic, permanent and always regular association that exists between forces, bodies and phenomena. . . . However, these correlations, these regular interactions, make up the essence of perceived nature.

The study of these interactions was to be the basis of a new and separate science:

The study of the complex and manifold correlations and interactions, as well as of the laws that govern their secular transformations.

and a science with

its own strict and well-defined problems and methods, in no danger of being confused with existing branches of the natural sciences, and thoroughly per-meated by geography.

He considered that geography as then practiced and conceived, was unable to take on the task because of its descriptive and chorologic traditions, and it is purely in the formal sense that he used the term 'geography' in the quotation.

More recent Soviet thinking holds out more hope for the subject and it is in the biogeocenology of more recent Soviet biogeography that the ideas of Dokuchaev now find coherent expression, particularly in the work of Sukachev. *Biocenosis,* a concept attributed to Möbius, is a well defined and established ecological concept, conveying the idea of a group of plants and animals living together in a particular habitat; the *biotope,* a term probably originated by Dahl, conveys the complementary idea of the habitat in which a particular group of plants and animals live. These terms linked together developed into the idea of the *ecosystem,* a term coined by Tansley, which involves reciprocal relationships between biocenosis and biotope. As Macfadyen points out, it is the result of the realization that:

not only is a characteristic community of organisms associated with and dependent upon a characteristic habitat, but also the habitat is modified and to a greater or lesser extent created by the activities of the organisms. The two components evolve together in such a way as to develop into a single system.

Both ecosystem and the broadly equivalent idea of biogeocenosis are unified by the fact that the biosphere, including the active part of the soil, is characterized by a:

constant and complex series of transformations of matter and energy among organisms, the lower layers of the atmosphere and the surface of the earth's crust.

Biogeocenosis, however, is wider in content than the ecosystem; it has an extrovert aspect as well as the essential introversion of the ecosystem. In his earliest rationalizations, Sukachev included topography in the biogeocenosis; but later it was excluded since topography was considered simply a manifestation of the lithosphere, and was in no sense a natural body, as soil or plants or animals. Rode, however, would include it, but primarily in the sense of the actual form of the surface within a particular unit. Surface form is of little direct significance to organisms, although correlations between slope form and biological phenomena may often be clearly demonstrated. This is largely the result of the relationships existing between slope processes, between surface slope and hydrological phenomena, such as lateral water movement in the soil, and groundwater level, and between surface form and local and microclimate. Altough important and significant correlations between slopes and biological communities are characteristic of large areas of the surface of the earth, investigation of the causal relationships involved often demonstrates the existence of a more direct influence than surface form itself. Communities involving man are more sophisticated in their responses, and it may be argued that slope as such has an importance of its own in such a context, as in soil erosion problems, and in settlement siting. Nevertheless, whether surface form be included or not, geomorphology in the conventional sense is clearly not a part of biogeocenology.

Climate is included, however, in the idea of biogeocenosis, but only insofar as there is a reciprocal relationship between the biological components and the physical factors, that is in microclimate and to a certain extent in local climate. Parent rock may be part of the unit if it is sufficiently close to the surface to influence plant growth, but in general, the reciprocal relationship is with the soil and not the rock. Reciprocity is thus the criterion for inclusion within the unit, and Sukachev distinguishes between *components* and *factors* within a biogeocenosis, and between dependent and independent factors according to whether they originate inside or outside the system.

Thus it is clear that the essential relationships between living and nonliving matter, between biological and physical phenomena, exist in operation of the biosphere and in its processes. The biosphere may be viewed as a series of distinct ecosystems or biogeocenoses, concepts which provide a convenient and useful tool for study of the biosphere from the point of view of the geographer, since each is clearly concerned with space relationships and the delimitation of areal units. Into these units man comes both as a component and as a factor. As a component he fills a number of distinct niches, and here lies the justification for considering human populations and their activities as communities rather than as societies, despite their monospecific character. As a factor man is a profound modifier of natural balances, a source of energy, and a final determinant in interspecific competition, both of plants and animals.

The complexity of the biogeocenosis is the complexity of a community of communities. Within the total ecosystem individual communities of plants, of animals, and of soils may be validly distinguished and studies, and within polyspecific phytocenoses and zoocenoses individual species-populations may also be studied. All are valid and valuable studies, and are essential to the understanding of the total community and its organization, but the more selective the study the less connected with geographical reality it becomes. In the selection of one community within the whole for special study, one must temporarily relegate the remaining communities to the status of environmental factors; but as has already been argued, the only truly environmental factors, in the sense of being completely independent and external, are macroclimate and parent rock. This is not to insist that the study of individual components is not a proper occupation for the geographer, but merely to suggest that it is desirable that such study should in some way be directed towards a fuller understanding of the total community.

The Meaning of the Term "Community"

The previous discussion clearly raises the problem of the content of meaning in the term "community." Macfadyen has an excellent discussion of the subject from a biological point of view, reviewing the whole range of meaning from merely "An assemblage of organisms" to

something with the attributes of organization which, in the absence of factual support, rivals the daydreams of the alchemists.

At one end of the scale, Clark implied that the actual association of species is a mere coincidence of range, whereas at the other, Emerson spoke of communities in terms hitherto restricted to individual distinct living organisms. From the mass of often contradictory material, Macfadyen distinguishes three main ideas involved in the concept of the community, namely:

1. the presence together of a range of animals (or plants), and the fact that the same groups of species recur both geographically and in time, and that there are thus many examples of a given community type, which can be recognized and distinguished from other types;
2. that communities have a tendency towards dynamic stability;
3. that communities possess characteristics which cannot be predicted from the properties of the constituent organisms, and that thus the community represents a different and higher level of organization.

This last idea may be carried further and the community may be considered a superorganism. There is little or no evidence for this idea, but Macfadyen concludes that, provided the organismic concept be treated merely as an analogy, and not as an identity, these three ideas involve a valid and useful concept upon which to base one approach to ecological problems. He concludes:

because each community has its peculiar features, and because we have not yet collected enough information about any one community to analyze it fully, we cannot make very specific generalizations about the properties of all communities. Nevertheless, from the success of the working hypothesis and the clues so far discovered, we have a clear conception of what to expect and this includes the properties of species constancy, dynamic stability and organismic unity. At the same time the word community is also used, without prejudice, in the sense of an assemblage of species populations which can be segregated by means of the methods of ecological survey. . . . It remains for ecologists to demonstrate whether these two conceptions are in fact identical.

The basic features of the biological community are thus a definable species content, a certain quality of stability, and a clear organization; there may be strong analogies with the individual organism, but more than an analogy is probably not warranted.

It is relevant at this point to observe that, to the biologist, species composition of a community is an indication of individual function. The same species does not generally perform more than one function within a given community and, conversely, one niche is usually occupied by only one species. The character of the community involves essentially the presence of a number of different niches by which organization is expressed; whether these are in fact occupied by individuals of the same or different taxonomic classes is irrelevant to the notion as such. Thus associations of ants or bees or humans are more validly considered as communities than societies.

These ideas concerning communities, although discussed by Macfadyen largely in terms of animal populations, apply also with some modifications to plants as well. Important similarities do exist between plant and animal communities, although the nature, if not the very existence, of plant communities is a matter of much controversy. Macfadyen perceptively points out that much of the botanical confusion and controversy is due to the concentration of botanists:

on the formal study of plant associations and the neglect of the essential structure of the biotic community as a whole involving animals and other heterotrophic organisms.

Thus the botanical controversy largely revolves around the latter definition of a community contained in the extended quotation from Macfadyen; it is not germane to the basic idea of a community as a functioning entity, upon which the present argument is based.

The Place of Soil in the Community

At this stage it is necessary to examine in more detail the place of the soil in the community. Is it to be treated as a mere environmental factor to plant and animal communities, as largely inorganic and inert, or is its role more vital and important, and more closely linked with that of the ecosystem as a whole? Like plants and animals, the soil as such is validly considered an object of study as a whole and in its own right, but from one point of view the soil may be viewed as a distinct community, similar to, and yet essentially different from, plant and animal communities. It contains a distinct flora and fauna, it does tend toward a dynamic internal stability, and it does possess organization. Its distinctive feature is that its organization and stability is achieved by means of inorganic as well as by organic components and processes. It is, in fact, the link between organic and inorganic natural phenomena. Soil may be studied as a natural unit, that is, pedologically, but it may also be treated as a distinct component, a unique community within the ecosystem, that is, ecologically. Furthermore without the organic/inorganic link provided by the soil, plant and animal communities could not continue to exist.

Linkage between Plants, Animals, and Soil

Thus it is possible and valid to conceive of the ecosystem as a community composed of linked communities of plants, animals, and soils. What linkages then are present between them? Four types of relationship may be distinguished:

1. The influence of one community upon the others is essentially reciprocal, not independent, unilateral and environmental; each influences the others by cross-linkages of various types.
2. Each community takes part in a complex series of transformations of matter, embraced in biogeochemical cycles, such as the nitrogen cycle, the phosphorus cycle, and so on; with this group may also be included that part of the hydrological cycle which takes place within the ecosystem.
3. The whole system is the seat of complex energy transformations, based on photosynthesis by green plants, embracing food chain and web relationships, and involving other functions of living matter, such as respiration and transpiration, as well as the energy changes involved in inorganic reactions within the soil. These are of fundamental importance in the present context, since it is upon these that the whole concept of productivity is based.
4. Last, and related to the exchange of energy, each distinct ecosystem is characterized by a related microclimate, produced by the community components within the limits imposed by the macroclimate.

It is also significant that plant succession involves community changes. Changing plant associations are associated with modification of the habitat, and a change in characteristic fauna. This is strikingly illustrated in the classic work of Shelford and Clements in north-central Indiana, as well as in many other important studies of successional phenomena.

Parallels between Biological and Sociological Communities

It may be objected that human communities are so different from animal, plant, and soil communities that there is no point in seeking analogies between them, even though it may be conceded that human beings can be regarded as part of a larger community or natural complex. Human communities may be regarded in two ways:

1. Ecologically, as aggregates of different species focusing on man, including all the animals and plants which depend on man, and all those on which man in turn depends.

2. Socially, as aggregates of one species, man, consisting of individuals with a variety of interests and functions which, joined together, make possible one social and economic unit.

In the first sense there is no difference between the two notions of human community and of animal or plant community. In the second the only near analogies to the human community are in the insect world, particularly among ants, termites, and bees. Yet the two notions are not so very different for the important feature is the uniting of individuals with different functions. The fact of species differentiation in the one case and not in the other is not without significance, but is of lesser importance and is not fundamental to the notion of community.

The real parallels between biological and sociological communities are thus apparent. Each may be considered as a more or less complex system of organization, involving transformations of matter and energy by the complementary activities of particular organisms fulfilling distinct and more or less unique functions within the community. These transformations imply both movement in space and real space organization. Sociological and biological communities both involve properties and characteristics different from the sum of the properties of the individual organisms, or of the societies or single-species populations of which they are composed. Furthermore, they are linked together in reality by the dependence of man upon other animals and plants for his very existence. This is especially apparent in agricultural communities, but is no less true in urban organization and function, though here other factors attain greater importance in affecting the type and expression of the organization present.

Many sociological theorists have rejected all forms of organic analogy and have objected to the views of earlier organic or natural sociologists such as Herbert Spencer. Such attacks may, as Rex submits, be misleading. The organic model may provide "a source of verifiable hypotheses," and it is in this sense that both sociologists and geographers may look at the concept of the community in different fields. The purpose is not to study species, but to study the structure and functions of a community within a space or spaces. The analogy is made clear not only by Rex, but also by Radcliffe Brown who com-

pares social structures with organic structures and draws parallels between individual human beings and living cells, between the different
relationships of the basic units and between the different forms of
continuity. Rex admits that one problem in the analogy is that the
sociologist is less interested in the spatial arrangement of the individual units than is the biologist, but there precisely is the geographer's
field of interest. Admittedly, as Rex explains, "the biological model is
only useful in suggesting explanations for some human activities," and
therefore is only of limited use to the sociologist. For the geographer,
or rather perhaps for the social geographer, that limited use is of
great importance because the activities concerned are those which
maintain community structure and are of major interest in any spatial
studies. These activities have been described as having the function
of maintaining social structure and stress has been laid on the word
function and on the purposive nature of the activities. Similarly, the
social geographer may conceive of the community region as a functional region, that is an area purposively demarcated and used by
its occupants within which their space-using activities are related
closely to one another to maintain the structure of their community.

The Role of Biogeography

Biogeography is concerned with the study of the ecosystem, the community of communities, soil, plant, and animal, which exists at the
surface of the earth. It is different from pure ecology in that it is,
through the soil treated as a community, firmly linked to the earth. It
is different also because it concentrates its interest principally upon
the space organization as an areal expression of community function
and interrelationship; furthermore, it is distinct in its concentration
upon an attempt to appreciate total biological reality, including man
himself as an essential component, rather than as an external influence.
The study of biogeography provides the major link between man and
land, and between land and man. Few other functional relationships
can be so convincingly demonstrated.

It may well be objected that such study is no part of "geography"
because of the necessity for biological and ecological knowledge in
its understanding. In this connection it is relevant to point out that
the knowledge required is no more specialized, no more recondite,
and no more esoteric than that required as a matter of course, and
without question, in the case of geomorphology, climatology, or economic geography, or even historical geography. Furthermore, the founders of modern geography, notably but not exclusively von Humboldt,
were convinced of the fundamental importance of biological phenomena, so that the inclusion of biogeography in geography proper as a

fundamental and essential part of the subject is no innovation. It is rather a return to the saner days prior to the preoccupation with morphology.

The Role of Quantitative Study

It is important to notice that the biological community, both as a whole and as separate community-units, has shown itself capable of quantitative study. This is especially true of energy exchange and balance, limiting factors, and population dynamics. Statistical study of species association as an indicator of community structure has been a notable development, and many other applications of statistical techniques have been devised; indeed this constitutes one of the fields of more rapid advance in ecological study. Furthermore, such concepts as the *nodum* of Poore in relation to the definition and recognition of plant communities would seem to be worthy of wider application than to plants alone. The strong analogies between biological and sociological communities would suggest the profitability of the mutual exchange of techniques and methods.

Conclusion

We would suggest that geographical thinking would profit considerably from the adoption of the ecologic rather than the physiographic point of view. The physiographic elements in geography, slopes and macroclimate, are truly environmental, and are independent of, though influencing, biological phenomena in general, and man in particular. Thus they logically constitute a separate and distinct physical geography, for, if it be conceded that man is an essential element in geography, then interest logically should center on the biological relationship rather than on the physical one, for it is mainly through the biological relationship that any major link between man and land must be established. The idea of the community provides a focus for such thinking and study. Sufficient valid analogies exist between the biological concept and the sociological to provide a coherent focus for the study of the significance and character of the space organization of geographical phenomena. Such a formulation leads naturally to an ecological, rather than to a physiographic frame of reference, but is nevertheless related strongly to the surface of the earth. It could in part serve to remedy the valid complaint of Ackerman that:

morphology was not a particularly happy choice as an analogue method, and the hint given by Barrows on ecology was never seriously followed up by his colleagues.

5. Geography, Experience, and Imagination: Towards a Geographical Epistemology

David Lowenthal

This article demonstrates the significance of man's perception of his surroundings in explaining his interpretation of them. As Lowenthal says, "every image and idea about the world is compounded . . . of personal experience, imagination, and memory." The combination of experience of various kinds as interpreted through the culture, habits, and ideas of an individual or group helps shape impressions of the spatial chracter of the surface of the earth. Lowenthal makes a convincing case for the significance of these considerations.

"The most fascinating *terrae incognitae* of all are those that lie within the minds and hearts of men." With these words, John K. Wright concluded his 1946 presidential address before the Association of American Geographers. This paper considers the nature of these *terrae incognitae*, and the relation between the world outside and the pictures in our heads.[1]

SOURCE: *Annals of the Association of American Geographers,* LI (September, 1961), 241–60. The author is a research geographer with the American Geographical Society, New York City.

[1] John K. Wright, "Terrae Incognitae: the Place of the Imagination in Geography," *Annals,* Association of American Geographers, Vol. 37 (1947), pp. 1–15, on p. 15. The phrase "The World Outside and the Pictures in Our Heads" is the name of the first chapter in Walter Lippmann, *Public Opinion* (New York: Macmillan, 1922). As my subtitle suggests, this is not a study of the meaning or methods of geography, but rather an essay in the theory of geographical knowledge. Hartshorne's methodological treatises analyze and develop logical principles of procedure for geography as a professional science, "a form of 'knowing,'" as he writes, "that is different from the ways in which we 'know' by instinct, intuition, *a priori* deduction or revelation" (Richard Hartshorne, *Perspective on the Nature of Geography* [Chicago: Rand McNally, for Association of American Geographers, 1959], p. 170). My epistemological inquiry, on the other hand, is concerned with *all* geographical thought, scientific and other: how it is acquired, transmitted, altered, and integrated into conceptual systems; and how the horizon of geography varies among individuals and groups. Specifically, it is a study in what Wright calls *geosophy*: "the nature and expression of geographical ideas both past and present . . . the geographical ideas, both true and false, of all manner of people—not only geographers, but farmers and fishermen, business executives and poets, novelists and painters, Bedouins and Hottentots" ("Terrae Incognitae," p. 12). Because

The General and the Geographical
World View

Neither the world nor our pictures of it are identical with geography. Some aspects of geography are recondite, others abstruse, occult, or esoteric; conversely, there are many familiar features of things that geography scarcely considers. Beyond that of any other discipline, however, the subject matter of geography approximates the world of general discourse; the palpable present, the everyday life of man on earth, is seldom far from our professional concerns. "There is no science whatever," wrote a future president of Harvard, a century and a half ago, "which comes so often into use in common life." This view of geography remains a commonplace of contemporary thought. More than physics or physiology, psychology or politics, geography observes and analyzes aspects of the milieu on the scale and in the categories that they are usually apprehended in everyday life. Whatever methodologists think geography ought to be, the temperament of its practitioners makes it catholic and many-sided. In their range of interests and capacities—concrete and abstract, academic and practical, analytic and synthetic, indoor and outdoor, historical and contemporary, physical and social—geographers reflect man generally. "This treating of cabbages and kings, cathedrals and linguistics, trade in oil, or commerce in ideas," as Peattie wrote, "makes a congress of geographers more or less a Committee on the Universe." [2]

Geographical curiosity is, to be sure, more narrowly focused than mankind's; it is also more conscious, orderly, objective, consistent, uni-

geographers are "nowhere . . . more likely to be influenced by the subjective than in their discussions of what scientific geography ought to be" (*ibid.*), epistemology helps to explain why and how methodologies change.

[2] Most of the physical and social sciences are, both in theory and in practice, more generalizing and formalistic than geography. The exceptions are disciplines which, like geography, are in some measure humanistic: notably anthropology and history. The subject-matter of anthropology is as diversified as that of geography, and more closely mirrors the everyday concerns of man; but anthropological research still concentrates predominantly on that small and remote fraction of mankind—"primitive" or nonliterate, traditional in culture, homogeneous in social organization—whose ways of life and world views are least like our own (Ronald M. Berndt, "The Study of Man: an Appraisal of the Relationship between Social and Cultural Anthropology and Sociology," *Oceania*, Vol. 31 [1960], pp. 85–99). More particularistic, more concerned with uniqueness of context than geography, history also comprehends more matters of common interest (especially the acts and feelings of individuals); but because the whole realm of history lies in the past, most historical data is secondary, derivative. Although "geography cannot be strictly contemporary" (Preston E. James, "Introduction: the Field of Geography," in *American Geography: Inventory and Prospect* [Syracuse University Press, for Association of American Geographers, 1954], p. 14), geography is usually *focused* on the present; direct observation of the world plays a major role in geography, a trifling one in history. In theory, at least, the remote in space is everywhere (on the face of the earth) personally accessible to us, the remote in time accessible only through memories and artifacts.

versal, and theoretical than are ordinary queries about the nature of things. Like geography, however, the wider universe of discourse centers on knowledge and ideas about man and milieu; anyone who inspects the world around him is in some measure a geographer.

As with specifically geographical concepts, the more comprehensive world of ideas that we share concerns the variable forms and contents of the earth's surface, past, present, and potential—"a torrent of discourse about tables, people, molecules, light rays, retinas, air-waves, prime numbers, infinite classes, joy and sorrow, good and evil." It compounds truth and error, concrete facts and abstruse relationships, self-evident laws and tenuous hypotheses, data drawn from natural and social science, from history, from common sense, from intuition and mystical experience. Certain things appear to be grouped spatially, seriated temporally, or related causally: the hierarchy of urban places, the annual march of temperature, the location of industry. Other features of our shared universe seem unique, amorphous, or chaotic: the population of a country, the precise character of a region, the shape of a mountain.

Universally Accepted Aspects of the World View

However multifarious its makeup, there is general agreement about the character of the world and the way it is ordered. Explanations of particular phenomena differ from one person to another, but without basic concurrence as to the nature of things, there would be neither science nor common sense, agreement nor argument. The most extreme heretic cannot reject the essence of the prevailing view. "Even the sharpest dissent still operates by partial submission to an existing consensus," reasons Polanyi, "for the revolutionary must speak in terms that people can understand."

Most public knowledge can in theory be verified. I know little about the geography of Sweden, but others are better informed; if I studied long and hard enough I could learn approximately what they know. I cannot read the characters in Chinese newspapers, but hardly doubt that they convey information to the Chinese; assuming that there is a world in common, other peoples' ways of symbolizing knowledge must be meaningful and learnable.

The universe of geographical discourse, in particular, is not confined to geographers; it is shared by billions of amateurs all over the globe. Some isolated primitives are still ignorant of the outside world; many more know little beyond their own countries and ways of life; but most of the earth's inhabitants possess at least rudiments of the shared world picture. Even peoples innocent of science are privy to elements of our geography, both innate and learned: the normal relations between figure and ground; the distinctive setting of objects on the face of the earth;

the usual texture, weight, appearance, and physical state of land, air, and water; the regular transition from day to night; the partition of areas by individual, family, or group.

Beyond such universals, the geographical consensus tends to be additive, scientific, and cumulative. Schools teach increasing numbers that the world is a sphere with certain continents, oceans, countries, peoples, and ways of living and making a living; the size, shape, and general features of the earth are known by more and more people. The general horizon of geography has expanded rapidly. "Until five centuries ago a primal or regional sense of space dominated human settlements everywhere"; today, most of us share the conception of a world common to all experients.

The General Consensus Never Completely Accepted

The whole of mankind may in time progress, as Whittlesey suggests, to "the sense of space current at or near the most advanced frontier of thought." But no one, however inclined to pioneer, visits that frontier often, or has surveyed more than a short traverse of it. "Primitive man," according to Boulding, "lives in a world which has a spatial unknown, a dread frontier populated by the heated imagination. For modern man the world is a closed and completely explored surface. This is a radical change in spatial viewpoint." But the innovation is superficial; we are still parochial. "Even in lands where geography is part of a compulsory school curriculum, and among people who possess considerable information about the earth," Whittlesey points out, "the world horizon is accepted in theory and rejected in practice."

The "dread unknowns" are still with us. Indeed, "the more the island of knowledge expands in the sea of ignorance, the larger its boundary to the unknown." Primitive world views were simple and consistent enough for every participant to share most of their substance. Within Western scientific society, no one really grasps more than a small fraction of the public, theoretically communicable world view. The amount of information an individual can acquire in an instant or in a lifetime is finite, and miniscule compared with what the milieu presents; many questions are too complex to describe, let alone solve, in a practicable length of time. The horizons of knowledge are expanding faster than any person can keep up with. The proliferation of new sciences extends our powers of sense and thought, but their rigorous techniques and technical languages hamper communication; the common field of knowledge becomes a diminishing fraction of the total store.

On the other hand, we tend to assume things are common knowledge which may not be; what seems to me the general outlook might be mine alone. The most devoted adherents to a consensus often mistake their own beliefs for universal ones. For a large part of our world view, we take on faith much of what we are told by science. But we may have got it wrong; as Chisholm points out, "we are all quite capable of believing falsely at any time that a given proposition is accepted by the scientists of our culture circle." In our impressions of the shared world view we all resemble the fond mother who watched her clumsy son parade, and concluded happily, "Everyone was out of step but my Johnnie."

The World View Not Shared by Some

The most fundamental attributes of our shared view of the world are confined, moreover, to sane, hale, sentient adults. Idiots cannot suitably conceive space, time, or causality. Psychotics distinguish poorly between themselves and the outside world. Mystics, claustrophobics, and those haunted by fear of open space (agoraphobia) tend to project their own body spaces as extensions of the outside world; they are often unable to delimit themselves from the rest of nature. Schizophrenics often underestimate size and overestimate distance. After a brain injury, invalids fail to organize their environments or may forget familiar locations and symbols. Impairments like aphasia, apraxia, and agnosia blind their victims to spatial relations and logical connections self-evident to most. Other hallucinatory sufferers may identify forms but regularly alter the number, size and shape of objects (polyopia, dysmegalopsia, dysmorphopsia), see them always in motion (oscillopsia), or locate everything at the same indefinite distance (porrhopsia).

A fair measure of sensate function is also prerequisite to the general view of the common world. No object looks quite the way it feels; at first sight, those born blind not only fail to recognize visual shapes but see no forms at all, save for a spinning mass of colored light. They may have known objects by touch, but had nothing like the common conception of a space with objects in it. A purely visual world would also be an unreal abstraction; a concrete and stable sense of the milieu depends on synesthesia, sight combined with sound and touch.

To see the world more or less as others see it, one must above all grow up; the very young, like the very ill, are unable to discern adequately what is themselves and what is not. An infant is not only the center of his universe, he *is* the universe. To the young child, everything in the world is alive, created by and for man, and endowed with will: the sun follows him, his parents built the mountains, trees exist because they were planted. As Piaget puts it, everything seems intentional; "the child behaves as if nature were charged with purpose," and therefore conscious. The clouds know what they are doing, because they have a goal. "It is not because the child believes things to be alive that he regarded them as obedient, but it is because he believes them to be obedient that he regards them as alive." Asked what something is, the

young child often says it is *for* something— "a mountain is for climbing"
—which implies that it has been *made* for that purpose.

Unable to organize objects in space, to envisage places out of sight,
or to generalize from perceptual experience, young children are especially poor geographers. To learn that there are other people, who
perceive the world from different points of view, and that a stable, communicable view of things cannot be obtained from one perspective
alone, takes many years. Animism and artificialism give way only
gradually to mechanistic outlooks and explanations. "No direct experience can prove to a mind inclined towards animism that the sun and
the clouds are neither alive nor conscious"; the child must first realize
that his parents are not all-powerful beings who made a universe centered on himself. Piaget traces the development in children of perceptual and conceptual objectivity, on which even the most primitive
and parochial geographies depend.[3] Again in old age, however, progressive loss of hearing, deficiencies of vision, and other infirmities tend
to isolate one from reality and to create literally a second geographical
childhood.

Different as they are from our own, the perceived milieus, say, of
most children of the same age (or of many schizophrenics; or of some
drug addicts) may closely resemble one another. But there is little communication or mutual understanding of a conceptual character among
children. No matter how many features their pictures of the world may
have in common, they lack any shared view of the nature of things.

Mutability of the General Consensus

The shared world view is also transient: it is neither the world our
parents knew nor the one our children will know. Not only is the earth

[3] *Child's Conception of the World,* pp. 384–385; *Construction of Reality in the
Child* (New York: Basic Books, 1954), pp. 367–369. Piaget and his associates have
worked chiefly with schoolchildren in Geneva. How far their categories and explanations apply universally or vary with culture and milieu remains to be determined. Margaret Mead ("An Investigation of the Thought of Primitive Children,
with Special Reference to Animism," *Journal of the Anthropological Institute,* Vol.
62 [1932], pp. 173–190) found that Manus children rejected animistic explanations
of natural phenomena. They were more matter-of-fact than Swiss children (and
Manus adults) because their language was devoid of figures of speech, because
they were punished when they failed to cope effectively with the environment,
because their society possessed no machines too complex for children to understand, and because they were barred from animistic rites until past puberty. In
Western society, on the other hand, "the language is richly animistic, children are
given no such stern schooling in physical adjustment to a comprehensible and easily
manipulated physical environment, and the traditional animistic material which is
decried by modern scientific thinking is still regarded as appropriate material for
child training" (p. 189). (Indeed, books written for children show clearly that
adults think children ought to be animists.) Elsewhere, however, child animism appears to be significant and tends to decline with age and maturity (Gustav Jahoda,
"Child Animism: I. A Critical Survey of Cross-Cultural Research," *Journal of Social
Psychology,* Vol. 47 [1958], pp. 197–212).

itself in constant flux, but every generation finds new facts and invents new concepts to deal with them. "You cannot step twice into the same river," Heraclitus observed, "for fresh waters are ever flowing in upon you." Nor does anyone look at the river again in the same way: "The vision of the world geographers construct must be created anew each generation, not only because reality changes but also because human preoccupations vary."

Because we cherish the past as a collective guide to behavior, the general consensus alters very slowly. Scientists as well as laymen ignore evidence incompatible with their preconceptions. New theories which fail to fit established views are resisted, in the hope that they will prove false or irrelevant; old ones yield to convenience rather than to evidence. In Eiseley's phrase, "a world view does not dissolve overnight. Rather, like . . . mountain ranges, it erodes through long centuries." The solvent need not be truth. For example, in the seventeenth century many scholars believed that the earth—the "Mundane Egg"—was originally "smooth, regular, and uniform, without Mountains, and without a Sea"; to chastise man for his sins, at or before the Deluge, God crumpled this fair landscape into continents and ocean deeps, with unsightly crags and chasms; modern man thus looked out on "the Ruins of a broken World." This version of earth history was overthrown, not by geological evidence, but principally by a more sanguine view of God and man, and by a new esthetic standard: to eighteenth century observers, mountains seemed majestic and sublime, rather than hideous and corrupt.

Anthropocentric Character of the World View

Mankind's best conceivable world view is at most a partial picture of the world—a picture centered on man. We inevitably see the universe from a human point of view and communicate in terms shaped by the exigencies of human life. " 'Significance' in geography is measured, consciously or unconsciously," says Hartshorne, "in terms of significance to man"; but it is not in geography alone that man is the measure. "Our choice of time scale for climatology," according to Hare, "is conditioned more by the length of our life span than by logic"; the physics of the grasshopper, Köhler points out, would be a different physics than ours. "All aspects of the environment," as Cantril puts it, "exist for us only in so far as they are related to our purposes. If you leave out human significance, you leave out all constancy, all repeatability, all form."

Purpose apart, physical and biological circumstances restrict human perception. Our native range of sensation is limited; other creatures experience other worlds than ours. The human visual world is richly differentiated, compared with that of most species, but others see better in the dark, perceive ultraviolet rays as colors, distinguish finer detail, or see near and distant scenes together in better focus. To many creatures the milieu is more audible and more fragrant than to us. For every sensation, moreover, the human perceptual world varies within strict limits; how bright the lightning looks, how loud the thunder sounds, how wet the rain feels at any given moment of a storm depends on fixed formulae, whose constants, at least, are unique to man.

The instruments of science do permit partial knowledge of other milieus, real or hypothetical. Blood ordinarily appears a uniform, homogeneous red to the naked eye; seen through a microscope, it becomes yellow particles in a neutral fluid, while its atomic substructure is mostly empty space. But such insights do not show what it is actually like to see normally at a microscopic scale. "The apparently standardized environment of flour in a bottle," Anderson surmises," would not seem undifferentiated to any investigator who had once been a flour beetle and who knew at firsthand the complexities of flour-beetle existence." The perceptual powers and central nervous systems of many species are qualitatively, as well as quantitatively, different from man's. We can observe, but never experience, the role of surface tension and molecular forces in the lives of small invertebrates, the ability of the octopus to discriminate tactile impressions by taste, of the butterfly to sense forms through smell, or of the jellyfish to change its size and shape.

The tempo of all varieties of experience is also specific. Time yields humans on the average eighteen separate impressions, or instants, every second; images presented more rapidly seem to fuse into continuous motion. But there are slow-motion fish that perceive separate impressions up to thirty each second, and snails to which a stick that vibrates more than four times a second appears to be at rest.

As with time, so with space; we perceive one of many possible structures, more hyperbolic than Euclidean. The six cardinal directions are not equivalent for us: up and down, front and back, left and right have particular values because we happen to be a special kind of bilaterally symmetrical, terrestrial animal. "It is one contingent fact about the world that we attach very great importance to things having their tops and bottoms in the right places; it is another contingent fact [about ourselves] that we attach more importance to their having their fronts and backs in the right places than their left and right sides." Up and down are everywhere good and evil: heaven and hell, the higher and lower instincts, the heights of sublimity and the depths of degradation, even the higher and the lower latitudes have ethical spatial connotations. And left and right are scarcely less differentiated.

Other species apperceive quite differently. Even the fact that physical space seems to us three-dimensional is partly contingent on our size, on the shape of our bodies (an asymmetrical torus), and, perhaps, on our semicircular canals; the world of certain birds is effectively two-dimensional, and some creatures apprehend only one.

Man's experienced world is, then, only one tree of the forest. The difference between this and the others is that man knows his tree is not the only one; and yet can imagine what the forest as a whole might be like. Technology and memory extend our images far beyond the bounds of direct sensation; consciousness of self, of time, of relationship, and of causality overcome the separateness of individual experiences. Thanks to what has been likened to "a consummate piece of combinatorial mathematics," we share the conception of a common world. Whatever the defects of the general consensus, the shared world view is essentially well-founded. "We are quite willing to admit that there may be errors of detail in this knowledge," as Russell wrote, referring to science, "but we believe them to be discoverable and corrigible by the methods which have given rise to our beliefs, and we do not, as practical men, entertain for a moment the hypothesis that the whole edifice may be built on insecure foundations."

Personal Geographies

Separate personal worlds of experience, learning, and imagination necessarily underlie any universe of discourse. The whole structure of the shared picture of the world is relevant to the life of every participant; and anyone who adheres to a consensus must personally have acquired some of its constituent elements. As Russell put it, "If I believe that there is such a place as Semipalatinsk, I believe it because of things that have happened to *me*." One need not have been in Semipalatinsk; it is enough to have heard of it in some meaningful connection, or even to have imagined (rightly or wrongly) that it exists, on the basis of linguistic or other evidence. But if the place did not exist in some—and potentially in all—personal geographies, it could scarcely form part of a common world view.

Individual and Consensual Worlds Compared

The personal *terra cognita* is, however, in many ways unlike the shared realm of knowledge. It is far more localized and restricted in space and time: I know nothing about the microgeography of most of the earth's crust, much less than the sum of common knowledge about the world as a whole and larger parts, but a great deal about that tiny fraction of the globe I live in—not merely facts that might be inferred from general knowledge and verified by visitors, but aspects of things that no one, lacking my total experience, could ever grasp as I do. "The entire earth," as Wright says, is thus "an immense patchwork of miniature *terrae incognitae*"[4]—parts of private worlds not incorporated into the general image. Territorially, as otherwise, each personal environment is both more and less inclusive than the common realm.

Complex Nature of Personal Milieus

The private milieu is more complex and many aspects of it are less accessible to inquiry and "so expressive a phrase as 'the mind's eye'" is current, Smythies points out, because there is "something very like seeing" about having sensory mental images.

Illusions do not long delude most of us; "we see the world the way we see it because it pays us and has paid us to see it that way." To find our way about, avoid danger, earn a living, and achieve basic human contacts, we usually have to perceive what is there. As the Sprouts express it, "the fact that the human species has survived (so far) suggests that there must be considerable correspondence between the milieu as people conceive it to be, and as it actually is." If the picture of the world in our heads were not fairly consistent with the world outside, we should be unable to survive in any environment other than a mental hospital. And if our private milieus were not recognizably similar to one another, we could never have constructed a common world view.

Range and Limits of Personal Knowledge of the World

However, a perfect fit between the outside world and our views of it is not possible; indeed, complete fidelity would endanger survival. Whether we stay put or move about, our environment is subject to sudden and often drastic change. In consequence, we must be able to see things not only as they are, but also as they might become. Our private milieus are therefore flexible, plastic, and somewhat amorphous. We are physiologically equipped for a wide range of environments, including some of those that we create. But evolution is slow; at any point in time, some of our sensate and conceptual apparatus is bound to be vestigial, better suited to previous than to present milieus.

As individuals, we learn most rapidly about the world not by paying

[4] Wright, "Terrae Incognitae," pp. 3–4. On the other hand, the consensual universe of discourse includes elements from an infinite number of private worlds—not only those of existing persons, but also those that might conceivably be held. No square mile of the earth's surface has been seen from every possible perspective, but our view of the world in general is based on assumptions about such perspectives, as analogous with those that have been experienced. The Amazon basin would look different in design and detail from the top of every tree within it, but we know enough of the general character and major variations of that landscape to describe it adequately after climbing—or hovering in a helicopter over—a small fraction of its trees.

close attention to a single variable, but by superficially scanning a great variety of things. "Everyday perception tends to be selective, creative, fleeting, inexact, generalized, stereotyped" just because imprecise, partly erroneous impressions about the world in general often convey more than exact details about a small segment of it. The observant are not necessarily most accurate; effective observation is never unwaveringly attentive. As Vernon emphasizes, "changing perceptions are necessary to preserve mental alertness and normal powers of thought." Awareness is not always conducive to survival. He who fails to see a tiger and hence does not attract its attention "may escape the destruction which his more knowing fellow invites by the very effects of his knowledge." So, Boulding concludes, "under some circumstances, ignorance is bliss and knowledge leads to disaster."

Essential perception of the world, in short, embraces every way of looking at it: conscious and unconscious, blurred and distinct, objective and subjective, inadvertent and deliberate, literal and schematic.

Perception itself is never unalloyed: sensing, thinking, feeling, and believing are simultaneous, interdependent processes. A purely perceptual view of the world would be as lame and false as one based solely on logic, insight, or ideology. "All fact," as Goethe said, "is in itself theory." The most direct and simple experience of the world is a composite of perception, memory, logic, and faith. Looking down from a window, like Descartes, we say that we see men and women, when in fact we perceive no more than parts of hats and coats. The recognition of Mt. Monadnock, Chisholm demonstrates, is a conceptual as well as a visual act:

Suppose that you say to me, as we are riding through New Hampshire, "I see that that is Mt. Monadnock behind the trees." If I should ask, "How do you know it's Monadnock?" you may reply by saying, "I've been here many times before and I can *see* that it is." . . . If I still have my doubts about what you claim to see . . . I may ask, "What makes you *think* that's Monadnock that you see?" . . . An appropriate answer would be this: "I can see that the mountain is shaped like a wave and that there is a little cabin near the top. There is no other mountain answering to that description within miles of here." . . . What you now claim to see is, not that the mountain is Monadnock, but merely that it has a shape like a wave and that there is a cabin near the top. And this new "perceptual statement" is coupled with a statement of independent information ("Monadnock is shaped like a wave and there is a cabin near the top; no other mountain like that is within miles of here")—information acquired prior to the present perception.

And each succeeding perceptual statement can similarly be broken down into new perceptual claims and other additional information, until "we reach a point where we find . . . no *perceptual* claim at all."

Uniqueness of Private Milieus

Despite their congruence with each other and with the world as it is, private milieus do diverge markedly among people in different cultures, for individuals within a social group, and for the same person as child and as adult, at various times and places, and in sundry moods. "The life of each individual," concludes Delagado, "constitutes an original and irreversible perceptive experience."

Each private world view is unique, to begin with, because each person inhabits a different milieu. "The fact that no two human beings can occupy the same point at the same time and that the world is never precisely the same on successive occasions means," as Kluckhohn and Mowrer put it, that "the physical world is idiosyncratic for each individual." Experience is not only unique; more significantly, it is also self-centered; I am part of your milieu, but not of my own, and never see myself as the world does. It is usually one's self to which the world attends; "we will assume that an eye looks at us, or a gun points at us," notes Gombrich, "unless we have good evidence to the contrary."

Each private world view is also unique because everyone chooses from and reacts to the milieu in a different way. We elect to see certain aspects of the world and to avoid others. Moreover, because "everything that we know about an object affects the way in which it appears to the eye," no object is apt to seem quite the same to any two percipients. Thus "in some respects," as Clark says, "each man's appraisal of an identical situation is peculiarly his own."

Cultural Differences in Aspects of World Views

Appraisals are, of course, profoundly affected by society and culture. Each social system organizes the world in accordance with its particular structure and requirements; each culture screens perception of the milieu in harmony with its particular style and techniques.

Consider social and cultural differences in habits of location and techniques of orientation. Eskimo maps, Stefansson reports, often show accurately the number and shape of turns in routes and rivers, but neglect lineal distances, noting only how far one can travel in a day. The Saulteaux Indians do not think of circular motion, according to Hallowell; to go counterclockwise is to move, they say, from east to south to west to north, the birth order of the four winds in their mythology. To find their way about, some peoples utilize concrete and others abstract base points, still others edges in the landscape, or their own locations. The Chukchee of Siberia distinguish twenty-two compass directions, most of them tied to the position of the sun and varying with the seasons. The precise, asymmetrical navigation nets of Micronesian voyagers made use of constellations and islands. Tikopians, never far from the ocean, and unable to conceive of a large land mass, use *inward* and *seaward* to help locate anything: "there is a spot of mud on your seaward cheek." In the Tuamotus, compass directions refer to winds, but places on the atolls are located by reference to their direction from the principal settlement. Westerners are more spatially egocentric than Chinese or Balinese. The religious significance of cardinal directions controls orientation indoors and out on the North China plain, and the Balinese give all directions in terms of compass points. Where we would say "go to the left," "towards me," or "away from the wall," they say "take the turn to the West," "pull the table southward," or, in case of a wrong note on the piano, "hit the key to the East of the one you are hitting." Disorientation is universally disagreeable; but inability to locate north quite incapacitates the Balinese. The English writer Stephen Potter was amazed to find that most Americans neither knew nor cared what watershed they were in, or which way rivers flowed— facts he maintained were second nature to Englishmen.

Apperception of shape is also culturally conditioned. According to Herskovits, an electrical engineer working in Ghana complained that "When a trench for a conduit must be dug, I run a line between the two points, and tell my workers to follow it. But at the end of the job, I invariably find that the trench has curves in it." In their land "circular forms predominate. . . . They do not live in . . . a carpentered world, so that to follow a straight line marked by a cord is as difficult for them" as drawing a perfect freehand circle is for most of us. Zulus tested with the Ames trapezoidal window actually saw it as a trapezoid more often than Americans, who usually see it as a rectangle; habituated to man-made rectangular forms, we are apt unconsciously to assume that *any* four-sided object is a rectangle.

Territoriality—the ownership, division, and evaluation of space—also differs from group to group. In American offices, workers stake out claims around the walls and readily move to accommodate new employees; but the Japanese gravitate toward the center of the room, and many Europeans are loathe to relinquish space once pre-empted. Eastern Mediterranean Arabs distinguish socially between right and left hand sides of outer offices, and value proximity to doors. In seeing and describing landscapes, Samoans emphasize the total impression, Moroccans the details. The Trukese sharply differentiate various parts of open spaces, but pay little attention to dividing lines or edges—a trait which makes land claims difficult to resolve.

As with shapes, so with colors. Our most accustomed hues, such as blue and green, are not familiar in certain other cultures; whereas gradations scarcely perceptible to us may be part of their common experience. "There is no such thing as a 'natural' division of the spectrum," Ray concludes. "Each culture has taken the spectral continuum and has divided it into units on a quite arbitrary basis. . . . The effects of brightness, luminosity, and saturation are often confused with hue; and the resulting systems are emotional and subjective, not scientific." Among the Hanunóo of Mindoro, Conklin shows, the most basic color terms refer to degrees of wetness (saturation) and brightness; hue is of secondary interest.

As the diverse views of color suggest, it is not merely observed phenomena that vary with culture, but whole categories of experience. A simple percept here may be a complex abstraction there. Groupings of supreme importance in one culture may have no relevance in another. The Aleuts had no generic name for their island chain, since they did not recognize its unity. The Aruntas organize the night sky into separate, overlapping constellations, some out of bright stars, others out of faint ones. To the Trukese, fresh and salt water are unrelated substances. The gauchos of the Argentine are said to have lumped the vegetable world into four named groups: cattle fodder, bedding straw, woody material, and all other plants—including roses, herbs, and cabbages. There is no natural or best way to classify anything; all categories are useful rather than true, and the landscape architect rightly prefers a morphological to a genetic taxonomy. The patterns people see in nature also vary with economic, ethical, and esthetic values. Esthetically neutral to Americans, colors have moral connotations to Navahos; an Indian administrator's attempt to use colors as impartial voting symbols came to grief, since the Navahos viewed blue as good and red as bad.[5]

The Significance of Linguistic Differences in Apperception of the Milieu

The very words we use incline us toward a particular view of the universe. In Whorf's now classic phrase, "We dissect nature along lines laid down by our native languages. . . . We cut nature up, organize it into concepts, and ascribe significances as we do, largely because we are parties to an agreement to organize it in this way—an agreement that holds throughout our speech community." To be sure, language also adjusts to the world view, just as environment molds vocabulary: within a single generation the craze for skiing has given us almost as many different words for *snow* as the Eskimos have.

Linguistic patterns do not irrevocably imprison the senses, but rather,

[5] Hall, *Silent Language*, pp. 132–133. Many landscape features exist as separate entities only in our minds. As Gombrich says (*Art and Illusion*, p. 100), "There is a fallacy in the idea that reality contains such features as mountains and that, looking at one mountain after another, we slowly learn to generalize and form the abstract idea of mountaineity." Owing to the 19th-century popularity of Alpine climbing, the English standard of mountains changed dramatically: for Gilbert White the 800-foot Sussex Downs were "majestic mountains"; today anything below 2,000 feet is at best a "hill" (Vaughan Cornish, *Scenery and the Sense of Sight* (Cambridge: University Press, 1935), p. 77.

Hoijer judges, "direct perception and thinking into certain habitual channels." Things with names are easier to distinguish than those that lack them; the gauchos who used only four floristic terms no doubt saw more than four kinds of plants, but "their perceptual world is impoverished by their linguistic one." Classifications into animate or inanimate, masculine, feminine, or neuter, and mass (sand, flour, grass, snow) or particular nouns (man, dog, thimble, leaf) variously affect the way different speech communities view things. We tend to think of waves, mountains, horizons, and martinis as though they were composed of discrete entities, but conceive surf, soil, scenery, and milk as aggregates, principally because the former terms are plurals, the latter indefinite nouns.[6]

The structural aspects of language influence ways of looking at the world more than do vocabularies. Seldom consciously employed, usually slow to change, syntax pervades basic modes of thought. In Shawnee, La Barre suggests, "I let her have one on the noggin" is grammatically analogous to "The damned thing slipped out of my hand." Lacking transitive verbs, Greenlanders tend to see things happen without specific cause; "I kill him," in their language, becomes "he dies to me." In European tongues, however, action accompanies perception, and the transitive verb animates every event with purpose and cause. The Hopis have subjectless verbs, but most Indo-European subjects have objects,

[6] "English terms, like 'sky, hill, swamp,' persuade us to regard some elusive aspect of nature's endless variety as a distinct THING, almost like a table or chair (Whorf, *Language, Thought, and Reality*, p. 240; see also pp. 140–141). But Roger W. Brown (*Words and Things* [Glencoe, Ill.: Free Press, 1958], pp. 248–252) maintains that the distinction between mass and specific nouns makes perceptual sense and corresponds well with perceived reality.

One can easily, as critics of Whorf have pointed out, make too much of such distinctions. The fact that the word for *sun* is masculine in French and feminine in German, whereas that for *moon* is feminine in French and masculine in German, cannot easily be correlated with the habits of thought or *Weltanschauung* of either people. The fact that in Algonquian languages the gender class of "animate" nouns includes such words as *raspberry, stomach*, and *kettle*, while "inanimate" nouns include *strawberry, thigh*, and *bowl* does not imply "that speakers of Algonquian have a shrine to the raspberry and treat it like a spirit, while the strawberry is in the sphere of the profane" (Joseph H. Greenberg, "Concerning Inferences from Linguistic to Nonlinguistic Data," in Harry Hoijer, ed., *Language in Culture*, American Anthropological Association, Memoir No. 79 [Chicago, 1954], pp. 3–19, on pp. 15–16). In short, "If grammar itself was once founded on an unconscious metaphysic, this linkage is now so vestigial as to have no appreciable bearing on the structure of philosophic ideas" (Lewis S. Feur, "Sociological Aspects of the Relation Between Language and Philosophy," *Philosophy of Science*, Vol. 20 [1953], pp. 85–100, on p. 87). This may be true of most aspects of language, and of philosophical ideas in their broadest sense. On the other hand, the fact that English-speaking mid-Victorians clad table and piano legs in ruffs and deplored direct reference to them in mixed company was not a necessary outgrowth of prudery but depended also on the metaphorical extension of the word for human limbs to furniture —a connection not made by speakers of other languages. In this respect, language certainly altered the English—and still more the American—home landscape.

which gives expression a dualistic, animistic stamp. In Piaget's illustration, to say "the wind blows" "perpetrates . . . the triple absurdity of suggesting that the wind can be independent of the action of blowing, that there can be a wind that does not blow, and that the wind exists apart from its outward manifestations." Important differences also occur within linguistic families. The French distinction between the imperfect tense (used for things and processes) and the perfect (used for man and his actions) contrasts the uniformity of nature with the uniqueness of man in a way that English does not ordinarily express.

That such distinctions can all be conveyed in English shows that language does not fetter thought; with sufficient care and effort, practically everything in any system of speech can be translated. Nevertheless, a concept that comes naturally and easily in one tongue may require awkward and tedious circumlocution in another. The difference between what is customary for some but difficult for others is apt to be crucial in terms of habits of thought and, perhaps, orders of events. European scientists, whose languages lump processes with substances as nouns, took much longer to account for vitamin deficiencies than for germ diseases, partly because "I have a germ" was a more natural locution than "I have a lack of vitamins." In short, as Waismann says, "by growing up in a certain language, by thinking in its semantic and syntactical grooves, we acquire a certain more or less uniform outlook on the world. . . . Language shapes and fashions the frame in which experience is set, and different languages achieve this in different ways."

Personal Variations in Aspects of the World View

Private world views diverge from one another even within the limits set by logical necessity, human physiology, and group standards. In any society, individuals of similar cultural background, who speak the same language, still perceive and understand the world differently. "You cannot see things until you know roughly what they are," comments C. S. Lewis, whose hero on the planet Malacandra at first perceives "nothing but colours—colours that refused to form themselves into things." But what you think you know depends both on what is familiar to you and on your proclivities. When the well-known is viewed from fresh perspectives, upside down or through distorting lenses, form and color are enhanced, as Helmholtz noted; the unexpected has a vivid, pictorial quality. On the other hand, prolonged observation may change red to apparent green, or shrink a figure in proportion to its surroundings.

The purpose and circumstances of observation materially alter what is seen. The stage electrician cares how the lights look, not about the actual colors of the set; the oculist who tests my eyes is not interested in what the letters are, but in how they appear to me. Intent modifies the character of the world.[7]

Outside the laboratory, no two people are likely to see a color as the same unless they similarly identify the thing that is colored. Even then, preconceptions shape appearances, as Cornish points out: "The exquisite colours which light and atmosphere impart to a snowy landscape are only half seen by many people owing to their opinion that 'snow is really white.'" Such stereotypes may outweigh other physiological facts. The United States Navy was advised to switch the color of survival gear and life jackets from yellow to fluorescent red, not so much to increase visibility as to buoy the confidence of the man lost at sea; dressed in red, he imagines, "They can't fail to see me."

The way a landscape looks depends on all the attendant circumstances, for each sense is affected by the others. Velvet looks soft, ice sounds solid, red feels warm because experience has confirmed these impressions. The sight of gold and blond beech trees lit by sunlight made Cornish forget that he was cold; but he could not appreciate a "frosty" blue landscape seen from a cold railway carriage. "Quite often," notes H. M. Tomlinson, "our first impression of a place is also our last, and it depends solely upon the weather and the food."

Circumstance apart, each person is distinctively himself. "The individual carries with him into every perceptual situation . . . his characteristic sensory abilities, intelligence, interests, and temperamental qualities," according to Vernon; and his "responses will be coloured and to some extent determined by these inherent individual qualities." Ability to estimate vertical and horizontal correctly, for example, varies with sex and personality as well as with maturity: strongminded men are better at telling which way is up than are women, neurotics, and children, whose kinesthetic sense reinforces visual perception less adequately. The story of the Astronomer-Royal, Maskeleyne, who dismissed a faithful assistant for persistently recording the passage of stars more than half a second later than he did, is often told to illustrate the inevitability of perceptual divergence under the best of circumstances. Each of us warps the world in his own way and endows landscapes with his particular mirages.

People at home in the same environments, for example, habitually select different modes of orientation. There is only one published "New Yorker's Map of the United States," but Trowbridge found a great

[7] "Without the conception of the individual and his needs, a distinction between illusion and 'true' cognition cannot be made" (Horace B. English, "Illusion as a Problem in Systematic Psychology," *Psychological Review*, Vol. 58 [1951], pp. 52–53). The size and shape of objects seem appropriately and necessarily constant, but most of us can afford to be "fooled" by the apparent bending of a stick half-submerged in water.

variety of personal imaginary maps. Individual deviations of direction ranged from zero to 180 degrees off course; some were consistent, others more distorted at Times Square than at the Battery, or accurate about Albany but not about Chicago. Still others assumed that streets always point towards cardinal directions, or imagined all distant places as lying due east or west. A few know which direction they face the moment they emerge from subways and theatres, others are uncertain, still others are invariably mistaken. Lynch characterizes structural images of the environment as positional, disjointed, flexible, and rigid, depending on whether people orient themselves principally by distant landmarks, by memories of details in the landscape, by crossings, street turns, or directions, or by maps.

Subjective Elements in Private Geographies

Another reason why private world views are irreducibly unique is that all information is inspired, edited, and distorted by feeling. Coins look larger to the children of the poor, the feast smells more fragrant to the hungry, the mountains loom higher to the lost. "Had our perceptions no connexion with our pleasures," wrote Santayana, "we should soon close our eyes on this world." We seldom differentiate among people, places, or things until we have a personal interest in them. One American town is much like another to me, unless I have a good motive for telling them apart. The most exhaustive study of photographs and ethnological evidence does not enable us to distinguish among individuals of another race with the ease, speed, and certainty generated by strong feeling. All Chinese may look the same to me, but not to the man—however foreign—with a Chinese wife. Only the flea circus owner can tell you which is which among his performing fleas.

Stereotypes influence how we learn and what we know about every place in the world. My notions of Australia and Alaska are compounds of more or less objective, veridical data and of the way I happen to feel about deserts, icefields, primitive peoples, pioneers, amateur tennis, and American foreign policy. Similar evanescent images come readily to mind; to Englishmen in the 1930's, according to one writer, Kenya suggested "gentleman farmers, the seedy aristocracy, gossip columns and Lord Castlerosse"; South Africa "Rhodes and British Empire and an ugly building in South Parks Road and Trafalgar Square." Education and the passage of time revise but never wholly displace such stereotypes about foreign lands and people. The present consensus of teen-aged geography students in an English school is that "South Africans break off from the Boer War to eat oranges, make fortunes from gold and diamonds, and oppress natives, under a government as merciless as the ever-present sun." [8] Those who think of China as an abode of laundrymen, France as a place where people eat snails, and the Spanish as hotblooded are only a trifle more myopic than anyone else; it is easier to deplore such generalizations than to replace them with more adequate and convincing images.

Because all knowledge is necessarily subjective as well as objective, delineations of the world that are purely matter-of-fact ordinarily seem too arid and lifeless to assimilate; only color and feeling convey verisimilitude. Besides unvarnished facts, we require fresh firsthand experience, individual opinions and prejudices. "The important thing about truth is not that it should be naked, but what clothes suit it best." The memorable geographies are not compendious texts but interpretative studies embodying a strong personal slant. A master at capturing the essence of a place, Henry James did so by conveying "less of its appearance than of its implications." In Blake's lines,

> This Life's dim Windows of the Soul
> Distorts the Heavens from Pole to Pole
> And leads you to Believe a Lie
> When you see with, not thro', the Eye.

The ideal traveler, according to one critic, ought to be "aware not only of the immediate visual aspect of the country he visits, its history and customs, its art and people, but also of his own relation to all these, their symbolic and mythic place in his own universal map." We mistrust science as the sole vehicle of truth because we conceive of the remote, the unknown, and the different in terms of what is near, well-known, and self-evident for us, and above all in terms of ourselves. What seems to us real and true depends "on what we know about ourselves and not only on what we know about the external world. Indeed," writes Hutten, "the two kinds of knowledge are inextricably connected."

The Role of the Individual Past
in Apperception of the Milieu

Personal as well as geographical knowledge is a form of sequent occupance. Like a landscape or a living being, each private world has had

[8] John Haddon, "A View of Foreign Lands," *Geography*, Vol. 65 (1960), pp. 286–289, on p. 286. If their view of South Africa is recognizable, the students' impressions of America leave more to be desired: "America is a country of remarkably developed, highly polished young women, and oddly garbed, criminally inclined young men travelling at great speed in monstrous cars along superhighways from one skyscraping city to the next; the very largest cars contain millionaires with crew-cuts; everyone is chewing gum" (p. 286). Such stereotypes die hard, even face to face with contrary realities, as one traveler noted among Americans in Russia (Richard Dettering, "An American Tourist in the Soviet Union: Some Semantic Reflections," *ETC.*, Vol. 17 [1960], pp. 173–201.

a career in time, a history of its own. Since personality is formed mainly in the earliest years, "we are determined, simultaneously, both by what we were as children and by what we are experiencing now." In Quine's words, "We imbibe an archaic natural philosophy with our mother's milk. In the fullness of time, what with catching up on current litera-ture and making some supplementary observations of our own, we become clearer on things. But . . . we do not break with the past, nor do we attain to standards of evidence and reality different in kind from the vague standards of children and laymen."

The earlier mode of thought continues throughout life. According to Portmann, we all remain to some extent pre-Copernican: "The decisive early period in our contact with nature is strongly influenced by the Ptolemaic point of view, in which our inherited traits and responses find a congenial outlet. . . . Nor is the Ptolemaic world merely a phase to be outgrown, a kind of animal experience; it is an integral part of our total human quality."

As every personal history results in a particular private milieu, no one can ever duplicate the *terra cognita* of anyone else. An adult who learns a foreign word or custom does not start from *tabula rasa,* but tries to match concepts from his own language and culture—never with com-plete success. Among "children, exposed serially to two cultures," notes Mead, ". . . the premises of the earlier may persist as distortions of perception into later experience, so that years later errors in syntax or reasoning may be traced to the earlier and 'forgotten' cultural exper-ience."

We are captives even of our adult histories. The image of the en-vironment, as Boulding says, "is built up as a result of all past experi-ence of the possessor of the image. Part of the image is the history of the image itself." I have touched on this in connection with color per-ception: "The color in which we have most often seen a thing is im-printed ineffaceably on our memory and becomes a fixed attribute of the remembered image," says Hering. "We see through the glass of remem-bered colors and hence often differently than we should otherwise see them." The sitter's family invariably complain that the painter has made him look too old, because they view as a composite memory the face the painter confronts only today. "Everyone sees the world as it was in the past, reflected in the retarding mirror of his memory."

Memory need not be conscious to influence images; as Hume pointed out, aspects of our past that we fail to recall also leave their imprint on mental maps. "The unconscious inner world," writes Money-Kyrle, "is peopled by figures and objects from the past, as they are imagined often wrongly to have been." Correct or not, recollections can virtually efface aspects of the actual contemporary landscape. Pratolini's *Il Quartiere* portrays inhabitants of a razed and empty section of Florence who instinctively continued to follow the lines of the former streets, instead of cutting diagonally across the square where buildings had stood.

Memory likewise molds abstract ideas and hypotheses. Everything I know about America today is in part a memory of what I used to think about it. Having once conceived of the frontier as a cradle of democracy, it is quite another thing for me to learn that it was not than it is for someone else to learn the "true" fact without the old error. What we accept as true or real depends not only on what we think we know about the external world but on what we have previously believed.

Shared perspectives of whole cultures similarly incorporate the past. "Meanings may reflect not the contemporary culture but a much older one." The landscape in general, Lynch remarks, "serves as a vast mnemonic system for the retention of group history and ideals."

Conclusion

Every image and idea about the world is compounded, then, of personal experience, learning, imagination, and memory. The places that we live in, those we visit and travel through, the worlds we read about and see in works of art, and the realms of imagination and fantasy each contribute to our images of nature and man. All types of experience, from those most closely linked with our everyday world to those which seem furthest removed, come together to make up our individual picture of reality.[9] The surface of the earth is shaped for each person by refraction through cultural and personal lenses of custom and fancy. We are all artists and landscape architects, creating order and organizing space, time, and causality in accordance with our apperceptions and predilections. The geography of the world is unified only by human logic and optics, by the light and color of artifice, by decorative arrangement, and by ideas of the good, the true, and the beautiful. As agreement on such subjects is never perfect nor permanent, geographers too can expect only partial and evanescent concordance. As Raleigh wrote, "It is not truth but opinion that can travel the world without a passport."

[9] As natives of places we acquire and assimilate information differently than we do as travelers; and personal observation, whether sustained or casual, yields impressions different in quality and impact from those we build out of lectures, books, pictures, or wholly imaginary visions.

6. The Ecology of Early Food Production in Mesopotamia

Kent V. Flannery

Archeological evidence gives us clues to the way people lived in the prehistoric past. The natural environment or habitat may not have been altered as drastically as was the culture of an area, but in many cases that too has undergone marked change. The Near or Middle East and particularly that part called Mesopotamia appears to have changed from a fertile, densely populated area to an arid or semi-arid region inhabited largely by nomadic herdsmen. Evidence exists that the climate of the area has changed significantly, but Flannery questions its role in changing cultures.

Flannery studies food production in relation to the contrasting physical characteristics of the area, particularly climate, and the needs of early farmers and herders of the area. He stresses the biological limitations of early agriculture, and describes the genetic changes that resulted in improvements in both the crops and animals of the time. The revolution in food production of southwestern Asia is viewed "not as the brilliant invention of one group or the product of a single environmental zone, but as the result of a long process of changing ecological relationships between groups of men and the locally available plants and animals which they had been exploiting on a shifting seasonal basis." Cultural and physical change are characteristically slow, and this reading stresses the importance of ecological change.

Greater Mesopotamia—broadly defined here as the whole area drained by the tributaries of the Shatt al-Arab—has long been the scene of popular interest and scholarly research. In recent years attention has been drawn to the fact that this was one of the few areas in the world where agriculture and animal husbandry seem to have arisen autonomously. A number of excellent cultural-historical reconstructions of the way food production began in the Near East are already available,

SOURCE: *Science*, CXLVII 3663 (March, 1965), 1247–56. The author is an associate curator of archeology in the United States National Museum, Smithsonian Institution, Washington, D.C.

but most of these reconstructions do not deal directly with some of the ecological questions most commonly asked by the interested non-specialist. This article examines some of those questions.

The Environment

From the standpoint of agriculture and grazing potential, the area under consideration includes four main environmental zones: the alluvial plain of Mesopotamia proper, the steppeland of Assyria, the woodland belt of the Zagros Mountains, and the edge of the high central plateau of Iran (see Figs. 1 and 2). The first three of these zones have already been described by Hatt; I have added the high plateau, although it is not actually drained by the Shatt al-Arab system, because its mineral resources figured prominently in the early village period.

1. The central plateau of Iran

Central Iran is an interior drainage basin at altitudes of 900 to 1500 meters, with annual rainfall as low as 100 to 230 millimeters. The basin is filled with sierozem and desert soils, overlain in places by shallow brackish lakes surrounded by salt-crusted flatland. Rugged mountains jut unexpectedly from the plain, some of them ore-bearing; there are veins of copper just east of the prehistoric site of Tepe Sialk, and one of the world's major turquoise sources lies in the northeast corner of the plateau near Meshed. Both turquoise and copper were traded as far as the Assyrian steppe zone by 6500 B.C.

Herds of gazelle (*Gazella subgutturosa*) and wild ass (*Equus hemionus*) would have been available to hunters in the area, but without irrigation the high plateau is very marginal agricultural land; the only source of hope for the early farmer would have been the alluvial aprons of mountain soil produced where streams break through the Zagros to enter the salt lake basins. Despite the uncertain rainfall, some of these "oasis" locations appear to have been permanently settled by 550 B.C., especially those near copper sources.

2. The oak-pistachio woodland belt

The Zagros Mountains break away from the eastern edge of the high plateau and descend in tiers toward the Tigris-Euphrates basin. In places the mountains form parallel ridges which are separated by long, narrow, synclinal or anticlinal valleys, frequently poor in surface water; in other areas there are irregular mountain masses bordering wide flat valleys. Acting as aquifers, these porous mountain masses may trap tremendous quantities of winter snow or rain and release it through springs, which in turn feed permanent poplar-bordered streams. At elevations of 600 to 1350 meters there are alluvial valleys of cherno-

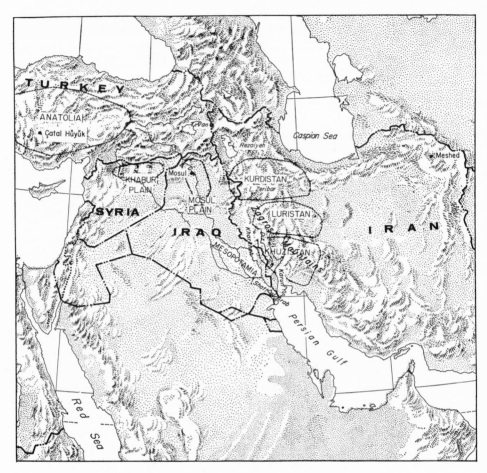

FIGURE 1: Map of Greater Mesopotamia and adjacent areas (1965).

zem, chestnut, brown, or reddish-brown soils, with alpine meadows
scattered through the surrounding peaks. Summers are warm and dry,
winters cool and wet; depending on altitude and topography, the annual rainfall varies from 250 to 1000 millimeters, and hillsides have
varying densities of oak, maple, juniper, hawthorn, pistachio, and wild
pear. On well-watered slopes grow hard-grained annual grasses like
wild emmer wheat *(Triticum dicocoides)*, barley *(Hordeum spontaneum)*, and oats *(Avena fatua)*.

Much of the area is too rugged for large-scale agriculture, but even
the narrower and drier valleys have been used for sheep or goat grazing
since at least 8500 B.C.; broad valleys with annual rainfall in excess of
300 millimeters have been farmed for at least the same length of time.

3. The Assyrian steppe

The Zagros Mountains fall away through a series of foothills and eventually level off onto a steppe region of great natural winter grassland at elevations of 150 to 300 meters; these plains have reddish-brown or brown prairie soils of high fertility. Here the mountain streams have collected into larger rivers like the Tigris, Karkheh, Diz, and Karun, which flow into the area erosional valleys and have wide, farmable floodplains. Hot and dry in the summer, the Assyrian steppe is transformed by 250 to 380 millimeters of winter rain into meadows of Bermuda grass, canary grass, and wild narcissus. Herds of gazelle, wild ass, and wild cattle once roamed the plain, and the rivers had carp and

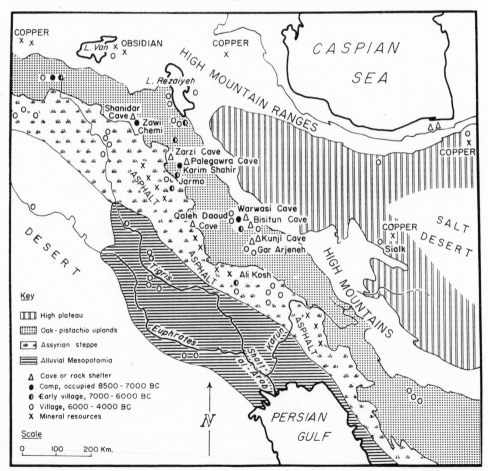

FIGURE 2: Map of Greater Mesopotamia, showing environmental zones, mineral resources, and archeological sites. Only sites mentioned in the text are labeled.

catfish. The Assyrian steppe is oil country, and one of its most widely traded commodities in prehistoric time was bitumen or natural asphalt, used for cementing flint tools into their handles.

Some parts of the steppe, too salty for effective agriculture, are used for winter grazing. Other areas are real breadbaskets for winter wheat (like the upper Khabur plain; the area near Mosul, Iraq; or the Khuzistan plain of southwest Iran), and the density of prehistoric villages in these regions is staggering. Adams' comments on northern Khuzistan—that the adequate rainfall, underlying gravels, and consequent good drainage in this zone facilitated the crucial transition from dry farming to irrigation—may apply to other favored parts of the steppes.

4. Southern Mesopotamia

Below 150 meters the Assyrian steppe gives way to the lower drainage of the Tigris, Euphrates, and Karun, as they flow together and empty into the Persian Gulf. Here the annual rainfall is under 250 millimeters (an amount usually inadequate for dry farming) and the grassland is replaced by two kinds of biotopes: alluvial desert and blowing sand dunes on higher ground, and reed-bordered swamps in the low-lying areas. The delta area is a subsiding geosyncline, slowly settling and filling with river alluvium, across which the big rivers run between their own natural levees, flooding and changing courses periodically. Contrary to what was once believed, the area has never been under the waters of the Persian Gulf (at least not since the Pliocene), and in prehistoric times it must have looked much as it does today. It was in this environmental zone that urban life, civilization, and writing began, about 3000 B.C. When permanent settlement began here is undetermined, but villages dating back to 5500 B.C. are known even in the bleak area west of the Euphrates. Surely these villages must have followed the old swamps and watercourses, beyond which agriculture would have been impossible and grazing difficult.

The Local Climatic Sequence

The possibility that the environment in the Near East might have been different during the beginnings of agriculture has intrigued archeologists for generations. The few prehistoric pollen sequences we have suggest that, although some climatic fluctuations did occur, they were not on a scale capable of creating or destroying the complex of plants and animals that were eventually domesticated. The facts we have are too few to permit us to say dogmatically that climatic change played *no* role, but it appears that the problem is cultural rather than climatic; the inescapable conclusion is that agriculture began in an area where, then as now, only about 10 percent of the land surface is suitable for dry farming.

One pollen sequence comes from Lake Zeribar in the wooded mountains of western Iran, at an altitude of about 1200 meters. Studies by van Zeist and Wright show that during the late Pleistocene the area was steppe, characterized by the sagebrush-like *Artemisia,* which implies a cool dry climate. About 11,000 B.C., at the end of the Pleistocene, the area became warmer and the vegetation made the transition to savanna, with scattered oaks and pistachios. The savanna thickened to oak forest about 3500 B.C., either through increased precipitation or through lowered temperature. Cereal-type pollen (possibly wild wheat and barley?) is present throughout the entire sequence, so climatic fluctuation would seem not to have been a determining factor in the beginning of agriculture there.

Six hundred meters lower, in the Zagros Mountains of Iraq, a slightly conflicting pollen story is available from human occupational debris in Shanidar Cave. More striking climatic fluctuations are implied, one of which Solecki interprets as the "shock stimulus" which triggered the beginnings of food production. Actually, however, the late-Pleistocene to early-recent pollen sequence from Shanidar is not in much conflict with that from Lake Zeribar: at about 10,000 B.C. a "relatively cool climate" changed to "a warmer one similar to the present climate." Cereal pollen is known at least as early as 14,000 B.C., and potential animal domesticates (sheep and goat) are present in the cave debris even at 40,000 B.C.

Neither of these pollen sequences supports the age-old myth that the Near East was once lush and well watered, then suffered from desiccation. Nor do any of the inferred climatic fluctuations imply the sudden, overnight appearance of wheat, barley, sheep or goats. I do not feel qualified to evaluate the "shock stimulus" theory, but I suspect that, although drastic climatic change explains why certain plants and animals become extinct, it does not explain how or why cultures change.

Pre-agricultural Subsistence Pattern

Scattered caves, rock shelters, and open-air sites have given us only hints of how man lived in this part of the world before domestication of plants and animals. All appearances are that his way of life conformed to a flexible, "broad-spectrum" collecting pattern, keyed to the seasonal aspects of the wild resources of each environmental zone, with perhaps a certain amount of seasonal migration from zone to zone. The less mobile members of society appear to have collected such resources as snails, turtles, fresh-water clams and crabs, and the seeds of wild annuals and perennials, while more mobile members pursued wild ungulates by special techniques, according to the species involved. Al-though cave remains include fish, birds, and small mammals, the bulk of the meat diet—often more than 90 percent—came from ungulates, like the wild sheep, goat, ox, pig, wild ass, gazelle, and deer. Note that the first four were early domesticates.

Hunting patterns were influenced by the topography of the region. In the steep, rugged rockslide area around Shanidar Cave, wild goat *(Capra hircus)* was the animal most frequently taken. The goat, a resident of the limestone crags, is difficult to hunt by means of drives; it is best pursued by small groups of agile men who know their country well and are equipped with light projectiles. Rock-shelters or caves overlooking broad, flat valleys are usually rich in the bones of the wild ass, a plains-dwelling animal which could best have been hunted by drives or surrounds, then dispatched with a larger weapon, like a thrust-ing spear. Gazelles and hares are also creatures of the flat valley, while the wild sheep of the Near East *(Ovis orientalis)* frequent rolling, round-top hills and are hunted today by ambush in the brushy stream-canyons where they hide during the noon hours. Some of the smaller rock-shelters excavated in the Zagros Mountains seem to have been stations or overlooks used mainly for hunting or butchering a single species of ungulate, or two species at most.

In recent years the oak-pistachio uplands, in the 400- to 1000-milli-meter rainfall belt at altitudes of 450 to 900 meters, have been singled out as an "optimum" zone which includes all the potential domesticates. Actually, topography is a much more important ecological factor for wild sheep and goats than either altitude or rainfall; sheep range down to sea level along the Caspian Sea, and up to 2700 meters in the Zagros Mountains, if rolling mountain meadows are available. Goats reach sea level on the foothills flanking the Persian Gulf, and are as much at home on the last rugged sandstone hills separating southwest Iran from southern Mesopotamia (180 meters above sea level) as they are on the 3000-meter crags of the northern Zagros. Pigs range over a wide area, from sea level to timberline, and if we knew more about the ecological requirements of wild cattle we might find their range equally broad. The crucial factors for hunters of wild ungulates, or early herders of semiwild ungulates, would have been the ability to move from upland to lowland as seasonal pasture was available, a pattern known as "trans-humance."

Let me give one example. Khuzistan, the Iranian arm of the Assyrian steppe, is lush winter grassland from December to April while many of the mountains to the east are covered with snow. Through late spring and summer the steppe becomes blisteringly hot and dry, while the melting snow on the mountains gives rise to good spring and summer grassland. The Persian herder classifies the steppe as *quishlaq* (winter pasture) and the mountains as *yehlaq* (summer pasture), and he moves his herd from one to the other as the season demands. Prehistoric hunters may have followed game over the same route; and as for prehistoric herders, Adams reminds us: "It is, in fact, erroneous to consider the upper plains as a zone of occupance distinct from the surrounding uplands. Both together constitute a single natural ecosystem, whose seasonal alternation of resources provides as strong an inducement to migratory stockbreeding as to intensive, settled agriculture."

The wild plants of southwestern Asia have much the same seasonal aspect. MacNeish's work in the New World has shown that a long period of intensive plant collecting preceded agriculture there; archeologists have long assumed that this was the case in the Near East, but preserved plant remains were not available to tell us which specific plants were used in the pre-agricultural era. New light was thrown on the problem in 1963 by a collection of some 10,000 carbonized seeds from basal levels at the site of Ali Kosh in lowland southwestern Iran. The area, a part of the Assyrian steppe, lies outside the range of wild wheat and barley, but locally available plants were intensively collected; the most common were wild alfalfa (*Medicago*) and the tiny-seeded wild legumes *Astragalus* and *Trigonella*, as well as fruits like the wild caper *(Capparis)*, used today mainly as a condiment. These data indicate that intensive plant collecting may have been the pattern everywhere in southwest Asia, not merely at the altitude where wild wheat grows best. Moreover, the fact that *Astragalus* and *Trigonella* occur in the mountains as well as the lowlands suggests that prehistoric collectors could have harvested one crop on the Assyrian steppe in March, moved up to 600 meters for a harvest in April or May, and arrived at 1500 meters for another harvest in June or July. Somewhere between 600 and 1200 meters these migrant collectors could have harvested the seeds of the annual grasses ancestral to domestic wheat, barley, and oats. These cereals, which are dependent on annual rainfall of 400 to 750 millimeters, do not range down to the Assyrian steppe today, although they are available over a surprisingly wide area; according to Helbaek, wild barley "grows in the mountain forest, on the coastal plain, in the shade of rock outcrops in semidesert areas, and as a weed in the fields of every conceivable cultivated crop" from Morocco to Turkestan.

Other plants useful to the collector—and eventually, in some cases, to the primitive cultivator—were ryegrass *(Lolium)*, *Aegilops* grass, wild flax *(Linum bienne)*, and large-seeded wild legumes like lentil, vetch, vetchling, chick pea, and *Prosopis* (a relative of mesquite). The lowlands had dates; the foothills had acorns, almonds, and pistachios; and the northern mountains had grapes, apples, and pears.

Most of the important species occurred in more than one zone, and

their months of availability were slightly different at different altitudes—
key factors from the standpoint of human ecology. An incredibly varied
fare was available to the hunter-collector who knew which plants and
animals were available in each season in each environmental zone;
which niche or "microenvironment" the species was concentrated in,
such as hillside, cliff, or stream plain; which species could be stored best,
and which it was most practical to hunt or collect. From 40,000 to
10,000 B.C., man worked out a pattern for exploiting the natural resources of this part of the world, and I suspect that this pre-agricultural
pattern had more to do with the beginnings of food production than
any climatic "shock stimulus."

Beginnings of Food Production

Leslie White reminds us that "we are not to think of the origin of agriculture as due to the chance discovery that seeds thrown away from a
meal subsequently sprouted. Mankind knew all this and more for tens
of thousands of years before cultivation of plants began." The cultivation of plants required no new facts or knowledge, but was simply a
new kind of relationship between man and the plants with which he was
most familiar.

One striking aspect of the late pre-agricultural pattern in the Greater
Mesopotamian area was the trading of obsidian from its source in central and eastern Turkey to cave sites in the central Zagros, such as
Zarzi and Shanidar. Natural asphalt was traded in the opposite direction, up from the tar pits of the Assyrian steppe to campsites in the
mountains, wherever flints had to be hafted. By 7000 B.C., handfuls of
emmer wheat from the oak-pistachio belt had reached the lowland
steppe of Khuzistan. Typical of the prehistoric Near Easterner was this
penchant for moving commodities from niche to niche within environmental zones, and even from zone to zone.

It has been argued that the last millennia of the pre-agricultural era
were a time of "settling in" to one's area, of increasing intensification
and regionalization of the exploitation of natural resources. This is indeed reflected in the flint tools, but such "regional specialization" may
not be the essential trend which led to food production. From the standpoint of human ecology, the single most important factor may have
been the establishment of the above-mentioned pattern of interchange
of resources between groups exploiting contrasting environmental situations—a kind of primitive redistribution system. It was this pattern
that set the stage for the removal of certain key species of edible grasses
from the niches in which they were indigenous, and their transferral to
niches to which they were foreign.

With the wisdom of hindsight we can see that, when the first seeds had been planted, the trend from "food collecting" to "food producing" was under way. But from an ecological standpoint the important point is not that man *planted* wheat but that he (i) moved it to niches to which it was not adapted, (ii) removed certain pressures of natural selection, which allowed more deviants from the normal phenotype to survive, and (iii) eventually selected for characters not beneficial under conditions of natural selection.

All that the "settling in" process did for the prehistoric collector was to teach him that wild wheat grew from seeds that fell to the ground in July, sprouted on the mountain talus in February, and would be available to him in usable form if he arrived for a harvest in May. His access to those mature seeds put him in a good position to bargain with the goat-hunters in the mountain meadow above him. He may have viewed the first planting of seeds merely as the transfer of a useful wild grass from a niche that was hard to reach—like the talus below a limestone cliff—to an accessible niche, like the disturbed soil around his camp on a nearby stream terrace. Happily for man, wild wheat and barley both grow well on disturbed soils; they will sprout on the back-dirt pile of an archeological excavation, and they probably did equally well on the midden outside a prehistoric camp. It is obvious from the rapid spread of agriculture in the Mesopotamian area that they grew as readily on the midden outside the forager's winter camp at 180 meters as they did in his summer camp at 900 meters, in the "optimum" zone.

Viewed in these terms the advent of cultivation may have been a rather undramatic event, and the concept of "incipient cultivation" becomes rather hard to define. Was it a fumbling attempt at cultivation, or only the intensification of an already existent system of interregional exchange?

Biological Obstacles to Early Food Production

The transfer of species from habitat to habitat made the products of all zones available to all people; but it was a process not without difficulty, since some of the plant and animal species involved had not yet developed the most tractable or productive phenotypes, from man's point of view.

Some of the biological obstacles faced by early agriculturalists were as follows.

1. The difficulty of harvesting wild, brittle-rachis grains. One adaptive mechanism for seed dispersal in wild wheat and barley is a brittle rachis or axis which holds the seeds together in the mature head of grain. When a dry, ripe head of wild barley is struck by a twig or a gust of wind, the rachis disintegrates and the seeds are spread far and wide. The disadvantages of this mechanism for the prehistoric collector are ob-

vious: the slightest tug on the stem of the plant or the slightest blow with a flint sickle might send the seeds scattering in every direction.

2. The difficulty of removing the grain from its husk. Even after a successful harvest, the prehistoric collector's troubles were not over. Primitive grains like emmer or einkorn wheat have a tough husk, or glume, which holds each kernel in a stubborn grip long after the brittle rachis has disintegrated. Even vigorous threshing will usually not release these primitive grains from the glume so that they can be eaten.

3. The difficulty of farming in the niche to which the grain was adapted. Both wild wheat and barley are grasses of hillsides and slopes, and they usually do not occur on the flat stream floodplains, where it would have been most convenient for prehistoric man to farm. The deep alluvial soils in the valley centers, prime areas from an agricultural standpoint, were already occupied by competing grasses and wild legumes.

Research on archeological grain remains by Danish botanist Hans Helbaek has shown us some of the ways in which early farmers either consciously or unconsciously overcame these three obstacles.

1. Selection for tough-rachis grains. Within the gene pool of wild wheat and barley were variants whose rachis was tough enough so that it did not shatter on contact. Normally these variants would have left few descendants, because of the inadequacy of their seed-dispersal mechanism. When man harvested with sickles or flails, however, he automatically selected *for* the tough-rachis grains because their heads stayed intact despite the rough treatment of the harvest. When seeds from the harvest were planted, the next generation of plants contained an abnormally high proportion of tough-rachis individuals, and each successive generation reinforced the trend.

2. The development of techniques for removing the seeds from their glumes. Sometime before 7000 B.C. man discovered that by roasting the grain he had collected he could render the glumes so dry and brittle that they could be crushed by abrasion; roasting, moreover, killed the wheat or barley germ so that it would not sprout, and the grain could be stored even through the winter rainy season. Many of the preceramic villages excavated throughout the Near East contain clay ovens appropriate for roasting grain in this manner, and nearly all seem to have stone grinding slabs of one kind or another on which the dry grain could be abraded out of its glume. Further grinding resulted in "groats," or coarse grits of grain which could be cooked up into a mush or gruel. (By and large, the tough-glumed primitive grains were unsuitable for bread-making.)

3. Actual genetic change in the grain species themselves, resulting in new strains. Because early cultivated grain was somewhat shielded by man from the natural selection pressures to which uncultivated grain

was subjected, the chance that random mutants would survive was much greater. One of the first mutations that occurred, apparently, was a change from the standard adhering-glume kernel to a "naked" kernel which could be easily freed by threshing. According to Stubbe, a single gene controls the difference between "hulled" and "naked" barley, and when a mutation took place at that locus, sometime before 7000 B.C., free-threshing barley was born. A second genetic change was that which transformed standard wild barley *(Hordeum spontaneum)*, which has only two fertile kernel rows, into mutant barley with six fertile rows *(Hordeum hexastichum)*. Helbaek, who has actually produced the six-row mutant in his laboratory by subjecting wild two-row barley to x-rays, feels that ecological factors probably determined the early distribution of these two strains: two-row barley is adapted to the fairly late (April and May) rainfall on the cool Zagros Mountain uplands, while mutant six-row barley may be more successfully adapted to much drier spring weather and the irrigation farming of the Mesopotamian plain. Archeological remains tend to support this. The two-row form seems to be the only one known so far from the highlands before 5000 B.C., while six-row barley is known from lowland Khuzistan by 6000 B.C.; the two-row strain does not seem to have caught on in the lowlands, possibly because it was poorly adapted to the climate there. Present data, in fact, suggest that although the cool uplands probably contributed the original ancestor (two-row hulled barley) it may have been the lowland ecology which stabilized the important "naked" and "six-row" strains.

Another important early genetic change was polyploidy, an actual increase in the chromosome number, which produced new strains of wheat. Wild emmer wheat *(Triticum dicoccoides)* is tetraploid—that is, it contains 4×7 chromosomes and has tough glumes enclosing the kernels. A native annual grass of well-watered mountains, it prefers the 400- to 750-millimeter rainfall zone, from Palestine and Syria to the Zagros Mountains of Iran and Iraq. By 6000 B.C., however, on the Anatolian plateau of central Turkey, a mutant had been produced which was free-threshing: this was hexaploid wheat *(Triticum aestivum)*, with 6×7 chromosomes. Such polyploid strains, together with irrigation, were instrumental in the spread of free-threshing wheat throughout southwest Asia.

Mutations and changes in gene frequency also played a role in the establishment of races of domestic animals, and once again there were biological obstacles to be overcome by early herders. Some of the adaptive and nonadaptive changes which took place were as follows.

1. A change in the sex and age ratios within the captive population. If early herds of domesticated sheep or goats were small, as we assume they were, how did the animals avoid being eaten during the winter

and survive until the spring lambing season? Work by Charles A. Reed and Dexter Perkins on archeological bones from early villages in Kurdistan suggests that some kind of conservation may have been practiced. Perkins notes that the proportion of immature sheep relative to adult sheep at Zawi Chemi, Iraq, was far higher than that in any normal wild herd, an observation from which he infers domestication. Evidently the young animals were eaten, while the older breeding stock was saved. The practice was much the same at the village of Jarmo, where Reed noted a high proportion of butchered young males, as if the females were being held back for breeding. Such practices would have resulted in an abnormally high proportion of adult females in the herd, and consequently in milk surpluses in late winter and early spring. Although wild sheep and goats produce very little milk in comparison to today's domestic breeds, such seasonal surpluses may eventually have been exploited by early herders. Today, milk, yogurt, and cheese are part of the whole trading complex of southwest Asian pastoralists.

2. Changes leading to wool production. Wild sheep (*Ovis orientalis*) have a coat like a deer or gazelle, and are no woolier than the latter. Microscopic examination of their skin reveals two kinds of follicles: "primaries," or hair follicles which produce the visible coat, and "secondaries," which produce the hidden, wooly underfur. In the skin of wild *Ovis* the secondary follicles lie intermingled with the primaries in groups of three to five. After domestication, genetic changes moved the secondaries out to the side, away from the primaries, and greatly increased their numbers; while wild strains of sheep or goat may have a ratio of only two to four secondaries for each primary, the ratio may be as high as seven to one in fine Merino sheep. The wool of the domestic sheep grows from these dense clusters of secondary follicles. Wool may already have been spun as early as 6000 B.C. at Catal Hüyük in Anatolia. Both "hairy" and "wooly" sheep were known by 3000 B.C. in Mesopotamia, and the now-famous Dead Sea Scrolls, dating to the time of Christ, have been shown by Ryder to have been written on parchment made both from hairy and from wooly sheep.

3. Nonadaptive genetic changes, such as the twisted horns of domestic goats. One of the most interesting (if poorly understood) changes which followed domestication was one affecting the horns of the goat (*Capra hircus*). The wild goat of the Near East has scimitar-shaped horns whose bony cores are quadrangular or diamond-shaped in cross section near the skull. Sites dating from 8500 to 7000 B.C. are known where goat domestication is inferred from the ratio of immature animals to adult animals, but no changes in the cross section of the horn during this period are noted. By 6500 B.C., from the Jordan Valley to the Zagros Mountains, there are scattered occurrences of goats whose horn cores show a flattening of the medial surface, and thus a triangular or almond-

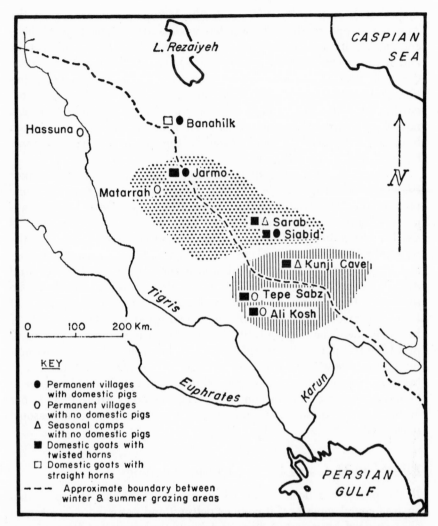

FIGURE 3: Map of Greater Mesopotamia, showing areas where transhumance is believed to have been of importance in prehistoric times. Ceramic objects from sites in the stippled area (Jarmo, Sarab, Matarrah) all have one set of traits; those from sites in the hachured area (Kunji, Ali Kosh, Tepe Sabz) all have another set. The rapid spread of the twisted-horn goat in both areas suggests that flocks may have been moved from one elevation to another seasonally; so does the almost complete absence of the domestic pig, an animal unsuitable for transhumant herding. In the summer grazing area (northeast of the dashed line), many sites appear to be seasonal shepards' camps in caves or on valley floors. These camps seem to have stronger ties, from the standpoint of traits of ceramic objects, with sites in the adjacent winter grazing area (southwest of the dashed line) than with other sites in their own environmental zone (see text).

shaped cross section. By 6000 B.C. in the Mesopotamian area, from the Assyrian steppe to the oak-pistachio woodlands, a new type of horn core makes its appearance: the core is medially flattened in section, and it also shows signs of a corkscrew twist like that of the modern domestic goat in southwest Asia. The irregular geographic distribution of the trait suggests that it was strongest in the Iran-Iraq area, occurring only sporadically elsewhere before 4500 B.C.; even at 3500 B.C. not all sites in the Palestinian area show goats of a uniformly "twisted horn" type. Possibly its rapid spread in the Zagros was due to transhumant herding (see Fig. 3).

4. The problem of pig domestication. One of the questions most frequently asked is why the pig was domesticated at 6000 B.C. in some parts of the Near East, like the Zagros Mountain valleys, but was apparently never domesticated in prehistoric time in other areas, such as the Khuzistan steppe. The most common answer is that this was the result of religious or dietary laws; but in fact, the reasons may be ecological. According to Krader, "the disappearance of the pig from Central Asia is not the clear-cut case of religious determination that might be supposed. The pig is not a species suitable to pastoral nomadism . . . it is nomadism with its mastery of the steppe ecology and movements of herds and herdsmen which is the decisive factor in the disappearance of pigs from this part of the world." Figure 3 shows the sites where domestic pigs are known either to have been, or not to have been, present in the Mesopotamian area between 6000 and 5000 B.C. Since pigs seem to be incompatible with transhumant herding, the areas where they do *not* occur may be those where there was greatest reliance on seasonal movement of flocks.

Effects on Human Life and Cultural Ecology

In the past it has been customary to treat each of the Mesopotamian environmental zones as if it were a "cultural and natural area"—a region characterized by a certain flora and fauna and exploited by a certain group of inhabitants who knew it particularly well. There are hints that such a situation obtained in Palestine, for there Perrot has distinguished two archeological traditions, one adapted to the moist Mediterranean side of the mountains, the other adapted to the arid eastern foothills.

In 1956 Fredrik Barth pointed out that the "cultural and natural area" concept did not fit northern Pakistan, and there are a considerable number of data to suggest that it does not fit the Mesopotamian area at 6000 B.C. either. Barth showed that a single valley system might be occupied by three distinct ethnic groups, each of which occupied only a portion of the total resources, leaving the rest open for other groups to exploit. The first group consists of sedentary agriculturalists who practice intensive irrigation agriculture on the river floodplain, growing two crops a year and never moving to a higher elevation. A second group raises one crop a year in this same floodplain area, but its members also migrate annually with their flocks up through five seasonal camp-sites to high mountain meadows. Still a third group is made up of pas-toral nomads who are assimilated into the society of the intensive agri-culturalists as a special "herder caste," contributing milk and meat in ex-change for grain; they are permitted to use prime grazing land not needed by the sedentary farmers.

At 6000 B.C. there are striking contrasts between archeological sites in the oak-pistachio belt and the Assyrian steppe of the Greater Meso-potamian area which suggest Barth's model. Jarmo, at an elevation of 750 meters in the oak woodlands, was a village of permanent, mud-walled houses with courtyards and ovens; Tepe Sarab, at an elevation of 1260 meters, has no obvious houses, and only the kind of ashy refuse beds that might occur around a tent camp. The pottery objects at the two sites are nearly identical, but Jarmo has goats, sheep, and even domestic pigs, along with two strains of wheat and one of barley, whereas Tepe Sarab has only goats and sheep, and no grinding stones suggestive of local agriculture. The ages of the domestic goats show that Tepe Sarab was occupied in late winter or early spring. In this case we suspect that the camp at 1260 meters may have been occupied by seasonal herders who obtained their grain from more permanent farming villages at 750 meters.

From the Assyrian steppe of Khuzistan, southwestern Iran, come further data of the same type. From 7000 to 6500 B.C. at the site of Ali Kosh, goat grazing and tiny amounts of agriculture supplemented the collection of wild legumes: from 6500 to 6000 B.C. the growing of wheat and barley greatly increased at the expense of wild plants. At 6000 B.C. a striking expansion of sheep and goat grazing occurred, and amounts of wild wheat and wild barley lessened, while the pod-bearing perennial *Prosopis* came to the fore. We doubt that this was a simple case of abandonment of agriculture; *Prosopis*, Helbaek reminds us, is intimately associated with herding peoples in southwest Asia, and the increase in domestic sheep and goats suggests that this was a time when, in con-formity with Barth's ecological model, Ali Kosh became primarily a "herding village" coexisting in a symbiotic framework with "farming villages" in adjacent areas.

Finally, we have the occurrences of typical Khuzistan pottery at a shepherds' camp in Kunji Cave, 1200 meters up, in the mountains of western Iran. This part of Luristan seems to have stronger cultural ties with lowland Khuzistan than with other mountain areas in the same environmental zone, suggesting that at 6000 B.C. some valleys in Luri-stan were summer grazing land for herds that wintered in Khuzistan.

Summary and Speculation

The food-producing revolution in southwestern Asia is here viewed not as the brilliant invention of one group or the product of a single environmental zone, but as the result of a long process of changing ecological relationships between groups of men (living at varying altitudes and in different environmental settings) and the locally available plants and animals which they had been exploiting on a shifting, seasonal basis. In the course of making available to all groups the natural resources of every environmental zone, man had to remove from their natural contexts a number of hard-grained grasses and several species of ungulates. These species, as well as obsidian and native copper, were transported far from the biotopes or "niches" in which they had been at home. Shielded from natural selection by man, these small breeding populations underwent genetic change in the environment to which they had been transplanted, and favorable changes were emphasized by the practices of the early planter or herder.

Successful cultivation seems to have intensified exchanges of natural resources and cultivars between groups, and there are hints that the diversity of environments made village specialization in certain commodities the best means of adapting to the area. We have suggestive evidence that by 4000 B.C. the redistributive economy had produced regional temple-and-market towns which regulated the produce of a symbiotic network of agriculturists engaged in intensive irrigation, transhumant herders, and perhaps even traders who dealt in obsidian, copper, salt, asphalt, fish, and regional fruits.

7. Man Against His Environment: A Game Theoretic Framework

Peter R. Gould

Scholars continue to search for a framework to categorize information, make it more meaningful, and result in useful concepts. Many theories have application in more than one discipline and on several types of problems. In this selection, Gould illustrates the "possible utility of the Theory of Games as a tool of research and as a conceptual framework in human and economic geography." With Ghana as the laboratory in which to apply the theory, he attempts

> to predict certain best choices for an agricultural
> economy in an uncertain environment.

Without cataloging the many and various definitions of human geography by professional geographers over the past few decades, it is safe to say that most have included the words *Man* and *Environment*. Traditionally, geographers have had a deep intellectual curiosity and concern for the face of the earth and the way it provides, in a larger sense, a home for mankind. Much of what we see upon the surface of the earth is the work of Man, and is the result of a variety of decisions that men have made as individuals or groups. Unfortunately, we have all too often lacked, or failed to consider, conceptual frameworks of theory in which to examine Man's relationship to his environment, the manner in which he weighs the alternatives presented, and the rationality of his choices once they have been made. Underlining a belief that such theoretical structures are desirable, and that they sometimes enable us to see old and oft-examined things with new eyes, this paper attempts to draw the attention of geographers to the Theory of Games as a conceptual framework and tool of research in human geography.[1] Upon its initial and formal appearance in 1944, a reviewer stated: "Posterity may regard this . . . as one of the major scientific achievements of the first half of the twentieth century," and although the social sciences have been relatively slow in considering the Theory of Games, compared to the widespread application of all forms of decision theory throughout engineering, business, and statistics, its increasing use in our sister disciplines of economics, anthropology, and sociology indicates a sure trend, fulfilling the extravagant praise heaped upon it at an earlier date.

The Theory of Games, despite its immediate connotation of amusements of a frivolous kind, is an imposing structure dealing, in essence, with the question of making rational decisions in the face of uncertain conditions by choosing certain strategies to outwit an opponent, or, at the very least, to maintain a position superior to others. Of course, we do not have to think in terms of two opponents sitting over a chessboard; we may, as geographers, think in terms of competition for locations

SOURCE: *Annals of the Association of American Geographers,* LIII (September, 1963), 290–97. The author is associate professor of geography, Pennsylvania State University.

[1] References to Game Theory in geographic literature are almost nonexistent. What few references there are usually appear as peripheral points to a larger discussion on linear-programming solutions, for example: William L. Garrison, "Spatial Structure of the Economy II," *Annals,* Association of American Geographers, Vol. 49, No. 4 (December, 1959), pp. 480–81. It should be noted, parenthetically, that much of the mathematics used in Game Theory is the same as that used in linear programming, and one of the hopeful things about the new ways of looking at old problems is that a common mathematics underlies many of the same theoretical structures. In terms of efficiency, a key made from a little modern algebra may often open many doors.

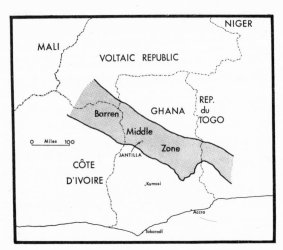

FIGURE 1: The Barren Middle Zone of Ghana of low population density and extreme variability of rainfall.

whose value depends upon the locational choices of others; or, perhaps more usefully, in terms of man choosing certain strategies to overcome or outwit his environment. A good example of the latter is a Jamaican fishing village, where the captains of the fishing canoes can set all their fishing pots close to the shore, all of them out to sea, or set a proportion in each area. Those canoes setting pots close to the shore have few pot losses, but the quality of the fish is poor so that the market price is low, particularly when the deep-water pots have a good day and drive the price of poor fish down still further. On the other hand, those who set their pots out to sea catch much better fish, but every now and then a current runs in an unpredictable fashion, battering the pots and sinking the floats, so that pot losses are higher. Thus, the village has three choices, to set all the pots in, all the pots out, or some in and some out, while the environment has two strategies, current or no-current. Game Theory has successfully predicted the best choice of strategies and the proportion each should be used, a proportion very close to that arrived at by the villagers over a long period of trial and error.

Man continually finds himself in situations where a number of different choices or strategies may be available to wrest a living from his environment. Indeed, without soaring to those stratospheric heights of philosophical, or even metaphysical, discussion, to which all discourse in the social and physical sciences ultimately leads, let it be said that to be Man rather than Animal is, in part, to be able to recognize a variety of alternatives, and in a *rational* manner, reasoning from those little rocks of knowledge that stick up above the vast sea of uncertainty, choose strategies to win the basic struggle for survival. The perception that alternatives exist, and the recognition that their specific value, or utility, for a given time and place may depend upon an unpredictable environment, about which Man has only highly probabilistic notions based upon past experience, is clearly central to any discussion of man–environment relationships within a game theoretic framework. Thus, growing concomitantly with, and, indeed, embedded in, the Theory

FIGURE 2: Payoff matrix for two-person-five-strategy-zero-sum game; crop choices against moisture choices (farmers of Jantilla).

	ENVIRONMENT MOISTURE CHOICES	
	Wet Years	*Dry Years*
Yams	82	11
Maize	61	49
Cassava	12	38
Millet	43	32
Hill rice	30	71

of Games, is a theory of utility intuitively raised, axiomatically treated, and experimentally tested in the real world.[2]

The Barren Middle Zone of Ghana (Fig. 1), a belt which, for environmental and historical reasons, has a very low population density, has one of the severest agricultural climates in West Africa, with heavy precipitation followed by the extreme aridity of the Harmatten, which sweeps south from the Sahara. A further problem is that the high degree of variability of the precipitation makes it difficult for the farmers to plan effectively.

Let us assume that the farmers of Jantilla, a small village in western Ghana, may use the land to grow the following crops, each with different degrees of resistance to dry conditions, as their main staple food: yams, cassava, maize, millet, and hill rice. In Game Theory terms the cultivation of these crops represents five strategies. In the same terms, and to simplify this initial example, let us make the somewhat unrealistic assumption that the environment has only two strategies; dry years and wet years. These strategies may be put into matrix form (Fig. 2), called the payoff matrix, and represent a two-person-five-strategy-zero-sum game, in which the values in the boxes represent the average yields of the crops under varying conditions, perhaps in calorific or other nutritional terms. For example, if the farmers of Jantilla choose to grow only yams, they will obtain a yield of eighty-two under wet year conditions,

[2] The barbarous treatment of utility theory by those who fail, or refuse, to see the difference between a man declaring a preference because of the supposedly existing greater utility, rather than assigning a higher utility to a man's preference after it has been declared, did much damage at one time in the field of economics. The latter must always be kept in mind to avoid confusion; see Luce and Raiffa, *Games and Decisions*, (New York: John Wiley and Sons Inc., 1958), p. 22.

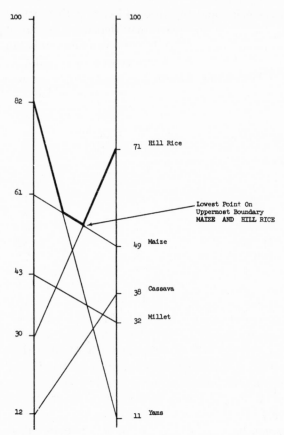

FIGURE 3: Graphical solution to assign critical pair of strategies in two-person-five-strategy-zero-sum game.

but the yield will drop to eleven if the environment does its worst. It should be noted that the values in the boxes have been chosen simply to provide an example of Game Theory, but this, in turn, emphasizes the close relationship of these methods to direct field work, for only in this way can we obtain these critical subcensus data. In a very real sense, our tools are outrunning our efforts to gather the necessary materials. We might also note, parenthetically, that extreme accuracy of data, while always desirable, is not essential in order to use Game Theory as a tool, since it can be shown that payoff matrices subjected to a fairly high degree of random shock by injecting random error terms still give useful approximations and insights upon solution.[3]

[3] In linear-programming terms this would follow from the notion that the boundary conditions would have to change quite drastically, in most cases, in order for there to be a change in the mini-max point which would alter, in turn, the choice of strategies (see Fig. 2).

A payoff matrix in which one opponent has only two strategies can always be reduced to a two-by-two game which is the solution for the complete game, in this case a five-by-two. We may, if time is no object, and we like dull, tedious work, take every pair of rows in turn and solve them for the maximum payoff to the farmers; but, fortunately, we also have a graphical solution which will point to the critical pair at once (Fig. 3). If we draw two scales from zero to one hundred, plot the values of each of the farmer's strategies on alternate axes, and connect the points, then the lowest point on the uppermost boundary will indicate which crops the farmers should grow to maximize their chances of filling their bellies.[4] Now we can take this pair of strategies, maize and hill rice (Fig. 4), and by calculating the difference between each pair of values and assigning it, regardless of sign, to the alternate strategy, we can find the proportion each strategy should be used. Thus, maize should be grown 77.4 per cent of the time and hill rice 22.6 per cent of the time, and if this is done the farmers can assure themselves the maximum return or payoff over the long run of fifty-four.

These proportions immediately raise the question as to how the solution should be interpreted. Should the farmers plant maize 77.4 per cent of the years and hill rice for the remaining 22.6 per cent, mixing the years in a random fashion; or, should they plant these proportions each year? As Game Theory provides a conceptual framework for problems where choices are made repeatedly, rather than those involving choices of the unique, once-in-history variety, the cold-blooded answer is that *over the long haul* it makes no difference. However, when men have experienced famine and have looked into the glazed eyes of their swollen-bellied children, the long-run view becomes somewhat meaningless. Thus, we may conclude that the farmers will hold strongly to the short-term view and will plant the proportions *each year* since the truly catastrophic case of hill rice and wet year could not then occur.

It is interesting to note, simply as an aside, that solving this two-by-two matrix vertically tells us that over the long run we may expect dry years 58.5 per cent of the time (Fig. 5), if we assume the environment

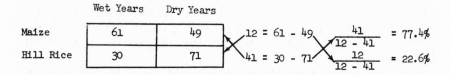

FIGURE 4: Solution of two-by-two payoff matrix to achieve most efficient choice of crop proportions.

[4] This is simply the graphical solution to the basic linear-programming problem. The values, and the resulting slopes, have been deliberately exaggerated for the purposes of illustration.

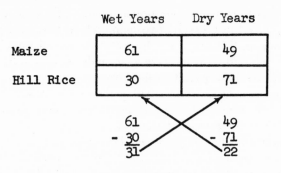

$$\text{Dry Years Expected } \frac{31}{53} = 58.5\%$$

FIGURE 5: Vertical solution of two-by-two payoff matrix to yield proportion of dry years expected.

to be a totally vindictive opposing player trying to minimize the farmers' returns.

The solution of this little game raises some interesting questions for the geographer. Does the land-use pattern approach the ideal? And if not, why not? If the land-use pattern does not approach the ideal, does this imply a conscious departure on the part of the people, or does their less-than-ideal use of the land reflect only the best estimate they can make with the knowledge available to them, rather than any degree of irrationality? Do the farmers display rational behavior in our Western sense of the term despite all the warnings of the anthropologists about the illusory concept of economic man in Africa? If one were in an advisory position, would this help to make decisions regarding the improvement of agricultural practices? If the solution exceeds the basic calorific requirements of the people, is it worth gambling and decreasing the proportion of one or both crops to achieve a better variety of foods —if this is desired by the people? How far can they gamble and decrease these proportions if inexpensive, but efficient, storage facilities are available, either to hold the surpluses of one year to allay the belt-tightening "hungry season" of the next, or to sell in the markets of the south when prices are high? Thus, the usefulness of the tool is not so much the solving of the basic problem, but the host of questions it raises for further research.

A further example from Ghana will make this clear (Fig. 6). For centuries the people living south of the great Niger arc have raised cattle and have driven them along the old cattle trails to the markets of Ghana. The driving of cattle is a chancy business because, while Man can overcome cattle diseases such as rinderpest with modern veterinary medicines, he cannot yet predict the very dry years in this area of high rainfall variability through which the cattle have to be driven to market. Let us assume that the northern cattle traders of the Voltaic Republic, Mali, and Niger have the choice of selling their cattle in five markets: Ouagadougou, Navrongo, Tamale, Prang, and Kumasi. Each market thus represents a strategy and the traders may choose any one, or a mixture, of these in which to sell their animals. Let us further assume that Nature, or the environment, also has five strategies ranging from years with intensely dry conditions to unusually wet years. Thus, the strategies available to the cattle traders and the environment form a two-person-five-by-five-zero-sum game and may be represented by a five-by-five matrix which indicates, for example, the average price of an animal in various markets under different conditions. The matrix indicates that a trader may gamble upon the season being a very wet one, in which case he would drive all his animals to Kumasi; but, if he guessed wrong, and the season was a less than average one, cattle would die or lose a great deal of weight on the way and he would get much less in Kumasi than

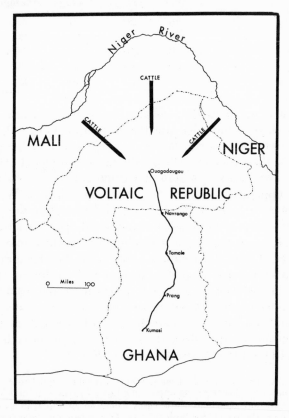

FIGURE 6: Areas of cattle production and main route to traditional cattle markets.

if he had sold them in another market such as Ouagadougou. This, of course, is a deliberate simplification, for we are not taking into account the possibility of varying demands, the question of alternative local supplies at some of the markets, nor the probability of Ghanaian consumers substituting one source of protein for another, for example, fresh fish from the coast or dried Niger perch. It might be possible to gather data to fill payoff matrices for other suppliers, but the situation would become much more difficult since we would be in the realm of non-zero-sum games that are, both conceptually and computationally, much more complex.[5]

FIGURE 7: Payoff matrix in two-person-five-by-five-zero-sum game; market choices against available moisture choice (cattle traders).

| Markets | ENVIRONMENT AVAILABLE MOISTURE CHOICES | | | | |
	Very Wet	Above Average	Average	Below Average	Intense Drought
Ouagadougou	15	20	30	40	50
Navrongo	20	15	15	20	5
Tamale	40	30	20	15	10
Prang	60	50	40	20	15
Kumasi	80	70	40	25	10

Given the above strategies, what are the best markets the cattle traders can choose, and what are the best proportions?—"best" in the sense that over the long run the traders selling certain proportions of their cattle in these markets will get the maximum payoff. The solution of a five-by-five matrix in a zero-sum game is not as easy as the case where one opponent has two, or even three, choices. We do have, however, ways of choosing the strategies and *estimating* the proportions that should be used, the estimation being based upon a relatively simple iteration which converges upon the solution and which may be carried to any degree of required accuracy (Fig. 8). In the above example, the iteration has been carried out sixty times, and by counting the number of asterisks in each row of a market, which mark the maximum figure in each column of the estimating process, we can calculate that the traders should sell thirty-two sixtieths, or 53.4 per cent, of their cattle in Ouagadougou and then drive the remainder right through Navrongo, Tamale, and Prang to the Kumasi market (Fig. 9).

[5] Zero-sum games are so called because upon choosing a particular strategy one competitor's gain (+) becomes the opponent's loss (−), the gain and loss summing to zero. Non-zero-sum games are those cases where an aletration in strategic choice *may* raise or lower the payoff for both players. Two-person-non-zero-sum games can be handled using the notion of imaginary side payments. N-person-non-zero-sum games may best be described as computationally miserable.

FIGURE 8: Solution by iteration of payoff matrix (cattle traders).

Markets	Environment available moisture choices					1	2	3	4	...	59	60	Total
Ouagadougou	15	20	30	40	50	15	65	115*	165*	...	2,060	2,110*	32
Navrongo	20	15	15	20	5	20	25	30	40	...	870	875	0
Tamale	40	30	20	15	10	40	50	60	70	...	2,045	2,055	0
Prang	60	50	40	20	15	60	75	90	105	...	1,875	1,890	0
Kumasi	80	70	40	25	10	80*	90*	100	110	...	2,065	2,075	28
	15*	20	30	40	50								
	95	90	70	65	60*								
	175	160	110	90	70*								
	.	.	.	.	.			OUAGADOUGOU	32				
	.	.	.	.	.					$\frac{32}{60} = 53.4\%$			
	.	.	.	.	.			KUMASI	28				
										$\frac{28}{60} = 46.6\%$			
	2,190	2,250	1,880	1,845	1,830								

ETC.

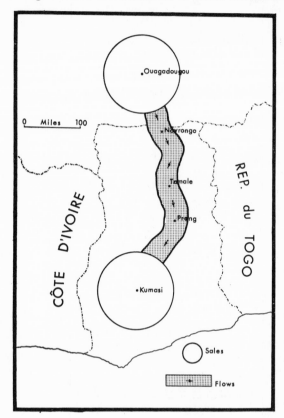

FIGURE 9: Proportional sales and flows of cattle prior to road improvements and trucking.

Let us pose the question, now, of what might happen if a really strong transportation link were forged between Tamale and Navrongo, such as the remaking and tarring of a road, so that upon arrival at the Voltaic-Ghanaian border cattle would no longer have to make their way on the hoof, but could be driven in trucks to the southern markets

FIGURE 10: New payoff matrix indicating price changes in markets as a result of new road link between Tamale and Navrongo (cattle traders).

Markets	Very Wet	Above Average	Average	Below Average	Intense Drought
Ouagadougou	15	20	30	40	50
Navrongo	20	15	15	20	5
Tamale	80	80	70	70	80
Prang	100	100	90	80	70
Kumasi	130	130	120	90	60

FIGURE 11: Solution by iteration of new payoff matrix (cattle traders).

Environment
Available Moisture Choices

Markets							1	2	3	4	. . . 160	TOTAL
Ouagadougou	15	20	30	40	50		50	100	150	190	.	0
Navrongo	20	15	15	20	5		5	10	15	35	.	0
Tamale	80	80	70	70	80		80*	160*	240*	310*	.	100
Prang	100	100	90	80	70		70	140	210	290	.	40
Kumasi	130	130	120	90	60		60	120	180	270	.	20
	130	130	120	90	60*	ETC.	.	.	.	.	.	
	210	210	190	160	140*		.	.	.	.	.	

$$\text{TAMALE } \frac{100}{160} = 62.5\%$$

$$\text{PRANG } \frac{40}{160} = 25.0\%$$

$$\text{KUMASI } \frac{20}{160} = 12.5\%$$

119

arriving in much better condition even in the very driest of seasons (Fig. 10). The payoff matrix would obviously change, and we might expect very much higher prices to prevail in Tamale, Prang, and Kumasi for the fat, sleek animals, rather than the bags-of-bones that often stumbled into these markets in former years. Again, the payoff matrix can be solved using the iterative method 160 times on this occasion (Fig.11), to produce completely different choices and proportions from the previous example. Now it is no longer worthwhile for the traders to sell cattle in the Ouagadougou or Navrongo markets, but sell instead 62.5 per cent in Tamale, 25 per cent in Prang, and 12.5 per cent in Kumasi. Thus, an improved road link, a visible sign on the landscape of a technological improvement, changes Man's perception and evaluation of the same choices available to him before, and as a result changes the patterns of flows and sales (Fig. 12). Now the flow has increased over the northern portion of the route, and it has become desirable to sell portions of the herds in the Tamale and Prang markets, the increases at

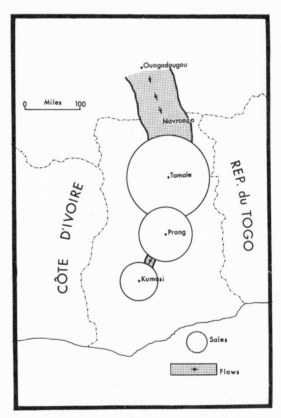

FIGURE 12: Proportional sales and flows of cattle after road improvements and trucking.

these markets coming from former sales at Ouagadougou and Kumasi. Again, solving the payoff matrix points up some interesting questions for the geographer. First, it raises the whole question of estimating the effects of improving a transportation link—what will the flows be before and after? Can we obtain payoff values from one part of West Africa and use them to estimate changes of flows in other parts? Secondly, the question, again: how close does the behavior of the cattle traders approach that required to obtain the maximum payoff over the long run? Thirdly, what would be the effect of increasing the speed of communication so that cattle traders who started early in the season could inform others on the trail to the north about the conditions they find? And, finally, we should note the way an improved transportation link in effect extends the influence of one or more markets over others as the effect of distance is broken down allowing the demands of one center to impinge upon another.

By taking two examples from the traditional economy of Ghana, this paper has tried to point out the possible utility of the Theory of Games as a tool of research and as a conceptual framework in human and economic geography. That such frameworks are needed is evident, for without these broad conceptual constructions in which to place our facts and observations it becomes an almost impossible task to raise and tackle, in a meaningful and lasting fashion, questions of Man's equilibrium with his environment, his perceptions and judgments about it, and the rules by which he reacts at different points in time and space. The work of Man is all around us upon the face of our earth, and is the result of men perceiving a variety of alternatives, subsequently limiting the range of choices according to their idea of what is useful and good, and *deciding* upon certain strategies to gain those ends. Thus, the whole body of decision theory, of which the Theory of Games is but one part, has an increasingly important role to play. Perhaps, in the same way that information theory has illuminated old problems of central-place structure, linear-programming solutions have helped our understanding of shifting flows and boundaries, and the theory of queues is throwing light upon problems ranging from those of the Ice Age to those of livestock production, the Theory of Games may also have a role to play.

IV. POPULATION
AND SETTLEMENT

The demands of a rapidly growing world population upon available resources and physical space is without doubt one of the most serious problems of our time. Many aspects of these problems are of interest to the geographer who is concerned with the spatial characteristics of both people and land. The uneven distribution of people over the face of the earth and within individual countries, smaller political units, and regions is of major significance to geographic study. The ratio of people to available resources and economic opportunity varies from region to region, and thus affects the degree of severity of the population problem. Experts disagree on the seriousness of the problem—as many prophets of gloom are heard as are disciples of a solution through human technology. Harkavy sets the theme for this section by stressing the ramifications of the population explosion and the resulting economic problems.

The individual abodes of man as well as his collective settlement patterns are excellent indicators of culture past and present. The nature and pattern of man's habitations constitute the core of settlement geography. The structures built by man for shelter as well as for economic, political, and social activities varies with such factors as landforms, climate, and culture. The settlement types also evolve over time and reflect changes in the culture and abilities of man to cope with the problems of a given region. Thus the study of such man-made structures is important to understanding a cultural landscape.

Settlement types can be roughly classified as urban or rural. The urban type is becoming more predominant as the proportion of city population steadily grows throughout the world. In some areas such as the eastern United States and western Europe, villages and cities predominate. In other regions such as southern and eastern Europe and southeast Asia, villages are characteristic even for rural people.

Houses in cities, villages, and on farms differ in structure, appearance, and function. A complex city differs greatly within its own sections, even from one street to the next, or one house to the next. All such distinctions help give character to the earth space occupied by man. The selections in this section include a theory on location of settlement, rural and urban studies from many parts of the world, and concludes with an article on the city or the country as a focus of change.

8. Economic Problems of Population Growth

Oscar Harkavy

*The rapidly expanding world population has been a concern
of scholars from many disciplines. Much research is done
through grants to individuals, universities, and even
directly to countries; India, for example, received a grant
to study "motivational factors in India's many population
groups." India is a good example of a country facing economic
problems as a result of population growth. Harkavy places
the population problem which faces most of the world
in proper perspective, and so lends orientation to the
articles that follow in this section.*

Population Density

The picture that first comes to mind in confronting the "population explosion" is a mass of humanity, like rush-hour passengers in the New
York subway, struggling for two square feet of standing room. But
crowding is not necessarily synonymous with poverty. There are about
327 people per square mile in India and twenty-one people per square
mile in Laos. Both have *per capita* income of about $80 a year. On
the other hand, the megalopolis stretching from Boston to Washington
has a population density of more than 2,000 per square mile, while enjoying a median family income of nearly $7,000 a year. Were this area
dependent on agriculture or mining and unable to trade with the rest
of the United States or with the rest of the world, 2,000 people crowded
together on each square mile would be able to eke out but a miserable
livelihood. To take another example, *per capita* income in Hong Kong,
with a density of 8,000 per square mile, has risen between 7 and 10
per cent a year since World War II. Despite a huge influx of refugees
from mainland China, Hong Kong is one of the most prosperous countries in Asia because of its vigorous industry and world trade.[1]

Overcrowding is undesirable for many reasons. But those responsible

SOURCE: The Ford Foundation, 447 Madison Avenue, New York, N. Y. The author is
director of the population program of the Ford Foundation.
[1] A. J. Coale: "The Economic Effects of Fertility Control in Under-developed
Areas" on Human Fertility and Population Problems (ed. R. O. Greep), 1963.

124

for a nation's population policy will make a grave mistake if they focus exclusively on population density. Latin America, where one-fourteenth of the world's population lives on one-seventh of the world's land mass, does not suffer from "over-population" in terms of density per square mile. But Latin America faces major problems because of its high rate of population growth. It is hard pressed to provide adequate food, housing, and education for its children, and productive employment for new entrants to the labor force. And as I shall point out further on, the great proportion of dependent children in a fast-growing population is a heavy handicap to poor nations that wish to lift themselves by their bootstraps.

Food and Natural Resources

Writing in eighteenth century England, Malthus saw famine, war, and pestilence as the inevitable deterrents to excessive population growth. Today, once more, there is grave question whether continued growth of world population will not outrun our food supply. But the more closely one examines the balance of food and population, the more difficult it is to come to an unequivocal conclusion. Long-term projections of food supplies are notoriously unreliable. We can only roughly estimate the current rate of growth of agricultural output. Projections based on these estimates become increasingly shaky if extended far into the future. Furthermore, one can only speculate about the effect of changes in agricultural technology and organization on future output. Artificial photosynthesis or vastly improved methods of gathering food from the sea may lead to quantum jumps in technology.

Between 1934-1938 and 1961, world *per capita* grain production increased by an estimated 14 per cent. But at the same time, output of grain per person *decreased* 2 per cent in Asia and 16 per cent in Latin America. It rose by 8 per cent in Africa and 5 per cent in Eastern Europe and Russia, but the major progress has come in Australia-New Zealand (up 51 per cent), North America (up 44 per cent), and Western Europe (up 19 per cent). Global or continental estimates of food deficits are based on fragmentary data supplemented by somewhat informed guesses. They gloss over the very great differences in food production and consumption from one country to another within a continent and from one region to another within a country. But:

. . . the accumulation of clinical evidence and medical judgment supports the more recent studies based on food balance sheets which indicate that in many countries millions of people get insufficient calories and that there is an

2 G. R. Allen: The World's Food Shortage: Nutritional Requirements and the Demand for Food. Paper presented at Iowa State University Seminar, 1962.

even wider and nutritionally more serious shortage of proteins, minerals, and vitamins, and probably of fats.[2]

India, with more than 450 million people, will have 187 million more in fifteen years. Thus, in the next fifteen years, India will have to find a way of feeding an increase in population about equivalent to the present population of the United States. Since India has little additional land that can be brought into cultivation, her farmers must increase yields per acre on existing farm land by at least 50 per cent between now and 1980. One expert calculates that an additional 24 million tons of fertilizer a year must be applied to achieve this performance, but the entire world production of fertilizer is now only 28.6 million tons a year.[3]

Nonetheless, it is entirely possible for India and most other countries in the world to grow or import enough food at least to keep its people from starving in the next few decades. But this would require a revolution in traditional agricultural technology, land tenure, credit, marketing, and transportation. The kinds of changes in attitudes and behavior that are likely to produce increased crop yields are analogous to those that would be required to bring down birth rates. India, in fact, is engaged in two large-scale, complementary efforts. One is a series of intensive experiments in which a "package" containing all elements required to improve agricultural productivity is applied to the land. The other is an intensive district program in family planning intended to apply the best technology and administration to a reduction in birth rates.

The future of the world's supply of raw materials other than food is also far from hopeless. The world's entire stock of fossil fuels (coal and oil) may be depleted in 150 to 200 years, but alternate energy resources, produced by atomic fission (possibly atomic fusion) and even by the sun, will probably mean that there will be sufficient energy for the world's use in the foreseeable future. It has been estimated that by the year 2000, from 10 to 20 per cent of energy consumption will be provided by means of electric generating plants that are powered by atomic energy.[4]

There will probably be enough iron, aluminum, and manganese to supply projected demands for the next forty years without significantly increasing costs, but there are likely to be shortages in copper, lead, and zinc. There are good substitutes for these metals, however, which will be used increasingly as the prices of the scarce metals rise. It is doubtful whether the world's forests will long be able to withstand

[3] L. R. Brown: *Man, Land and Food—Looking Ahead at World Food Needs*. U.S. Department of Agriculture, 1963.
[4] J. L. Fisher and N. Potter: "Resources in the United States and the World" in *The Population Dilemma* (ed. P. M. Hauser), American Assembly, 1963.

the demands made upon them. But again, it will be possible to substitute steel, aluminum, and other building materials for wood.

Water demand and supply is very difficult to estimate far into the future. Assumptions must be made as to the extent of future investment in massive river development projects. Brackish water, even ocean water, can be demineralized with existing technology and will become increasingly economic as inexpensive sources of energy, such as solar energy, are developed. But these optimistic predictions assume timely investment of huge amounts of capital to anticipate the demands of the growing population.

Burden of Dependency

Developing countries are kept poor by shortages of productive capital, fertilizer and farm machinery, industrial plant and equipment, and of highly trained and motivated technicians, engineers, and managers who can make optimum use of that capital which is available. Capital accumulation is the essence of economic development. It is the primary path to increased income *per capita*. Aside from foreign economic aid and investment, a nation accumulates capital by investing that part of its income not spent on consumption. In other words, the more a nation saves, the more is available for investment in productive capital.

In rich countries, which already have accumulated large amounts of capital, savings of individuals and business firms run between 10 and 20 per cent of national income. These savings are usually sufficient to provide as much new investment as is required by business and government. The problem in the developed countries is to maintain a level of investment high enough to absorb all the savings that individuals and business generate during periods of prosperity. On the other hand, in the capital-poor, developing world only a trickle of savings (up to 7 per cent of national income at most) can be turned into productive capital. One reason lies in the age profile of the newly developing countries.

The dramatic declines in mortality experienced in the developing countries have primarily affected infant and child mortality; they have not appreciably extended life expectancy at the upper end of the age scale. Thus, declining mortality, combined with relatively stable birth rates, has produced a "youngling" population, not an aging population. In the industrialized countries, the proportion of children under the age of fifteen ranges from about 25 to 30 per cent; in the developing countries, children under fifteen constitute between 35 and 50 per cent of the population. These children—who are consumers for many years before they are producers—constitute a great burden of dependency that hinders economic development.

Employment

Countries with a rapidly growing population must spend a greater proportion of their income feeding their children, clothing and housing them, and providing them with a rudimentary education than is necessary in those nations in which population increases more slowly. With a given national income, a fast-growing population must spend so much on primary education to achieve minimum levels of literacy of its young children that it has little left over for the training of engineers. Also, it must spend on family housing what it otherwise could invest in hydroelectric plants and steel mills.

With the passage of time, dependents under the age of fifteen will enter the fifteen to sixty-four age group, and look for work. It is obvious, but sometimes forgotten, that mere additions to the labor force do not necessarily mean that total production is increased. If the ratio of labor to productive capital is already high, as is the case in developing countries, more entrants to the labor force may mean more unemployment and underemployment. For example, in India it is estimated that, from 1956 to 1961, eight million new jobs were created, but the working population increased by ten million. As stated in the U.N. Report on the World Social Situation: [5]

. . . even if all the liberal provisions and estimates for the creation of additional employment that are contained in the various Asian development plans were to be completely fulfilled, the problem of rural unemployment and underemployment in most countries of the region will not be solved unless the efforts to control population growth prove more successful than they have in the past.

In the United States, the postwar bumper crop of babies is entering the labor force at a time when technological advances require fewer, but more highly skilled, workers to achieve a given level of output. An intensified version of the same problem faces the developing country. Modern technology is directed toward producing more and more with less and less labor. With limited capital and an excess of labor, it would be logical to install new plant and equipment that maximize the use of labor and minimize the use of capital. But a country that desperately needs all the goods it can produce seeks the most "efficient" factories, and these do not use much labor. Furthermore, when a developing nation invests its scarce resources in a new steel mill or cement plant, it wants the latest model, not something that was obsolete in the West fifty years ago. Thus, in the developing world, the very process of introducing and modernizing technology is likely to exacerbate the unem-

[5] United Nations Economic and Social Council Report on World Social Situation, 1963.

ployment problem, at least in the short run. In any event, an increased number of unskilled laborers is hardly the key to economic development.

Urbanization

The process of economic development has historically involved a movement of people from the countryside to the cities in response to opportunities for gainful industrial employment. While large-scale urban migration takes place in the developing countries, much of the mass movement to the cities is not inspired by the call of employment but by the desperate hope that some menial job or governmental relief will be available there. Too often, a man exchanges rural underemployment for urban underemployment or unemployment. Kingsley Davis [6] esti-

[6] K. Davis: "Population" in *Scientific American*, May 1963.

mates that if the population of India increases as expected, there will be between 100 and 200 million migrants to cities between 1960 and the end of this century. In the year 2000, the largest city, Calcutta, will contain between 36 and 66 million people. Calcutta, sprawling for hundreds of square miles, with a population of 66 million inadequately employed people, does not suggest elevated levels of living. It suggests, instead, a concentration of misery that can only have explosive consequences. The sheer density of population under these circumstances presents problems of the greatest magnitude.

Waiting for the Demographic Transition

Despite the obstacles to capital accumulation presented by population growth, the emerging countries are gradually becoming more industrialized, and great urban complexes are rapidly growing. Some argue, therefore, that the developing countries are bound to go through the demographic transition of late nineteenth century Europe and the United States, when a reduction in birth rates was a concomitant of increasing urbanization and industrialization. Thus it is asserted that scarce resources and administrative effort would be more wisely applied to speed up the pace of industrial development than to finance national programs of fertility limitation.

With improvements in medicine and agriculture, and with economic well-being enhanced by technological and organizational advances in industry and commerce, mortality began to decline slowly in nineteenth century Europe. Birth rates continued to average around thirty per 1,000 well into the century, but began to decline beginning about 1875 in Western Europe, and somewhat earlier in France. Despite some interesting demographic research on isolated vital statistics records, there is little comprehensive empirical data on which to construct an unassailable theory that accounts for the demographic transition. The introduction of the condom and diaphragm toward the end of the century is claimed to be an important influence, but there is evidence that *coitus interruptus*, practiced since antiquity, was, in fact, the most prevalent method of contraception. Kingsley Davis bases an explanation for the decline in birth rates on one of the most important forces that motivate human beings, "keeping up with the Joneses," or, as he identifies it in his presidential address before the Population Association of America,[7] the avoidance of "invidious deprivation." According to Davis, families strove to enhance their share of the new prosperity brought on by the industrial revolution (in Great Britain, for example, real *per capita* income in 1910-1914 was 2.3 times greater than in 1855-1859), and thus improve their social status relative to their neighbors. But declines in mortality meant that more children were living to share the family substance. Davis concludes:

. . . if each family is concerned with its prospective standing in comparison to other families within its reference group, we can understand why the peoples of the industrializing and hence prospering countries altered their demographic behavior in numerous ways to have the effect of reducing the population growth brought about by lowered mortality.

There are, however, profound differences between the situation that prevails today in the developing countries and the circumstances under which the industrialized western nations, followed by Japan, underwent their demographic transition. The surge in population brought about by swift declines in mortality through imported public health measures is taking place at an earlier stage of development than was the case in the West. Davis [8] points out that in Great Britain "the peak of human multiplication came when the country was already highly industrialized and urbanized, with only one-fifth of its working males in agriculture," while declines in fertility did not occur until much later. If European patterns are duplicated, it may take the developing countries at least thirty to sixty years to arrive at a state of industrialization that will bring with it declines in fertility. But in the meantime, population is growing much more swiftly than ever before in history. The rate of natural increase (births minus deaths) rarely rose above 1.5 per cent in nineteenth century Europe, but between 1950 and 1960 it averaged 3.2 per cent per year in Taiwan, 2.7 in Ceylon, 3.2 in Malaya, and 3.4 in El Salvador.[9]

With rates such as these, *per capita* income is more likely to fall than

[7] K. Davis: "The Theory of Change and Response in Modern Demographic History" in *Population Index*, October 1963.
[8] K. Davis: "Population" in *Scientific American*, May 1963.
[9] K. Davis: "The Theory of Change and Response in Modern Demographic History" in *Population Index*, October 1963.

to rise during the coming decades. The growth in prosperity that Davis sees as a condition precedent to fertility reduction in the face of declining mortality is not likely to be achieved by the masses in the developing countries. When poverty is all-pervasive, one child more or less does not seem to make much difference, particularly if he is part of an extended family in which brothers, and even first cousins and their families, live under one roof, pool their property and earnings, and share responsibility for rearing the young. On the other hand, the urbanized prosperous elite almost universally take the lead in limiting the size of their families. Unfortunately, they constitute only the thinnest layer of population in these countries. Unless their example influences the behavior of the people at large, their action will have little effect on national birth rates.

Economics of Fertility Limitation

One cannot escape the conclusion that it is wishful thinking to expect the forces of industrialization and urbanization alone to bring down birth rates in the developing countries within the next few decades. Goverment officials sometimes talk about levying a tax that rises progressively with the number of children in a family, or of removing the rice subsidy that is awarded in some countries on the basis of family size. But this would be inhumane as well as politically suicidal. A much more attractive measure politically would be the establishment of a social security scheme under which parents would no longer feel the need for many children as old-age insurance. But developing countries, according to many observers, already devote too much of their limited substance to welfare benefits; they could ill afford a really effective social security system.

The dollar-and-cents benefits derived from a reduction in the birth rate are so great that governments are justified in allocating a substantial share of national resources to programs of fertility limitation—provided, of course, the programs are effective. Economists who have attempted estimates conclude that a dollar invested in preventing a birth is many times as effective in increasing income *per capita* as a dollar invested in plant and equipment. One economist calculates that for India the present value of a representative newborn baby's lifetime consumption is $200 while the present value of his lifetime future production is about $75. He concludes that the government can afford to pay $125 for each birth prevented.[10] But there still remains the much more uncertain determination of the number of births prevented per dollar of expenditure on a given family-planning program. Nonetheless, those

[10] S. Enke: "The Economics of Government Payments to Limit Population" in *Economic Development and Cultural Change,* July 1960, pp. 339–348.

responsible for the direction of economic and social development of
their nations must do the best job they can with the knowledge available to calculate the costs—in political, social, and ethical terms, as well
as in rupees or pesos—of national programs of fertility limitation and
to balance these costs against the political, social, ethical, and monetary
costs of letting the growth of population take its natural course.

9. Theoretical Considerations Regarding the Distribution of Settlement in Inner North Sweden

Erik Bylund

*Explaining the form and distribution of settlement types
often is a difficult problem of research. We are only in the
incipient stages of developing meaningful findings on the
spread of various kinds of settlement. This article
suggests ways of analyzing the distribution
of settlement in northern Sweden.*

When searching for the factors affecting the distributional pattern of
settlement in inner Norrland, and bearing in mind the colonization process, we will find, on the whole, a preference for areas more attractive
from a physical point of view. Areas with better conditions have been
exploited before districts with inferior qualities. Good soil, favourable
climate or mineral resources have often determined the location of
settlement. However, we also find that the settlement distribution
is not only determined by natural conditions. For example, Rudberg
(1957) called attention to this in the summary of his investigation into
the causes for the distribution of settled and unsettled areas in northern
Sweden, and Enequist wrote in 1959: "Yet even relatively favourable
natural and geographic conditions have not always attracted settlement." My own investigations in central Lappland show that some good
land close to established settlements and well suited for colonization
may remain unsettled. On the contrary, other localities in remote dis-

SOURCE: *Geografiska Annaler,* XLII (1960), 225–31. The author is associate professor of geography, University of Uppsala, Sweden.

tricts and with inferior natural conditions may have been cultivated surprisingly early. Our problem is to explain this.

This paper is a theoretical approach to the problem, to a great extent based upon results from investigations of the colonization process in Lappland; however, it is not intended as a final answer, only a simple contribution to the discussion.

Four theoretical models of settlement development are shown in Fig. 1. The basic assumption for all of them, and also for the following discussion, is that the physical conditions are equal all over the area, settled or unsettled. The first concept (A-model) means that one area after another is colonized starting from an original settlement area in such a way, that a more remote area will be settled first when the area nearer the origin is fully occupied, even if the colonists are not able to leave the origin area or their mother settlements at the same time. For example no new settlement within stage 3 has been established before every one of the 6 settlements within stage 2 have been built. As a simplification the settlements each are assumed to use an equally great area. In this case we will have a colonization wave, which moves parallel in to a line, a "shore line", where the limit of the physical colonization conditions will be reached.

The B-model is a variation of the A-model; in that opposite to the A-development one supposes that new settlement spreads concentrically and radially from settlements established earlier, i.e., like waves from a stone plunged into the water. Moreover, the assumptions are the same as those relating to the A-concept, with one exception, and that is that the origin is here represented by one settlement unit only. In th B-development one assumption is that the mean area within the different zones are the same as the origin settlement area; that is why the number of settlements increase from the centre outwards.

Both these models involve purely theoretical concepts and show no similarity at all with the actual colonization development in inner North Sweden. Possibly, it may be correct to say, that the B-model is a little more realistic than the A-model in that the starting point is only one origin settlement and not a great number of different settlements. The real development shows very few such initial points, not a great number of them. There has been no question of great colonization waves consisting of a lot of people entering the Lappish lands, but rather only a handful of persons, who appeared as pioneers in the wilderness. Afterwards the following colonization was carried out by sons of the first pioneers and then their sons, generation after generation. I have called this development clone-civilization (clone from the Greek word clon meaning branch) i.e., a development from one genealogical tree.

Before 1870 about three fourths of the settlements in Pite lappmark

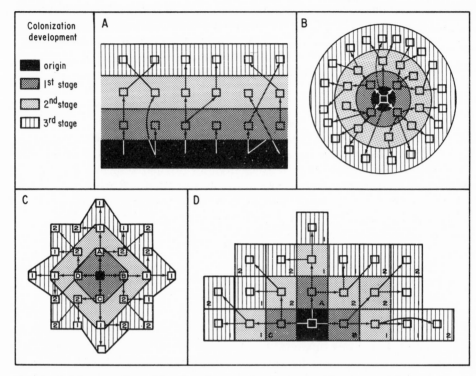

FIGURE 1: Theoretical models of settlement development. (Squares=settlements.)

were results of the clone-colonization or an inner colonization, not the result of immigration.

The C-model, like all the following models, is built upon an assumption of a pure clone-colonization. The mother settlements A, B, C, D have been established with the starting point in one origin settlement, and two sons from each one of the mother settlements have been assumed to be pioneers in the following order A 1, B 1, C 1, D 1, A 2, B 2, C 2, D 2, A 11, B 11, C 11, D 11, A 12, B 12 etc. It has been considered an important endeavour of the colonists to find and choose new land as near the mother settlement as possible, but, on the other hand also to have the new settlement in a position as free as possible from land competition from other pioneers coming from other mother settlements. This is an assumption which is based upon facts from the colonization development in Pite lappmark. In a choice between two or more equivalent land areas a random decision is made. With these assumptions in mind we are able to construct a development, illustrated by the C-model.

The D-model in its turn is a variation of model C. The difference is that the vertical component in the C-model is prevented from developing downwards. Certain factors are responsible for this, e.g., physical, or the vertical area is already fully colonized and is assumed to reach up to the baseline on the D-model. A consequence of this is that the competition for new land in free positions is harder in the D-model, and the settlement pattern more irregular than in the C-model. Besides, the chronology of the settlement development in model D is the same as that for the C-model, described above.

The clearly noticeable irregularity of the D-model indicates, however, an approach to reality, and upon the assumptions of that model the E-model (Fig. 2) is built. The E-model shows evident similarities to realistic colonization by using only a few more simple complicating factors, based upon reality. These new assumptions are:

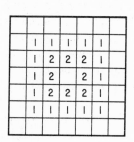

	2	4	4	2	l		
l	2	4	4	2	l		
l	2^1	4^1	4^1	2^1	l^1	l	
l	2^1	4^3	4^3	2^3	l^3	l	
l	2^1	4^3	⊕		l^3	l	
l	2^1	4^3	4^3	2^3	🌸	l	
l	🌸	4^1	Cl	2^1	l^1	l	
l	2	4	4	2	l		
l	2	4	4	Bl	l		
l	Al	4	4	2	l		

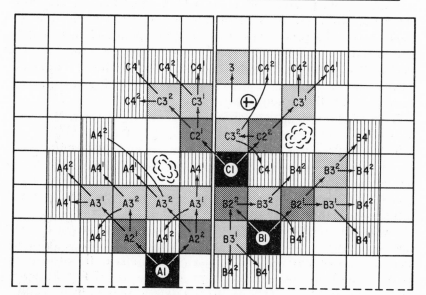

FIGURE 2: A theoretical colonization model which shows good similarities to the real development. Cf. Figure 3. (Squares=settlers' lands. Legend: See Figure 1.)

1. The attraction of the settlers' lands is inversely proportional to the perpendicular distance from the road, which is assumed to be straight and to go through the middle of the area (indicated by small dots in the figure).

2. The church and market-place (cross with a circle round it) are assumed to exercize a certain attraction on the settlement.

Otherwise the basic assumptions for the C- and D-models about the pure clone-colonization development and the endeavor to find land free from competition are still used—i.e.:

3. The settlers' lands are colonized by settlers who go out from within the area of previously existing settlement (mother settlements).

4. Settlers' land lying at the shortest distance from the mother settlement is occupied before land situated further away. (A diagonally adjoining square—settlers' land—is considered to lie at the same distance from the mother settlement as squares directly adjoining vertically and horizontally.) However, in choices between other equivalent settlers' lands, that is preferred which is most free from competition from the nearest existing settlement which is not a mother settlement.

The other principles for the construction of the E-model will be described as follows:

5. The first three settlements quoted, A 1, B 1, and C 1, are established one after the other, as regards time, in the order A 1, B 1, and C 1.

6. Each mother settlement sends out an equal number of son-colonists, i.e., two. These are designated by two numerals of which the first (1–4) means the generations from the first up to and including the fourth, and the second, which may be 1 or 2, designates son No. 1 and son No. 2 respectively. In order that it may be possible to distinguish among sons, their descent is given in the text by inserting earlier generations as well within parentheses: A $(1\ 2\ 3^1)\ 4^1$.

7. These sons take up new settlements on coming of age in the following order: A $(1)\ 2^1$, B $(1)\ 2^1$, C $(1)\ 2^1$, A $(1)\ 2^2$, B $(1)\ 2^2$, C $(1)\ 2^2$, etc.

8. The settlers' lands not already taken up by settlements are only found within the Lappland boundary (the line of short dashes at the foot of the figure).

9. Certain squares have been assumed to be totally unfit for settlement, waste land ("smoke rings").

The fundamentally new thing with the construction of the E-model, however, is that an attempt has been made to give the presumptive new settlers' lands certain attraction values (which refer to the assumptions 1–3). In the half-scale squared diagram on the left of Fig. 2, starting with the settlers' land which we desire to test as regards its competitive attraction, a valuation is made of surrounding settlers' land in which the squares situated nearest are given the value 2, and those round about the bordering frame the value 1. If any of the settlers' land squares are already occupied when a settler's son is to be placed, these are deducted from the maximum total of 32, a value which can be assigned to every presumptive settlers' land, if all surrounding settlers' lands on which values have been placed are available. If any of the squares falls on waste land, its value is, of course, also deducted.

This left-hand diagram is consequently regarded as movable and transferable onto the right-hand diagram in the figure, which gives, on the one hand, the increasing value of the squares with shorter distance to the road according to the scale 1–2–4 and, on the other hand, the value with regard to the church and market-place, in which adjacent settlers' land is assigned the value 3 and the settlers' land beyond that the value 1 (marked in the upper right-hand part of the squares). Waste land is also marked.

A summation of the numerical value of each square (maximally three different values) is then made, after which the settlers' land which has the largest total value is considered to have the largest competitive attraction and is therefore assumed to be settled.

By this method every settlers' land which conceivably can be colonized by removal from an existing mother settlement accordingly is evaluated on purely theoretical grounds. The distribution pattern shown in Fig. 2 must be considered wholly a result of the three numerical scales applied in the evaluation. Many but largely similar patterns are possible, depending on the value we wish to assign to the attraction in assumptions 1–3 in relation to each other. A very difficult problem is to give the true, realistic, and not only theoretical, attraction value to the presumptive settlers' land in order to produce a closer adaptation to reality. But for this further investigations are necessary.

However one proceeds in each individual model experiment, the result is in all cases a considerably more disturbed pattern than when one disregards the fact that the settlers' lands have different attractions. Thus, for example, it may happen—as is evident from the figure—that settler's sons belonging to the same generation may be compelled to take up new farmsteads at very variable distances from the mother settlement; A $(1\,2^2\,3^2)\,4^2$, for example, moves twice as far away as his brother A $(1\,2^2\,3^2)\,4^1$. And settlers belonging to the same generation who started out originally from the same settlement in the first generation may come to develop their settlements at very considerable distances from each other [cf., for example, C $(1\,2^1\,3^2)\,4^2$ with C $(1\,2^2\,3^1)\,4^1$].

Fig. 3 gives a generalized picture of the real process of colonization in Arvidsjaur parish during the different epochs stated. (The numerals indicate height above sea-level in metres.) Its similarity with the theoretical model (Fig. 2) cannot be said to be immediately striking

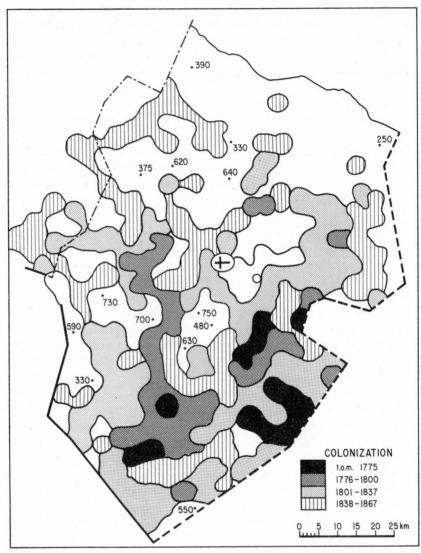

FIGURE 3: The colonization of Arvidsjaur parish, Norrbotten county, during stated periods. (Black=area settled before 1776.)

as regards the formation of the pattern. But strictly speaking, it is not right to expect any detailed agreement. In reality further complications supervene, to which no regard has been paid in the theory; for example, the fact that from each mother settlement a varying number of settler-sons has gone out, while from certain of them none at all. Besides, we may, in reality, have to reckon with several roads which wind in and out of the colonization area.

In spite of the pronounced and expected differences in the distribution pattern between the model and reality, essential similarities are nevertheless manifest.

We may note in particular that the areas do not only adjoin each other in, so to say, chronological order but also mingle with each other both in the model and in reality. Thus, according to the model, both the third and the fourth generations' colonization areas adjoin in several ways the areas settled by the first generation. Furthermore, as is evident, the second and the fourth generations' areas may border on each other. We may also note that the fifth generation also will adjoin settlements A 1 and B 1 with its settlement buildings and cultivations in a number of cases.

In reality we find, as has already been said, corresponding phenomena. Areas which were colonized as late as the 1838–1867 period and the immediately preceding 1801–1837 period adjoin in certain cases the areas colonized first, before 1776. Similarly, we find that areas colonized in 1776–1800 and 1838–1867 have common boundaries. All the surface designations of the figures are thus mixed with each other.

The similarity between the figures is not restricted to areas *with* settlement. As regards the uninhabited areas, we can demonstrate that both in the theoretical pattern and in the real one non-settled areas may appear which are not waste land, enclosed in areas *with* settlement. At a later stage of settlement development we may find these areas used by settlers.

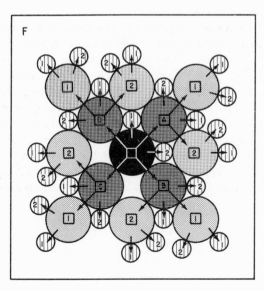

FIGURE 4: Refined model of settlement development. Cf. Figure 1, model C. (Circles=settlers' lands.—Legend: see Figure 1.)

This fact, that land with equally good conditions for new settling as other lands already settled lies unexploited a surprisingly long time, may, of course, in reality depend upon the fact that the land is initially of inadequate size to support a settler but that under new conditions it can be large enough. For example, the conditions for colonization in Lappland were changed, in any case from about 1820 onwards, in such a way that the colonists by aid of different irrigation methods suitable to the prevailing natural hydrophilous vegetation (Carex and Equisetum) could bring the hay yield to increase from 2 to 10 times. Besides, from that time potatoes were used generally, and so the conditions of maintenance for the colonists were much better than before. Thus it was possible to earn a living from a far smaller area than earlier. With regard to this, the F-model (Fig. 4) is constructed. The principles for the construction are the same as for the C-model but with two exceptions. These are (1) that the colonization during the third stage claims only about 1/5 of the mean area which was necessary for the older settlements established during the earlier stages, and (2) that every settlement, the older ones as well, even the origin and the mother settlements A–D, sends out two pioneers during the third stage.

As may be seen from the F-model presumptive settlers' lands during the two earlier stages are left unsettled, even in the nearest neighbourhood of the origin settlement. However, during the third stage these unsettled areas begin to be occupied and certainly will be filled up by settlements later on during times with the same economic conditions and with a still increasing population.

In this paper I have only intended to point out that with the guidance of some good assumptions it is possible to draw theoretical patterns for the spread of settlement, which can contribute explanations to complicated settlement developments which are otherwise difficult to interpret. In order to adapt the models still better to reality, attention, of course, must also be paid to other facts which have not been discussed or considered here; amongst other things, the natural advantages of the settlers' lands, e.g., the occurrence of good soils or of profitable fishing lakes. It is, however, obvious, that the very complicated pattern of the spread of settlement does not in every case admit of explanation by physico-geographical conditions alone, however important these may otherwise be.

10. A Theory of Location for Cities

Edward Ullman

*Central-place theory is of concern to the urban, economic,
and cultural geographer. This concept is generally attributed
to Walter Christaller, who in 1935 published "Die Zentralen
Orte in Suddeutschland." His theory provides a framework
for studying and explaining the distribution of cities and has
been adapted by many other scholars. Ullman reviews the
development of this theory and the contributions of others
working in the same general area. The growth and
distribution of cities is an important part of the urbanization
process, affecting parts of the world particularly
when they industrialize.*

I

Periodically in the past century the location and distribution of cities
and settlements have been studied. Important contributions have been
made by individuals in many disciplines. Partly because of the diversity
and uncoordinated nature of the attack and partly because of the complexities and variables involved, a systematic theory has been slow to
evolve, in contrast to the advances in the field of industrial location.

The first theoretical statement of modern importance was von Thünen's *Der isolierte Staat*, initially published in 1826, wherein he postulated an entirely uniform land surface and showed that under ideal
conditions a city would develop in the center of this land area and concentric rings of land use would develop around the central city. In
1841 Kohl investigated the relation between cities and the natural and
cultural environment, paying particular attention to the effect of transport routes on the location of urban centers. In 1894 Cooley admirably
demonstrated the channelizing influence that transportation routes,
particularly rail, would have on the location and development of trade
centers. He also called attention to break in transportation as a city-
builder just as Ratzel had earlier. In 1927 Haig sought to determine
why there was such a large concentration of population and manufacturing in the largest cities. Since concentration occurs where assembly

SOURCE: *American Journal of Sociology*, XLVI (May, 1941), 835–64, and Edward
Ullman, *Geography as Spatial Interaction: Studies in Regional Development, Cities,
and Transportation* (Seattle: University of Washington Press, 1968). The author
is professor of geography, University of Washington.

of material is cheapest, all business functions, except extraction and transportation, ideally should be located in cities where transportation is least costly. Exceptions are provided by the processing of perishable goods, as in sugar centrals, and of large weight-losing commodities, as in smelters. Haig's theoretical treatment is of a different type from those just cited but should be included as an excellent example of a "concentration" study.

In 1927 Bobeck showed that German geographers since 1899, following Schlüter and others, had concerned themselves largely with the internal geography of cities, with the pattern of land use and forms within the urban limits, in contrast to the problem of location and support of cities. Such preoccupation with internal urban structure has also characterized the recent work of geographers in America and other countries. Bobeck insisted with reason that such studies, valuable though they were, constituted only half the field of urban geography and that there remained unanswered the fundamental geographical question: "What are the causes for the existence, present size, and character of a city?" Since the publication of this article, a number of urban studies in Germany and some in other countries have dealt with such questions as the relations between city and country.

II

A theoretical framework for study of the distribution of settlements is provided by the work of Walter Christaller. The essence of the theory is that a certain amount of productive land supports an urban center. The center exists because essential services must be performed for the surrounding land. Thus the primary factor explaining Chicago is the productivity of the Middle West; location at the southern end of Lake Michigan is a secondary factor. If there were no Lake Michigan, the urban population of the Middle West would in all probability be just as large as it is now. Ideally, the city should be in the center of a productive area. The similarity of this concept to von Thünen's original proposition is evident.

Apparently many scholars have approached the scheme in their thinking. Bobeck claims he presented the rudiments of such an explanation in 1927. The work of a number of American rural sociologists shows appreciation for some of Christaller's preliminary assumptions, even though done before or without knowledge of Christaller's work and performed with a different end in view. Galpin's epochal study of trade areas in Walworth County, Wisconsin, published in 1915, was the first contribution. Since then important studies bearing on the problem have been made by others. These studies are confined primarily to smaller trade centers but give a wealth of information on distribution of settle-

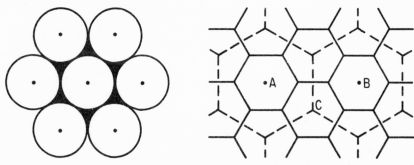

FIGURE 1: Theoretical shapes of tributary areas. Circles leave unserved spaces, hexagons do not. Small hexagons are service areas for smaller places, large hexagons (*dotted lines*) represent service areas for next higher-rank central places.

ments which independently substantiates many of Christaller's basic premises.

As a working hypothesis one assumes that normally the larger the city, the larger its tributary area. Thus there should be cities of varying size ranging from a small hamlet performing a few simple functions, such as providing a limited shopping and market center for a small contiguous area, up to a large city with a large tributary area composed of the service areas of many smaller towns and providing more complex services, such as wholesaling, large-scale banking, specialized retailing, and the like. Services performed purely for a surrounding area are termed "central" functions by Christaller, and the settlements performing them "central" places. An industry using raw materials imported from outside the local region and shipping its products out of the local area would not constitute a central service.

Ideally, each central place would have a circular tributary area, as in von Thünen's proposition, and the city would be in the center. However, if three or more tangent circles are inscribed in an area, unserved spaces will exist; the best theoretical shapes are hexagons, the closest geometrical figures to circles which will completely fill an area (Fig. 1).

Christaller has recognized typical-size settlements, computed their average population, their distance apart, and the size and population of their tributary areas in accordance with his hexagonal theory as Table 1 shows. He also states that the number of central places follows a norm from largest to smallest in the following order: 1:2:6:18:54, etc.

All these figures are computed on the basis of South Germany, but Christaller claims them to be typical for most of Germany and western Europe. The settlements are classified on the basis of spacing each larger unit in a hexagon of next-order size, so that the distance between similar centers in the table above increases by the $\sqrt{3}$ over the preceding

TABLE 1.

	TOWNS		TRIBUTARY AREAS	
Central place	Distance apart (Km.)	Population	Size (Sq. Km.)	Population
Market hamlet (*Marktort*)	7	800	45	2,700
Township center (*Amtsort*)	12	1,500	135	8,100
County seat (*Kreistadt*)	21	3,500	400	24,000
District city (*Bezirksstadt*)	36	9,000	1,200	75,000
Small state capital (*Gaustadt*)	62	27,000	3,600	225,000
Provincial head city (*Provinzhauptstadt*)	108	90,000	10,800	675,000
Regional capital city (*Landeshauptstadt*)	186	300,000	32,400	2,025,000

smaller category (in Fig. 1, e.g., the distance from A to B is $\sqrt{3}$ times the distance from A to C). The initial distance figure of 7 km. between the smallest centers is chosen because 4–5 km., approximately the distance one can walk in one hour, appears to be a normal service-area limit for the smallest centers. Thus, in a hexagonal scheme, these centers are about 7 km. apart. Christaller's maps indicate that such centers are spaced close to this norm in South Germany. In the larger categories the norms for distance apart and size of centers appear to be true averages; but variations from the norm are the rule, although wide discrepancies are not common in the eastern portion of South Germany, which is less highly industrialized than the Rhine-Ruhr areas in the west. The number of central places of each rank varies rather widely from the normal order of expectancy.

The theoretical ideal appears to be most nearly approached in poor, thinly settled farm districts—areas which are most nearly self-contained. In some other sections of Germany industrial concentration seems to be a more important explanation, although elements of the central-place type of distribution are present. Christaller points out that Cologne is really the commercial center for the Ruhr industrial district even though it is outside the Ruhr area. Even in mountain areas centrality is a more important factor than topography in fixing the distribution of settlements. Christaller states that one cannot claim that a certain city is where it is because of a certain river—that would be tantamount to saying that if there were no rivers there would be no cities.

III

Population alone is not a true measure of the central importance of a city; a large mining, industrial, or other specialized-function town might have a small tributary area and exercise few central functions. In addition to population, therefore, Christaller uses an index based on number of telephones in proportion to the average number per thousand inhabitants in South Germany, weighted further by the telephone density of the local subregion. A rich area such as the Palatinate supports more telephones in proportion to population than a poor area in the Bavarian Alps; therefore, the same number of telephones in a Palatinate town would not give it the same central significance as in the Alps. He claims that telephones, since they are used for business, are a reliable index of centrality. Such a thesis would not be valid for most of the United States, where telephones are as common in homes as in commercial and professional quarters.

Some better measures of centrality could be devised, even if only the number of out-of-town telephone calls per town. Better still would be some measure of actual central services performed. It would be tedious and difficult to compute the amount, or percentage, of business in each town drawn from outside the city, but some short cuts might be devised. If one knew the average number of customers required to support certain specialized functions in various regions, then the excess of these functions over the normal required for the urban population would be an index of centrality. In several states rural sociologists and others have computed the average number of certain functions for towns of a given size. With one or two exceptions only small towns have been analyzed. Retail trade has received most attention, but professional and other services have also been examined. These studies do not tell us actually what population supports each service, since the services are supported both by town and by surrounding rural population, but they do provide norms of function expectancy which would be just as useful.

A suggestive indicator of centrality is provided by the maps which Dickinson has made for per capita wholesale sales of cities in the United States. On this basis centers are distributed rather evenly in accordance with regional population density. Schlier has computed the centrality of cities in Germany on the basis of census returns for "central" occupations. Refinement of some of our census returns is desirable before this can be done entirely satisfactorily in the United States, but the method is probably the most promising in prospect.

Another measure of centrality would be the number of automobiles entering a town, making sure that suburban movements were not included. Figures could be secured if the state-wide highway planning surveys in forty-six states were extended to gather such statistics.

IV

The central-place scheme may be distorted by local factors, primarily industrial concentration or main transport routes. Christaller notes that transportation is not an areally operating principle, as the supplying of central goods implies, but is a linearly working factor. In many cases central places are strung at short intervals along an important transport route, and their tributary areas do not approximate the ideal circular or hexagonal shape but are elongated at right angles to the main transport line. In some areas the reverse of this normal expectancy is true. In most of Illinois, maps depicting tributary areas show them to be elongated parallel to the main transport routes, not at right angles to them. The combination of nearly uniform land and competitive railways peculiar to the state results in main railways running nearly parallel and close to one another between major centers.

In highly industrialized areas the central-place scheme is generally so distorted by industrial concentration in response to resources and transportation that it may be said to have little significance as an explanation for urban location and distribution, although some features of a central-place scheme may be present, as in the case of Cologne and the Ruhr.

In addition to distortion, the type of scheme prevailing in various regions is susceptible to many influences. Productivity of the soil, type of agriculture and intensity of cultivation, topography, governmental organization, are all obvious modifiers. In the United States, for example, what is the effect on distribution of settlements caused by the sectional layout of the land and the regular size of counties in many states? In parts of Latin America many centers are known as "Sunday towns"; their chief functions appear to be purely social, to act as religious and recreational centers for holidays—hence the name "Sunday town." Here social rather than economic services are the primary support of towns, and we should accordingly expect a system of central places with fewer and smaller centers, because fewer functions are performed and people can travel farther more readily than commodities. These underlying differences do not destroy the value of the theory; rather they provide variations of interest to study for themselves and for purposes of comparison with other regions.

The system of central places is not static or fixed; rather it is subject to change and development with changing conditions. Improvements in transportation have had noticeable effects. The provision of good automobile roads alters buying and marketing practices, appears to make the smallest centers smaller and the larger centers larger, and generally alters trade areas. Since good roads are spread more uniformly over the land than railways, their provision seems to make the distribution of centers correspond more closely to the normal scheme.

Christaller may be guilty of claiming too great an application of his scheme. His criteria for determining typical-size settlements and their normal number apparently do not fit actual frequency counts of settle-

ments in many almost uniform regions as well as some less rigidly de-
ductive norms.

Bobeck in a later article claims that Christaller's proof is unsatisfactory. He states that two-thirds of the population of Germany and England live in cities and that only one-third of these cities in Germany are
real central places. The bulk are primarily industrial towns or villages
inhabited solely by farmers. He also declares that exceptions in the rest
of the world are common, such as the purely rural districts of the Tonkin
Delta of Indochina, cities based on energetic entrepreneurial activity, as
some Italian cities, and world commercial ports such as London, Rotterdam, and Singapore. Many of these objections are valid; one wishes that
Christaller had better quantitative data and were less vague in places.
Bobeck admits, however, that the central-place theory has value and applies in some areas.

The central-place theory probably provides as valid an interpretation
of settlement distribution over the land as the concentric-zone theory
does for land use within cities. Neither theory is to be thought of as a
rigid framework fitting all location facts at a given moment. Some, ex-
pecting too much, would jettison the concentric-zone theory; others,
realizing that it is an investigative hypothesis of merit, regard it as a
useful tool for comparative analysis.

V

Even in the closely articulated national economy of the United States
there are strong forces at work to produce a central-place distribution of
settlements. It is true that products under our national economy are
characteristically shipped from producing areas through local shipping
points directly to consuming centers which are often remote. However,
the distribution of goods or imports brought into an area is characteristically carried on through brokerage, wholesale, and retail channels in
central cities. This graduated division of functions supports a central-
place framework of settlements. Many non-industrial regions of relatively uniform land surface have cities distributed so evenly over the
land that some sort of central-place theory appears to be the prime explanation. It should be worth while to study this distribution and compare it with other areas. In New England, on the other hand, where
cities are primarily industrial centers based on distant raw materials and
extraregional markets, instead of the land's supporting the city the reverse is more nearly true: the city supports the countryside by providing
a market for farm products, and thus infertile rural areas are kept from
being even more deserted than they are now.

The forces making for concentration at certain places and the inevitable rise of cities at these favored places have been emphasized by

geographers and other scholars. The phenomenal growth of industry and world trade in the last hundred years and the concomitant growth of cities justify this emphasis but have perhaps unintentionally caused the intimate connection between a city and its surrounding area partially to be overlooked. Explanation in terms of concentration is most important for industrial districts but does not provide a complete areal theory for distribution of settlements. Furthermore, there is evidence that "of late . . . the rapid growth of the larger cities has reflected their increasing importance as commercial and service centers rather than as industrial centers." Some form of the central-place theory should provide the most realistic key to the distribution of settlements where there is no marked concentration—in agricultural areas where explanation has been most difficult in the past. For all areas the system may well furnish a theoretical norm from which deviations may be measured. It might also be an aid in planning the development of new areas. If the theory is kept in mind by workers in academic and planning fields as more studies are made, its validity may be tested and its structure refined in accordance with regional differences.

11. The Assimilation of Nomads in Egypt
Mohamed Awad

People in ancient times wandered from place to place in search of food and shelter for themselves and their animals, and even today small numbers of Eskimos, Lapps, and desert nomads continue that way of life. Nomads wander over large semi-arid and arid regions of the world, particularly in North Africa and the Middle East. As they come in contact with a sedentary civilization or acquire land for cultivation, their nomadic characteristics disappear. The nature of this assimilation process and culture change in Egypt is described by Awad.

The gradual transition from total nomadism to a completely sedentary life, in which agricultural pursuits replace the herding of flocks, is a well-known social phenomenon common to many parts of the world.

SOURCE: *Geographical Review*, XLIV (1954), 240–52. The author is a geographer and president of Alexandria University, Egypt.

There are, however, interesting variations, due to local conditions. Egypt offers a particularly suitable illustration. In Egypt, when nomads become assimilated, they are said to have become *fellahin* (singular, *fellah*), a word meaning literally "tillers of the soil," but with a cultural and social significance beyond this.

Egypt is a country of sharp contrasts. The narrow alluvial valley of the lower Nile and its delta, both intensively cultivated, lie between two vast deserts, the eastern excessively arid, the western containing a few scattered oases. These desert areas constitute some 95 per cent of the whole country. This juxtaposition of a region of great fertility and one of extreme barrenness, with scarcely any zone of transition, is almost without parallel. The waters of the Nile flood reach to the edge of both deserts; it is often possible to stand with one foot on the desert and the other on a cultivated field.

However, a zone of transition can be artificially created, when parts of the border cultivable areas are occupied by pastoral people who are not interested in tilling the soil. Such artificial zones of transition have, in fact, existed in Egypt at certain times, in both the eastern and the western limits of cultivation, and have strongly influenced the relationships between nomads and cultivators. At present such transition areas are insignificant, having been steadily brought under cultivation of one kind or another.

The population of Egypt is naturally concentrated in the region of intensive cultivation, but the adjoining deserts, though too barren in part even for nomads, are not at present, and have never been in the past, without their own inhabitants, whose ethnic and cultural composition may have changed from time to time, but whose role in the life of the country has remained almost unaltered. These desert folk are sometimes established on the borders of the cultivated lands and maintain regular relations with the settled peasant population in their neighborhood. They are also established in the heart of the desert to the east or to the west, where they live their own lives, with a minimum of contact with the peasant people of the valley. To the average Egyptian, even the names of these tribes are unknown.

But the problem for the settled population has been how to deal, not with the desert dwellers of Egypt as such at any given time, but with continuous streams of nomadism, flowing from vast and almost inexhaustible reservoirs to the east and west. The eastern desert of Egypt, reaching to the Red Sea and the wilderness of Sinai, is only the nearest part of a desert area embracing the whole of the Arabian Peninsula and extending to the Persian Gulf and to the Gulf of Aden and the Indian Ocean. On the west, the Libyan Desert is also merely a fraction of a much larger desert, extending across the great Sahara to the shore of the Atlantic. Thus we have a desert region curving in a great arc, some five thousand kilometers in length, from the Indian Ocean to the Atlantic, interrupted at the center by an area of cultivation and sedentary life. Had it been merely a question of dealing with the "local" desert folk, the problem might have been solved, once and for all, in early Pharaonic times. But it has recurred, time and again, throughout Egyptian history.

The Nomad Streams

The two streams of nomadism, from the east and from the west, have been distinct and independent, each having what might be called its own sphere of influence. The routes from the east into Egypt are affected by geographical circumstance, notably by the extension of the Red Sea in the Gulfs of Aqaba and Suez within 150 kilometers of the Mediterranean. The path of ingress is thus limited to the Isthmus of Suez. The influence of this convergence of routes is concentrated in one part of Egypt, and it has therefore been more profound than if the routes were scattered over a wide area.

The western, or Libyan, routes, on the other hand, cover a much larger area, and their influence embraces the whole of western Egypt. Nevertheless, free movement of nomads is hampered by vast areas of sand dunes in certain latitudes, a handicap partly compensated for by the existence of a line of oases from Siwa in the north to Kharga and Dakhla in the south, and of the Wadi el Natrun and the Faiyum depressions, which act as corridors to the Nile Valley.

But by far the most important Libyan route, in both ancient and modern times, has been the strip of land, 20 or 30 kilometers wide, bordering the Mediterranean from Egypt to Tunisia. This coastal strip has abundant pasture and has been sporadically cultivated. Its rainfall, though too uncertain for regular crops, is adequate for the growth of herbs and shrubs for the flocks of nomads, even when they do not possess camels. In ancient times, long before the camel was introduced into Africa, there were large migrations of nomadic tribes, such as the earlier Tehenu and the later Temehu, which for several centuries affected the settled population of Egypt.

Although the eastern nomadic stream normally affects the eastern Nile Valley and Delta, and the Libyan the western, including the Faiyum, there have been notable exceptions, such as the settlement of the western Hanadi tribe in Sharqiya Province by the orders of Mohamed Ali. Besides the two main streams of nomadism, there has been a certain amount of movement from the southeast, the country of the Beja people, who were known to the ancient Egyptians as the Mazoi. Their wanderings, however, have been felt far more in the Sudan than in Egypt proper.

Nomadism in Egyptian History

In remote antiquity, it must be assumed, the population of Egypt consisted of wandering folk, living on the products of the chase or edible roots or fish caught from the river and the pools. In some remote prehistoric period the people took to agriculture and a settled life, and the almost continuous struggle with nomadic intruders began—one of the most disturbing factors in Egyptian history, ancient, medieval, and modern.[1]

The legend of the long feud between Osiris and Set has perpetuated the bitter struggle in mythological form. Even more definite proof of an early predynastic invasion from the eastern desert is found in the language, which emerges in the early dynastic period with strong Semitic characteristics.

When the Egyptian rulers began to record the principal events of their times, they gave frequent accounts of punitive expeditions or even full-scale wars against "troglodytes" from the east and different varieties of Libyans from the west. The country was organized for defense against their sudden inroads. The copper mines in Sinai were protected by fortifications, though sometimes they were abandoned in the face of overwhelming attack. Special elaborate fortifications were constructed at the eastern and western approaches to the Delta, which were probably adequate in small raids but powerless to stem an overwhelming tide.

The introduction of the camel into Africa[2] notably affected the manner and character of the raids. The earlier nomads possessed flocks of sheep and goats as well as some donkeys, and the range of their wanderings was limited. The camel greatly increased the mobility of the nomads. They were able to travel longer distances, and to wander around for generations until a chance for penetration offered. This is true of both the eastern and the western deserts, though a later development in the latter. In the east people of Arabian stock wandered into Egypt so persistently that in the Ptolemaic period the eastern nome (province) came to be known as the Arabian Nome, several centuries before the

---

[1] Distinction must be made at this point between invasion by a foreign power—Assyrian, Persian, Roman, or Arab—with its special organization and established culture, and the persistent but unsystematic intrusions of rude nomads, with pillage, not conquest, as their motive. Conquest by a foreign power has been relatively rare; the inroads of nomads are chronic.

[2] Apparently the camel was known to exist in Egypt at a very early date, but it was not introduced in any numbers until the Persian conquest (525 B.C.), and its use did not become widespread until Ptolemaic times.

Arab conquest of Egypt. Branches of well-known Southern Arabian tribes [3] began to settle in the eastern part of the Delta, and when these became absorbed by the settled population, a fresh contingent moved in to occupy their place. The nature of the country helped the process. A tribe moving from southern Arabia, perhaps with no definite intention of reaching the Nile Valley, was brought by decades, even centuries, of wandering to the northern part of the peninsula. In the land of Petra, east of the Gulf of Aqaba, the roving clans found suitable grazing and occasional springs and wells for watering their flocks. To the west, they found in Sinai a similar land, with even more abundant grazing and springs. In time, some wandered across the Isthmus of Suez, beyond which the Wadi Tumilat extended from the Delta eastward to the gates of Sinai. This area, the well-known Land of Goshen, sub-sequently the Arabian Nome, has from the most ancient times received immigrant nomads from the east, and for a long period the land was seldom brought under cultivation. A large part of what is now Sharqiya Province suffered the same fate, and its agricultural life never enjoyed long stability. This is one of the artificial transition zones referred to earlier, which only in recent times has been brought under permanent cultivation.

It is difficult to assay the relative influence of east and west, the more so since the North Africans have adopted Islam and have also come to be known as "Arabs." But Libyan influence must have been strong indeed. The people of Siwa, the oasis of Jupiter Ammon, speak a Libyan Hamitic dialect to this day, and the predominance of Libyan Arabs in every province of Upper Egypt as well as in the western Delta shows how far Libyan elements have penetrated into the agricultural lands of Egypt.

Arab medieval writers were in the habit of dividing the country, especially northern Egypt, into four parts: the Eastern "Hauf" (District), containing the Wadi Tumilat and its surroundings; the Western Hauf, the corresponding part in the western Delta (these two are the artificial transition zones between the wilderness and the sown, which constituted the special domain of nomads when they approached the purely agricultural lands); the middle of the Delta, known as the "Rif" (or land of tillage and agricultural pursuits), the domain of the settled fellahin, though not entirely free from nomadic encroachments; and the strip of coastland bordering the Mediterranean, better represented in Libya than in Sinai, and known to Arab writers as the "Gufar."

[3] Students of Arab genealogies divide the tribes of Arabia into Southern, or Kahta-nite, and Northern, or Adnanite. The former, the more numerous of the two branches, and originally from the Yemen and surrounding countries, has subsequently migrated to other parts of Arabia.

Process of Nomad Penetration

Though there may have been slight variations throughout the centuries, the process of nomad penetration has remained more or less the same. Since the Arab conquest of Egypt, the prevailing nomadic elements have been Arab. At first they were pure Arab tribes, coming directly from Arabia; later the Libyan elements came to be described as Arabs also, though they certainly contained a high percentage of Berber blood. Such has been the case to the present day, so that the distinction between sedentary peasants and nomads is now described as between "fellahin" and "Arabs."

It was natural that in early Islamic times, when Egypt was a province of the Muslim Empire, conditions should be favorable for Arab immigration. The nomination of a prominent Arab as governor of Egypt was invariably the occasion for the immigration of large numbers of the tribe to which he belonged, who were given lands in the Eastern Hauf. These authorized, large-scale immigrations were accompanied by the usual unauthorized waves of infiltration and penetration, so that the numbers of nomads through the ages must have been enormous. It is safe to assume that in due course these nomad elements gradually departed from the nomadic form of life and in the end were completely absorbed into the native population, only to be replaced by fresh nomad elements. Maqrizi,[4] writing in the fifteenth century, tells us that the Arabs who entered Egypt with the conquest in A.D. 640 and subsequent years had completely vanished in his time and could not be traced.

Naboulsi,[5] who wrote at the beginning of the thirteenth century, in a careful description of the Faiyum under the Ayubid dynasty divides the inhabitants into nomads and peasants, using the words "nomad" and "Arab" indiscriminately, though actually he is referring to tribes no longer wholly nomadic but of nomadic origin. He says: "The majority of the population of the Faiyum are Arabs divided into tribes, sections, and clans. The settled population is relatively small, and is not left alone, for the Arabs place them under their protection and exact the price by taking parts of their crops and their lands, and in addition look upon them with contempt, and are always humiliating them." Naboulsi divides the Arabs into three large tribes, Kilab, 'Aglan, and Luwata, and gives a fairly complete list of the clans of each tribe and the districts they occupied. Comparing his accounts with that of Maqrizi two centuries later, we find that some changes had already occurred. The Kilab tribe was still represented, but the other two were insignificant. At the

[4] Al-Maqrizi: Al-Bayan wa 'l-I'rab (Cairo, 1916), pp. 20–21.
[5] Al-Naboulsi: Description du Fayoum au VIIe siècle de l'hégire, Publs. Bibliothèque Nationale, Cairo, 1899.

present time, out of some 20 tribal divisions mentioned by Naboulsi, only one, "Samalus," a Berberized clan, remains, in a much-subdued condition; and the whole section of the Faiyum population claiming Arab descent, in different forms of assimilation, does not exceed 20 per cent of the total. Even at the time of the French expedition to Egypt, at the end of the eighteenth century, the Samalus were completely sedentary, and today they are in a state of advanced assimilation.

The names of some clans, both in the Faiyum and elsewhere, have survived in the names of villages where scarcely any trace of the original clan or tribe remains. Many well-known towns, such as Saqqara (near ancient Memphis), Maghagha in Middle Egypt, Beni Suef, and Beni Mazar, bear names of old Berber or Arab tribes or clans that have completely disappeared. In both Lower and Upper Egypt there are several villages called Juhaynah or Fezara, names of two famous Arab tribes; but there is no trace in the neigborhood of any groups belonging to those tribes, and though some of the more sophisticated members of the community may claim adherence to them, nothing in their social or cultural condition supports such a claim. The same process occurred in ancient times, when groups of Libyans occupied districts, like that of Meir in Upper Egypt, and were gradually absorbed. There can be little doubt that assimilation is the ultimate end of the nomad elements that penetrate the desert and settle in the borderlands of cultivation. Once in the borderlands, they cannot resist the temptation to penetrate farther; moreover, they are often forced to move on by the pressure exerted by new waves behind. The pace of such penetration is usually accelerated at a time of weak central government, for by themselves the fellahin can offer little resistance to encroachment. Throughout the last half century the number of nomads inside the frontiers of Egypt has steadily diminished. The following figures indicate the general trend but must not be considered accurate.

Year	1898	1907	1917	1927	1937	1947
Arab nomads	70,472	97,381	32,663	40,000	12,000	49,000

The figures for 1917 and 1947 are naturally affected by the conditions prevailing during the two World Wars; in the first, nomads were discouraged, and in the second many sought refuge in Egypt.

Stages in Assimilation

It is possible to divide the "Arabs" in Egypt, including the Berberized Arabs from Libya, into four categories, representing different stages of progress toward complete assimilation. The country as a whole can thus

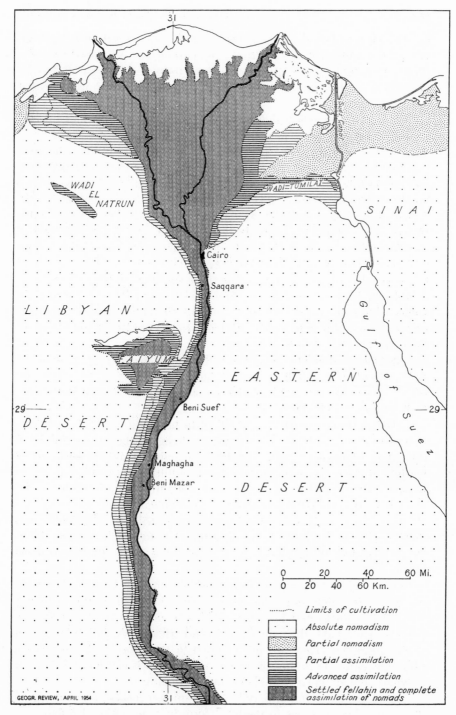

FIGURE 1: Map showing stages in the assimilation of nomads.

Labels within the map:

WADI EL NATRUN

LIBYAN

DESERT

FAIYUM

SINAI

EASTERN

DESERT

Gulf of Suez

WADI TUMILAT

Suez Canal

Cairo

Saqqara

Beni Suef

Maghagha

Beni Mazar

29

31

0   20   40   60 Mi.
0   20   40   60 Km.

.... Limits of cultivation
· ·   Absolute nomadism
      Partial nomadism
      Partial assimilation
      Advanced assimilation
      Settled fellahin and complete
      assimilation of nomads

GEOGR. REVIEW, APRIL 1954

155

be divided into five different zones (Fig. 1): (1) absolute nomadism; (2) partial nomadism; (3) partial assimilation; (4) advanced assimilation; (5) complete assimilation. Each of these five categories has its peculiar characteristics, though an exact sociological description has yet to be attempted.

1. The pure nomads wander in Sinai, and in the lands immediately west of the Suez Canal; farther south, the Maʿaza tribe dwells between the Red Sea and the Nile. The Libyan Arabs usually occupy the zone between Cyrenaica and the Nile Delta, with the exception of the oases and the narrow strip of coast. They are not all equally rich in flocks and numbers, but all possess camels and live in the usual goat-hair tents. Tribal organization is fairly strong, and each tribe has its own area, though tribal boundaries are always contested. Wealth is reckoned in camels, and to a smaller extent in other flocks. The nomads have their own unwritten, strictly observed law, which even the present frontier administration of Egypt has to take into consideration.

Many of these nomads have "Arab" relatives in the Rif agricultural lands, whom they visit at certain seasons to render services, such as carrying crops, for which they are paid. In the course of time some of them are persuaded to stay behind.

This zone of complete nomadism is the almost exclusive domain of the Arab nomad. The sedentary population is confined to a few oases and scattered monasteries, both of which have been subject to raids from their turbulent neighbors.

2. The partial nomads occupy the strip of Mediterranean coastland, some 20 kilometers wide. Here many of them engage in agriculture to the extent of raising a crop of barley, though not always successfully because of the uncertainty of the rains. In addition, they cultivate figs in the part closest to the coast and olives slightly farther south. In the Wadi el Natrun, which has become an Arab domain, cultivation depends on water from wells and springs. Usually the tribe divides labor, part following the flocks, part raising the crops. The two sections have different chiefs, and those engaging in agriculture have *omdas*, or local heads.

In their figs and olives, and sometimes also in their barley, the partial nomads have a new source of income. They begin to reckon in money and not in camels, and the *diya*, or blood money, is paid in Egyptian pounds. They have their own courts and tribal laws, but their power is circumscribed. They are not exposed to the process of assimilation until they emigrate to the Rif, where assimilation is accelerated by their previous acquaintance with elementary agriculture.

Though the condition of partial nomadism is specially characteristic of northern Libya, it exists in modified form in some parts of Sinai.

3. The Arabs undergoing partial assimilation occupy the agricultural

zone immediately adjoining the desert, where they live in villages of their own, completely separate from those of the fellahin. Their houses are usually built, partly at least, of stone, often on the desert edge; there may be some tents.

The villages are small at first. The inhabitants live on their flocks and for some time do not own any land. They usually serve as "guards" to protect the crops of the fellahin, to whom also they sell some of their sheep, goats, or camels. They are not above stealing from, or black-mailing, the settled peasants, whom they despise and with whom they never intermarry. In the course of time they become more numerous and stake a claim to a piece of land on which they have grazed their flocks. The peasant owner is usually obliged to accept the nominal price offered, to avoid worse consequences. The Arab chiefs have another, and more legal, method of acquiring land. They hire from a large landowner, who is usually an absentee landlord, the whole or a large part of his land at a greatly reduced rent and sublet it in small portions at much higher rents to the fellahin or even to members of their own tribe who have taken to agriculture. These chiefs become quite rich and begin to buy land for themselves, though they continue to pursue their tribal habits and are still intimately connected with their nomadic or seminomadic cousins in the desert. But the possession of land leads to an interest in crops and prices. Wealth is no longer reckoned in camels, but in land and money; and cattle are now added to their flocks, which they still love.

4. In the state of advanced assimilation the Arabs have usually emigrated farther into the heart of the Rif. Having realized the value of owning land, they wish to own the better land farther from the desert. Here they cannot hope to have villages of their own and are obliged to share the villages of the fellahin, whom they still consider inferior. But day-to-day intercourse helps bring them socially closer. Their sole occupation is now agriculture, at which they soon become nearly as good as the fellahin. They no longer have a close tribal or-ganization, though they still consider themselves Arabs of such and such a tribe. For a time, depending on the strength of the tribe and its traditions, they continue to marry among themselves. The Hawara of Upper Egypt, an Arabicized Berber tribe that at one time ruled the whole of southern Egypt, still refuse to give their daughters to a fellah, however rich he may be. But since they themselves do not object to marrying rich fellah girls,[6] many of their women are doomed to be old maids. It is unlikely that this state of affairs can last much longer.

Eventually, however, intermarriage becomes inevitable, especially when the Arabs are in a small minority, not exceeding 10 per cent of the

[6] In fact, marrying a rich fellah woman has been one of their means of acquiring land.

population. In any case, they begin to adopt many of the customs of the native fellahin. An interesting example is the practice of clitoridectomy, common among Egyptians but absent in all Arab communities. Sophisticated Egyptians are beginning to drop the custom, but it has existed in Egypt for a very long time, probably since the Pharaohs, and it is found in the oases of the desert, with the exception of Farafra, whose inhabitants claim to be Arabs. In an exaggerated form it exists also among the Nubians and most of the tribes of the northern Sudan. Although the Arabs of both the eastern and the western deserts practice circumcision and celebrate it with special rites, they never practice clitoridectomy until they are in an advanced state of assimilation.

5. Complete assimilation is inevitable when intermarriage has been going on for several decades. New relationships replace the old, and the Arabs of nomadic origin become fellahin, indistinguishable from the native fellahin. Assimilation has for some time been retarded by the law exempting "Arabs" from military service, which encouraged even many non-Arabs to claim Arab descent. But this law no longer operates except as regards pure nomads, and the process has continued, so that when we reach the heart of the Delta, we find no groups claiming an Arab connection of any kind.

These five different stages are likely to exist for some time to come. But a good administration and an orderly government can help remove the more violent aspects of assimilation and reduce the feuds between the Arab tribes themselves, and between Arabs and fellahin.

1 2. Farmsteads in Puerto Rico and Their Interpretative Value

John F. Lounsbury

Farmsteads are "highly indicative of the type of economy that exists in a given rural area." Types of buildings, their size, number, and location are related to agricultural activity and cultural background of Puerto Ricans.

In the last few years the study of rural settlement has been receiving attention from American geographers. A few of their studies are con-

Source: *Geographical Review*, XLV (1955), 347–58. The author is professor of geography, Eastern Michigan University.

cerned with the significance of the farmstead in the North American rural landscape. French and British geographers have made similar studies, over a longer time, in various parts of Europe, but few settlement studies devoted to the description and interpretation of farmsteads have been undertaken in the tropics. A general objective of the present paper in the field of settlement geography is to contribute to a better understanding of the types and occurrence of farmsteads in Caribbean America as exemplified by Puerto Rico.

Obviously, the farmstead is highly indicative of the type of economy that exists in a given rural area. No other settlement form is so closely associated with agriculture, for the farmstead is the first step in the echelon of the production and distribution of agricultural goods, and its distinctive structures are built with that end in mind. A specific objective of this paper is to demonstrate the relationship between the structure of farmstead complexes and the type of rural economy in which they exist.

The farmstead is also indicative of the level of the technology practiced in its particular type of agriculture. Thus the farmstead complex varies in structure from place to place and from time to time with differences in farming techniques. For example, farmsteads in the tobacco regions of the world, though similar, will not be identical.

The island of Puerto Rico is admirably suited for the study of farmsteads in Caribbean America. The diversity in climate, topography, and soils has resulted in practically every type of agricultural or pastoral activity that can be carried on in a tropical or semitropical region. Farmsteads associated with the major types of farming have been studied and compared to determine their basic differences and to find why those differences exist. These farmsteads, producing sugar cane, pineapples, tobacco, coffee, minor subsistence crops, or dairy products, together make up more than 95 per cent of the farms in Puerto Rico. No attempt is made here to discuss relatively unimportant types of agriculture, such as those producing beef cattle, bay rum, cotton, citrus fruits, or vanilla. In all the research areas a specific type of agriculture was found in its optimum setting and had reached its full development.

These optimum agricultural areas were determined by a detailed and quantitative method using the land-mapping data of the Rural Land Classification Program of Puerto Rico of 1949–1951; these data included a land-use map at the scale of 1:10,000 and several hundred interviews. Briefly, the types of agriculture were delimited by a formula adding the percentage of land occupied by each type of land use to the percentage contributed to the farm income by each major crop and dividing the result by two. An index figure was thus derived that not only could be used to delimit agricultural areas but also indicated the intensity of

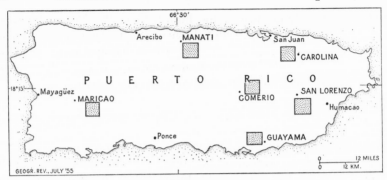

FIGURE 1: Location of selected research areas.

each type of farming.[1] The research was then carried out in areas where particular types of farming were most intensive: Guayama for sugar cane, Manatí for pineapples, San Lorenzo for tobacco, Maricao for coffee, Comerio-Naranjito for minor crops, and Carolina for dairying (Fig. 1). Within each research area, of 4–10 square miles, all farmsteads were analyzed; a summary is given in Table 1.

TABLE 1.

	Sugar Cane	Pine- apples	Tobacco	Coffee	Minor Crops	Dairying
Farmsteads per sq. mi.	3.1	4.2	27.5	5.0	104.0	2.2
Features per farmstead						
Dwellings	31.3	2.3	1.5	2.5	1.1	9.2
Tobacco barns		1.1	1.1		0.1	
Coffee barns				1.0		
Coffee drying floors				1.0	0.2	
Dairy barns	1.0					2.5
Packing houses		3.1				
Large garages		3.0				
Machine sheds	3.0					
Seedbeds			1.0			
Irrigation tanks	0.5					

By the use of these data, it is possible to determine the typical farmstead for each type of farming. The farmsteads described in this article were selected as being as close to typical as possible.

Sugar-Cane Farmsteads

The farmsteads in the most favorable sugar-cane areas are actually small hamlets. They are large, averaging about three to a square mile.

[1] For example, in a specific area it was determined that sugar cane occupied 55 per cent of the land and contributed 87 per cent to the farm income. The index figure, therefore, was 71, and the area was one of sugar-cane farming.

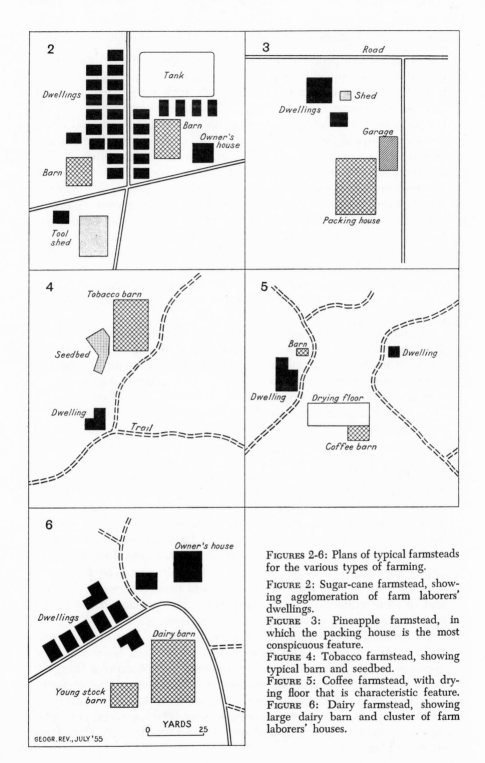

2

Dwellings

Tank

Barn

Owner's house

Barn

Tool shed

3

Road

Dwellings

Shed

Garage

Packing house

4

Tobacco barn

Seedbed

Dwelling

Trail

5

Barn

Dwelling

Dwelling

Drying floor

Coffee barn

6

Owner's house

Dwellings

Dairy barn

Young stock barn

YARDS

0   25

GEOGR. REV., JULY '55

FIGURES 2-6: Plans of typical farmsteads for the various types of farming.

FIGURE 2: Sugar-cane farmstead, showing agglomeration of farm laborers' dwellings.

FIGURE 3: Pineapple farmstead, in which the packing house is the most conspicuous feature.

FIGURE 4: Tobacco farmstead, showing typical barn and seedbed.

FIGURE 5: Coffee farmstead, with drying floor that is characteristic feature.

FIGURE 6: Dairy farmstead, showing large dairy barn and cluster of farm laborers' houses.

161

The elements that make up the farmstead complex (Fig. 2) are a substantial house occupied by the owner or manager, characteristic of the larger farms in all types of farming; a large, single-story machine or tool shed to house cane carts, tractors, and other machinery; one or more low barns to shelter milch cows and saddle horses; and the several small, flimsy dwellings of the *agregados*, or farm laborers, clustered around the farmstead or on poor land unsuitable for cane cultivation. Often there is a country store, occasionally a small church or school. Generally there is a water tank or reservoir, in the form of a shallow basin a few acres in size. In a semi-arid area, accessibility to water largely governs choice of site. In Puerto Rico, practically all irrigated land is devoted to sugar cane, and the best cane lands are in the southern coastal plain. It is imperative to transport the cut cane rapidly to the mill, or *central*, and this necessitates a well-developed road pattern, so that the farmsteads are always served by one or more motor roads. Around and among the structures of the farmstead, subsistence crops are grown in small, irregular plots.

The hamletlike farmstead is found consistently only in the sugar-cane areas. It reflects the intensive farm economy of the optimum areas and the great numbers of people necessary to produce the crop. In the less favored areas, where production is less intensive, the hamletlike structure is not so well developed. Generally, three or four laborers' dwellings, a garage or machine shed, a large house for the owner, and a small shed or two make up the farmstead complex.

Pineapple Farmsteads

The farmsteads in the more favorable pineapple areas are also large—usually two to five to a square mile. The most conspicuous feature is the packing house (Fig. 3), often more than 100 feet long and 50 feet wide, invariably an integral part of the pineapple farmstead and an important functional structure in the efficient handling of the crop. Here the pineapples are graded, wrapped, and crated for shipment. The grading is done by large rollers; sufficient room is also needed to wrap the fruit and to store crates and other equipment. The packing house is not found in farmsteads of other types of agriculture.

The dwelling of the owner or manager is usually a substantial structure. A large garage is also characteristic, since each farm ordinarily possesses one or more trucks for transporting the pineapples from the fields to the packing house or cannery and from the packing house to the docks for ocean shipment. On the smaller farms in the less favorable areas, the garage is smaller or may be lacking. The farmstead is located on one or more motor roads and serves as a focus for secondary farm roads and lanes.

Tobacco Farmsteads

The tobacco farmsteads are relatively small: there may be 20 to 30 to a square mile. Tobacco can be successfully cultivated on a small farm, with little or no specialized equipment. Consequently, the tobacco farmstead is characterized by its simplicity (Fig. 4)—an unsubstantial dwelling and a large, high, well-constructed tobacco barn. Like the pineapple packing house, the tobacco barn is the most distinctive feature of the farmstead. The tobacco leaves must be dried for 30 to 40 days where it is well ventilated and dry, and the barn is built for this purpose. The barns vary in size: the smallest is about the size of a small dwelling (20 by 20 feet), the largest more than 150 feet long; the commonest is some 80 feet long and 40 feet wide. The sides are generally made of thatch and the roof of sheet metal, but the larger barns are most frequently made of wood. The site of the barn is usually a low ridge which ensures good ventilation but which is not exposed to hurricane winds.

Since the annual income of most tobacco farms is meager, the house is generally small and flimsily built. Tobacco is relatively nonperishable and does not have to be processed or transported to market rapidly. Consequently, most tobacco areas do not have a well-developed network of roads, and many farmsteads are located on unimproved trails. During the fall, small cloth-covered seedbeds are constructed to protect the seedlings, which are later transplanted to the tobacco fields. These seedbeds, only a fraction of an acre in size, may be laid out within the farmstead or scattered throughout the area.

Coffee Farmsteads

Coffee is grown on large or medium-sized farms; in the more important coffee areas there are three to six farmsteads to a square mile. Except in rare instances, the farmstead complex is characterized by three elements (Fig. 5): the house, the coffee barn, and the concrete drying floor. In addition, a small shed for miscellaneous uses is not uncommon.

The most distinctive feature of the farmstead is the drying floor, which ranges in length from 30 feet to more than 150. The coffee bean must be dried for three to ten days, and the drying floors or mobile racks are used for this purpose. The coffee barn is also distinctive. After the picking, the coffee berries are dropped from a height of several feet through a hopper, where they are hulled and the two beans within each berry are separated and washed. The coffee barn houses this equipment, and the height of the machine makes a double-story structure most practical.

The dwelling is generally large. Where drying racks are used, built to be rolled under the house in inclement weather, it is of unique construction. In areas where large farmsteads predominate, the dwelling may resemble a barracks, in order to house coffee pickers during the harvest. In areas of exceptionally large farms, a cluster of five to ten small houses may be erected for the laborers. Coffee farms are not always served by motor roads. The dried coffee beans withstand long periods of storage and do not have to be rapidly transported to market. Unimproved trails can be used to transport the crop, and many farmsteads, especially those of the medium-sized farms, are located away from the motor roads.

Dairy Farmsteads

The dairy farms are among the largest farms in Puerto Rico; generally only two or three farmsteads are found to a square mile in the optimum dairy areas. The main feature of the farmstead is the low, open-sided dairy barn (Fig. 6), conspicuously different in structure and appearance from those in the mid-latitudes. The absence of a dormant season enables year-round pasturing and makes unnecessary the high barns and silos that are an essential part of the dairy farmstead in the mid-latitudes. Only in the less favorable dairy areas where there is a distinct dry season, especially along the south coast of the island, is it necessary to construct silos or other structures to store feed. The dairy barn, connected with each field by a trail or lane, serves as an assembly place into which feed is brought daily and cattle are collected to be milked and fed at least twice a day. Within the barn, in addition to the cattle stalls, there is a chopping machine, which cuts the harvested forage grasses and other feed into small enough particles to be used as fodder for the cattle. Occasionally a farmstead has two barns or more; a small corral may serve as a temporary enclosure. Generally, in addition to the large barns for the milking cattle, there is a smaller one for the young stock.

The dwelling of the farm owner or manager is ample and well constructed. On the larger dairy farms in the more favorable dairy areas, five to ten small buildings house the farm laborers. Every farmstead is served by a motor road, for the milk is transported by truck, and it must be shipped at least once a day.

Minor-Crop Farmsteads

The minor-crop farms most frequently average from 60 to more than a hundred to a square mile. They do not have farmsteads, in the sense of several associated structures, for usually a dwelling and a shed are the only buildings. This extreme simplicity lacking distinctive features differentiates the minor-crop farmstead from those in other types of farming and may be explained by the fact that small amounts of many crops are produced and are consumed in a short time. Subsistence crops alone are cultivated, which are relatively nonperishable and are commonly consumed locally.

Because of the low income of the tiny farms, the dwelling is generally small and flimsy. Where attempts are made to produce small amounts of commercial crops, a diminutive coffee drying floor or a little shed to dry tobacco may be present. A well-developed road network is unnecessary, and most of the dwellings are not located on a motor road.

Some General Observations

It is apparent, then, that in most cases the farmstead complex reflects not only the predominant type of agriculture but also the level of technology on which that agriculture is practiced. The sugar-cane farmsteads of the past, when roads and large *centrales* had not yet been developed, were different from the farmsteads of the present. Then each farmstead had its own small sugar mill and crude refinery. Occasionally these relict features may still be seen in the landscape, and in less-developed parts of Caribbean America the old-type farmsteads are still in operation. On the other hand, during recent years a few large coffee farmsteads have installed oil or wood-burning driers, which dry the coffee beans in huge rollers in a matter of hours. This development makes the drying floor and mobile rack obsolete, and they are no longer a part of the farmstead using the advanced technique.

The farmstead may also reveal the manner in which specific crops are marketed. For example, about half of the pineapple crop is shipped fresh to the continental United States, and the remainder is processed by canneries. The packing house within the pineapple farmstead grades and crates the fruit that is to be shipped fresh; the pineapples that are to be processed are trucked directly from the fields to the cannery. The presence of the packing house, therefore, not only is indicative of a pineapple farmstead but also reveals that the fruit is to be shipped fresh.

In addition, the farmstead may reflect conditions of the physical environment. For example, dairy farmsteads in the tropics, as we have seen, differ from those in the mid-latitudes, where a cold season prevails.

In Puerto Rico, as in numerous other areas with dense populations, acute rural problems exist. Progress in defining and solving many of these problems is being made by sound planning. An understanding of the relationship of the farmstead to the total economy of a given area is a major prerequisite to effective planned development. The analysis of farmsteads in problem areas along with a study of the agricultural economy will determine which features of the rural landscape are significant and which are inefficient or superfluous. In this way it may increase the total production of a given area. Further, in planning resettlement programs, it is important to establish the most effective structures to handle or process the dominant crops. Obviously, effective resettlement units will vary considerably in structure from one type of agriculture to another. Also, in areas that are undergoing a change in agricultural economy, whether planned or not, it is possible to predict and encourage the ensuing changes in the morphology of the farmstead.

13. The Empty Areas of the Northeastern United States

Lester E. Klimm

Gottmann, in Selection 14, stresses the growing urbanization of the eastern United States, while Klimm here points out the large areas of empty land near this same part of the country. Men throughout history have clustered in favored areas and avoided others. Even areas that are generally considered densely populated such as Belgium, the Ruhr, or New York City have some completely unoccupied space. Empty areas are of as much interest to the geographer as are densely settled ones.

When an expanding people with an active industrial and commercial culture have used an area for two or three centuries, it should be of interest to see what parts they have passed by or tried and abandoned. Further, the information is now available, and the time seems appropriate, to consider the geography of some parts of the United States in units of the order of one mile in least dimension. . . .

These empty areas are not used for farming, no one lives in them, they contain virtually no recreational or commercial structures. Most of the surface is in woods or brush, ranging from "barrens," burnt-over land, or bog to large tracts of managed commercial forest in Maine, New Hampshire, and New York and extensive areas of state and national forest. Forestry and recreation are the principal present uses. Where they have resulted in structures, the areas occupied have been classified as not being empty.

An "empty area" is defined as one (1) containing no used structures (dwellings, factories, mine buildings, oil wells, hunting lodges, recreational buildings, and so on); (2) containing no land used for agriculture (including even the roughest pasture) or for industry; and (3) having a minimum dimension of at least one mile but not approaching a used structure nearer than a quarter of a mile. . . .

SOURCE: *Geographical Review*, XLIV (July, 1954), 325–45. The author was professor of geography, University of Pennsylvania.

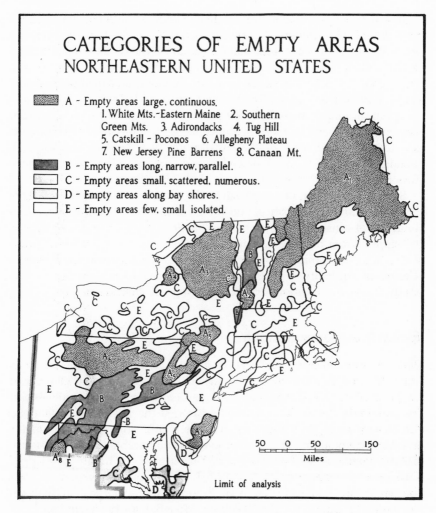

CATEGORIES OF EMPTY AREAS
NORTHEASTERN UNITED STATES

A - Empty areas large. continuous.
   I. White Mts.-Eastern Maine 2. Southern
   Green Mts. 3. Adirondacks 4. Tug Hill
   5. Catskill - Poconos 6. Allegheny Plateau
   7. New Jersey Pine Barrens 8. Canaan Mt.
B - Empty areas long. narrow. parallel.
C - Empty areas small. scattered. numerous.
D - Empty areas along bay shores.
E - Empty areas few. small. isolated.

50 0 50   150
Miles

Limit of analysis

Figure 1.

The Regionalization of Emptiness

The distribution of the empty areas will be analyzed first as to pattern and texture. The names of classical physiographic features are used purely as reference points for location.

The pattern lends itself to a broad grouping in five major categories (Fig. 1): A–empty areas are large and continuous; B–empty areas are long, narrow, and parallel; C–empty areas are small, scattered, and numerous; D–empty areas are grouped along bay shores; E–empty areas are few, small, and isolated.

It will be apparent that this regionalization is based on the "grain," or "texture," of emptiness. Categories A and E, at the two extremes, are relatively homogeneous, and that fact is the basis of their separateness. In the others, the size, shape, and frequency of empty areas are the criteria by which they are differentiated. Such a regionalization is almost naive; however, it is probably the most serviceable for the possible uses of a map of empty areas. It is not proposed to enumerate these possible uses at length here, or those of the concept of empty areas. Suffice it to say that here is a map of the distribution of a kind of landscape. It should contribute to the knowledge and understanding of—and therefore the ability to "plan" for—parts of the Northeast.

Such a regionalization emphasizes the distinction between two kinds of distribution: the statistical and the geographical. It would be possible to arrive at a useful guess as to *how much* of the land in the Northeast is "empty" from the charts, maps, and discussion in the excellent "Land Utilization: A Graphic Summary" published as part of the United States Census of Agriculture, 1950. . . .[1] The map accompanying the present study shows the *location, extent,* and *shape* of such areas.

Relation to Generalization

How do the presence and size of empty areas affect generalizations about the northeastern United States? This region has some 30 per cent of the nation's population; the average density per square mile is 244. In the middle states (Massachusetts through the District of Columbia) the density averages 326 per square mile. Within the United States this is a dense population: even in Europe it is comparable to 200 for France, 260 for Denmark, and 400 for Italy. Yet within this "highly developed," "urbanized," "commercial," "intensively industrialized" region most of the empty areas of category A of Figure 1 are so large that they can be shown to scale at 1:20,000,000, or 316 miles to the inch.

Even at so small a scale it would seem necessary to show empty areas on any map that purports to depict the distribution of almost any phenomenon that involves people and their works. The prevailing emptiness of Maine, New Hampshire, and Vermont, as well as the exceptions to it, should certainly be shown because it is the dominant surface characteristic. Isn't a geographer or cartographer under an implied obligation to show any feature which affects his generalization, and for which the information is available, that *can* be shown on the map scale used?

[1] United States Census of Agriculture: 1950, Vol. 5, Special Reports, Part 4, U. S. Bureau of the Census, 1952.

Relation to Regional Study

Generalizations about the distribution of phenomena are usually made through the process of regionalization. The concept of "region" has been variously defined, but the definition usually involves delimiting areas within which there is some degree of homogeneity or unity with respect to one criterion or an association of criteria. It would seem that the presence of empty areas, if it is to affect regionalization at all, should be most significant in regionalizing about people and their activities.

In such "human use regions," then, how do empty areas affect the concept of homogeneity? The nature of the problem can be illustrated by stating two opposite approaches to it. First, people and their activities are the major interest: homogeneity applies to what people do in the region, even if they do it dispersed over a wide area with empty spaces between units. Or, second, geography is popularly defined as "areal differentiation": even if people's activities are to be the dominant interest, the "homogeneity" of a region in which there are substantial areas with no people and none of the activities being studied will be dubious.

There are, of course, numerous ways of avoiding the horns of this dilemma, and many students and users of regions have followed them. The simplest is to make the map showing the regionalization at the largest feasible scale and indicate all empty areas that can be shown to scale as "empty," "vacant," or "unclassified," and so on. Such a procedure adds refinement to maps of population distribution and density, in particular, and is useful in other forms of regionalization. Freeman in his studies of Ireland has used this method effectively.

As a basis for certain maps in "New England's Prospect: 1933" John K. Wright delimited "sparsely settled or uninhabited lands and non-farming areas." For the large areas in Maine, New Hampshire, and Vermont his delimitation anticipated to a remarkable degree our results for those states. . . . There is less resemblance in the smaller areas and in the three southern New England states.

However, strict adherence to the rule that every empty area that *can* be shown to scale *should* be so shown is necessary if the regionalization is not to be confusing, perhaps misleading. On the map in the Department of Agriculture's "Generalized Types of Farming in the United States" all or parts of categories A1, A2, A3, and A7 of Figure 1 are excluded from the classification and are labeled "Nonfarming." Categories A5 and A6 and the neighboring parts of B are certainly large enough to be shown and are, even "statistically," "nonfarming" but are not so indicated. Many other empty areas appearing on our map could be shown on the Department of Agriculture map to the benefit of the user, but some of them do not show up statistically because of the county basis for the information hitherto available.

In a regionalization of economic or social phenomena there may well be significant differences between a region including, for instance, small, relatively evenly spaced empty areas, as in south-central Maine (in category C, Fig. 1), and a region, such as central Pennsylvania (B), where long, narrow empty areas prevail. Statistically, the regions may be similar according to the criteria of regionalization, but the "grain" or "texture" will differ.

The presence, size, and distribution of empty areas would seem to be especially significant in any attempt at regionalization that is designed to establish "composite," or "social," or "economic" regions, or to give the "flavor" or "personality" of an area. Examples would be "The South," "The West," "Maine," "Cape Cod," all of which are geographical or political areas in their simplest sense, but all of whose names may have connotations of character and personality. The presence of small, scattered empty areas, for example, implies a wooded landscape (at least in the Northeast), game, fish, berries, recreation, distance between groups of people—all of which contribute to the personality of a region, even if they are concealed by the usual statistical analysis.

Empty areas have a special bearing on the problem of boundaries in regionalization. There is a temptation to regard empty areas, especially large ones, as transition zones between adjacent regions and to place the boundary more or less arbitrarily in the middle. If the regions are "nodal"—that is, based on relations between two centers of force or circulation, such as the market areas of two cities—the boundary may actually be in the middle of the empty area, but it is of doubtful wisdom to make the assumption unless other evidence points in the same direction. In the case of a "uniform" region, one based on some single criterion or combination of criteria, to regard an empty area as a transition zone is absolutely erroneous, because, by definition, it is sterile and has none of the characteristics of the region on either side.

This tendency to regard an empty area as a transition zone is due to a semantic trap into which most students of regional methodology have fallen. This is the assumption that in any uniform region there is a section, near the center, where the regional characteristics are "pure" and that outward from this center they become diluted. The Whittlesey Committee report implies that in some types of region this "pure" section may be off-center or even reach the edge; nevertheless, it adopts the term *core* for this section and poses the contrast between "cores and boundaries" or "cores and peripheries." This unconsciously reinforces the assumption that the pure part is at the regional center; for there surely is no concept of "core" in English that does not involve centrality.

Actually, an empty area may occupy the physical center of a region and therefore, by location, be the "core." A volcanic cone with empty upper slopes might have population and economic activities symmetrically arranged around the lower slopes. If the sterile part were too small to be set off separately, the resultant region would have an "empty" "core" and the greatest intensity of its characteristic at the "periphery."

The Tug Hill Plateau in north-central New York (A4, Fig. 1) was treated this way in Foster F. Elliott's regionalization of American agriculture. Elliott set up a region called "Tug Hill plateau—Intensive dairy," which includes an empty area at its center and extends to his "Adirondacks—Part-time, resort" on the east and Lake Ontario on the west. According to his statistical analysis, 55 per cent of the land in the region was in farms. Inasmuch as most of the land *not* in farms was in the center and use became more intensive toward the periphery, the term "core," with its implication of centrality, is hardly suitable to represent the nature or location of the characteristic part of this region, nor does the term "periphery" justify the usual implication.

Relation to "Cause"

The . . . distribution of empty areas will, in general, not surprise anyone who is familiar with the northeastern United States. It is safe to go further and say that geomorphologists, even structural geologists, may be pleased to see so much evidence of accordance with the classic regionalization of this part of the country in their fields. In Pennsylvania, Maryland, and northern New Jersey the empty areas conform dramatically to Appalachian structure. The Catskills, Tug Hill, the Adirondacks, the Green Mountains and the White, the Berkshires and the Taconics, can all be distinguished, and terminal moraine is identifiable in southeastern Massachusetts and Long Island. In the New Jersey Pine Barrens the too well drained sands and gravels of the Beacon Hill formation, which remained above water during the Pensauken submersion of the remainder of the nearby Coastal Plain, are apparent. In other parts of the Coastal Plain, especially on the coast and bay margins, large marshes are reflected by empty areas. In northern Pennsylvania, New York, and New England the large empty areas have, in addition, short growing seasons, because of altitude, or latitude, or both.

With regard to the empty areas of the Northeast as a whole, it is safe to say that perhaps 85 per cent of their surface is characterized by steep slope or poor drainage or poor soil, and perhaps 60 per cent also has some climatic handicap. That this is so, should surprise

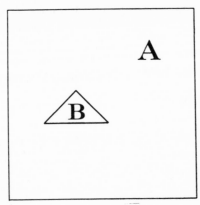

FIGURE 2: A (including B) is a region of steep slope; B is an empty area. The remainder of A is occupied by various residential and recreational uses. B is not too steep for these uses but is not so used. Is the steepness of slope A the "cause" of the emptiness of B, because the slope is too steep for agriculture, another possible use?

no one. Man is a pretty rational creature and has a strong tendency to choose the easier way and the better land if there is choice.

But the relation between empty areas and unfavorable terrain or climate is by no means simple and merits the adjective "causal" only partly. The difficulty is immediately revealed if a statement of generalization is attempted; for instance, "Most empty areas have terrain handicaps, but much of the area with difficult terrain is not in empty areas." Obviously, therefore, difficult terrain does not "cause" empty areas, or there would be what James calls "coincidence" or "in situ correspondence" of their boundaries. What is badly needed is a term to describe this somewhat nebulous relationship, illustrated in Figure 2. A is related to B as a partial cause, but the sizes and shapes of the two outlines are dissimilar and have neither "coincidence" nor "correspondence." Other land in A is "occupied" for any of a hundred reasons or is empty in units too small to fall within our definition.

Exactly this situation prevails where the Hudson River cuts through the Highlands. On the map a few small scattered empty areas trace the classic New England Upland, from Connecticut to the Hudson. These empty areas are certainly connected causally with the nature of the terrain, if only in a leftover sort of way.

The cultural factors influencing the distribution of empty areas are almost fantastically complex. This is bound to be so, because the very concept is negative and relates to three centuries of history. Some areas, as in western Massachusetts and southern Vermont, are now empty because people tried them and found them unsatisfactory as compared with alternative areas. Others, as in north-central Pennsylvania and the Adirondacks, are empty because, when settlement got to them, people already "knew better," that is, knew there was better and easier land elsewhere. Large parts of both types will probably remain empty, because society has concluded they are fit for no more intensive use than forestry and recreation and has set them aside as state or national parks.

It is obvious that unsuitability for agriculture does not always put territory in the empty-area class and that there are many uses of land for which location overweighs great terrain handicaps. The location and size of many of the parts of category E show evidence of the influence of urban centers.

For some uses, terrain or climatic features that hamper agriculture are advantageous. This is true of resort and recreational development and accounts for many of the "windows" in the large empty areas and many of the irregularities around their edges. Near urban centers rugged terrain may even be considered superior for high-class residential and institutional use. This is one of the major reasons for the small amount of empty area in the Highlands of the Hudson and obscures the fact that the leftover land is empty for the same part cause (steep slope) that encourages use of the occupied land.

The large empty areas in southern New Jersey are a special case. They are not rugged, and over large tracts they are well drained. But the soil in many of these so-called "Pine Barrens" is too sandy or gravelly to encourage field agriculture in competition with better soil in apparent abundance nearby, and the agriculture is largely poultry raising or, in a few favored places, specialized cranberry or blueberry culture. Since there are no agricultural advantages, the potentials would seem to lie in the direction of commercial, industrial, or recreational uses. Apparently, however, in spite of the nearness of large urban populations and excellent transportation, all the land for which there is demand is being used, and this extensive area, or at least the well-drained parts of it, is simply "leftover."

This part of New Jersey also suffers from a sort of isolation. It is increasingly "peninsular" southward and eastward, and Cape May is relatively "remote." The lines of through traffic flow to the west and cross the Delaware before it widens into the bay.

In contrast with the large empty areas in New Jersey, the small and scattered ones in the Delmarva Peninsula (between Delaware and Chesapeake Bays), with only one small exception, are on marsh or swamp. However, the soil is probably better, and the narrowing of the Delmarva Peninsula toward the south adds shore industries to the agriculture. There is also an added advantage: the Delmarva Peninsula is not a cul-de-sac. Its linear roads and railroad go somewhere, and it is possible to get off its southern tip (or near it) and go on to the mainland.

Relation to Appalachian Structure

South of the New York State border and west of the Hudson the empty areas conform strikingly to the trend of the Appalachian folding. As on a physiographic diagram, one may trace the Blue Ridge, many of the ridges of the Ridge and Valley province (some are too narrow to qualify as empty under the definition used), the ridges overlooking the Allegheny Front, and Chestnut and Laurel Ridges on the Allegheny Plateau. The trend of these last may be traced in an arc northeastward that apparently extends the influence of the folding across what is usually regarded as "plateau" almost to the New York border on the north and well into the glaciated section. These obvious adjustments of the empty areas to the Appalachian structure are included in category B of Figure 1 because they are distinctive in shape and consistency of trend. The boundary between this category and the neighboring categories of A should not be regarded as firm, but it was considered illuminating to suggest the approximate location of the change.

Isolation as a Factor

Isolation as a part cause of emptiness may be considered in three aspects. In the first and most important sense, isolation means distance from the centers of economic activity. In this sense the northern parts of Maine, New Hampshire, Vermont, and New York are "isolated" from the centers of population and economic activity centering well south of a line Boston–Albany–Buffalo. But it seems impossible to point to strong and obvious evidence of the power of this factor. The remotest corner of Maine, Aroostook County, is by no means all empty and is a surprise to the traveler along U.S. 1 who has watched the north woods close in on him for nearly a hundred miles between Calais and Houlton. And although New Hampshire would seem a nice example of increasing isolation northward, Vermont is turned upside down and is more economically active, and has greater population, in the northern half. In the St. Lawrence Valley of New York empty areas are few, though markets are distant and the empty Adirondacks lie as a great sterile area to the south. Nevertheless, isolation certainly affects the kind of agriculture that is profitable and is a large cost factor in the marketing of milk and potatoes from these remote areas.

The major influence of the distance factor would seem to bear on industrial and commercial activities. It is probably safe to say that some of the remoter empty areas which are not rough and poorly drained would be occupied for commercial, industrial, residential, or recreational purposes if they were nearer to New York, Philadelphia, or Pittsburgh. However, the large amount of flat, well-drained land still empty in the Pine Barrens of New Jersey would seem to indicate that there are decided qualifications to this conclusion.

There is isolation of another kind—remoteness, not from the centers of activity, but from the historical routes of most intensive circulation between them. Probably the best single indicator of these flows is Ullman's map [2] of United States railroads classified according to their facilities. The traffic pattern runs largely east–west from Boston–Buffalo on the north to Baltimore–Pittsburgh on the south, but the greatest intensity occurs in the roughly north–south New York–Baltimore line, which intersects the seabord ends of the east–west lines. Thus northern New England and New York, peninsular New Jersey, and the Delmarva Peninsula do seem to be truly peripheral, since the lines that penetrate them go virtually nowhere else. It has already been pointed out that this is a probable part cause of the lack of nonagricultural use of the New Jersey Pine Barrens, and it is probably contributory in the other areas mentioned. The scarcity of empty areas along the Mohawk Valley would seem to be related to the railroad, but empty areas to the south are disposed largely with relation to the trend of Appalachian structure, almost at right angles to the routes of traffic.

Empty areas and isolation may be considered in still a third sense: the degree to which emptiness is related to lack of local routes. In particular, many empty areas are the leftover country between roads. This is most likely to be true of otherwise well-settled country and of small or isolated empty areas. Certainly almost everyone in the Northeast lives on or close to a road, and the track of a road is less likely to be empty. But the road acts on development as only a part cause, and a lot of territory with excellent road connections is empty. For example, the Pine Barrens of New Jersey are especially well served with roads and railroads connecting the short resorts with the New York and Philadelphia urban areas. U.S. Routes 30, 40, and 322 carry almost bumper-to-bumper traffic on weekends through long stretches of wilderness and past signs warning of deer crossing and appealing to the motorists not to run over game. New Jersey Route 72 from Four Mile to Manahawkin probably runs through more empty area and more spectacular "barrens" than any of the other "shore" roads.

All over the Northeast, so many empty areas are so well served by

[2] E. L. Ullman: The Railroad Pattern of the United States, *Geogr. Rev.*, Vol. 39, 1949, pp. 242–256; map on pp. 244–245.

local roads that it must be concluded that, if roads *are* lacking in empty areas, the lack is not the *principal cause* of the emptiness but largely *a result* of it.

The "Problem Element"

What to do about empty areas in the Northeast is not a primary concern of this study, but a few brief observations may be made. Presumably most of the possibilities fall within two categories: (1) attempt to fill them in with population, or with industrial or agricultural uses; (2) set them aside, perhaps even enlarge them, and zone them for forest, watershed protection, recreational use, and so on.

Programs looking toward filling these empty areas would assume that there is need for land in the Northeast. So far as agricultural uses are concerned, the historical trend has been in the opposite direction. Land in farms decreased by 26 million acres between 1880 and 1950, and cropland showed a general downward trend.[3] The fact that during the years of World War II the Northeast expanded its land in farms and cropland harvested, then by 1949 had resumed the decrease in both,[4] shows that there is potential farmland to spare, and even usable cropland that could be developed in times of intense agricultural demand and high prices without trespassing on the empty areas. In general, the better lands have long been exploited, but there is still much land in empty areas that is as good, physically, as some agricultural land nearby was *when it was cleared.* But two or three centuries of use has removed stones and improved soil to the point where the long-used land is now better than the nearby unused land. To clear and improve empty areas at present labor costs and in competition with used land as good or better seems economically unfeasible.[5]

[3] United States Census of Agriculture: 1950, Vol. 5, Special Reports, Part 4, U. S. Bureau of the Census, 1952, p. 6.

[4] United States Census of Agriculture: 1950, Vol. 2, General Report, gives the following statistics for the New England and Middle Atlantic States and Delaware, Maryland, and the District of Columbia, in thousands of acres:

	1950	1945	1940
Land in farms	49,310	54,028	52,106
	1949	1944	1939
Cropland harvested	16,937	20,590	18,854
Cropland not harvested and not pastured	3,403		

It should be noted that many careful students of the census figures on agricultural land do not regard the data for the decennial census as strictly comparable with those for the census on the fifth year of the decade. Here, however, it is the trend that is important.

[5] J. D. Black: The Rural Economy of New England (Cambridge, Mass., 1950) analyzes the land economics of New England. In Chapter 35 (pp. 757–766), "Trends, Prospects, Potentials," he concludes that "no basis exists for anything except a very moderate recovery [of agriculture] in the future" (p. 757).

Recreational land use in this "urbanized" part of the country will probably expand, especially if population and standard of living keep on rising. Such use, if it results in structures and formal recreational facilities, will probably be the most effective force in filling up parts of empty areas.

The New England Planning Commission recommended the expansion of state and federal holdings of land in New England until they comprised 15 per cent of the land.[6] In the Middle Atlantic States an active program of state acquisition of unused lands has been pursued for years. The Pennsylvania Game Commission, for instance, now owns 897,864 acres,[7] which it has purchased with hunting and fishing license funds. The land is managed to encourage the increase of game, and most of it is open for public hunting in season. The greater part is included in Pennsylvania empty areas.

Presumably most of the land now in empty areas is better suited to growth of forest than to any other use, though a large amount is not very good even for that. Increased use for this purpose will not fill in empty areas but will instead perpetuate them, as it probably should.[8]

With a few outstanding exceptions, any large-scale dispersal of industry into the empty areas of the Northeast seems unlikely. In general, they have steep slopes or poor drainage, and construction costs would be high, especially when relatively flat land with low intensity of use is available nearby. Further, the mere existence of an empty area, if of any size, denotes lack of population, and therefore of labor. The large empty areas apparently best suited to industrial dispersal are the Pine Barrens of New Jersey and similar scrub-clad "plains" in southern Maine. It must be remembered that the size definition of an empty area (a mile in least dimension) leaves out extensive tracts of low-use country within the occupied areas that might well be used for industrial and residential expansion before there is much need to call upon even the better-suited empty areas.

The broad, general classes of empty areas have been indicated. To carry classification much further would necessitate analysis of individual empty areas, and, although that might be profitable locally, it is beyond the scope of this paper. Extensive field experience has led this observer to the conclusion that many details of the present landscape represent the "frozen history" of decisions—once with some rational explanation but now incomprehensible—by people long since dead. Faced with such a conclusion, the geographer can at least point

[6] Black, *op. cit.*, pp. 166–167.
[7] *Pennsylvania Manual*, Vol. 90, 1951–1952, Bureau of Publications, Harrisburg, 1953, pp. 972–973.
[8] The *Philadelphia Inquirer* of January 17, 1954, reports that the State of New Jersey has appropriated funds to purchase 56,000 acres in the Barrens for a forest and water preserve and is negotiating for 41,000 additional acres.

to his map and his description and say, "Here is where they are and what they are like!" and hope that that knowledge may, in itself, prove useful.

14. Megalopolis, or the Urbanization of the Northeastern Seaboard

Jean Gottmann

Continuous urbanization is a major phenomenon in many parts of the world. Associated with such a development arise problems of congestion which are a challenge to the planner, urban geographer, and other scholars as well as the businessman and homeowners. Gottmann has coined the word "megalopolis" to describe such merging urbanization. As the world population grows, such areas are destined to become an even more dominant feature of the earth's landscape. Is it possible that a continuous city will stretch from Chicago to New York by 1980 or 2000 to link up with the current eastern seabord development? In any case, dense areas of urbanization reflect as well as have an impact upon culture and all human activity.

The frequency of large urban units scattered along the Atlantic seabord in the northeastern United States was a striking realization to the foreigner who first visited the area, even 15 years ago. In February, 1942, after a first trip from New York to Washington, the writer, being asked by Isaiah Bowman in Baltimore what was the most striking impression he had had as a geographer in his first months in this country, answered: "The density of great cities along this coast, from Boston to Washington."

In 1950, on the basis of the new census, the Bureau of the Census prepared a map, later published as an illustration to a booklet of statistics on *State Economic Areas*, which showed clearly the continuity of an

SOURCE: *Economic Geography* XXXIII (July, 1957), 189–200. The author is a member of the Institute for Advanced Study, Princeton, N.J., and a French geographer at the University of Paris.

area of "metropolitan" economy from a little north of Boston to a little south of Washington, more precisely from Hillsborough County in New Hampshire to Fairfax County in Virginia. This seemed to be a first statistical demonstration on the map of the existence of a continuous stretch of urban and suburban areas, the main NE-SW axis of which was about 600 miles long, and within the frame of which dwelt even in 1950 some 30 million people.

In the geography of the distribution of habitat this was a phenomenon unique by its size not only in America but in the world. It resulted obviously from the coalescence, recently achieved, of a chain of metropolitan areas, each of which grew around a substantial urban nucleus. The super-metropolitan character of this vast area, the greatest such growth ever observed, called for a special name. We chose the word *Megalopolis*,[1] of Greek origin, and listed in Webster's dictionary as meaning "a very large city."

Indeed, the name "Megalopolis" appears on modern maps of Greece, designating a plateau in the Peloponnesus. A city was established there in ancient times, the founders of which dreamt of a great future for it and of an enormous size. But the Greek town of Megalopolis never grew to be much of a city. What has developed now in the northeastern seabord surpasses everything dreamers of the past may have visualized. Aristotle, however, wrote in his *Politics*: "When are men living in the same place to be regarded as a single city? What is the limit? Certainly not the wall of the city, for you might surround all Peloponnesus with a wall. Like this, we may say, is Babylon and every city that has the compass of a nation rather than a city."

A few years ago the reviewer of a book on the history of eastern railroads referred to the stretch of land along the tracks of the Pennsylvania and Baltimore and Ohio Railroads from New York City to Washington, D.C., as the "Main Street" of the nation. To be quite correct, such a "Main Street" ought to be prolonged along the rail tracks from New York City to Boston. There is, however, some truth in this symbolical expression. This section of U.S. 1 has come to assume within the

[1] The term *Megalopolis* was preferred to others after careful consideration of various possibilities. We wish to express our appreciation for the help received in this matter from several distinguished classicists at the Institute for Advanced Study, especially from Professors Harold Cherniss, Benjamin Merritt, and the late Jacob Hammer. "Megalopolis" was used by various authors in connection with quite different meanings: ancient philosophers described sometimes by it the "world of ideas"; recently Lewis Mumford used it to describe the whole trend towards large cities. We have felt it appropriate to describe a unique geographical region, characterized more than any other by enormous urban and metropolitan growth, and to assess the present status of a vast region in the northeastern seaboard section of the United States. Our statistical definition as on the maps is based on the map accompanying the Bureau of the Census publication: *State Economic Areas* by Donald J. Bogue, Washington, 1951.

American nation a special function, or a whole group of intertwined functions, which is hinted at in less urbanized areas by the concept of Main Street.

What Is the Meaning of a Study of Megalopolis?

Geographers are of course convinced of the value of a study describing a given geographic region endowed with some unity and originality, and thus differentiated from neighboring areas. Although such a region may be unique in the world, investigating its features, problems, and structure has generally been recognized as a worthwhile enterprise. As the data describing unique cases piled up, the endeavor developed in the geographical profession to look for general principles and for studies of cases, the outcome of which would be more immediately valuable because they are applicable to some extent in more than one area or place.

Although unique today, *Megalopolis* obviously has been and still is an extraordinarily interesting laboratory *in vivo* where much of what may well be accepted as the "normalcies" of the advanced civilization of the latter part of the twentieth century is slowly shaping. It still is too early to assess the full meaning of a study of Megalopolis in the frame we have outlined. The study must first be carried out. The many questions it involves could not be listed, let alone discussed, in such a brief article. A few hints may be given, however, of what such a survey could mean and of the main problems it could tackle.

By its size and mass, Megolopolis is both an exceptional growth and a pioneer area; exceptional, for nowhere else could one find another concentration of population, of industrial and commercial facilities, of financial wealth and cultural activities, comparable to it. However, in several other points in America and on other continents growth of continuously urbanized spaces may be observed. More of such enormous "metropolitan" bodies can be expected to arise as the evolution, already well advanced in and around New York, Philadelphia, Boston, Washington, reaches other cities and their environs. In this sense Megalopolis is a pioneer area: the processes which develop therein will help toward an understanding of, and will forecast ways and obstacles to, urban growth in various other parts.

In fact Megalopolis has already been pioneering in the organization of urban life for quite some time. Such features as skyscrapers, building elevators, city and suburban networks of trains, traffic lights, and one-way streets started here on a large scale to gain later world-wide adoption. Megalopolis grew up from the network provided by the early mushrooming of sea-trading towns along the coast from Boston to New

York and then, along the Fall line, from New York to Washington. The size of its principal urban nuclei, especially New York and Philadelphia, caused the subsequent mushrooming of suburbs filling in the spaces between the larger cities. James Madison defined New Jersey as a "barrel tapped at both ends"; that this state's function was essentially to link the area of New York and Philadelphia was apparently understood by such a clever observer at the end of the eighteenth century. But the polynuclear origin of Megalopolis is beginning to be repeated in other regions. A vast urban and suburban area is rapidly expanding around Los Angeles, for instance; inland it has already reached, in fact, San Bernardino; it may unite with San Diego on the coast. Around Chicago, on the shore of Lake Michigan, another impressive urban continuity is shaping. The metropolitan areas stretching in Ohio between Cleveland and Pittsburgh are close to coalescence; and the St. Lawrence Seaway, once opened, may accelerate and expand these trends in the area south of Lakes Erie and Ontario. And as more metropolitan areas are pushing forth suburban tentacles one towards another throughout the nation, additional but smaller Megalopolis-like clusters will be formed. This is a process involving considerable changes in the American modes of living. The trends may become better understood once the case of the largest and most advanced of these areas, the present Megalopolis, is thoroughly analyzed.

What Are the Problems of Megalopolis?

Within such a vast area the problems are, of course, many and diversified. It may not be necessary, nor very useful, to survey all of them, in their local variety, in the different parts of Megalopolis. A few basic questions must, however, be asked: How did Megalopolis happen to arise and with such a shape? What are the present main functions of this area, its role within the American economy and the North Atlantic system of relations? What are the present problems of internal organizations, and what solutions have been attempted?

Here are three sets of questions, each of which requires detailed consideration, involving a great deal of research.

Megalopolis' growth in the past sums up a good part of the economic history of the United States. It has not often been examined as to how the sequence of events and trends in the past growth of the nation affected local developments. Although it is, in area, only a small section of the Northeast, Megalopolis had a crucial part in determining national trends; on the other hand, the main swings of its own history were usually the consequence of shifts in national policies.

Why was Megalopolis' growth throughout its history more rapid and continuous than that of many other urban areas in the world? This question leads into an examination of the factors motivating or determining urban expansion in a given area. In a first inquiry concerning the matter conducted by this writer a few years ago were listed some 40-odd factors that in different ways and at different periods helped the upbuilding of Megalopolis. The two major among these factors appear to be, on the one hand, the polynuclear origin and the part played by the series of northeastern seabord cities as a *hinge* of the American economy. The federal organization of government and the division of the Atlantic seabord into so many states (each with access to tidewater) that engaged in a fruitful rivalry made all nuclei compete one with another until their growth joined them together.

The role of the "hinge" is more difficult to perceive, but is easily demonstrated by the material accumulated in regional economic history. This seaboard had from the inception of the United States the opportunity and the responsibility of serving both as an oceanic façade for relations abroad and as a springboard for the settlement and development of the continent inland. At different periods the main weight of the northeastern interests oscillated from sea trade to continental development and back again; in New England one of these oscillations in the bginning of the nineteenth century was defined as the period when the main interest shifted "from the wharf to the waterfall." In many towns which, on the Fall, were later integrated with the area of Megalopolis, wharf and waterfall were very close to one another. Whether the general trends of the American economy threw the door open towards the outside or closed it to turn the main endeavors inland, the hinge remained fixed at the series of eastern cities, extending from Boston to Washington, which alone had the geographical position, the authority, the capital, and the skill to elaborate such policies and put them into application.[2]

The inheritance of the past still influences heavily present situations and trends. Whether the eastern seaboard will keep the monopoly of the "hinge" advantages after the St. Lawrence Seaway is completed remains a burning question. However, the faculty of direct access to the sea was only one of many factors which favored Megalopolis and the others may still operate in the future. The relative part played by these various factors in shaping the present would be an important and suggestive aspect in the study of Megalopolis' historical background.

The present functions of Megalopolis would be the next step in the proposed research. These functions are several; there is, of course, a residential one expressed in the total figure of the population; but how

[2] See the historical sketch of the "hinge" function in J. Gottmann: "La région charnière de l'economie americaine," *Revue de la Porte Océane*, Le Havre, VII, Nos. 71 and 72, March, 1951, pp. 9–14, and April, 1951, pp. 11–20.

do the inhabitants make a living and why do they have to be concentrated in this area?

Megalopolis arose as a grouping of the main seaports, commercial centers, and manufacturing activities in the United States. To a large extent the *maritime façade function* still is carried on: most of the seaborne foreign trade of the country goes through Megalopolis' harbors. The *manufacturing function* never stopped developing within the area, although many industries have been brought into operation in other sections of the United States. Megalopolis seems to specialize rather in the more delicate finishing industries and in those involving a great deal of laboratory work and research. However, a good number of large plants (iron and steel, chemical and metallurgical industries) have been erected within the last 20 years in this same area. What the balance is and how much specialization is really shaping up would be interesting to ascertain.

The *commercial and financial functions* remain extremely important for Megalopolis. Despite decentralization trends many times stressed and advocated, this area remains a decisive one for the American economy as well as for international financial relations. If New York City is no longer the financial capital it was earlier in the century, it is because much of that function migrated to Washington, with the increasing role of federal authorities in the management of the nation's business. As a market, for goods as well as for money, Megalopolis as a whole still dominates the rest of the national territory. Not only does it comprise one-fifth of the nation: this fifth is obviously the best paid and the wealthiest. Though other centers of concentrated wealth have arisen and developed elsewhere, especially on the West Coast and along the Great Lakes' shores, none can yet boast a mass approaching that of the Boston-Washington region. Nor has any had such a traditional grouping of financial and social activities as that suggested by some of New York's thoroughfares: Wall Street, Park Avenue, or Fifth Avenue, all fractions of the national Main Street.

Whether or not related to the social stratification and the abundance of money in the area, Megalopolis acquired and retained a quite remarkable *function of cultural leadership,* despite the American endeavor at decentralization. Here are found the best-known universities, the better-equipped laboratories, the greatest density of learned institutions and large libraries in North America, and probably in the present world. The vast majority of nationally read periodicals and important publishing houses have their editorial offices in Megalopolis; some newspapers from this area have even a nationwide distribution, especially for their Sunday editions. The concentration of cultural leadership makes it difficult for institutions such as the Ford Foundation or the R.C.A. Research Laboratories to operate from headquarters located far from Megalopolis. This leadership is even more evident in the arts: whether theater, music, or galleries, the concentration attained in this area has no match elsewhere in America.

Finally, the question may arise, and would be more difficult to answer, as to the actual weight of Megalopolis in the political life of the country. Although the national capital is part of it, this region is only one-fifth of the nation and its votes do not necessarily make the decision of major states, parts of which are megalopolitan, such as New York and Pennsylvania. Nevertheless, Megalopolis has a definite political pattern which differs from that of the surrounding northeastern country.

Having thus analyzed the past growth and present functions of Megalopolis, we come to its actual problems. These are many. Two categories of problems, particularly pressing in all downtown sections of modern cities, have attracted attention and have been given much study: the traffic difficulties and the slums. Two other problems are nowadays receiving increasing attention in competent quarters: water supply and local government. Both appear inadequately set to answer the present needs of the huge cities and their quickly expanding suburbs. The rapidly mushrooming metropolitan commissions and committees seem to herald already deep changes forthcoming in the traditional concepts and practices of local government. Interstate compacts may arise to help solve transportation problems (such as the Port of New York Authority); experiments in metropolitan government may be more difficult to start in parts of Megalopolis because of the mass and variety of interests at stake—but the very difficulties make every attempt more significant.

Megalopolis as a unit has taken shape only within the last few years. Its laws and customs will take much longer to evolve into new forms better adapted to the needs and resources of such an enormous urban territory. A survey of the new problems, in their variety, should nevertheless be of some help even at this time. While legislation and institutions change slowly, modes of living evolve far more rapidly. Novelists have satirized certain aspects of megalopolitan life: a quarter century after the "cliff-dwellers" were strongly established on Fifth and Park Avenues, we hear about the "exurbanites." The basic fact is the double trend of the large cities: part of the population moves out and commutes from an "outer suburbia" which often extends 50 miles beyond; and parts of the cities are converted into immense apartment house groupings (paradoxically sometimes called "villages"). These two trends are particularly clear in Manhattan and in Washington, but they are gaining other big nuclei of Megalopolis as well. The threat of the recent spread of juvenile delinquency seems to increase the migration of families to the periphery of metropolitan areas. The new mode of life involves more daily traveling, more traffic jams, and more highways outside the downtown areas; a redistribution of marketing channels (illustrated by proliferating suburban shopping centers and department store branches); some changes in the type of goods needed; an increasing interest in zoning, gardening, and nature conservation.

Because more megalopolitan, the way of life of an increasing proportion of the population becomes more country-like although not really rural. The Bureau of the Census has had to revise several times its standards for the definition of metropolitan areas; the criteria of integration with the central urban district include such measurements as the proportion of commuters and the average number of telephone calls per subscriber from a suburban county to the central county of the area, etc. In 1950 the Bureau even had to revise its definition of "urban territory" and introduced the term "urbanized areas" to provide for a better separation between urban and rural territory in the vicinity of large cities, especially within metropolitan areas. New suburban types of farming are also developing, consisting both of a few highly mechanized and specialized large enterprises (such as the truck farming on Long Island) and a scattering of numerous small farms inhabited by people working in the cities and deriving their income from nonagricultural occupations.

The city, in the days of yore, was a well-defined, densely settled territory, often surrounded by walls or palisades. Some time ago it broke out of such rigid frames and developed outlying sections, *extra-muros*. In its most recent stage of growth, already characteristic of Megalopolis, it extends out on a rapidly expanding scale, along highways and rural roads, mixing uses of land that look either rural or urban, encircling vast areas which remain "green" (and which some wise endeavors attempt to preserve as recreation space for the future), creating a completely new pattern of living and of regional interdependence between communities.

The coming of age of Megalopolis thus creates, besides problems in legislation, traffic, engineering, marketing, etc., also new psychological problems: people have more difficulty thinking along the traditional lines of division into states when megalopolitan sections of different states are much more integrated in daily life than they could be with upstate areas of the same "Commonwealth"; people have also some difficulty adapting themselves to such a scattered way of life; and officials are often lost when trying to classify according to the traditional categories of urban, rural, rural non-farm, farming, etc. Such are, too briefly reviewed, the various problems of Megalopolis. They are worth analyzing for the conclusions that may follow.

Lessons from an Analysis of
the Megalopolitan Process

A detailed analysis of Megalopolis, as it appears today, seems a worthwhile enterprise despite the present unique character of this region. Its
trends acquire immediate national, and sometimes international, significance by the sheer size and weight of Megalopolis in economic and
social matters. But it is also, as has been shown, a pioneering area in
terms of urbanizaticn. What is observed and experimented with here
may serve, though on a smaller scale and in many cases only after some
time, to avoid delays and errors in other growing urban areas. It may
help improve our management of the intricate process of urbanization.

This process is an old one and has greatly contributed, as many
authors have shown, to the growth of western civilization. Far from
having reached its optimum, in the middle of the twentieth century,
the process of urbanization accelerated its pace. The United States has
demonstrated that enough agricultural commodities of all kinds can be
produced for a populous nation, enjoying a high standard of living, by
the work of only one-eighth of the total population. This proportion of
the farmers within the nation may and probably will be further reduced.
Thus 90 per cent of a prosperous nation must live from nonagricultural
pursuits, but not in congested slums. This momentous evolution, one of
the major American contributions to this century, leading to semiurban-
ized status, is most advanced in Megalopolis.[3]

The new forms thus attained, the intensity of the problems, the solutions attempted, must be compared to what happens in all these respects
in other principal metropolitan areas in the United States and perhaps
in Canada. A clearer mode of classification for both problems and possible solutions may thus be worked out, based on factual observation
rather than generalized theory. The whole survey may help to evaluate
this new expanding frontier of the American economy: the urbanization
of the land.

Outside the North American continent many other countries are already faced with a similar acceleration of the process of urbanization.
Their policies could greatly benefit from a full analysis of Megalopolis
today and its comparison with other urban growths in America. None
of the continuous chains of metropolitan areas or conurbations shaping
now in other parts of the world is indeed comparable in size or shape as
yet to the American Megalopolis. The one most nearly approaching it,
which may perhaps coalesce sometime within the next 20 years, would
be in our opinion in northwestern Europe, from Amsterdam to Paris,

[3] See J. Gottmann: *L'Amérique*, Paris, Hachette, 1954, 2nd ed. revised, pp. 170–177
and 244–246; also "La ville americaine," in *Geographia*, Paris, No. 48, September
1955, pp. 9–14; and *Virginia at Mid-Century*, New York, 1955, pp. 473–479.

including perhaps a bulge eastwards as far as the Ruhr and Cologne along the Rhine and Meuse Rivers.

Another possible super-metropolitan system of this kind could well be forming in England. A giant U-shaped urban chain surrounds the southern Pennines, extending from Liverpool and Manchester to Leeds and Bradford, via Birmingham and Sheffield. This U may some day unite southwards with the expanding suburbs of Greater London. Then the whole system may enter the megalopolitan family. It would remain, nevertheless, quite different from Megalopolis on the northeastern seaboard. Each large area of such kind will long keep its originality, resulting from its own past and its relation to a given zone of civilization. Large urbanized areas do not need, however, to grow up to megalopolitan size to be able to profit by the lessons in metropolitan organization obtained in Megalopolis.

How Far Could Megalopolis Grow?

Several important studies of the metropolitan areas around New York City, Philadelphia, etc., are now in progress. These surveys will attempt to forecast future growth, by projecting curves for the next 10 to 25 years. Urban and suburban territory is expanding at a fast pace in the United States, and this pace has been notably accelerated in recent years. A vast area like Megalopolis would not have arisen without it. The time has perhaps come to ask once more the question: How far could Megalopolis grow? And in which directions?

In 1955, a group of city planners at Yale University began to speak about a citylike, well-knit system extending from Portland, Maine, to Norfolk, Virginia. Such may be the impression provided by road transportation maps. This writer's observations on completion of a study of Virginia by January, 1955, did not seem to warrant as yet the absorption into Megalopolis of more than a few counties in northern Virginia. Richmond and the Hampton Roads area had not yet been consolidated with the Washington-to-Boston more intensely urbanized system. Beyond eastern Massachusetts northwards, urbanization was felt mainly in the summer as a seasonal migration of vacationing or semivacationing people from Megalopolis. However, there could be no doubt that Megalopolis is daily expanding its territorial scope. Our definition (see Fig. 1) based on the census of 1950 is certainly an underestimation in area for 1957.

Expansion proceeds in many directions, of course, all around the outer fringes. Consolidation of the urban land use within the 1950 limits goes on at the same time. The existing densities of population (see Fig. 2) and the trends of increase of this density by counties in the recent past (see Fig. 3) concur in stressing a relative saturation of most

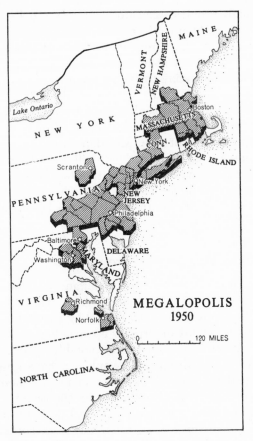

FIGURE 1.

of the areas within Megalopolis between Philadelphia and Boston. Although a great deal of new construction still goes on even in those parts, the more striking increases appear in the southern section of Megalopolis and an expansion in the Virginian Tidewater and northern Piedmont seems unavoidable.

Thus Megalopolis is pushing southwards and southwestwards. It may indeed reach Richmond and Norfolk some day in the foreseeable future. Another set of directions, this time inland, and breaking away from the fateful axis of U.S. 1, may be inferred from an attentive examination of the distribution already in 1950 of the metropolitan areas in the northeastern section of the United States, between the Atlantic seaboard, the Great Lakes and the Ohio Valley (see Fig. 4). A rather impressive density of such metropolitan areas is found inland along the route of the New York Central Railroad up the Hudson-Mohawk route and the southern shores of Lakes Erie and Ontario. Then from Cleveland southwards a little interrupted chain extends towards Pittsburgh,

Pennsylvania. Between Megalopolis on one hand and the trans-Appalachian urbanized and industrialized areas, the valleys and ridges of the Appalachian Mountains cause a clearcut break. But if the Pittsburgh-Cleveland-Syracuse-Albany chain would come to be consolidated, even mountain ranges could be overcome and an enormous sort of annular megalopolitan system could arise; the St. Lawrence Seaway, if it

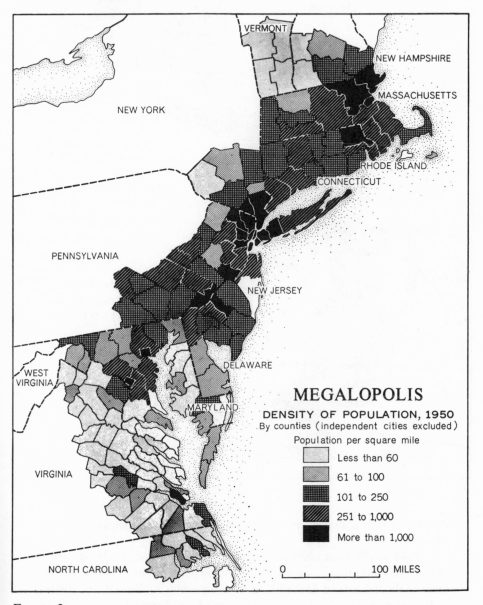

MEGALOPOLIS

DENSITY OF POPULATION, 1950
By counties (independent cities excluded)

Population per square mile

	Less than 60
	61 to 100
	101 to 250
	251 to 1,000
	More than 1,000

0   100 MILES

FIGURE 2.

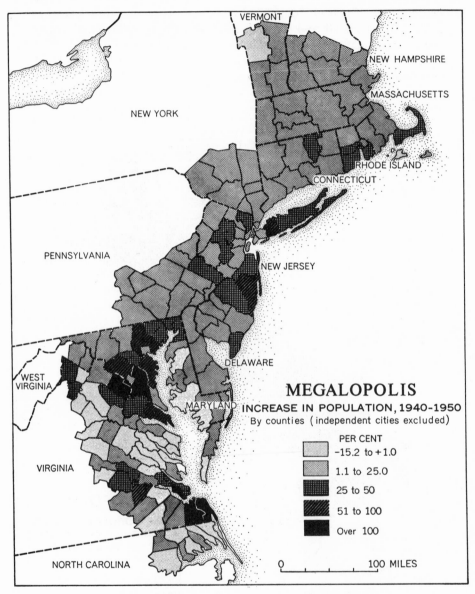

MEGALOPOLIS
INCREASE IN POPULATION, 1940-1950
By counties (independent cities excluded)

PER CENT
-15.2 to +1.0
1.1 to 25.0
25 to 50
51 to 100
Over 100

0   100 MILES

FIGURE 3.

developed into a major artery of navigation, could precipitate such a trend.

A much smaller but curiously "annular" urban system is already shaping in the Netherlands, as after the coalescence of the cities along the main seaboard axis of Holland, from Amsterdam to Rotterdam, urbanization is gaining inland, along the Rhine from Rotterdam to Arnhem, and along roads and canals from Amsterdam to Utrecht. The coalescence between Arnhem and Utrecht is on its way. In England the U-shaped chain of the metropolitan type outlined above from Manchester to Leeds has not been filled up in between these two cities along the shortest line into another annular formation because of the topographical obstacle of the Pennine range, still an empty area. This obstacle is comparable, though it is on a much smaller scale, to the Appalachian ridges back of Megalopolis.

Other trends of megalopolitan expansion in territory could be discussed either inside the mountainous obstacle itself or northeastwards in the seaboard area. But these trends are definitely seasonal. In the past Megalopolis has in fact *emptied* the neighboring mountains, northern New England, and even to some extent the province of Québec in Canada by attracting millions of people from difficult rural areas, less rich in opportunity. Now, with the rise of the standard of living, with

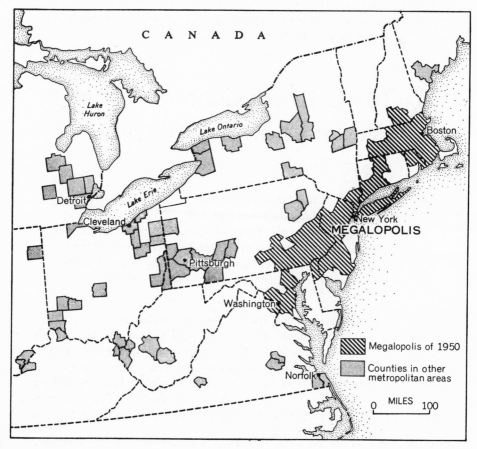

FIGURE 4.

more people taking longer summer vacations, the cooler New England seashore or hills, the Appalachian plateaus, attract a sort of *transhumance* of city folks to summer pastures. This transhumance seems to be constantly on the increase and creates for the summer months long-range commuting problems. If the contiguous areas, where the majority of the permanent population lives from the proceeds of summer residents and tourists, were to be included in the territorial concept of Megalopolis, the limits of our area would have to be rapidly and substantially enlarged.

Urban land utilization is indeed devouring land fast, in many ways. The old habit of considering it as a minor occupant of space will soon have to be revised. Our modern civilization has found the means to grow more and more agricultural products, to raise more and more livestock, on less space; but industrial, commercial, and residential uses are constantly increasing their space requirements. Our generation is probably witnessing the beginning of a great revolution in the geography of land use. Megalopolis heralds a new era in the distribution of habitat and economic activities.

15. The City as a Center of Change: Western Europe and China

Rhoads Murphey

Cities can be indicators of the character of the societies and cultures that brought them into being. In western Europe the city has been the focus of economic, political, and social change. In China the rural society has been the center of ferment and the cities, though functioning as trade centers, were administrative centers that fostered stability.

Every sedentary society has built cities, for even in a subsistence economy essential functions of exchange and of organization (both functions dealing with minds and ideas as much as with goods or with institutions) are most conveniently performed in a central location on behalf of a wider countryside. The industrial revolution has emphasized the economic advantages of concentration and centrality. But is it true to say that change, revolutionary change, has found an advantage in

SOURCE: *Annals of the Association of American Geographers*, XLIV (December, 1954), 349–62. The author is professor of geography, University of Michigan.

urbanization; in concentration and in numbers? The city has instigated or led most of the great changes in Western society, and has been the center of its violent and non-violent revolutions. In western Europe the city has been the base of an independent entrepreneur group which has successfully challenged and broken the authority of the traditional order. In China, while cities with the same universal economic functions arose, they tended until recently to have the opposite effect on the pattern of change. China has consistently reasserted itself as a single political unit, but it is otherwise the appropriate qualitative and quantitative counterpart of Europe, and provides a reasonable basis for comparison. China and Europe have been the two great poles of world civilization, and an examination of the different roles which their cities played may help to elucidate other differences between them.

The following generalized and capsulized discussion aims only to suggest this difference, as an example of what might be made of an approach to the study of society through an analysis of the city's role in the process of change. By cutting a familiar pie in another way we may arrive at useful insights. In doing so in the short space of an article the writer realizes that he must raise or beg more questions than he answers, and may in particular be guilty of oversimplification or distortion. But the virtue of such an attempt may lie in its disturbing or even irritating nature; it aims less to prove than to provoke. To quote from Karl Marx with this in mind, ". . . the whole economical history of society is summed up in the movement of this . . . separation between town and country." In distinguishing between European and Chinese civilization, we must of course assume a complex multiplicity of causes, many of which may elude us, and many of which may have little or nothing to do with geography. The distinctions and the arguments which follow do not imply that this basic fact is disregarded, but they pursue the matter from a point of view which has frequently been neglected and which may be suggestive of important factors.

The cities of western Europe have been, at least since the high middle ages, centers of intellectual ferment; of economic change; and thus, in time, of opposition to the central authority. They became rebels in nearly every aspect of their institutional life. It was trade (and to a somewhat lesser extent specialized manufacturing) which made them strong enough to maintain their challenge to the established order. Their spirit of ferment was the spirit of a new group, urban merchant-manufacturers, which could operate from a base large and rich enough to establish increasingly its own rules. This setting tended to ensure that the universities, which grew up in cities originally for convenience and centrality, would frequently nourish skepticism, heresy, and freedom of enquiry. Even where they did not overtly do so, the concentration of literacy and learning in the cities was a stimulus to dissent.

Most of the cities which rose out of the cultural and social chaos following the destruction of Roman unity and preceding the development of a new national unity grew in answer to new conditions, for northwest Europe was ideally situated for trade. Most of them were in their origins much older than this, and had begun as administrative, military, or ecclesiastical centers. But a score of major rivers, navigable and free from floods, silting, or ice throughout the year in this mild maritime climate, led across the great European plain to the open sea; the peninsular, indented nature of the coast critically heightened mobility. The invitation which this presented to inter-European trade furthered the ascendancy of the commercial function. The shift of commerce and associated urbanism from the Mediterranean to northwest Europe seems to have begun before the Age of the Discoveries, notably in the Hansa towns and in Flanders. This may be in part a reflection of the mobility inherent in the lands around the Baltic and North Seas, once they had learned from the Mediterranean the lessons of commerce and absorbed the civilizing influences of this earlier developed area. In any case, these northern cities came to be dominated by trader-manufacturers. Trade was a heady diet, and enabled urban merchants to command cities which had originally been administrative creations. While the cities did not alone destroy feudalism, they owed much of their prosperity and independence to its decline: freer trade, wider exchange, and failing power of the landed nobility. And their very growth as rival power bases accelerated the collapse of the old feudal order.

As the growth of national unity progressed, under the institutional and emotional leadership of monarchy, an alliance of convenience between king and city arose which met the crown's demands for funds and the city's demand for representation. Urban merchants had the money to support the king in his foreign wars and in his struggle with the divisive domestic ambitions of the nobility and the church. In return the city received an increasing voice in the affairs of state, through representation in parliaments, and indirectly through the making of policy in which the throne was obliged to follow. But while this alliance of revenue in exchange for concessions was one of mutual interest, its ultimate result was the strengthening of the urban commercial sector until it overthrew or emasculated the monarchy, and with it the traditional order as a whole. Having helped the king to power over the nobility, the city achieved a *modus vivendi* with him which left it in control of the affairs vital to it. As a current reminder of the development of urban independence, "the city" of London retains its originally hard-won privilege of excluding the reigning monarch, who is also excluded from the House of Commons, in part the city's creation and in part its weapon. To a certain extent the king, and even the nobility, were willing to go along with the process of economic change instigated by the city since they profited from it as the principal source of wealth in which they were often investors as well as tax collectors. But the new values which the city emphasized, and their institutional expression, were in direct conflict with the traditional society based on land; the city repeatedly bred overt revolutionary movements designed to establish its new order as the national way of life.

As centers of trade, the cities were free of the land and of its social and political limitations embodied in the institutions of post-Roman society. They developed their own law which was in differing degrees independent of the traditional, rural law. Their institutions were self-made, and they were not beholden to the traditional system which they challenged. The companies and corporations which the merchants organized went far beyond the scope of guilds in their successful attempt to order most of the social and economic fabric (instead of being limited to a trade-union function, as the guilds of China predominantly were). Traditional guilds were overlaid with new merchant organizations, or were clothed with new functions and powers, although some of the older guilds remained as conservative or retarding influences. The economic institutions which arose concurrently were also new-made sources of strength: banking, letters of credit, private property, interest, speculation and investment, representing needs and ideas which were almost wholly foreign to the traditional society of the countryside, and which were the accompaniment of an ever-widening trade. For the invitation to commercial expansion overseas was as strong in Europe's geography as the earlier invitation to trade among the lands surrounding the Baltic, Mediterranean, and North Seas. A leading agent of this process was necessarily the city, where trade flowed through break-in-bulk points such as the mouths of the Rhine or the English ports facing the Channel. Merchant corporations for overseas trade became the strongest and most progressive, or revolutionary, of the city's agents. Interestingly, the original charter of the British East India Company stated that "gentlemen" (by which was meant the landed gentry) "shall be excluded" from membership.

The city was the natural center of political change as it had been of economic change. The growth of modern Europe may be regarded as the steady progress of a new class of urban traders and manufacturers toward a position of control in a society and economy which their own enterprise had largely created. It was they who had realized the potential of Europe's location for world trade, and they who had developed and applied the technological and economic tools which made Europe the center of the world. The destruction of the old pattern was implicit in this process, and also implicit was the revolutionary expression, by the cities, of their claim to political power. City-country al-

liances were formed, and the dissident groups from the country often
bore the brunt of the effort, since they were the more numerous, as well
as sharing in the spoils. But the city was in the van, and even diverted
or perverted rural dissent and rural force to its own ends; leadership
and money were frequently more decisive than numbers. It is of course
true that at least in England this city-country alliance left and perhaps
still leaves the landed gentry with prestige and thus with considerable
power, while it left wealth with the urbanites. Characteristically this
wealth was used to acquire land and gentry status. This balance of
advantage was particularly pertinent in the matter of parliamentary
representation.

Revolutionary changes are nearly always the work of an alliance of
groups, but the history of modern Europe is suggestive of the city's key
role, despite the recurrent blurring of city-country distinctions. The first
great modern revolution, in seventeenth century England, was the work
of a city-country alliance, but London was mainly Puritan, and the
outcome might be regarded as the victory of urban merchants and their
country confreres over the traditional authoritarian alliance of cavalier
and peasant based on the land. Two centuries later Manchester and
Birmingham had joined London in the final stages of the contest between
urban "radicalism" and country "conservatism," epitomized in the struggle over the Corn Laws, the Reform Bills, free trade, and the Manchester
School. By this time cotton textiles had well supplanted woolen textiles
as the chief manufacturing industry; since it came relatively late it was
not greatly hampered by guild restrictions, as wool had been; it established itself in Manchester, which as a then unincorporated town lacked
formalized controls. It may irritate many readers as a loose generalization, but still seems worth stating for argument, that representative government and the industrial revolution, perhaps modern Europe's two
most significant products, were created by the city. The Low Countries
provide as good an illustration of this as does England.

In France the picture was less clear since urban merchant-manufacturers were less prominent in the national economy. Even so, it was
Paris which created and carried the revolution. Paris used peasant
distress and rebellion, but was never dethroned by it. One may say that
Paris later destroyed Charles X and Louis Philippe. By this time, however, the Napoleonic land reform had given the peasant a stake in the
status quo and helped to keep him a conservative counter-influence to
the city, after his revolutionary ardour of the 1790's had served its
purpose and cooled. Thus, in part, is derived the country's role in the
destruction of the Second Republic and the Paris Commune, "radical
city movements." Across the Rhine these distinctions become increasingly
blurred, as for example in the Peasant War in early Reformation Swabia
and Franconia. In eastern Europe it is difficult to draw distinctions

between city and country, or to find an independent urban-based group living on trade and challenging the existing order. Nevertheless even in twentieth century Russia, while the Soviet revolution was in part carried by peasant groups, leadership remained in the urban intellectual group which had instigated the change.

In northwest Europe, which is our concern here, the city has been a consistent seat of radicalism. This is not to overlook the recurrent Jacqueries which in every society have been the desperate recourse of an oppressed peasantry. But in the West these have often been closer to reaction than to revolution—the peasants were demanding the restoration of the status quo ante, not the establishment of a new order. Where they did attack the old order it was characteristically on specific points, such as Wat Tyler's demand in the fourteenth century England for the disendowment of the church. The same pattern is apparent in rural opposition in America, in uprisings like the Whiskey Rebellion or in political parties like the Populists. The removal of abuses does not necessarily mean revolutionary change, despite the violence or the "levelling" sentiments which usually characterized rural dissidence.

In China, while the peasant and the countryside were in some respects like the West, the city's role was fundamentally different. Chinese cities were administrative centers. With few exceptions this function dominated their lives whatever their other bases in trade or manufacturing. Their remarkably consistent, uniform plan, square or rectangular walls surrounding a great cross with gates at each of the four arms, suggests their common administrative creation and their continued expression of this function. Local defensive terrain, such as at Chungking, occasionally made this common plan unsuitable, but the stamp of governmental uniformity is nonetheless apparent. This was true for cities which had originally risen as trade centers, or which became more important commercially than they were administratively. It is possible to find a clear separation in many provinces between administrative and commercial cities, where the capital is not the most important commercial base: Chungking and Chengtu in Szechuan, Chengchow and Kaifeng in Honan, Hankow and Wuchang in Hupeh, Hsiangtan and Changsha in Hunan, Soochow and Nanking in Kiangsu, Wuhu and Anking in Anhwei, Tientsin and Peking in Hopeh; and other less clear cases. But despite this degree of functional specificity, little urban independence or urban-based revolutionary change appeared until the traditional fabric was rent by the growth of Western-inspired treaty-ports. Even in the exceptional cases where trade or manufacturing was the sole or predominant basis of the city: Chingtechen, the site of the Imperial Potteries, or Canton, the consistent focus of foreign trade, there never developed a merchant-controlled urban base free in any significant sense of the traditional state order.

A case in point is Shanghai. Long before the city became a treaty-port under foreign domination, it was the leading commercial hub of the Yangtze Valley and may even have exceeded Canton in the volume of its trade. A British visitor in 1832 maintained that it did, and his count of junk traffic suggests that Shanghai was then among the leading ports of the world. It nevertheless remained well down on the list of delta cities by size despite its lion's share of the trade. Another British visitor in 1843, the year in which Shanghai was opened to foreign trade as a treaty-port, estimated its population at 270,000, Hangchow at one million, Soochow, Ningpo, and Nanking at half a million each, and six other delta cities at figures equal to or greater than Shanghai's. Shanghai has never performed any administrative functions outside its own metropolitan limits, and it may be for this reason that it did not dominate the delta until Western entrepreneurs largely took over its development. In bureaucratic China, trade alone could not rival administration as an urban foundation. Outstanding locations for trade, such as Hankow (or Shanghai), as advantageous as Amsterdam or London, were frequently not put to full use until European traders built major cities there. Wuchang, opposite the mouth of the Han, was an almost exclusively administrative city before 1850, while Hankow itself was only a moderate sized town.

Large cities seem to have been proportionately more numerous in China than in Europe until the nineteenth century, and until the eighteenth century urbanism may have been higher. Perhaps a quarter or more of the population lived in towns and cities of more than 2500 population, and perhaps 10 or 15 per cent in cities over 10,000. The big cities of the East as a whole were huge by European standards; this was a consistent feature of what has been called "Oriental society." In China most cities or towns of 5,000 or more had well-defined commercial or manufacturing districts, and special areas for each important enterprise: banking, metal goods, food markets, textiles, woodwork, and so on. This pattern remains in most contemporary Chinese cities. But the cities were not decisive centers of change in a commercialized economy. They served as imperial or provincial capitals, seats for garrison troops, and residences for governors, viceroys, and the ubiquitous cloud of officials and quasi-officials with their "service-providers." Their business was administration, and exploitation, of the countryside. Marco Polo, in describing the magnificence of Peking, accounts for it as follows:

... and this happens because everyone from everywhere brings there for the lord who lives there and for his court and for the city which is so great and for the ladies and barons and knights of whom there are so many and for the great abundance of the multitude of the people of the armies of the lord, which stay round about us well for the court as for the city, and of other people who come there by reason of the court which the great lord holds there, and for one and for another . . . and because the city is in too good a position and in the middle of many provinces.

Here is a clear picture of a city based on administration from a central location, where trade flows in largely in response to the existing structure of officials, troops, court, hangers-on, and the host of people necessary to support them, from secretaries and servants to bakers and dancers. Six hundred years later at the end of the nineteenth century European travellers in China reported the same phenomenon, on a smaller regional scale: large cities whose sole function appeared to be administration, or important trading cities at key locations which were nevertheless dominated by officials and the magistrate's *yamen* (office). Thus Archibald Little, describing the city of Kweichowfu in Szechuan where the manufacture of salt brine and coal dust balls, and trade on the Yangtze River, were the apparent sources of its prosperity, writes that the city was a main station for the collection of *likin* (internal customs tax) and "the town is studded with the numerous mansions of the wealthy officials and their dependents." With the opening of Chungking as a treaty-port, *likin* was collected at Kweichowfu only on local hauls and the city rapidly decayed despite its apparently strong economic base in manufacturing and trade.

The trade process appears to have lacked the dynamic quality by means of which Europe's cities rose to power. Pre-eighteenth century China had a trade as great as or greater than pre-eighteenth century Europe, but Europe's subsequent commercial expansion left China far behind. Why this happened, and why China never produced the revolutionary economic and political changes which remade Europe into an arbiter for the rest of the world is a vital question. An analysis of the city's role may help to suggest some relevant factors. Why was the Chinese city not a European-style center of change?

China is geographically isolated by a formidable assemblage of barriers. To landward lies the greatest mountain mass in the world, with its extensions from the Pamir Knot, reinforced on the south by rainforests and spectacular river gorges, on the north by the barren wastes of Siberia, and on the west and northwest by a vast sweep of desert. Seaward a coast deficient in harbours faces a huge and until recently commercially underdeveloped ocean, by European standards. Chinese trade with Japan was at several periods considerable, and with southeast Asia even larger, but it did not approach eighteenth or nineteenth century European levels. It tended to be characterized by luxury goods, strategic goods (such as copper for coinage), or specialties such as Chinese porcelain. With these exceptions, especially the highly developed and diversified trade between southeast coastal China, and southeast Asia, China did not greatly extend herself commercially, and was for the most part content to send specialized goods, like silk, to the rest of the world through middlemen intermediaries: the Arabs by sea and the Turkish peoples of central Asia by land. Significantly, the largest concerted Chinese attempt in foreign trade was an imperial government project (the famous Ming expeditions of the fifteenth century), which lasted only some 30 years and apparently found no solid base in the Chinese economy or in its merchant group.

Internally, trade moved largely on the great river systems, running fortunately east and west, but there was no such close interconnection between these river basins as in Europe, by sea or across plains. Physically China is built on a grander scale, but the landscape presents no such invitation to exchange as has sparked the development of Europe. Europe is multi-peninsular, each peninsula tending toward economic distinctiveness and political independence, but joined by cheap sea and river routes. This plethora of complementary areas and their transport links magnified the basis and the means of exchange. Although its early trade development was not larger than China's, by the middle of the eighteenth century commercial expansion overseas had joined and accelerated commercialization at home, and Europe stood in a class by itself. The cities of western Europe were both the creators and inheritors of this development. But in China the cities remained centers of the unitary national state and of the traditional order rather than its attackers, epitomes of the status quo. As direct links in the official hierarchy, they were the props of the empire. The universities were urban, for convenience as in Europe, but they stimulated no dissent. Their accepted function was to train scholars who could staff the imperial civil service, and they fed their graduates into the imperial examination system. This, and the better economic and social position of scholars generally in China than in Europe, encouraged the universities and the literati to support the status quo; European intellectuals may have taken a vow of poverty, but they remained a dissident or discontented group.

Physically, China lacked Europe's outstanding advantages for trade, and on the other hand presented a base for highly productive agriculture, through irrigation. Wittvogel's revealing work on the organic connection between the need for mass organized water control and the growth of a monolithic bureaucratic state in China lends insight into the origins and pattern of the institutional structure. With China's environmental advantages, water control made agriculture the massive core of the economy, and at the same time left the bureaucracy in a position of ramified command. It was not possible for urban merchants to win independence from this system. They had less economic leverage than the rising European merchants because, with the preponderant position of agriculture, they never occupied proportionately as large a place in the economy.

The state of course did its part to prevent the development of a rival group, and by taxation, requisition, and monopoly ensured that the merchants would be kept relatively impotent. This was a job which European states and monarchs, though equally determined, failed to accomplish; their merchants were in a stronger position, and the state was weaker: it was merely *primus inter pares*. Land hunger in China, as a reflection of a population too large for the available arable land (increasingly serious during the past 200 years, but even in Han times worse than in most other parts of the world, including Europe), also acted to restrict commercial development, since it meant high land rents. Capital could almost always be invested with greater profit and safety in land, or in rural loans, than in productive or capital-generating enterprises outside the agrarian sphere.

Where extra-agricultural opportunities for investment did exist, the individual entrepreneur was at the mercy of the bureaucratic state. Many of the major trade goods were government monopolies. Elsewhere the essentially Western concepts of private property and due process of law, in a word, of the entrepreneur, were lacking in a society dominated by agriculture and officials. Extortion, forced levies, confiscation, and simple financial failure as the result of arbitrary government policies were the daily risk of the merchant. Some individuals did indeed become very rich, for example the famous *hong* merchants of Canton, but their wealth came necessarily through official connection: by possession of gentry status, by office holding or official favour, or by trading as part of a government monopoly (such as foreign trade under the Canton system and at most other periods was). Even so their gains were never secure. The greatest and richest of the *hong* merchants died in poverty, having lost official favour. While this also happened to many of the pre-eighteenth century European capitalists, it did not prevent the survival and growth of individual capitalist families or firms or of a moneyed group. The famous Ch'ing dynasty billionaire Ho Shen, said to have been worth the equivalent of nearly a billion and a half U. S. dollars, was not a merchant at all, but a favourite minister of the emperor Ch'ien Lung, which demonstrates the real source of wealth in traditional China. Yet he too died in poverty and disgrace (by suicide in place of a suspended death sentence in 1799) at the hands of Ch'ien Lung's successor.

In China merchant-capitalists did not use their money to establish their independence, as did the merchants of London or Antwerp, or to stimulate the growth of a new economic pattern. Unfortunately for the Chinese merchants, the imperial revenue was at most periods derived largely from the land tax and from the government trade monopolies. Agriculture was proportionately more productive than in Europe, and revenue from trade less necessary. Peking thus did not need the merchants as the king had needed them in Europe to finance the ascendancy of the national state, to pay for its wars with rival states, or to meet its normal bills. No concessions were necessary; the merchants could be squeezed dry, and were, with no harm to the state. The commanding position of the bureaucracy, and the fact of the bureaucratic state, are perhaps explainable by a similar process of default. Merchants were necessary or useful to perform essential (and, to the state, profitable) commercial functions; they were tolerated, but kept under strict control, and this was simpler and cheaper than for the state to manage all commercial dealings itself.

But the merchants were also identified with the state as well as being stifled by it. Their numbers were recruited largely from the gentry class, who had the capital and the official connections essential to commercial success. Gentry merchants worked willingly with gentry officials in the management of the state monopolies, including foreign trade. Outside the monopolies, the same partnership operated, as a matter of mutual interest. In addition, most gentry members, whether or not they were engaged in trade, also performed other semi-official functions, comparable in some degree to the British landed gentry. These "services" represented a considerable part of their income; they were not likely to attack the system which nourished them. In a more general sense, the tradition of revolt in this hierarchical society did not include the reordering of social or economic groups, but concentrated on the removal of bad government. Individual or group improvement was not to be won by destroying the fabric, but by making optimum use of one's position within it.

Finally, China had maintained since Han times and with few breaks a remarkable degree of unity and a central power which no single European state achieved until quite late in its modern development. In China even towns of the *chen* (market town) rank (population c. 3000–5000) were seats of garrison troops, whatever their prominence in trade. In Europe in the course of the crown's contest with the nobles, and of the international rivalries which also developed among the plethora of separate national states, urban merchants found an opportunity which contrasted sharply with the rooted monolithic nature of the Chinese state.

The cities of China were consequently microcosms of the empire, not deviants. They were not backwaters, for necessarily learning, art, and the trappings of cosmopolis were concentrated in them. Yet, each was a symbol of the imperial system, operating not only under the direct thumb of Peking, but according to its precepts. Obvious considerations of convenience made them central places, market towns, transport termini or break-in-bulk points, and exchange centers of varying degrees of sophistication. But these universal urban functions do not automatically bring with them the character of rebellion or innovation which we have rightly come to associate with cities in the West. The main distinction of the Chinese city was concentration, as the node of the traditional society and as its power base. Imperial authority filtered down more slowly into the countryside, becoming more dilute with every level. Every government with ambitions of central power attempted to control the peasant. In a largely pre-commercial and pre-industrial society of a basically molecular character, this could never be perfect control. China lacked not only the tools of control for its huge area, such as communications and literacy, but the bond of common interest and attitude which a completely commercialized economy tends to create, often by sublimating or suppressing conflicting interests. In the absence of such tools or conditions to implement rural control in China, the importance of the city as a center of political and military power on the side of authority was magnified.

Change in China, as elsewhere, has been the work of a city-country alliance, with the leadership coming usually from the gentry based in cities or towns. But the origins of dissent and the main force of attacks on the status quo have been far less urban in China than in the West. While the rebellions were in many cases closer to the usually unsuccessful Jacqueries of the West than to the really revolutionary changes generated in Western cities, they were the predominant agents of what change did take place. They were successful where their Western analogues failed because there was no more potent agent of change, no other group (if we except the several nomadic invasions and conquests) and no other economic base by which change might even superficially be forced. The similarity with the Jacqueries lies in the fact that Chinese rebellions rarely challenged the basic nature of the existing order, but only its administration. The new dynasty which resulted might mean new blood, but seldom new institutions.

Given a largely closed, agrarian system, it is understandable that each dynasty, as it lost its momentum, lacked the means of maintaining a high productivity and effective distribution as population increased, and that it eventually declined into corruption. This was especially so in the rural sphere, easy prey to tax and rent manipulation (and the source of most of the national revenue and income), but marginal enough to be sensitive to oppression. At the same time, the lack of large extra-agricultural economic bases for an independent group prevented the growth of new ideas or new institutions to challenge the old, even while the old lay in ruins. The city-country alliance which in Europe made revolution made only a change of administration in China. The city was too dependent on the traditional order to attempt its destruction.

The accelerated impact of the West on China during the nineteenth century has by the twentieth centry set in train profound changes, and it is natural to find that these are reflected also in the city's role. The

Kuo Min Tang was a largely urban-based movement, and though its revolutionary aspects became less and less prominent under the more compelling problems of security against Communists and Japanese, it was far more than a change of administration. It was in fact the political vehicle of a new group, nurtured not only in Western thought, but in the essentially Western milieu of the treaty-ports. Negatively also the cities have made a new impression. The present Communist regime had prominent rural roots, and came to power with an announced resentment and distrust of cities, calling them the centers of reaction (and also of degeneracy, softness, and vice), though its venom was directed particularly against the foreign-created treaty-ports.

It was basically the impact of the West, including the Soviet Union, which ensured that this latest of rebellions would for the first time successfully destroy the existing fabric. In the treaty-ports themselves development had been too brief, and too much limited by the inertia of the agrarian economy, to produce an effective base for change to rival Communism in its originally rural base. Nevertheless these urban centers, many of them new as large cities dependent on trade, played much the same role as the cities of late medieval Europe. They were rebels against the traditional order because for the first time in the history of China they provided opportunity for the merchant. Money could not only be made, but invested, in trade or manufacturing, with safety, profit, and prestige. Private property, and all of the values of R. H. Tawney's "Acquisitive Society" had been enthroned in the treaty-ports by the West, and to the Chinese businessman Shanghai or Tientsin were all that traditional China was not. He was prepared to work for the establishment of a government and society which would make a respectable place for a commercial industrial bourgeoisie, based, as the term implies, in cities.

This new group, shaped by the West, largely created the Kuo Min Tang. They formed an alliance with some of the landed gentry, for example Chiang Kai-shek, who was both landed and bourgeois, but they were never in any sense a peasant party, and their ties with the land were feeble. While they answered, or promised to answer, many of the needs of the new class of treaty-port Chinese, and kept peace with the gentry, they did not seriously attempt to answer the questions and strivings of the Peking intellectuals, nor the more compelling needs of the peasants. Communism ultimately rode to power in part as a crusade against the "merchant capitalists" of Shanghai on the one hand and the Western-inspired intellectuals of Peking on the other.

To be sure, the Chinese Communist Party and its leaders are urban-trained Marxists operating intellectually and practically in an urban framework, and dedicated to an industrialization program which necessarily centers in the cities. Their political control also depends substantially on their control of city populations and city enterprises. Insofar as they thus push the city toward the middle of the stage as a recognized base at least for economic and technological change, they continue the about-face in the city's role which the Western impact began in the treaty-ports. In any case, active urban agency for change is a recent phenomenon in China, perhaps one may say a direct transmittal from the West.

This analysis, in attempting to particularize the city's role in the two great centers of world civilization, has necessarily dealt with institutions as much as with place. The urban differences were expressions of distinct societies. It was broadly speaking the bureaucratic state in China which stifled the growth of European-type cities despite the volume of trade or the regional specialization of commerce and manufacturing which existed. In Europe, too, wherever bureaucratic and/or persistently authoritarian governments ruled, commercialization and industrialization were late and/or little, and the urban-based entrepreneur usually exerted small influence. Some other common ground may exist between these bureaucracies, and the suggestion that physical conditions required or invited central control, and that geographic factors helped to minimize the opportunity of the merchant, are perhaps as applicable to eastern Europe, or to Spain, as to China. The imprint of Roman Law and of Mediterranean urban traditions may also help to account for the east-west distinction in Europe. In any case, maritime western Europe followed a course whose urban direction lay at the root of its wealth, its power, and its distinctiveness.

Sir George Sansom, in a characteristic series of lectures given at Tokyo University in 1950 and published in 1951 under the title *Japan in World History*, typifies the modern European attitude and contrasts it with the Tokugawa Japanese by quoting as follows from Alexander Pope's "Windsor Forest," written about 1712:

> The time shall come when free as seas or wind
> Unbounded Thames shall flow for all mankind,
> Whole nations enter with each flowing tide
> And seas but join the regions they divide.

This is so revealingly and typically English, and so untypically Chinese, because it shows the world through the eyes of the London merchant. Ironically, merchant towns of a European type had begun to develop in Japan by the sixteenth century around the Inland Sea (perhaps an oriental Mediterranean?), including self-governing Sakai, living on the trade with China and southeast Asia. Sakai, with its own army and its council of merchants, was so close to the European pattern that contemporary Jesuit observers compared it with Venice. This promising development was crushed, despite its apparently strong economic base, by the feudal revival of the Togukawa and its superior armies reacting to the political threat which they felt was posed by the existence of even quasi-independent merchant cities. Here we may perhaps see an expression of Japan's insularity and strategic commercial location, and perhaps *inter alia* of the weight of influence from China. The latter was earlier expressed in the great period of Japanese borrowing from T'ang China when Nara, Japan's first real city, was built on the Yamato plain as a smaller scale copy of Ch'ang An, the T'ang capital. Nara omitted Ch'ang An's massive walls, and walled towns as such have never existed in Japan at any period, one reflection of a basically different set of geographic and social conditions.

But our purpose here has been only to suggest. The city has been a center of change in western Europe, while it has been the reverse in traditional China, despite the broad similarity in urban economic functions in both areas. Urban character and urban roles may be useful indicators of the nature and dynamics of the diverse entities of society.

V. SOCIAL FORCES
AND PROCESSES

The nature of a society and its culture are important forces in shaping the geographic character of any given area as to how its physical and human resources are utilized. Racial, linguistic, ideological, and religious factors are important criteria that help differentiate the geography of various parts of the world. The discipline of geography has only quite recently begun to examine the importance of these variables. A number of scholars are directing their major research toward this effort, and this section presents a sample of the available material.

It could be assumed that, with increased mobility of people and more abundant and rapid means of communication, social differences between diverse peoples would gradually disappear. This may eventually be the case, but there is little evidence currently to support such a conclusion.

As an example, Augelli points out the misconceptions that exist in the United States concerning Latin America, and similar misconceptions are true for most if not all other parts of the world. Similarly, the image of the United States in other lands is often far from accurate. The linguistic barrier is one of the problems that prevents accurate understanding, as Wagner points out. Religious differences have long produced cleavages between peoples and areas. The Negro ghetto, which Morrill discusses, has been emphasized by the recent concern for civil rights. Other ghettos have now or in the past existed for the Jews in Warsaw and the Arabs in North African cities and many others. Varying ideological points of view are major sources of antagonism in today's world and their effects produce remarkably different landscapes. All of the above elements have impact on an area and are major agents of change in both rural and urban areas, perhaps more rapid in the latter. The following articles highlight the importance of these social forces and processes to the student of geography.

16. The Controversial Image of Latin America: A Geographer's View

John P. Augelli

*Ignorance of foreign lands, peoples, and their cultures
unfortunately is prevalent among citizens of the United States
A national survey testing knowledge of world place-names
among American college students indicated a 10-per cent
level of accuracy. Augelli describes this ignorance about Latin
America, and stresses that there is not only lack of
knowledge but also numerous dangerous misconceptions.
Because Latin America is a diverse, complicated culture region,
it is difficult to make meaningful generalizations about the
area. Latin America is important to the United States; our
citizens must be better informed if we are to assume
our proper role in the world.*

Myths die hard, especially when they serve as facile answers to un-comfortable challenges. And so it is with those that color much of our current thinking about Latin America. Teachers who introduce the study of this vast and culturally complex area can seldom start with a clean slate. Too frequently their first task is to erase the cluttering of mythical concepts and irrational attitudes which the students have acquired elsewhere; less frequently the teachers themselves are carriers of ill-founded notions with reference to the nature of things south of the border. This paper will attempt to challenge a few of the more pernicious myths which tend to warp the popular image of Latin America and to suggest how geographers and teachers may help to mold a more realistic picture of this important complex of lands and people.

Of Yankee Myths and Other Fables

In retrospect, Latin America seems to have loomed as an enigma and a fertile subject for myths almost from the dawn of discovery by Euro-peans. The early Spanish *conquistadores* fell for the treasure fable of "El Dorado," for the exciting figment of *amazona* communities ruled by

SOURCE: *Journal of Geography*, LXII (March, 1963), 103–12. The author is
professor of geography, University of Kansas.

fierce but (presumably) romantic women warriors and for the fanciful notion of fountains of youth which were always just on the other side of the horizon. Later, Protestant historians nourished the "Black Legend," a tale of Catholic Spain's brutal slaughter of Indians in the New World— conveniently forgetting that along the Anglo-Saxon sector of the American frontier, "the best Indian was a dead one." [1] Nineteenth century American businessmen fell victim to the pipe dream of Latin America's rich, untapped markets and huge reservoirs of natural resources whose development merely awaited a few Yankee dollars and a dash of Yankee ingenuity. Also worthy of mention are the mystique of "Pan Americanism," the soothing opiate of the "Good Neighbor Policy" and other fables and foibles of yesteryear, too numerous to enumerate.

Today's Latin American myths tend to come in "giant, economy sizes." Note, for example, the reassuring belief that by pumping billions of Alliance for Progress dollars into the area one can buy the answer to the challenge of Communism. But to the geographer, who is keenly attuned to areal differentiation and who is steeped in environmental studies, perhaps the most disturbing of the current *latino* fables are: (1) the "uniformity and homogeneity" which are often read into Latin American cultures and (2) the stigma of environmental impossibility which is frequently attached to the climate and terrain of much of the area.

A Dubious Homogeneity

The term "Latin America" was originally coined by the French presumably in an effort to differentiate those areas of the American hemisphere which were conquered and colonized by Europeans of Latin culture such as the Spaniards and Portuguese from those settled by Anglo-Saxon stock. If this were the only implication of the term, there would be no quarrel. Unfortunately, however, with the passage of time "Latin America" has come to signify a homogeneity of place and culture, of peoples and institutions and of problems and possibilities which simply does not exist. It may be convenient to lump into a neat pigeonhole labeled "Latin America" virtually all of the lands and people between the United States-Mexican border and Tierra del Fuego, but in so doing, one perpetuates a myth, a myth which geographers are admirably equipped to dispel.

The geographer viewing this broad area finds little homogeneity in terms of physical environment, resource complexes and most other visible patterns. Any freshman enrolled in an introductory geography

[1] There is a vast amount of historical literature dealing with the "Black Legend." For a concise exposition see John A. Crow, *The Epic of Latin America,* Doubleday and Co., New York, 1948, pp. 160–61.

course may observe that the environmental and resource phenomena of Latin America run virtually the entire gamut of possibility. All this freshman need do is to study a few generalized maps such as those of climate, soils, minerals and the like.

From an economic point of view it is true that most of Latin America may be classified as "depressed," "underdeveloped" or what have you. But to cite only a few contrasts, it would take a long stretch of the imagination to conjure similarity between the commercial, pastoral and farming economy of Argentina with its large land holdings and surplus food production and the dominantly subsistence agriculture of Haiti with its characteristic peasant plots; between the oil-rich exports of Venezuela and the sugar plantation structure of the Dominican Republic; and between the relative stability of Costa Rican economics and the runaway inflation of Brazil. (Suggest to that freshman that he look at a commercial flow map, or one of transportation, or land use or of economies, etc.).

Still more misleading is the implied uniformity of the so-called "Latin" cultural flavor of the lands between the Rio Grande del Norte and Cape Horn. The nineteenth century intellectuals of the newly emancipated nations to the south were quick to adopt the French "Latin" label.[2] But how valid is such a label in an area peopled largely by Indians, *mestizos*, and Negroes who have only an incidental connection with the white, Roman Catholic, aristocratic tradition of Latin Europe? In the words of Luis Alberto Sanchez, "Existe America Latin?"—does "Latin" America, in fact, exist?

Many Latin American intellectuals continue to feel that all *latinos* have something in common. For example, the distinguished Chilean Nobel Prize winner, Gabriela Mistral, once said, "What unites us in Spanish America is our beautiful language and our distrust of the United States." Few would argue with Mistral's observation of the common distrust of the *yanqui*, but her generalization concerning language is subject to question. It does not apply to Portuguese-speaking Brazil, a country which (contrary to Mistal's view) has been traditionally friendly to the United States. More questionable, however, is the dubious role of the Spanish language as a unifying cultural instrument in an area where such a large percentage of the population is illiterate. The educated minorities who read each other's literature and are able to communicate ideas may feel united by the beautiful Spanish language, but the masses are largely deprived of this means of communication and its unifying influence. Equally significant, while Spanish is the official

---

[2] "Latin America" came into popular usage during the 19th century and was quickly adopted by *latino* intellectuals who wished to identify themselves with French (Latin) culture. At that time (and to a large extent even today) Paris rather than Madrid ruled as the cultural Mecca to which Latin Americans turned.

language and the instrument of the literati in most of Latin America, it remains that millions of people especially in the heavily Indian regions of Andean South America, Paraguay, Mexico, and Central America, either do not speak Spanish or use it only as a second tongue. (Suggest to that poor, overworked freshman that he glance at maps of race and language and at some statistics on illiteracy!)

As to the role of religion which is often cited as a homogenizing force, virtually all Latin Americans are nominally Roman Catholic, but the emphasis should be on "nominally." In many territories, particularly those with large indigenous and Negro populations, Catholicism tends to be "skin-deep" with ritual and form (such as the cult of saints, public processions and sodalities), as its primary attraction. Proof for the nominal hold of the Church is abundant: (1) Latin America is not ordaining enough priests to man the existing Catholic organization; (2) Protestant missionaries, especially those from the United States, have probably made more inroads into Catholicism in Latin America than they have anywhere else in the world during recent decades and (3) the Vatican itself has come to recognize Latin America as a religious frontier in need of a missionary renaissance and a strong counterreformation movement. The Catholic Church as an institution continues to wield a strong influence in many Latin countries, but this seems to be due more to the almost inbred tradition for the non-separation of church and state inherited from Iberia and to the cultural place of pride which Catholicism occupies in the upper classes than to burning faith and strong religious conviction of the masses.

Lest the case for diversity be overstated, it should be stressed that there are some common denominators stemming from Iberian culture which support the argument of cultural uniformity for most of Latin America. One can not escape the considerable similarity of architecture styles with their typical patio, barred windows and houses flush with the street; the structure of the towns with their Hispanic "plaza pattern"; the imprint of Moorish arches on public buildings, etc. Similarly, viewing Culture (spelled with a capital "C"), one is aware that in much of Latin America this culture is "humanistic rather than puritanical"; that it is characterized by logic and dialectics rather than empiricism; and that conversation is better developed than mechanics. There are also common features of social organization (such as the "extended family," official male dominance, double standards of sex morality), and a comparable juridical framework stemming from Roman law is characteristic of most Latin American countries.

While it may be true, however, that these and other common denominators provide a basis for claim to cultural unity in Latin America, it is equally true that the most important cultural links seem to be most often centered on the predominantly white and wealthy upper classes which represent only a tiny minority (five per cent or less) in most countries. It is essentially this minority which is aware of its cultural history, which is capable of transmitting its ideas across mountain boundary and jungle frontier, and which shares a common pride in its white, European and Latin cultural tradition. The masses, however, are often only incidental heirs to this common bond of European tradition. More frequently, their cultural outlook is molded by local Amerindian or even imported African traditions, rather than by European. They are unable to communicate, and both their cultural and physical horizon is often limited to the *pueblo* in which they live, the *hacienda* on which they work, and the local traditions and mores whose roots may reach back to the pre-Columbian or to some long-forgotten nook of West Africa. Thus, it may well be that upper class Bolivians, Chileans, Argentines and Cubans share some similar cultural traits, but to suggest that the Bolivian Indian, the Chilean mixed-blood *inquilino*, the Argentine-Italian porteño and the Cuban mulatto cane cutter fit a common cultural framework is to play upon a myth.

That "Impossible" Environment

And then there is that other grand-daddy of a *latino* myth which often comes to haunt geographers. This is, of course, the old rationalization which suggests that, in most of Latin America, the physical drawbacks of the land pose an almost insurmountable barrier to economic development and a more uniform distribution of population. For many (including some geographers) this seems to be a valid assumption, but for others, it smacks of a facile explanation based on skimpy knowledge and age-old prejudices.

Viewed objectively, the picture of man-land relations in Latin America appears to be a composite of anomalies. On the one hand, it is known that: (1) the rapidly increasing population tends to be concentrated within a few hundred miles of the sea, leaving considerable empty or thinly settled areas to the interior (especially in South America); and (2) the gross pattern of population distribution is characterized by clusters separated by what James has called a "hollow" frontier. On the other hand, it is obvious that the expanding population is not effectively occupying the empty lands; and worse, there is an artificial country-to-town movement which is depleting the countryside of what is often badly needed labor while it creates slums and swells unemployment in the cities. As an added joker to this anomalous set of conditions, some people insist that agrarian reform is one of the absolute "musts" to meet the revolution of rising expectations and the threat of Communism in rural Latin America.

If one poses the question—"why not seriously investigate the possibilities of large-scale occupance of the lightly settled interior lands?", the stock answer is likely to be—"these lands are too hot, too wet, too dry, too isolated, too inconvenient," etc. Moreover, why bother with such prosaic approaches when one can dream of spectacular solutions like agrarian reform, industrialization and the like.

This argument of environmental impossibility reminds some geographers of that old wives' tale in United States history known as the "Great American Desert." Frontiersmen, emerging from the humid eastern forests and carrying with them the typical European distrust of new and untried environmental conditions, jumped at an unwarranted conclusion when they gazed upon the great grasslands of North America. "Any land that won't grow trees won't grow crops," they claimed. But experimentation and adaptation soon proved them wrong, and today this same "Great American Desert" is one of the world's great producers of cereals and meat.

Is it conceivable that our present negative conclusions vis-a-vis the "green hell" of the Amazon Basin, for instance, are equally false? We do not really know because we have found it more convenient to let prejudices determine judgment rather than expend the effort and capital to arrive at a rational conclusion. There are at least four Japanese agricultural colonies that refused to be discouraged by the "green hell" of the Amazon. After only a few decades of effort, these settlements loom as striking successes. They produce the bulk of their own food with a surplus for sale, and they have found convenient cash crops in the form of black pepper and jute. The conclusion appears inescapable that among the many obstacles to economic development in rural Latin America is a built-in prejudice against (and an abysmal ignorance of) the potential of untried environments, especially tropical environments.

The Challenge to Geographers

These are only two of the myths which warp the image of Latin America, but they are of special interest to geographers because of the competence they claim with problems of man-land relations and with areal differentiation. What can geographers do to dispel these fables?

With reference to the notion of environmental impossibility, the answer is research and more research. After the efforts of at least two generations of geographers, knowledge of Latin America's environment can still be measured largely by the often-unwarranted textbook generalization. Field geographers have frequently stuck to the beaten paths, and there is still little realization in this profession that the most pressing research need in Latin America is to evaluate in realistic detail the conditions, the problems, and the possibilities of the underpopulated and underdeveloped areas lying outside the orbit of present settlement.

The present slogans in Washington not withstanding, there have been too few "frontiersmen" among geographers.

With reference to the fable of uniformity, one can begin by pointing out that despite the claim to unifying influence based on "Latin" heritage, it remains that Latin America emerged from its colonial experience as a politically fragmented mosaic. Virtually every nucleus of colonial settlement became the seat of an independent "nation." Such dreams of unity as Bolivar's "Greater Colombia" were shattered by the localism of the supposedly culturally related upper class families of Caracas, Bogotá, and Quito. Romanticists claim that the splintering of Hispanic America into a large number of independent nations merely reflects the fierce "individualism" of the *latino*. Geographers suspect, however, that this individualism may be still another myth, and that the considerable physical and cultural diversity of Latin America is a sounder reason for the area's political fragmentation.

The diversity which created this multiplicity of "nations" (despite the common Hispanic ancestry of much of the population in Latin America) stems from many causes. Chief among these are: (1) differences in physical environment (including location and resources) and the consequent variety in human adjustment and economic development and orientation; (2) a post-Columbian history of limited interaction among the Latin communities stemming from inadequate transportation, physical barriers and other factors; (3) differences from place to place in the number, level of civilization and cultural resistance of Amerindian population and (4) variety of the non-Iberian cultural intrusions such as the Italian in Argentina, the German in Chile, the North American in Cuba and Puerto Rico and the African in much of the tropical lowland zones.

Regardless of what the causes for their emergence may have been, however, it remains that once established, the numerous nation states of Latin America gave further impetus to the theme of diversity. Differences in government policies, political stability, ideologies, national military history—these and other influences stemming from the state reinforced national differences. Thus, there is ample justification for approaching the study of areal differentiation in Latin America on the basis of the political unit or state as many geography teachers do.

But while recognizing the importance of "state" and "nation," the effort to drive home the culture-areal diversity of Latin America should not stop at the national frontier. Geographers know that national boundaries in Latin America seldom delimit territories which are uniform in patterns and problems of resource utilization, economic development and other cultural manifestations. For example, while both are included within the national boundaries of Brazil, the states of São Paulo and Pernambuco are cultural worlds apart in matters of environment, race,

economics, settlement history, etc. In fact European São Paulo is culturally far more closely related to Uruguay and the Argentine Pampas
than to its sister state of Pernambuco; in turn the patterns and problems
of Pernambuco may be more akin to those of the Guiana lowlands and to
other regions with a comparable tropical plantation history than to Sao
Paulo and the Brazilian south. Moreover, the cultural uniformity and
emotional bond evoked by "nation" in Latin America are often of a different order than they are in Europe or the United States or Japan. For
example, the third-generation German in southern Chile may have
changed his first name from "Karl" to "Carlos" but he may still consider
himself a German first and then a Chilean. To be a *Paulista* or a *Carioca*
in Brazil implies a much higher degree of local loyalty and attachment
than to be a Texan or Brooklynite in the United States. It is important
to raise the question: To what extent does the illiterate, poverty-stricken,
Quechua-speaking Indian of the Andes think of himself as a Peruvian,
a Bolivian or an Ecuadorian?

A Suggestion for Regionalization

This leads to the suggestion that geographers apply their often-vaunted
capacity for integration and regional generalization to create a more
realistic image of Latin America than one based on national cultures or
on the assumed uniformity stemming from Iberian influence. Taking
only South America as an example (and using as a point of departure
the culture-sphere division proposed by Wagley, Gillin, and others), the
continent may be broken down into five crudely differentiated cultural
complexes (Fig. 1): (1) the European-Commercial; (2) the Tropical
Plantation; (3) the Indo-Subsistence; (4) the Mestizo-Transitional and
(5) Undifferentiated. This breakdown goes beyond political divisions to
what may be more realistic boundaries based on patterns of physical environment and human adaptation, economic geography and history and
population characteristics. A summarized rationale for this division is
given below, but a detailed defense of the scheme is both beyond the
scope of this paper and all-but-impossible on the basis of available information.

Rationale for Proposed Culture-Sphere
Division of South America

A. *European Commercial.*

1. Mid-latitude climates; other physical conditions apt for European
mixed farming and grazing.

2. Sparse aboriginal population at low level of technology; post-

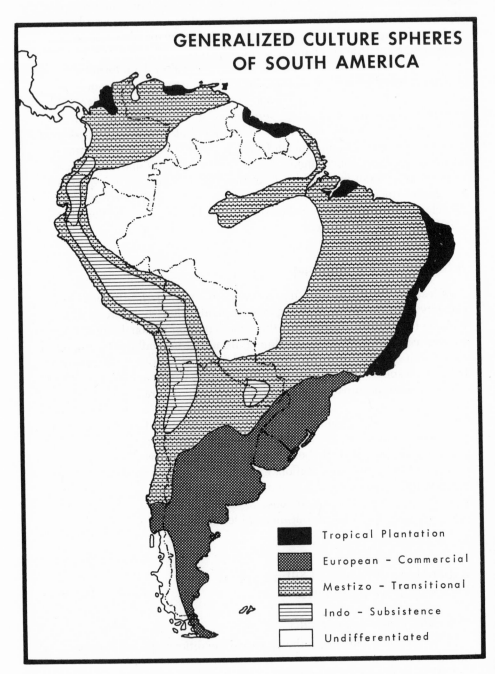

GENERALIZED CULTURE SPHERES
OF SOUTH AMERICA

Tropical Plantation
European – Commercial
Mestizo – Transitional
Indo – Subsistence
Undifferentiated

FIGURE 1: Latin America.

216

Columbian influence of Amerindians on race and culture limited or absent.

3. Low in attraction for early Iberian colonists because areas were poor in precious metals, had few Indians, and were incapable of producing "dessert" crops such as sugar; limited economic development and population growth until after mid-19th century.

4. Significant economic development during the past century based on commercial agriculture, grazing, and (to a lesser extent) industry; economic growth attracted millions of European immigrants and gave the areas a dominantly white population.

5. Measured by the usual yardstick (standard of living, literacy, transportation network, etc.) "European" sphere ranks well above the rest of the continent; the bulk of the labor force is involved in a commercial rather than a subsistence economy, and the overall development compares favorably with that in many parts of Europe.

B. Tropical Plantation.

1. Tropical climates, lowland terrain, and coastal location.

2. Aboriginal population too sparse and undisciplined to supply adequate labor force for tropical commercial agriculture.

3. Areas poor in precious metals but a combination of clay soils and climate made them attractive to early colonists for the production of valuable plantation crops such as sugar.

4. Millions of Negro slaves imported to form a population base dominated by a small, white "plantocracy"; African influence on racial composition and many facets of culture continues to the present.

5. Spectacular wealth produced by plantation during 17th and 18th centuries by exploiting slaves and "mining" the soil; rapid decline and decay with emancipation and other conditions of the past century; the old plantation areas are now among the poorest regions of South America, and the labor force depends primarily on a subsistence economy.

C. The Indo-Subsistence.

1. Except for Paraguay, this sphere focuses on tropical highlands and conincides with the "high culture" centers of pre-Columbian Indian civilizations in the Andes.

2. Early colonists attracted to the area because of large pool of labor or precious metals; colonies were considered the most important possessions by Spaniards; a feudal socio-economic structure was erected by the whites on the Indian base, and in large measure, this structure continues to the present.

3. Indians were easily conquered but not easily assimilated; currently

the Indian continues to make up the bulk (or a large percentage) of the total population, and he remains culturally apart from the "national life" of the country in which he lives.

4. Such commercial economies as exist in these areas tend to be in the hands of white or *mestizos*, and the Indians form a large, landless peonage living by subsistence agriculture or by laboring on the *haciendas*.

5. Areas rank with plantation zones as among poorest on the continent.

D. Mestizo-Transitional.

1. The climates and terrain of these areas vary, but they most commonly fall within the broad range of tropical upland fringes.

2. Aboriginal population was "moderate" in numbers, and the present matrix tends to be dominantly mixed European and Indian.

3. While Indian cultural remnants are not unknown, the *mestizo* has largely embraced the European way of life.

4. The economy of these areas is termed "transitional" because it tends to be less commercial than the European sphere but less subsistent in orientation than dominantly Indian areas.

5. In most areas the *mestizo* racial blend stems from European and Indian; in much of Brazil as well as in the coastal zones of Colombia and Venezuela the racial mixture may include Negro.

E. Undifferentiated.

(This is a "catchall" division applied largely to areas where differentiation is especially difficult. For example, the Pacific coast of Columbia and several areas in interior Brazil have a Negro population which is not associated with a past or present plantation economy; southernmost Chile's combination Indian remnants and European intrusions defy facile classification. Despite the difficulty of differentiation, however, some common characteristics are apparent for the areas labeled "undifferentiated.")

1. Climates vary but tend to extremes.

2. Areas are of low population density and limited economic development.

3. Location and poor transportation give rise to comparative isolation.

4. Much of the sphere only slightly modified in post-Columbian period.

In conclusion, the author is keenly aware of the numerous exceptions and questionable assumptions glossed over by the classification. Despite this awareness, the writer is bold enough to submit it in part because it may serve as a crude pedagogic device for use in beginning courses.

More important, however, this article may serve as a "bee in the bonnet," an "irritant" for teachers of geography to scratch more deeply into the complexity which is Latin America. The burgeoning political importance of this area and the challenge of reform-or-revolution which it poses for the United States are too immediate, too close to the bone to be met by misconceptions and myths. Geographers may not be competent to attack all of the *latino* mythology, but if they fail to take the lead in attacking those myths which stem from misunderstanding of physical environment and areal differentiation, then they deny the very *raison d'être* of their professional existence and function.

17. Remarks on the Geography of Language

Philip L. Wagner

The inability of one people to understand clearly the language of another, whether they be next-door neighbors or contestants in the struggle for world power, is of fundamental significance to world peace and the exchange of goods and ideas. The number of languages and dialects utilized by the world's peoples is overwhelming: just that region roughly bounded by the Baltic, Black, and Caspian Seas is said to have 163 different languages and dialects. This "shatterbelt" of eastern Europe has been a trouble spot over the years, with language differences contributing to the unrest. In other countries such as Switzerland bi- and trilingual people have successfully unified into one nation. Language difference is a major obstacle to the successful operation of the United Nations.

Wagner illustrates how a "geography of language" can be developed as an aid to cultural geography. There is no doubt that language is a major key to problems in the study and explanation of many cultures.

Language exercises a decisive influence on the composition and distribution of intercommunicating social units—on who talks to whom—and thus on the activities in which men are able to participate in groups.

Source: *Geographical Review*, XLVIII (January, 1958), 86–97. The author is associate professor of geography, University of California, Davis.

Without linguistic communication no organized social undertaking can proceed, and without a single, shared language such an undertaking becomes cumbersome and subject to many potential misunderstandings. There are only a few nations—for example, Belgium, Canada, and Switzerland—where leadership is successfully shared by two speech communities or more.

I once heard a prominent American geographer ask whether the Latvians spoke Russian or German or perhaps a mixture of both. His unawareness that a Latvian language exists, and that it is affiliated to a well-studied and important branch of Indo-European—the Baltic— is all too typical of a large part of the geographical profession.

The structure and internal characteristics of language are properly the concern of professional linguists, and the function of language in communication is traditionally studied by some of the social scientists. But the distribution of linguistic usages and of social groupings based thereon is another important aspect of language, which is of major consequence for the geographer.

Linguistic heterogeneity is one of the most obvious, most absolute, and most fixed of the categories of diversity that apply to human populations. The sharp discontinuities and the relatively uniform blocs that characterize modern linguistic communities strongly influence human behavior, and particularly the association of people and their interaction. Political, social, and economic structures are often closely correlated with linguistic usage, and distributional patterns of these phenomena tend to coincide strikingly with linguistic areal patterns.

It is my purpose to set forth here some of the understandings of linguistic geography as pursued by the linguist; to consider the categories and classification of languages per se, and of the social units marked by certain consistencies of linguistic usage; and to invite the attention of geographers to the pertinence of linguistic geography for their own work.

The history of linguistic geography begins with the history of geography itself; for a good part of the ancient geographies is simply the enumeration and location of peoples and tribes, of whom perhaps the majority were distinguishable chiefly as separate linguistic groups speaking their own distinct languages or dialects. We find in Herodotus or Strabo or Ptolemy, and again in the Arab geographers and the medieval Europeans, a preoccupation with the fixing of name and site for innumerable peoples who were otherwise undescribed.

As geography has expanded its scope and become accustomed to dealing with regions in their manifold aspects, it has failed significantly to maintain and extend its concern with the linguistic correlates of area. The study of the variation of linguistic forms in space has become the province of specialists within linguistics, whose precise scientific techniques and numerous detailed investigations have produced a rich literature in this geographical field.

The Nature of Linguistics

As in other sciences, the selection of the unit of observation and the identification of the universe of discourse are prerequisites to the study of linguistic geography. The plotting of linguistic distributions has depended on the establishment of categories of linguistic facts, and on the development of theories of relationship among these categories. The raw material of linguistic science is of course the single utterance or, less satisfactorily, some transcription of it; but the sounds made by the human vocal apparatus, together with the associated gestures, attitudes, and overtones, are so numerous and so variable among individuals that they alone do not provide suitable units of observation. Nor can any scheme of "meanings" be introduced, a priori, as a basis for selecting such units.

Linguists had observed and worked with a basic speech unit long before it was isolated and described as the "phoneme." All sounds that fall within the same conventional range are treated as identical and form the essential and significant units of linguistic communication.

Just as each utterance has its distinctive sound characteristics, so the speech of different persons, over a period of time, will fall into individual patterns. Every human being develops more or less perceptible idiosyncrasies in his speech. Communication among individuals of slightly different speech patterns is effective only when the individual ways of speaking can be equated to some set of linguistic conventions. The standardization of phonetic values through the discrimination of phonemic elements provides the primary mechanism for bringing the sounds employed by one speaker into operational correspondence with those employed by any other speaker of the same idiom. This phonemic equivalence is a necessary but not sufficient condition for linguistic communication and is one of the several internal criteria for defining a distinct communicating group.

Given this prerequisite, a further mechanism must be introduced—symbolic equivalence. Sounds have no absolute "natural" meanings.[1] Meanings are arbitrary: any language is a large but finite set of symbolic values arbitrarily assigned to phonemic units and sequences.[2]

Like the values assigned to phonetic features (units of phonemic discrimination, based on conventional intervals or ranges of sound rather

[1] It is of course true that some sounds uttered by the human voice are onomatopoetic, or suggestive of sounds occurring elsewhere in nature, and thus suggest things related to them.
[2] This is only a limited case of my working definition of culture as "a large but finite set of values assigned to conceived possibilities of state and behavior."

than on absolute and exact values), the symbolic value of an utterance may be regarded as embracing a range of infinite possible meanings, limited by conventional agreement. Thus one may never state *exactly* the meaning of a given word or phrase but may readily infer the limits of its possible meaning and treat it operationally as if in fact it carried an exact value.

A speech community—or, roughly, a language group—is a group of persons who possess in common at least two sets of understandings or standards of discrimination, the phonemic and the symbolic. The membership of such a group varies greatly, according to the immediate situation; for example, a simple lingua franca may in a temporary wartime setting become the basis of successful communication among individuals of diverse backgrounds, or a group of scientists may at times become a small and exclusive communication group, whose jargon is unintelligible to other speakers of the same colloquial language.

Language and Language Groups

The word *language* is an ambiguous one. We may define the "language" of any individual as his habitual speech (or writing), with all its idiosyncrasies; we may speak of the "English language" as an entity, by which we imply the general set of phonemic and symbolic standards of a large body of speakers (but even here we embrace great diversity in phonemic discrimination, and some also in symbolism). We refer to the "language of peasants," as an entity transcending the speech of individual peasants, and to the "languages" of science, philosophy, and other fields. There are "national languages," "literary languages," "colloquial languages," and several other categories. The study of linguistic phenomena is itself described as the study of something called simply "language."

An empirical approach to the problem of clearing up this confusion of terms might begin with the language of an individual and arrive at an understanding of the nature, size, and composition of the speaker's language group simply by observing whom he could or could not communicate with. But in fact our notions of the nature and distribution of languages are not established in this manner. It is rather the group of persons who are in daily communication one with another, the "face-to-face group," that is taken as the basic unit of distribution.

Communication through the utterance of sounds is never perfect; there is a huge loss in meanings between speaker and hearer. But within a face-to-face group, and sometimes far beyond it, the habitual standards of phonemic and symbolic discrimination provide a satisfactory approximation to exact meaning, which drops off rapidly as we go beyond the social unit of everyday communication. There is a downward gradient of communicative intensity, which might be shown as a hyperbolic curve on rectangular coordinates, from the speaker himself downward and outward to persons and places remote from him in space or circumstance, where the point of complete linguistic incomprehension is reached. The linguistic usage of the speaker's face-to-face group bridges some part of the large interval of meaning through the employment of discriminated ranges of sound and symbol, but a limit is set on this device by the confusion that soon appears as wider and wider ranges of meaning must be allowed for a single unit of discrimination (phoneme or lexical element), and a critical range of the unit is ultimately reached, beyond which regular sustained communication cannot occur. In other words, a given word will take on more and more possible shades of meaning, or a given phoneme will be rendered in more and more different sound versions, as one gets away from the basic face-to-face group. This is not hard to account for. Imitative learning, from examples constantly repeated, and "feedback," which informs the speaker whenever he deviates from the correct usage, produce a high degree of likeness among the individual "languages" of different speakers in the same face-to-face group.[3] The fact of intensive mutual influence among speakers in a face-to-face group makes it possible to disregard individual speech peculiarities, and to base a scheme of linguistic distribution on the usage—the linguistic conventions embraced in phonemic and symbolic standards—of face-to-face groups. We may easily plot the patterns of phonetic values of index words on a map, and this procedure is the technical foundation of linguistic geography.

Linguistic Mapping

The fundamental assumption on which linguistic mapping rests may be stated as follows: "At any given point on the land surface of the earth, there is one and only one possible interpretation (of sound or meaning) for any given utterance." The corollary would be that between any two points there may be any degree of variation in the interpretation of a given utterance. Isopleths may be constructed to show such variation; these lines are referred to as "isoglosses."

Beginning at any given settlement, one might hypothetically construct a linguistic map of the world simply by plotting all isoglosses as they were encountered, that is, by making a notation on the map every time a change in linguistic usage was observed. In most areas this would produce a map on which the density of isoglosses, representing increas-

[3] The effectual face-to-face group may be very large, as in a modern industrial country with highly developed mass communications and considerable territorial mobility of individuals, but it may also be very small, as in a small isolated primitive group such as the Andamanese or the Seri.

ing divergence in speech forms, would increase rapidly in all directions away from the point of origin. At no great distance even a large-scale map would be completely black with isoglosses.

Two important qualifications must be introduced in order to overcome this difficulty. First, it is never necessary to plot all possible isoglosses; a small number of "critical" or representative sounds or lexical features is selected to provide an index to the whole body of speech, and only variations among these elements are plotted. Second, for smaller-scale maps the local language of face-to-face contact in each settlement is not used as a base, but rather some form more widely understood.

If we allow our interest to remain focused on local usage in face-to-face contact but limit ourselves to a few critical isoglosses, we produce a map on which the isogloss density increases less rapidly with increasing distance. Nevertheless, at some points we find that the isoglosses "bunch up" and make thicker lines of coincident or nearly coincident limits. We next discover that this is a recurrent but discontinuous phenomenon, and that it is beginning to block out greater or smaller areas of relative uniformity. These areas are indicated by nets of isoglosses spaced more or less evenly, at low density, and separated by the bunched-up isoglosses. Such cases of relatively homogeneous usage, at the scales used and with the testing criteria usually applied by linguistic geographers, correspond to dialect areas.

A dialect, in pure distributional terms, is thus a group of local speech systems more alike among themselves than any one of them is like any local speech system outside the group. There are also bases for the definition of dialects in historical linguistics, which complement the distributional approach. In practice, the two approaches are used concurrently.

If we continue the plotting of isoglosses, we eventually find that the isoglosses for all or almost all the criteria we have selected will coincide in a single massive line, and we infer that beyond this limit a totally new series of speech forms begins. This is the "linguistic frontier" between larger communities of linguistic descent and development. Often the linguistic frontier coincides with the limits of "national languages" in the common sense of the term, but this is by no means always the case. "National language" properly signifies something quite distinct from a collection of intergrading local usages.

Let us take the linguistic map of Western Europe as an example. If we were to follow the procedure just outlined, we should discover that one such frontier, thick and absolute, runs through Belgium, eastern France, Switzerland, and northern Italy, and along the western frontiers of Yugoslavia, Hungary, Czechoslovakia, and Poland. Other frontiers are represented by small enclaves in Brittany, western Ireland, Wales, and Scotland, and at the foot of the western Pyrenees, and in the area just south of Berlin in Germany.

These lines delimit the great areas of Western European speech groups of ancient lineage—Germanic, Romance, Celtic, and Slavic, and the small, isolated Basque stock. Within these heavy frontier lines are less prominent lines between the western part and the rest of the Iberian Peninsula, along the Pyrenees, in the Grisons region of Switzerland, down the spine of Scandinavia, through southern Jutland, and in the northeastern Netherlands. These less thick bundles of isoglosses represent subdivisions within the language groups of the first category. Successively less sharp limits will appear as we consider lesser subdivisions, for the differences in speech forms will decrease in number and degree within each area. The larger discontinuities clearly reflect a situation of long standing, which can be explained only by a history of migration, conquest, and linguistic succession. To bring these facts into some sort of meaningful order, we must have recourse to historical methods.

Derivation and Classification of Languages

Languages change gradually. The English spoken by this generation is the English of 50 years ago with numerous additions and replacements that have been fitted into the basic pattern without changing it too much. The English of 1900 is the English of Chaucer modified in the same gradual manner over a longer period. The speech of today's teen-ager is a bewildering but nevertheless legitimate descendant of the speech of some Neolithic warrior of 1957 B.C. The teen-ager's language might not be understood by his parents, much less by his Neolithic ancestor, but it is a descendant of the speech of both. We may say that language is a continuum in time, and that any speech of today may be derived, with infinite small modifications along the way, from the language of the first speaking human beings. Linguistic history and linguistic classification rest on the assumption that all languages have a direct line of descent from older forms. There are probably no true linguistic "hybrids" or "mixtures," since at any one time only a few additions are being made to the existing stock of sounds and symbols; a sudden total replacement is of course inconceivable, as anyone who has tried to learn a foreign language can testify. Hypothetically, long coexistence and mutual influence might produce a total convergence of two originally different languages, but no case of this has been discovered.

On the basis of this assumption, linguists classify languages into groups based on descent, much as taxonomists classify plants into orders, families, genera, and species on the basis of inferred common descent. The genetic classification of languages is dependent on historical documents and on internal evidence in the existing forms. Sounds, grammatical features, vocabulary, and other characteristics tend to preserve some measure of equivalence within the languages descended from a common source. Thus French, Spanish, Portuguese, Italian, Rumanian, and a few other groups of dialects share many features and are known to be descendants of Latin; together they are designated as the Romance languages. This group may be shown to belong, together with Celtic, Slavic, Baltic, Germanic, Greek, Albanian, Iranic, Indic, and a number of close relatives, to the Indo-European family of languages. The Indo-European tongues show certain features that lead some scholars to postulate for them remote connections with groups such as Finnic, Turkic, Semitic, Hamitic, and even Eskimo. Inferences for membership within the Indo-European family are strongly based on well-worked-out schemes of phonetic correspondence, numerals, and vocabulary relationships. Similar criteria have established tentative descent lines for Finnic, Semitic, Mongolic, Dravidian, Sino-Tibetan, and many other families. Such linguistic groups are often the categories employed on world maps of linguistic distribution.

If we were to confine our plotting of isoglosses on the map of Europe to samples selected only in certain kinds of places—say, army parade grounds, law courts, or university lecture halls—we should produce an entirely different kind of map. There would be large areas with few or no isoglosses crossing them, then concentrations of isoglosses at long intervals. The bunched isoglosses would tend to coincide with national frontiers.

These frontiers are those of "national languages," and the homogeneous areas within them are the areas of official use of the respective languages. Official languages may also be referred to loosely as "standard" or, often, "literary" languages. In accordance with linguistic doctrine, these standard languages must also have each a single line of descent; they cannot be mixtures, and there is of course no such thing as a natural common denominator among languages or dialects. The national, or standard, language must be derived at some point from some local system of linguistic conventions, in which numerous modifications may later take place. This is usually the speech of an elite group—military, political, religious, literary—or of commerce. It becomes widely diffused within the area where its speakers are active and is maintained and regulated by them. Historically, most of the standard languages have depended on a written or an oral literature to exemplify the desired standards and to inhibit excessive change. The writers or bards are in effect the arbiters of linguistic usage, a position that is symbolized by the institution of national academies (for example, the Académie Française or the Real Academia Española) or the publication of great national dictionaries such as Webster's and the Oxford English Dictionary.

We may differentiate between the literary language and the habitual spoken form, or "colloquial language," which together constitute the standard language. The standard language may overreach national frontiers, as English and Spanish do, and thus differ in extension from the national language as such. On the other hand, the colloquial and literary languages may coexist with another colloquial-national language, as is exemplified in Quebec, with its standard literary French alongside local "French" developed in the country.

National languages, if official—for some are not identified with a political state—become diffused through such institutions as the press, the school, the army, and the radio. In our time their use is expanding rapidly at the expense of local speech types, or dialects.

Languages of commerce are employed far beyond their original national boundaries. The great European languages—English, French, Spanish, Russian—are used widely even in places where few or none of their "native speakers" live. There have been many instances in history of the use of some particular language as the lingua franca of trade and cultural contact. Arabic, Greek, Aramaic, Latin, Sanskrit, Persian, Mandarin, and Nahuatl are prominent examples. Some of the languages of contact are much modified from their originals, but nevertheless all of them are based on a pre-existing language; such are pidgin English, the Chinook Jargon, and, more or less consciously, Esperanto. Occasionally a jargon gives rise to a regular language, which becomes the exclusive vehicle of communication of some population; colonial jargons based on standard European languages gave rise to Papiamento in Curaçao, Creole French in Haiti, Creole in Mauritius, and several other independent languages of the present day. Some languages of wide currency shrink to purely literary vehicles but may continue, like Latin, Attic Greek, Sanskrit, and Pali, to be written for millennia after they have ceased to function as means of everyday speech. Others are revitalized to serve a national independence movement, for example, Hebrew in Israel and Gaelic in Eire.

Some Potentially Profitable Geographical Studies

The larger implications of linguistic distributions for social phenomena are so evident that we shall not consider them here. It is to be noted, however, that a large task remains for geographers in the detailed study of the effect of areal patterns of language in the general geographical context. As examples of such subjects that might be approached by the geographer we may select a few at random.

The validity of the proposition that linguistic frontiers are the most desirable political frontiers has never been carefully examined, though the concept has been influential in the determination of national boundaries, especially in the twentieth century. This question deserves a thorough examination by a competent political geographer. The historical geographer might investigate the amazingly wide distribution of such groups of languages as the Turkic, the Malayo-Polynesian, and the Uto-Aztecan or consider the diffusion of words from Spanish and certain native languages in the Americas as a possible index of the time, kind, and content of cultural borrowings. For the economic geographer, the barriers that linguistic differences oppose to economic integration in Europe, India, and other areas, the implications of linguistic obstacles to world trade, and the language problems of international communication would be worth investigating. The cultural geographer might examine the relation between linguistic isolation and cultural distinctiveness, and the possible value of the linguistic region as a basic unit of regional research. The potential areas of geographical interest in the broad field of linguistic distribution are numerous and need exploration by geographers of many different specializations and talents.

It hardly needs to be pointed out that the experience of linguistic geography offers some useful methodological suggestions for the work of all geographers. The discipline has developed with a strong emphasis on conceptual clarity, and the admirable precision and economy of the linguist's distributional methods may well be taken as a model for further refinement in geographical method. Although the linguistic geographer is concerned with the variation of phenomena in space, he is less aware of the possibility of total regional synthesis than are other geographers. He does not hesitate, however, to draw on the evidence offered by other than linguistic data when it may serve to clarify some important point. Often enough a primarily linguistic study develops as by-products many valuable insights into the historical geography of a region.

The linguistic geographer employs his distributional studies chiefly in the investigation of problems of linguistic development and differentiation; distributional information serves to document the retention, loss, or alteration of phonemes and lexical elements, and to expose connections and borrowing that would be missed if only the data from the standard languages were used. However, this clearly subsidiary position of geography within linguistic science does not detract from the value of its methods.

Linguistic Geography and Culture

The use of the carefully defined basic units of phonemic and symbolic value and their plotting by the isogloss method present a promising approach to the study of the distribution of cultural phenomena, which might be applied more widely. The reduction of cultural features to similarly controllable and empirically testable categories and their systematic plotting by means of appropriate isopleths would provide a powerful tool to geography and greatly strengthen the regional approach.

Our understanding of culture and its concrete manifestations is still far from complete. Linguistics is one area of cultural science in which perhaps greater precision has been attained than is typical, and therefore linguistic geography is of special interest in connection with the methodology of cultural research. Geographers have resently heard a plea for greater attention to, and use of, the concept of culture in their work. The experience of linguistic geography suggests that means may be at hand for more and better cultural research in geography.[4]

[4] The literature of linguistics in general is extensive. It is summarized up to about the year 1930 by Leonard Bloomfield in his great work "Language" (New York, 1933), which also sets forth the new principles that were to dominate linguistics in America for a generation after its first publication. Other general works of great interest and importance are Edward Sapir's "Language: An Introduction to the Study of Speech" (New York, 1921), Louis Hjelmslev's "Prolegomena to a Theory of Language" (translated from the Danish, "Omkring sprogteoriens grundlæggelse," by F. J. Whitefield; Baltimore, 1953), and Tadeusz Milewski's "Zarys jezykoznawstwa ogólnego [Outline of General Linguistics]" (2 vols., Lublin, 1947–1948).

The current state of linguistics is outlined in "Linguistics Today," *Word: Journ. Linguistic Circle of New York*, Vol. 10, 1954, pp. 121–400, and the progress of the science may be followed in many journals, of which *Language*, published by the Linguistic Society of America, is perhaps the most important in the United States.

The special interests of linguistic geography are considered in a large number of works. Ernst Gamillscheg's "Die Sprachgeographie und ihre Ergebnisse für die allgemeine Sprachwissenschaft" (Bielefeld-Leipzig, 1928) gives an especially lucid account of the study of phonetic variation through geographical methods, which is also the subject of Eli Fischer-Jorgensen's "Dialektgeografiens betydning for opfattelsen af lydforandringer" (Copenhagen, 1934). A recent general survey is found in Gino Bottiglioni: "Linguistic Geography: Its Achievements, Methods and Orientations," *Word*, Vol. 10, 1954, pp. 375–387. Albert Dauzat's "La géographie linguistique" (Paris, 1922) shows the application of linguistic geography to problems of vocabulary, and the history of words. "La dialectologie: Aperçu historique et méthodes d'enquête linguistique" by Sever Pop (Louvain, 1950) surveys the whole field of linguistic geography and offers a vast bibliography of its literature. Another useful source on the literature of this subject is the "Essai de bibliographie de géographie linguistique générale" by Josef Schrijnen (Nijmegen, 1933).

A number of world atlases of language have been produced, and the consultation of these rich and probably neglected resources of geographical reference, despite the occasional disagreement that is to be expected among the authorities, can provide a much more reliable basis for the treatment of language in regional studies than a reliance on hearsay or works of general reference. The most important atlas accompanies "Les langues du monde," a comprehensive work with diagnostic sketches of the major languages and language groups, in addition to the maps, produced under the direction of A. Meillet and Marcel Cohen (new edit, Paris, 1952). The atlas volume of Milewski's work, previously cited (Vol. 2, Part 3, Lublin, 1948), A. Drexel's "Atlas linguisticus . . ." (Innsbruck, 1934), now being republished, and the atlas accompanying Father W. Schmidt's "Die Sprachfamilien und Sprachenkreise der Erde" (Heidelberg, 1926) are highly controversial in some features.

18. The Citron in the Mediterranean: A Study in Religious Influences

Erich Isaac

Religion influences many aspects of daily life for a large proportion of the world's people. India, for example, possesses the largest number of cattle of any country, yet the meat of this animal does not contribute to the food supply of a majority of the people because it is taboo in the Hindu religion. The location of churches and church-related schools often influences the choice of home locations by individual families. The control or lack of control of the birth rate and the future solution of the world population problem is in part related to religion. Ellsworth Huntington in his Mainsprings of Civilization *was one of the first geographers to point out the significance of the geography of the great religions. He traces the close relationships between religion and the worldwide differences in culture and civilization, and indicates that certain climates have fostered the development of religions. The following selection by Isaac demonstrates very well the effect of religion upon the distribution and shifting location of a specific crop, citron, in the Mediterranean area. Religion influences landholding systems, settlement patterns, food consumption, and many other spatially related practices and thus is of increasing interest to the cultural geographer. In Selection 21, English also considers the part played by religion in the organization and utilization of space.*

The citron, or *Citrus medica,* is today, commercially, the least important of cultivated citrus fruits. It is used primarily for the production of candied citron peel, and the leaves and blossoms of the tree provide essential oils used in the manufacture of perfume. But despite the citron's minor commercial role the fruit has a twofold significance for the economic geographer. Historically, the citron is important inasmuch as it was the first fruit of the genus citrus to be cultivated in the Mediterranean. There it was introduced and spread by the Jews, to whom the fruit is necessary for the ritual celebration of the holiday of the Feast

Source: *Economic Geography,* XXXV (January, 1959), 71–78. The author is associate professor of geography, The City College of the City University of New York.

of Booths. The citron, moreover, was in all probability responsible for the initial introduction of oranges and lemons to the Mediterranean, for whose early cultivation there we have evidence.[1] But of greater geographic significance is the illustration offered by the history of the citron of the role which religion may play in shaping the landscape and in determining regional and interregional economic relations. The citron is certainly an exceptional example of the religious factor at work; the present day location, and, historically, the shifting of areas of citron production in Mediterranean lands can be explained to a large extent in terms of religious needs and fashions.

Appearance and Significance of Citron

The spread of citron through the Mediterranean coincided with the growth of Jewish communities in the Mediterranean Diaspora. The extent of its distribution was, of course, limited by the requirements of the citron tree. A small evergreen with irregular branches, oval and slightly serrated leaves, the citron tree produces a fragrant yellow oblong fruit, from four to eight inches long, with a furrowed skin. Like other commercial citrus trees, it is unlikely to sustain damage if temperatures fall for short periods to 28° F., but is less able than other varieties of citrus to endure lower temperatures. The reason is that while in most citrus trees flowering takes place in early spring, the citron continues throughout the year to produce flowers in varying degrees of abundance. It is this absence of a period of dormancy which makes the tree more susceptible to frost damage. Growth is imperceptible above 95° F. While the water requirements of the tree are large, its cultivation can be carried out on a great variety of soils provided they have a favorable texture. The citron does best on fine sandy loams although in some commercially producing areas plantings occur on what is almost pure sand.

The citron is accepted by the Jews as the fruit commanded for use in the Feast of Booths. Leviticus 23:40 reads:

And you shall take unto yourself on the first day the fruit of a goodly tree, palm branches, foliage of a leafy tree, and willows of the brook, and you shall rejoice before the Lord your God seven days.

The citron is not mentioned by name here nor anywhere else in the Bible. Documentary evidence for the acceptance of the citron as "the fruit of a goodly tree" is not present until the second century B.C. The

---

[1] The Jews, who became leading arboriculturists and horticulturists in the first four centuries A.D., were familiar with varieties of citrus other than the citron and it is reasonable to believe that they transferred the skills developed in growing citron to the production of other citrus fruits with which they were familiar, and whose requirements were very close to those of the citron.

presumption of its acceptance at a much earlier period rests upon Rabbinic insistence in the first centuries of the Christian era that the citron was the fruit originally designated and that it had always been accepted as such.

Early Spread of Citron

The citron, or *etrog* as it is known to the Jews, appeared in the Peloponnesus, one of the first centers of dense Jewish settlement outside Palestine, probably in the first century, and was certainly to be found there in the second century A.D. In Mauretania, another area of early Jewish settlement, the citron was intensively cultivated at the beginning of the Christian era, and the tree appeared in Italy about the middle of the first century A.D. While the citron occasionally appeared in non-Jewish art of the period, it was many times more frequent in Jewish art—so much so, in fact, that its presence in non-Jewish art is considered a sign of Judaizing influences. While citrus cultivation died out in the centuries immediately following the fall of the Roman Empire and was not revived until the Arabs reintroduced it, the citron, despite great difficulties, continued to be grown because it fulfilled a religious obligation for a segment of the Mediterranean population.

Paradoxically, it was in the thirteenth and fourteenth centuries A.D., when the Jews had long since ceased to be numbered among the leading arboriculturists and horticulturists of Mediterranean Europe, that their influence on the distribution of centers of citron production became most marked. For a combination of reasons the Jews ceased to grow citron—partly because centers of Jewish population moved northward outside areas of possible citron production and partly because increasing legal restrictions were imposed upon Jewish landholding. It was precisely because Jews had to rely upon non-Jewish cultivation of citron that conflicts arose among the Jews concerning the conditions under which citron in given areas was produced. According to Rabbinic law, which derives its prohibition from a command in Leviticus 19:19 against sowing together diverse seeds, grafting is forbidden. In the case of the citron, grafting was considered peculiarly abhorrent since it meant that a forbidden object was used for a holy purpose.

The Italian Source for Citron

In the fourteenth century Italy was the source of citron for the Jews of Europe. So important had citron become that in 1329 victorius Guelph Florence prohibited the Republic of Pisa from engaging in the trade of citron and allocated to itself this lucrative export. Travel grants were obtained by Jews in other lands to procure citron in Italy; in 1389, for example, Archduke Albrecht III of Austria issued passports to Jewish merchants for this purpose.

By the middle of the sixteenth century the practice of grafting citron had become common in Italy. The rabbis took a firm stand against this development in emphasizing the prohibition against grafting. Noted Talmudic scholars and acknowledged authorities throughout European Jewry, such as Moses Alshech, prohibited the use of grafted etrogim, even though it might be impossible to distinguish grafted from ungrafted fruit on the basis of physical appearance. Similarly Samuel Katzenellenbogen of Padua, in the sixteenth century, forbade the use of grafted citron.

Within Italy itself there were, in the mid-sixteenth century, two major sources for etrogim. The region of Padua served primarily Jewish communities north of the Alps, while Apulia served Jewish communities in Italy itself, especially in times of scarcity in the crop from Padua. The prevalence of grafting, the difficulty of distinguishing the grafted from the ungrafted fruit, and the lack of alternative sources induced a minority of rabbinic authorities to allow the use of grafted citron in cases where it proved impossible to obtain the true etrog. Nonetheless the unreliability of etrogim, from Apulia especially, led to Jewish avoidance of this source and the eventual death of the citron industry there. Despite the presence of grafting, citron from northern Italy continued to be used up to the nineteenth century because Jews living in this region were able to detect the signs of the grafted fruit in their own area and avoided purchasing or exporting ritually unacceptable fruit.

Italian etrogim were sent northward by two main routes: On the route regularly used by the Levant trade via Bolzano (Bozen) and Innsbruck to Germany, and from the head of the Adriatic Sea through the Pear Tree Pass to Ljubljana (Laibach) and from there to Maribor (Marburg) and on to Wiener Neustadt. Transport of etrogim was a difficult matter because each fruit had to remain perfect in order to be ritually acceptable. The availability of markets along the route facilitated the trader's task.

The Shift to New Areas of Citron Production

By the seventeenth century, trade with Apulia had ceased and new sources of supply had been tapped. Jewry north of the Alps and northeast of Dalmatia obtained citron from areas of production which may be divided into two groups: Catalonia and the Balearic Islands, especially Majorca; the coast and islands of the Ligurian and Tyrrhenian seas, especially Corsica, Elba, and Sicily, and, on the mainland, the Riviera di Ponente and Riviera di Genoa, Campania, and Calabria. Genoa and San Remo acted as major points of assembly for the fruit from both these regional groupings and the fruit was then shipped north to the communities beyond the Alps. While the disrepute into which the citron of Apulia had fallen tended to cast doubt upon etrogim from southern Italy as a whole, proximity to the market explains in part the prolonged existence of citron groves as far north as Lago di Garda's Riviera di Salo, especially around Limone, where, despite climatic difficulty in maintaining orchards, the citron was grown extensively until the middle of the nineteenth century. A third major grouping began to emerge as a source for citron, although it did not assume major proportions until the nineteenth century. This was in the east, from the Adriatic shores of the Ottoman Empire and from the Venetian-held Ionian Islands, especially Corfu, Cephalonia, and Zante. Venice channeled the trade from these areas.

The Ottoman Monopoly

The emergence of the Adriatic shores of the Ottoman Empire as a major source for etrogim at the turn of the nineteenth century came in part because trade in the fruit was a state monopoly of the Porte, which maintained strict control over the purity of the stock. Attention of the Jews had turned to the Ottoman Adriatic as a result of the difficulty which developed in obtaining citron from the second major regional grouping we have described. The citrons of Corsica and Elba especially, which were imported via Genoa, had long been held in the highest esteem, for here the fruit grew in wild and indisputably ungrafted profusion. The First Republic of France and the swift rise of Napoleon had the effect of hardening boundary lines between French and Austrian possessions, so that Jews in Austrian territories, including such major Jewish concentrations as Austrian Galicia and Poland, and the Jews in Russia and the Russian-held territories of Poland and Baltic Samogitia, Courland, and Livonia had to rely largely on Adriatic sources for their supply of etrogim. Trieste took the place of Genoa as the great entrepôt port for citron. Official supervision of the growing of citron in the coastal areas of Ottoman Albania and Epirus, especially in the orchards of Parga, Ayia, and several other villages of the provinces of Thesprotia and Preveza, allowed the etrogim from this area to achieve as high a reputation among the Jews as that formerly enjoyed by the citrons of Corsica. The importance of the Ottoman Adriatic spelled the further decline of the Italian citron.

Decline of the "Corfu Etrog"

The seeds of the next shift came with the abandonment of the Sultan's monopoly of citron cultivation. By 1843 the growing and sale of citron was open to anyone interested in the fruit. The explanation for the state's giving up a monopoly which provided an excellent source of income may well have lain in the very fact of its lucrative character. Ottoman control over the Adriatic coast territories was never wholly successful, and when the local population became aware of the profit to be derived from trade in citron, it is likely that in defiance of the state monopoly they began to grow and trade in the fruit themselves. Official abandonment of the citron monopoly was, in all probability, merely the acceptance of a long since accomplished fact.

For the Jews the significance of these developments lay in the growing impossibility of distinguishing between grafted and ungrafted fruit exported from this region. The Sultan's groves were concentrated in Parga, but to the Jews the fruit from all the orchards in the region was known as the "Corfu etrog," for Corfu channelled the trade from the Ottoman Adriatic to Trieste. With the end of the monopoly, all the fruit from the region, including now most of Albania, the Ionian Islands, and Corfu itself, was exported under the name, and accorded the local rabbinical certification of the "Corfu etrog."

This situation gave rise to a great and heated controversy which did not end until the substantial abandonment of the region as a source for etrogim. European rabbis argued that local certification from Corfu was meaningless, since neither from superficial inspection nor on the basis of the botanical knowledge of the time could the grafted be distinguished from the ungrafted citron sent into Corfu and Trieste. The rabbis in both places were accused of self-interest in giving their certification indiscriminately under pressure from the local community which stood to gain from the trade.

One after another the rabbis of important Jewish communities on the traditional trade routes from Trieste to northeastern Europe banned the Corfu etrog. From opposite ends of the Austrian Empire—from Brod, in Austria Slavonia close to the border of Ottoman Bosnia, to Brody, at the time an Austro-Polish town near the Russian border—prohibitions were issued against the use of the Corfu etrog. These were duplicated by leading rabbis in Vienna, Cracow, Kishinev, and Jasi, as well as in other Jewish centers. Unfortunately, while the majority of important rabbis of western as well as eastern Europe united to ban the Corfu etrog, rabbinic opinion was not unanimous, nor, for that matter, were the masses of eastern European Jewry obedient to rabbinic authority. Hasidism had taken firm root primarily in Russia and Poland, and for these people the word of their own leaders had primary authority. Many of these Hasidic leaders, who, in the opinion of their flock, derived their authority from mystical intuition, maintained that the Corfu etrog was the divinely acceptable one.

However, while early rabbinic bans were only partially effective, the decline of the Corfu etrog was hastened by the sharp practices of the Corfiote merchants, who were anxious to profit further from an already profitable trade. Coming into contact with Hasidic Jews, these merchants formed an exaggerated view of the importance of the Corfu etrog to their Jewish market. They believed that Jewish superstition held that if a Corfu etrog was not used for the Feast of Booths, the man would die the same year. With his very life at stake, the merchants reasoned that the Jew would surely be willing to pay any price for the fruit. Accordingly they resorted to the practice of dumping the fruit into the sea to force up the price, and etrogim became prohibitively expensive.

In the 30-year period following 1846, when the first important series of bans against the Corfu etrog had been issued, more and more rabbis and with increasing effectiveness joined in the ban. In peaceful mid-nineteenth century Europe there were no longer difficulties in obtaining the Corsican citron, and this or the Palestinian, Moroccan, Campanian, Calabrian, and Portuguese citron were recommended by the rabbis. These alternatives would probably have been accepted more readily if the Corfu etrog had not greatly surpassed the others in appearance. Even those rabbis who were most doubtful of its ritual acceptability conceded that the alternative fruits could not compare to it in beauty. By 1875 we have indications that rabbinic bans, which may well have been aided by the rise in the cost of the Corfu etrog, had become highly effective, especially in those areas where Hasidism was not strong. In the Baltic provinces, for example, the Corfu etrog now found no market.

But the virtual death blow to the citron industry channelled through Corfu came as a result of the wave of persecution suffered by the island's Jewish inhabitants. Under Napoleon, civil equality had been granted to the Jews, but, under English and subsequently under Greek rule, intermittent outbreaks against them occurred. These came to a head with the pogrom of 1891, which produced a violent reaction in Jews throughout the world. It became exceedingly difficult to obtain buyers for the Corfu etrog in Europe and, as far from the scene as the United States, where traders concentrated their efforts, pamphlets urged the American Jew to boycott the fruit. The importers were described as "traders in the blood of Israel," who "since there is hardly a man in Europe who will touch them bought these etrogim dripping with the blood of the children of Zion."

Rise of the Palestinian Citron

Morocco, Tunisia, Corsica, and Calabria continued to be sources for etrogim and have remained so until the present day. There has been one major addition—Palestine, now Israel, which has become the most important single producer in the Mediterranean. The rise of the Palestine etrog coincided with the decline of that of Corfu. Etrogim were, of course grown from ancient times in Palestine and individual citron reached European Jewish dignitaries, but there was no significant trade until the latter part of the nineteenth century.

The chief impediment to widespread acceptance of the Palestinian etrog in Europe was the prevalence of grafting there as in Europe. A number of citron groves had been established in the coastal plain near Jaffa by foreign non-Jewish investors who grew the fruit for its commercial uses. Citron oil is an ingredient in some perfumes and the citron was also considered to possess medicinal properties. Sefardim, largely Jews of Spanish and North African descent, who held no deep convictions on the subject of grafting, in 1875 began to take advantage of the presence of these orchards to send citron to Europe for use in the Feast of Booths. Such practices, which were discovered by European Jews, almost killed Palestinian etrog exports in their inception.

The industry was saved by the presence in the interior around Um el Fahm on the southern slopes of Wadi Arah (Nahal Eron—ca. 10 miles southwest of Afula) and at Lifta, about 2.5 miles northwest of Jerusalem, and at Alma ca. 6 miles north of Safad of wild, untended groves held in high regard by the orthodox Jewish community of Jerusalem. Certain Jerusalem merchants undertook to make the Um el Fahm etrog a commercial product by transforming the wild groves into carefully cultivated orchards. They also undertook a publicity campaign to familiarize European Jews with these etrogim and to distinguish them in the public mind from the grafted etrogim of Jaffa exported by the Sefardim. In the process they established to the satisfaction of the majority of Jews the ritual acceptability of most untended citron groves, such as those of Lifta and Alma, outside the coastal plain of Palestine. To the Jews of Palestine, who were attempting to build up a Jewish agriculture, the development of the citron industry was of inestimable value because the fruit had a guaranteed overseas market. Further, the citron provided experience in the cultivation and export of one type of citrus product, an experience to prove of value in the subsequent development of large scale production of other types of citrus fruits. While Israel is the main producer of etrogim today, the citron nonetheless constitutes a minor percentage of the state's total citrus output.[2]

[2] Before World War II an average of 60,000 units were exported annually from Palestine. Due to the annihilation of European Jewry exports have been reduced since the war and fluctuated between 25,000 to 30,000 units annually. H. Oppenheimer, "Etrog," (Hebrew) *Encyclopaedia Hebraica*, Jerusalem, 1954, p. 491; *Israel Weekly Digest*, October 9, 1957.

The Religious Impact

We have shown that the present day location of citron groves in the Mediterranean; in Italy in the Calabrian province of Cosenza, and in the Campania of Salerno and Potenza; in Greek Epirus; in Corsica; and in North Africa has been influenced to a large degree by religious considerations. The historic shifts in the location of the industry, from Apulia to Calabria, from Corsica to Parga, Corfu, and the Ionian Islands, and then back to the western Mediterranean, mainly the Tyrrhenian islands and coasts, and finally the addition of Palestine were not primarily economically induced. Economic forces tend to bring an horticultural industry as close as possible to its markets, but as Jewish centers were concentrated ever more to the north and east of the Mediterranean, growing areas of citron shifted most inconveniently in relation to established trade routes.

The fact that religion has played a considerable role in the location of present day citron groves does not mean that citron today depends upon a Jewish market. With the virtual destruction of the Jewish communities of Europe during World War II, Europe ceased to be a significant market for etrogim. The Feast of Booths, moreover, has ceased to be an important holiday for the great majority of Jews. Its ritual celebration is confined to observant Jews, who are a small minority in Israel as well as in the Jewish Diaspora. Paradoxically, it is for this reason that religious influences continue to shape the location of citron groves within the state of Israel. In a society where there is prevailing indifference to traditional orthodox standards, and indeed often open hostility to them, the orthodox Jew has grown to prefer citron produced in villages or cooperative villages where an orthodox population is concentrated or where it is a substantial landowning minority, as at Petah Tiqva, Rehovot, Hadera, Ness Ziona, and Kfar Haroeh. Thus present citron groves in Israel are almost exclusively in those orthodox enclaves where citron growing is climatically possible.

Although citron production outside Israel is no longer primarily directed to a Jewish market, this market is still a factor in as much as there are minority groups within orthodox Jewry, even in Israel, which prefer, on traditional grounds, citron from Calabria, Corfu, Morocco, and Tunisia. Corsican production, in particular, has experienced a marked increase since World War II.

At the present time the greater part of citron production is used for candied citron peel. Since grafted trees tend to produce better fruit with greater immunity to plant diseases, grafting is almost universal. The growth of the citron industry in the western hemisphere, as, for example, in the Caribbean and in Latin America, owes nothing to religious influences. But though the religious need of the Jews, historically so decisive, has since World War II played a minor role in the citron industry as a whole, this need will continue to have some influence upon the future of the Mediterranean citron. Ungrafted groves, in particular, will owe their persistence to the Jewish market.

19. The Negro Ghetto: Problems and Alternatives

Richard L. Morrill

Minority groups, both ethnic and racial, have been a major component in shaping the spatial character of cities in both the United States and the rest of the world. Large concentrations of Italians and Jews are found in New York; Poles, in Detroit; Swedes and Norwegians, in Minneapolis-St. Paul; and Chinese, in San Francisco. The distinctive cultural backgrounds of these peoples have endured, and in many cases their homes have spread beyond the original areas of settlement.

Negroes in the United States, for example, live in most urban as well as rural areas in the South. They are often concentrated in the poorest sections of a city, and as their numbers increase they encroach upon nearby housing and commercial areas. Characteristically, the whites have moved to other parts of the city or the suburbs to avoid this encroachment. In this article, Morrill demonstrates effectively how the diffusion process of the Negro takes place in Seattle, a sample city. He also shows the value of diffusion analysis to the geographer, particularly the manner in which predictions can be made of future movements of Negroes within a city.

"Ghettos," as we must realistically term the segregated areas occupied by Negroes and other minority groups, are common features of American urban life. The vast majority of Negroes, Japanese, Puerto Ricans, and Mexican-Americans are forced by a variety of pressures to reside in restricted areas, in which they themselves are dominant. So general

SOURCE: *Geographical Journal*, IV (July, 1965), 339–81. The author is associate professor of geography, University of Washington.

is this phenomenon that not one of the hundred largest urban areas can be said to be without ghettos.

Inferiority in almost every conceivable material respect is the mark of the ghetto. But also, to the minority person, the ghetto implies a rejection, a stamp of inferiority, which stifles ambition and initiative. The very fact of residential segregation reinforces other forms of discrimination by preventing the normal contacts through which prejudice may be gradually overcome. Yet because the home and the neighborhood are so personal and intimate, housing will be the last and most difficult step in the struggle for equal rights.

The purpose here is to trace the origin of the ghetto and the forces that perpetuate it and to evaluate proposals for controlling it. The Negro community of Seattle, Washington, is used in illustration of a simple model of ghetto expansion as a diffusion process into the surrounding white area.

From the beginning of the nineteenth century the newest immigrants were accustomed to spend some time in slum ghettos of New York, Philadelphia, or Boston. But as their incomes grew and their English improved they moved out into the American mainstream, making way for the next group. During the nineteenth century the American Negro population, in this country from the beginning but accustomed to servitude, remained predominantly southern and rural. Relatively few moved to the North, and those who did move lived in small clusters about the cities. The Negro ghetto did not exist. Even in southern cities the Negroes, largely in the service of whites, lived side by side with the white majority. Rather suddenly, with the social upheaval and employment opportunities of World War I, Negro discontent grew, and large-scale migration began from the rural south to the urban north, to Philadelphia, New York, Chicago, and St. Louis, and beyond.

The influx was far larger than the cities could absorb without prejudice. The vision of a flood of Negroes, uneducated and unskilled, was frightening both to the whites and to the old-time Negro residents. As the poorest and newest migrants, the Negroes were forced to double up in the slums that had already been created on the periphery of business and industrial districts. The pattern has never been broken. Just as one group was becoming settled, another would follow, placing ever greater pressure on the limited area of settlement, and forcing expansion into neighboring areas, being emptied from fear of inundation. Only in a few cities, such as Minneapolis–St. Paul and Providence and other New England cities, has the migration been so small *and* so gradual that the Negro could be accepted into most sections as an individual.

America has experienced four gigantic streams of migration: the European immigration, which up to 1920 must have brought thirty million or more; the westward movement, in which from 1900 to the

present close to ten million persons have participated; the movement
from the farms to the cities, which since 1900 has attracted some thirty
million; and the migration of Negroes to the North and West, which
has amounted since World War I to about five million, including some
three million between 1940 and 1960 (Table 1). The pace has not

TABLE 1. Major Destinations of Net 3,000,000 Negroes Moving North, 1940–
1960 (*Estimates only*)

New York	635,000	Washington, D. C.	201,000
Chicago	445,000	San Francisco	130,000
Los Angeles	260,000	Cleveland	120,000
Detroit	260,000	St. Louis	118,000
Philadelphia	255,000	Baltimore	115,000

TABLE 2. Minority Populations of Major Urbanized Areas, United States,
1960

City	Minority Population	Total Population	Minority %
1. New York City	2,271,000	14,115,000	16
Negro	1,545,000		
Puerto Rican	671,000		
2. Los Angeles	1,233,000	6,489,000	19
Negro	465,000		
Mexican	629,000		
Asian	120,000		
3. Chicago	1,032,000	5,959,000	17
4. Philadelphia	655,000	3,635,000	18
5. Detroit	560,000	3,538,000	16
6. San Francisco	519,000	2,430,000	21
7. Washington, D. C.	468,000	1,808,000	26
8. Baltimore	346,000	1,419,000	24
9. Houston	314,000	1,140,000	28
10. San Antonio	303,000	642,000	47
11. St. Louis	287,000	1,668,000	17
12. Cleveland–Lorain	279,000	1,928,000	15
13. New Orleans	265,000	845,000	31
14. Dallas–Fort Worth	252,000	1,435,000	18
15. Atlanta	207,000	768,000	27
16. Birmingham	201,000	521,000	38
17. Memphis	200,000	545,000	37

SOURCES: Census of Population, 1960: Vol. 1, Chap. C, *General Social and Economic Characteristics;* Vol. 2, *Subject Reports: Nonwhite Population by Race.*

abated. Contributing also to the ghetto population have been 900,000 Puerto Ricans, who came between 1940 and 1960, largely to New York City; about 1,500,000 Mexicans, descendants of migrants to the farms and cities of the Southwest; and smaller numbers of Chinese, Japanese, and others. Economic opportunity has been the prime motivation for all these migrant groups, but for the Negro there was the additional hope of less discrimination.

The rapidity and magnitude of the Negro stream not only have increased the intensity and size of ghettos in the North but no doubt have also accelerated the white "flight to the suburbs" and have strongly affected the economic, political, and social life of the central cities. In the South, too, Negroes have participated in the new and rapid urbanization, which has been accompanied by increased ghettoization and more rigid segregation.

As a result of these migrations, the present urban minority population consists, in the North and West, of 7.5 million Negroes and 4 million others, together 12.5 percent of the total regional urban population; in the South, of 6.5 million Negroes, 20 percent; in total, of 18 million, 14 percent. The proportion is increasing in the North, decreasing in the South. Minority populations in large American cities are presented in Table 2.

The Nature of the Ghetto

If we study the minority population in various cities, we can discern real differences in income, education, occupational structure, and quality of homes. For example, median family income of Negroes ranges from $2600 in Jackson, Mississippi, to $5500 in Seattle; and as a proportion of median white family income, from 46 percent to 80 percent respectively. The United States median family income for Negroes in urban areas is only $3700, as compared with $6400 for whites, but it is more than double the figure for Negroes still living in rural areas, $1750. It is not hard, therefore, to understand the motivation for Negro migration to the northern cities, where striking progress has really been made.

But the stronger impression is of those general characteristics which are repeated over and over. The ghetto system is dual: not only are Negroes excluded from white areas, but whites are largely absent from Negro areas. Areas entirely or almost exclusively white or nonwhite are the rule, areas of mixture the exception. The ghettos, irrespective of regional differences, are always sharply inferior to white areas; home ownership is less and the houses are older, less valuable, more crowded, and more likely to be substandard. More than 30 percent of Negro urban housing is dilapidated or without indoor plumbing, as compared with less than 15 percent for whites. The ghetto is almost always in a zone peripheral to the central business district, often containing formerly elegant houses intermingled with commercial and light industrial uses. As poor, unskilled labor, Negroes settled near the warehouses and the railroads, sometimes in shacktowns, and gradually took over the older central houses being abandoned by the most recent segregated groups—for example, the Italians and the Jews—as their rise in economic status enabled them to move farther out. More than one ghetto may appear on different sides of the business district, perhaps separated by ridges of wealthy, exclusive houses or apartments.

The Negro differs fundamentally from these earlier groups, and from the Mexicans and Puerto Ricans as well. As soon as economic and educational improvements permit, the lighter-skinned members of the other groups may escape the ghetto, but black skin constitutes a qualitative difference in the minds of whites, and even the wealthy Negro rarely finds it possible to leave the ghetto. Color takes precedence over the normal determinants of our associations.

In the southern city Negroes have always constituted a large proportion of the population and have traditionally occupied sections or

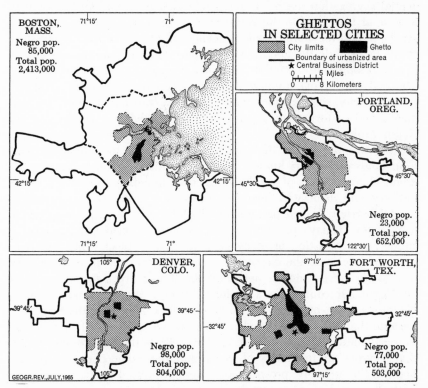

FIGURE 1: A group of representative ghettos. The dashed-line boundary on the Boston map indicates the inner urbanized area. Source: 1960 census data.

wedges, extending from the center of the city out into the open country. Indeed, around some cities, such as Charleston, South Carolina, the outer suburban zone is largely Negro. Figure 1 depicts the ghetto pattern for selected cities.

The impact of the ghetto on the life of its residents is partly well known, partly hidden. The white person driving through is struck by the poverty, the substandard housing, the mixture of uses, and the dirt; he is likely to feel that these conditions are due to the innate character of the Negro. The underlying fact is, of course, that Negroes on the average are much poorer, owing partly to far inferior educational opportunities in most areas, but more to systematic discrimination in employment, which is only now beginning to be broken. Besides pure poverty, pressure of the influx into most northern cities itself induces deterioration: formerly elegant houses, abandoned by whites, have had to be divided and redivided to accommodate the newcomers, maintenance is almost impossible, much ownership is by absentee whites. Public services, such as street maintenance and garbage collection, and amenities, such as parks and playgrounds, are often neglected. Residential segregation means de facto school segregation. Unemployment is high, at least double the white average, and delinquency and crime are the almost inevitable result. A feeling of inferiority and hopelessness comes to pervade the ghetto. Most important is the enormous waste of human resources in the failure to utilize Negroes to reasonable capacity. The real cost of maintaining the ghetto system is fantastic. In direct costs the city spends much more in crime prevention, welfare payments, and so forth than it can collect. The ghetto is the key to the Negro problem.

What are the forces that operate to maintain the ghetto system? Four kinds of barriers hinder change: prejudice of whites against Negroes; characteristics of the Negroes; discrimination by the real-estate industry and associated financial institutions; and legal and governmental barriers. Naked prejudice is disclaimed by a majority of Americans today. Today's prejudice is not an outright dislike; it is, rather, a subtle fear, consisting of many elements. The typical white American may now welcome the chance to meet a Negro, but he is afraid that if a Negro moves into his neighborhood it will break up and soon be all Negro. Of course, on a national average there are not as many Negroes as that—only one or two families to a block—but the fear exists because that is the way the ghetto has grown. A greater fear is of loss in social status if Negroes move in. This reflects the culture-bred notion that Negroes are inherently of lower standing. Some persons are terrified at the unlikely prospect of intermarriage. Finally, people are basically afraid of, or uncertain about, people who are different, especially in any obvious physical way. These fears combine into powerful controls to maintain segregation: refusal to sell to Negroes, so as not to offend the neighbors; and the tendency to move out as soon as a Negro enters, in order not to lose status by association.

The Negro himself contributes, however unwillingly, to ghettoization. It is difficult to be a minority as a group, but more difficult still to be a minority alone. Consequently the desire to escape the ghetto and move freely in the larger society is tempered by a realization of the problems in store for the "pioneer" and hesitancy to cut neighborhood ties with his own kind. Few people have such courage. In most cities, even if there were no housing discrimination, the ghetto would still persist, simply because a large proportion of Negroes could not afford, or would be afraid, to leave. Most Negroes achieve status and acceptance only within the Negro community. Usually Negroes who leave the ghetto prefer Negro neighbors; the risk is that this number, however small, is enough to initiate the conversion to full-scale ghetto.

The Negro today suffers from his past. The lack of initiative and the family instability resulting from generations of enforced or inculcated subservience and denial of normal family formation are still present and are a barrier to white acceptance. The far lower levels of Negro income and education, no matter how much they are due to direct neglect and discrimination by the white majority, are nevertheless a strong force to maintain the ghetto. Studies show that whites will accept Negroes of equivalent income, education, and occupation.

The strongest force, however, in maintaining the ghetto may well be real-estate institutions: the real-estate broker and sources of financing. It has always been, and continues to be, the clear-cut, official, and absolute policy of the associations of real-estate brokers that "a realtor should never be instrumental in introducing into a neighborhood a character of property or occupancy, members of any race or nationality, or any individuals whose presence will clearly be detrimental to property values in that neighborhood." Many studies have attempted to resolve this problem. In the long run, property values and rents exhibit little if any change in the transition from white to Negro occupancy.[1] Sales prices may fall temporarily under panic selling, a phenomenon called the "self-fulfilling prophecy"—believing that values will fall, the owner panics and sells, and thus depresses market values.

The real-estate industry opposes with all its resources not only all laws but any device, such as cooperative apartments or open-occupancy advertising, to further integration. Real-estate and home-building in-

[1] Luigi Mario Laurenti: Property Values and Race: Studies in 7 Cities: Special Research Report to the Commission on Race and Housing (Berkley, 1960); [Homer Hoyt:] The Structure and Growth of Residential Neighborhoods in American Cities (Federal Housing Administration, Washington, D.C., 1939); Lloyd Rodwin: The theory of Residential Growth and Structure, *Appraisal Journ.*, Vol. 18, 1950, pp. 295–317.

dustries base this policy on the desirability of neighborhood homogeneity and compatibility. Perhaps underlying the collective action is
the fear of the individual real-estate broker that if he introduces a
Negro into a white area he will be penalized by withdrawal of business.
There is, then, a real business risk to the individual broker in a policy
of integration, if none to the industry as a whole. Segregation is maintained by refusal of real-estate brokers even to show, let alone sell,
houses to Negroes in white areas. Countless devices are used: quoting
excessive prices, saying the house is already sold, demanding unfair
down payments, removing "For sale" signs, not keeping appointments,
and so on. Even if the Negro finds someone willing to sell him a house
in a white area, financing may remain a barrier. Although his income
may be sufficient, the bank or savings institution often refuses to provide
financing from a fear of Negro income instability, and of retaliatory
withdrawal of deposits by whites. If financing is offered, the terms
may be prohibitive. Similar circumstances may also result when a white
attempts to buy a house—for *his* residence—in a heavily minority area.

Through the years many legal procedures have been used to maintain segregation. Early in the century races were zoned to certain areas,
but these laws were abolished by the courts in 1917. The restrictive
covenant, in which the transfer of property contained a promise not to
sell to minorities, became the vehicle and stood as legal until 1948, since
when more subtle and extralegal restrictions have been used.

Until 1949 the federal government was a strong supporter of residential segregation, since the Federal Housing Administration required
racial homogeneity in housing it financed or insured. As late as 1963,
when the President by Executive order forbade discrimination in FHA-
financed housing, the old philosophy still prevailed in most areas.
Finally, many states, and not just those in the South, still encourage
separation. Even in the few states with laws against discrimination in
housing, the combined forces for maintaining segregation have proved
by far the stronger.

The Process of Ghetto Expansion

The Negro community in the North has grown so rapidly in the last
forty years, almost doubling in every decade, that even the subdivision
of houses cannot accommodate the newcomers. How does the ghetto
expand? Along its edge the white area is also fairly old and perhaps
deteriorating. Many whites would be considering a move to the suburbs
even if the ghetto were not there, and fears of deterioration of schools
and services, and the feeling that all the other whites will move out,
reinforce their inclination to move. Individual owners, especially in
blocks adjoining the ghetto, may become anxious to sell. Pressure of

Negro buyers and fleeing white residents, who see the solid ghetto a block or two away, combine to scare off potential white purchasers; the owner's resistance gradually weakens; and the transfer is made.

The role of proximity is crucial. On adjacent blocks the only buyers will be Negroes, but five or six blocks away white buyers will still be the rule. In a typical ghetto fringe in Philadelphia the proportion of white buyers climbed from less than 4 percent adjacent to the ghetto itself to 100 percent five to seven blocks away. Figure 2 illustrates the great concentration of initial entry of new street fronts in a band of two or three blocks around a ghetto. The "break" zone contains 5 percent or fewer Negroes, but 60 percent of the purchases are by Negroes. Typically, a white on the edge does not mind one or two Negroes on the block or across the street, but if a Negro moves next door the white is likely to move out. He is replaced by a Negro, and the evacuation-replacement process continues until the block has been solidly trans-

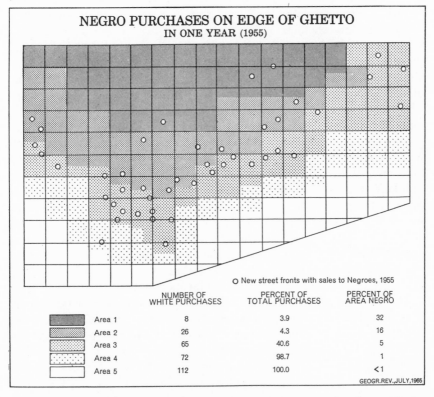

NEGRO PURCHASES ON EDGE OF GHETTO
IN ONE YEAR (1955)

O New street fronts with sales to Negroes, 1955

		NUMBER OF WHITE PURCHASES	PERCENT OF TOTAL PURCHASES	PERCENT OF AREA NEGRO
	Area 1	8	3.9	32
	Area 2	26	4.3	16
	Area 3	65	40.6	5
	Area 4	72	98.7	1
	Area 5	112	100.0	< 1

GEOGR.REV.,JULY,1965

FIGURE 2: Distribution of Negro purchases on the edge of the ghetto, showing initial entry of street fronts, 1955. Adapted from diagram in Rapkin and Grigsby, The Demand for Housing in Racially Mixed Areas (see text footnote 11 for reference) p. 76.

ferred from white to Negro residence. Expansion of the ghetto is thus a block-by-block total transition.

In this process the real-estate agent is also operative. If the demand for Negro housing can be met in the area adjacent to the ghetto, pressure to move elsewhere in the city will diminish. The real-estate industry thus strongly supports the gradual transition along the periphery. After the initial break the real-estate broker encourages whites to sell. The transition is often orderly, but the unscrupulous dealer sometimes encourages panic selling at deflated prices, purchasing the properties himself and reselling them to Negroes for windfall profits. The probability of finding a white seller is high in the blocks adjacent to the ghetto but falls off rapidly at greater distances, as whites try to maintain familiar neighborhood patterns and conceive this to be possible if the Negro proportion can be kept small. The process of transition is destructive to both groups, separately and together. Whites are in a sense "forced" to sell, move, and see their neighborhoods disband, and Negroes are forced to remain isolated; and total transition reinforces prejudice and hinders healthy contact.

Spread of the Negro ghetto can be described as a *spatial diffusion* process, in which Negro migrants gradually penetrate the surrounding white area. From some origin, a block-by-block substitution or diffusion of a new condition—that is, Negro for white occupancy—takes place. The Negro is the active agent; he can move easily within the ghetto and can, though with difficulty, "pioneer" outside it. The white is passive, an agent of resistance or inertia. Resistance against escape of Negroes from the ghetto takes two forms: rebuff of attempts to buy; and diminishing willingness to sell with increasing distance from areas or blocks that already have Negroes. On the average the Negro will have to try more than once to consummate a sale, or, conversely, the owner will have to be approached by more than one buyer. Once the block is broken, however, resistance falls markedly, and transition begins. Although a complete model would take into account that a few whites continue to purchase in transition areas, the rate is insufficient, the net flow clear-cut, and the transition inevitable.

The proposed diffusion model is of the probabilistic simulation type.[2] It is probabilistic rather than deterministic for several reasons. We do not have sufficient definite information concerning the motivations for specific house-to-house moves of particular persons, but only general ideas concerning the likelihood of movement and how far. We are not dealing with a large aggregate of migrants, but with only a few indi-

---

[2] Herbert A. Meyer, edit.: *Symposium on Monte Carlo Methods, Held at the University of Florida . . .* , March 16–17, 1954 (New York and London, 1956); Everette M. Rogers: *Diffusion of Innovations* (New York, 1962); Warren C. Scoville: "Minority Migrations and the Diffusion of Technology," *Journ. of Econ. History,* Vol. 11, 1951, pp. 347–360.

viduals in a short period of time in a small area. If we had a thousand migrants, we could safely predict how many would move how far, but at the micro-level a probabilistic approach is required to evaluate individual decisions in the face of a complex of possible choices. Rather than determine that a specific migrant moves from one particular house to another, we find the probability of a typical migrant's move from a block to any and all other blocks, and we use random numbers to decide which destination, among the many possible, he chooses. We thus obtain a spatial pattern of moves, which spreads settlement into new blocks and intensifies it in old blocks.

. . . . .

Alternatives to the Ghetto

The model attempted merely to identify the process of ghetto expansion and thus helps only indirectly in the evaluation of measures to control the ghetto. We know that such a diffusion process is common in nature— the growth from an origin or origins of something new or different within a parent body. Reduction of this phenomenon would seem to require a great weakening of the distinction between groups, here Negroes and whites, either naturally through new conceptions of each other or artificially by legal means.

In ghetto expansion the process is reduced to replacement of passive white "deserters" by active Negro migrants. Is there an alternative that would permit the integration of minorities in the overall housing market and prevent the further spread and consolidation of ghettos? Is it possible to achieve stable interracial areas, in which white purchasers, even after Negro entry, are sufficiently numerous to maintain a balance acceptable to both? Three factors have been found crucial: proximity to a ghetto; proportions of white and nonwhite; and preparation of the neighborhood for acceptance of Negro entry. Proximity to a ghetto almost forbids a stable interracial situation. Fear of inundation either panics or steels white residents. Only wealthy areas can maintain any interracial character in such a location, since few, if any, Negroes can afford to enter. Negroes entering areas remote from the ghetto are more easily accepted (after initial difficulties), because the great body of Negroes does not "threaten" neighborhood structures.

The proportion of Negroes in an area is critical for continued white purchasing. Whites are willing to accept 5 percent to 25 percent (with a mean of 10 percent) Negro occupancy for a long time before beginning abandonment—depending on such factors as the characteristics of the Negroes moving in, the proximity of the ghetto, and the open-mindedness of the resident white population. On the other hand, although the Negro is accustomed to minority status, he usually prefers a larger proportion of his own group nearby than the critical 10 percent. Thus a fundamental dilemma arises, and there are in fact few interracial neighborhoods. For cities with low Negro ratios, say less than 10 percent, the long-run possibilities are encouraging, especially with the rise of Negro education and income, increased enforcement of nondiscrimination laws, and the more liberal views of youth today. For urban areas with high Negro ratios, such as Philadelphia, with 20 percent (40 percent in the city proper), it is difficult to imagine an alternative to the ghetto. The same conclusion holds for southern cities. No spatial arrangement, given present levels of prejudice, will permit so large a proportion of Negroes to be spread throughout the city without serious white reaction.

Private interracial projects have begun integration and have been successful and stable, if few in number. From these experiments it has been learned that white buyers in such developments are not unusually liberal but are a normal cross section. Also, the spatial arrangement that permits the largest stable proportion of nonwhites has been found to be a cluster pattern—small, compact colonies of a few houses—rather than dispersed isolates.[3] This makes possible easy contact within the minority group, but also good opportunity for interaction with the white group, while minimizing the frequency of direct neighbors, which few whites are as yet able to accept.

Integrated residential living will become more acceptable as Negroes achieve equality in education and employment, but housing integration will probably lag years or decades behind. At most we may expect an arrest of the extension of existing ghettos, their internal upgrading, and prevention of new ones. Experience certainly indicates a long wait for goodwill to achieve even internal improvement; hence a real reduction in ghettoization implies a governmental, not a voluntary, regulation of the urban land and housing market—that is, enforced open-housing ordinances. Everything short of that has already been tried.

The suggested model of diffusion-expansion still describes the dominant ghettoization pattern. In the future we may be able to recognize an alternative "colonization" model, in which small clusters of Negroes or other minorities break out of the ghetto and spread throughout the urban area under the fostering or protection of government.

[3] Reuel S. Amdur: "An Exploratory Study of 19 Negro Families in the Seattle Area Who Were First Negro Residents in White Neighborhoods, Of Their White Neighbors and of the Integration Process, Together with a Proposed Program to Promote Integration in Seattle" (unpublished Master's thesis in social work, University of Washington, 1962); Arnold M. Rose and others: "Neighborhood Reactions to Isolated Negro Residents: An Alternative to Invasion and Succession," *Amer. Sociol. Rev.*, Vol. 18, 1953, pp. 497–507; L. K. Northwood and E. A. T. Barth: *Neighborhoods in Transition: The New American Pioneers and Their Neighbors* (University of Washington, School of Social Work, Seattle), pp. 27–28.

20. Ideology and Culture Exemplified in Southwestern Michigan

Elaine M. Bjorklund

Decision-making by man creates the spatial organization of his world. The decisions made are often influenced by the cultural background of a people. Bjorklund suggests that culture may be described as consisting of three components— works, ways of life, and ideology—and further indicates that in well-established cultures the first two components are expressions of and are based in the third. "Ideology refers to the set of ideas, concepts, values, attitudes, and goals accepted by a group of people." The article illustrates how the ideology of a Dutch-Reformed community in southwestern Michigan influences the decision-making process and thus the patterns of human occupance in that area. The idea has applicability in many other parts of the world.

The discipline of geography has a distinctive contribution to make to the study of culture and culture processes. There is an important advantage in the fact that elements of a culture which reflect even intangible qualities can be mapped and analyzed. Examination of the spatial context and the relatedness of culture forms, features, and other expressions of people reflecting distinctive ways of life, yield evidence of the value of a geographical appraisal of culture. The purpose of this paper is to offer a statement about a geographic view of culture and culture process, and to demonstrate that ideology contains the fundamental bases from which decisions are made and distinctive ways of organizing area are derived. These ideas are illustrated by their application to a specific culture group, the Dutch-Reformed community of southwestern Michigan. The study of this group provides some insights into the culture process by which area and its occupants are transformed.

SOURCE: *Annals of the Association of American Geographers*, LIV (June, 1964), 227–41. The author (now Elaine M. Philbrick) was assistant professor of geography, Vassar College.

A Geographic View of Culture

For geographic purposes, culture may be described as consisting of three components: ideology, "works," and "ways of life." Already developed cultures may be defined geographically by the area containing expressions created by people from the culture as an outgrowth and reflection of their ideology, implemented through their ways of life and embodied in their works. Taking the last item first, as viewed in this perspective, the "works" of any given culture consist of all the resultant forms produced by living. These include the institutions and establishments within which a culture operates. Works also include less tangible forms, such as language and other means of communication and ideological expression. "Ways of life" is a phrase applied to the gamut of procedures people evolve to meet both their physical and spiritual needs. Both "ways of life" and "works" in well-established cultures are manifestations of, and have roots in, ideology. Ideology refers to the set of ideas, concepts, values, attitudes, and goals accepted by a group of people. Ideology constitutes the bases for making decisions and choices affecting the ways of life and works.

Processes of Cultural Appraisal

The ideological component of culture stems from the mental and spiritual life of man. Every group and its leaders constantly evaluate problems and circumstances confronting them by applying their ideology. Such continuing evaluation may be referred to as the "processes of cultural appraisal," and normally involve innovation, selection, and continuation. Ideology functions in every culture to give a framework for the conscientious activities of its members. Though some aspects of cultural appraisal are evolutionary, since they represent processes by which procedures may originate or be adapted from contact with others, not all three operate equally or simultaneously, and not all three have the same degree of importance in any given culture. In the early stages of formation of a system of culture, innovation and selection processes may dominate. Continuation processes become more effective as the group advances, its maturing culture stabilizes, and the group becomes transformed from early radicalism to older conservatism. Inasmuch as innovation, selection, and continuation processes result from different applications of mental creativity which implement culture change and lead to different concrete expressions of ideology in area, it may be deduced that all cultural features are subject in one way or another to these processes. These fundamental processes are set forth in Table 1.

As Table 1 shows, the three processes may lead to four types of evaluations and, thence, to five kinds of results. Those elements or traits

TABLE 1. Processes of Cultural Appraisal

Process	Evaluation	Result
1. Innovation	1. Acceptance	1. Innovations
		2. Additions
	2. Modification	3. Alterations
2. Selection	3. Rejection	4. Abandonments
3. Continuation	4. Reaffirmation	5. Retentions

not possessed by a group of people but appraised as valuable and representir a felt need may be added or may originate. These may be described as innovations or as additions, depending on their source. Traits, features, or culture complexes already existing in a culture are subject to selection processes which evaluate them as useful or unimportant, thereby modifying or rejecting earlier known elements resulting in altered or rejected features. Finally, when appraisal reveals continued usefulness, reaffirming the trait or complex, the result is that the item is retained. It is through these kinds of appraisals that matters of community concern are measured, tested, and compared for their fit and application to ideology and to culture as a whole, and are given geographic expression by the occupant group.

Furthermore, ideology is given spatial expression because it manifests itself in human establishments and institutions. The establishment or institution is an expression of human purpose and can be characterized accordingly. Every individual has a place in some organized unit, whether part of an indigenous majority or foreign minority culture, a parent or an off-shoot group, whatever his role within it. By studying the composite activities of people within organized units and by analyzing the interactions among them, one can perceive the functional relationships in a culture.

An Example of Ideology and Culture

Beginning with the hypothesis that ideology, as one of the major parts of culture, contains the bases for the organization of areas, the Dutch-Reformed communities of southwestern Michigan, a parent body of a religious sect in the United States, have been investigated. These people of Dutch-Reformed affiliation are said to constitute a particular culture because they have created a distinctive way of life within the American culture complex. They occupy approximately 444 square miles of Ottawa, Allegan, and Kent counties between Grand Rapids and Lake Michigan.

These people present an opportunity to examine the relevance to the geographic study of culture of a clearly formed and well-established ideology. Although there are only about 40,000 people in this parent colony, and although they represent only one of several Dutch-Reformed communities in the United States and Canada and only a very small culture group in the United States, their processes of cultural appraisal reveal findings which have wide application to other groups of people.

Several carefully prepared histories made it feasible to trace both the development and functional geographical relationships of this culture "island" within the general context of the American culture system. These works, coupled with the candid commentary and thoughtful responses of many Dutch-Reformed people to my inquiries, have contributed greatly to this paper.

Basic Ideology

The basic principles followed by the adherents to Dutch-Reformed ideology can be stated simply as follows: (1) there are particular rules governing the conduct of life which must be obeyed literally; (2) man is obliged by these rules to perform both physical and spiritual work; and (3) opposition or intrusion of conflicting rules of conduct cannot be tolerated, because life after death depends upon the literal conduct of life on earth on a principled basis and is not subject to individual interpretation.[1] These essentially conservative codes of life are moralistic beliefs in accordance with which all judgments concerning the conduct of daily affairs are made. Scrupulous devotion to these binding principles, their attendant values, beliefs, and practices, and the resulting institutional forms within the organization controlled by the group have enabled them to maintain their identity and their distinctive geographical pattern. Based on these three main principles which follow from the doctrine of Calvinism, cultural features of the landscape created by the Dutch-Reformed people may be identified as a direct outgrowth of their ideology. To the casual observer traveling through Michigan on state Highway 21, which cuts across the heart of Dutch-Reformed territory between Grand Rapids and Holland, Michigan, there are only subtle visible manifestations of the distinctive ideology. This indicates that, besides maintaining the distinctiveness of their own culture, they are also part of the larger American culture system. Nevertheless, there are important relationships connecting the small, neat, specialized farms

[1] These are the practical beliefs predicated on the doctrines of "unconditional election," "limited atonement," "total human depravity," "irresistible grace," and the "perseverance of the saints" as originally set forth by John Calvin and his followers in the Lowlands in 1556. The basic dogmatic expression of these beliefs was prepared by Guido de Bres in 1561 in *The Belgic Confession*. In 1563 the *Heidelberg Catechism* presented the Biblical creed which became one of the statements of doctrinal unity.

and churches whose lean spires punctuate the horizon to the basic principles of Calvinist beliefs which characterize the Dutch-Reformed ideology.

The substance of the study of this community of Dutch-Reformed people is presented in condensed form in Table 2. It shows the stuff out of which the main thesis of this study emerged, gleaned from many interviews and from living among the Dutch-Reformed people in Zeeland, Michigan. It also must be noted that the remainder of the presentation of material is geared to the organization set forth in Table 2. Ordering material this way helps clarify the potency of ideology in shaping a culture area.

The material in Table 2 is arranged in five columns. There are also 14 rows which are to be read from left to right in order to establish the relationships among the ideological principles (column I), specific ideas expressing the principles (column II), resulting events (column III), and a set of tangible geographic manifestations (column IV). It also will be found useful to read each column from top to bottom to gain insight into the diversity of ideas, responses, and spatial expressions of the culture. Column III supplies the "verbs" or activating events which serve to identify the ways in which ideas, beliefs, values, or goals of the culture have been translated in practice into geographic expressions recorded in different tangible forms, each according to its nature.

The last column (V) summarizes the cultural appraisal processes by which the specific geographic expressions were evolved from their first recorded occurrence to the present day. The materials in this table enable one to follow some of the choices and decisions by which particular elements of the culture have developed. The cultural appraisal referred to in column V is the perception and decision-making process of a people living within a framework of an established culture. The final section of the paper is devoted to a point-by-point discussion of items in columns I through V of Table 2 in the application of the processes of cultural appraisal to the Dutch-Reformed group in southwestern Michigan.

The first of the three components of culture, ideology, is the subject of columns I and II in Table 2. All fourteen of the specific items in column II are direct outgrowths of basic ideology. Ideas, values, attitudes, and goals are often not made explicit in a culture and are hard to pinpoint. Those set forth in the table may not be the only ones which can be identified for Dutch-Reformed culture, but it is proposed here that these are among the basic goals which are recognized by the group, and that these have been given geographic expression.

The column marked "events" (III) illustrates some of the reactions of the group to ideas; these represent actions that bridge the gap between ideas and their spatial expression. Although such events could

TABLE 2. Selected Dutch-Reformed Culture Traits Traced from Ideology to Geographic Expression

I Cultural components	II Ideology: made specific through ideas, beliefs, attitudes, values, and goals	III Events or circumstances	IV Geographic expression or impact	V CULTURAL APPRAISAL PROCESSES			
				New condition	Modified	Reaffirmed	Abandoned
Fundamental Ideological Principles i Obedience to rules governing the conduct of life	A Belief in Calvinist ideology and the desire to both practice and promote it.	1. The State Church of the Netherlands founded in 1816 by followers of Calvin (*Hermvorde Kerk*).		x			
		2. The secession state Church and formation of the Reformed Church in 1834.	a Institution which became known as the Reformed Church of America.	x			
ii Obligation to perform both physical and spiritual work		3. Dissent of a group rejecting liberalization of Reformed Church role in 1872.	a Creation of institution known as Christian Reformed Church.	x			
iii Principled basis for Christian life which is not subject to change	B Protection and control of religion (ideology) and the way of life derived from it.	1. Decision to emigrate from the Netherlands in 1846.	a Formation of a "Kolonie."	x			
		2. "Kolonie" selection of southwestern Michigan for settlement in 1846.	a Settlement takes place on shore of Lake Michigan around Macatawa (Black) Lake.	x			

3. Building in Michigan of church-centered communities named after home provinces in the Netherlands.

   a Main center called Holland, others: *Zeeland, Vreisland, Drenthe, the Overisel, Noord Holland, Noordeloos, Groningen, Grafschap.*   x

   b Settlement organized by congregations (consistories) under the leadership of *dominies.*

4. Purchase of 3,000 acres and additional sections of land.

   a Complete ownership of territory to be developed.   x

1. Families encouraged to emigrate and have many children in order to create independent self-sufficient units of organization.   x

   a Single family, owner-operated farms, residences on the farms.

C Belief that the Calvinist family is the basic unit for development of physical and spiritual life by the individual, with responsibility for making own home and raising family.   x

258

TABLE 2. *Continued*

I Cultural components	II Ideology: made specific through ideas, beliefs, attitudes, values, and goals	III Events or circumstances	IV Geographic expression or impact	V CULTURAL APPRAISAL PROCESSES			
				New condition	Modified	Reaffirmed	Abandoned
	D Independence valued highly, recognized in terms of individual responsibility.	1. Highly developed self-determination, perseverance and/or "stubbornness."	a Individual church autonomy. Consistory ruled by minister and elected elders.			x	
		2. Resistance to outside authority and authoritarianism.	a Absence of strong church hierarchy and permanent church leadership center.		x		
	E The non-Dutch-Reformed world regarded as basically sinful and inferior. It has succumbed to many temptations and subscribes to many false values and ways of life.	1. Contact is avoided as much as possible except when necessary to gain a living. Outsiders have little place in the communities since they do not belong to the institutions around which life revolves.	a No taverns, movie houses, or dance halls, except in Holland, Michigan.	x			
			b Absence of other churches and non-Dutch-Reformed population, except in Holland, Michigan.	x			
			c Separation of any facilities for outsiders from core of community.	x			

Procedures or ways of doing, as related to ideology			
F Habits of dress should be simple, modest, and economical.	1. Garments from the Netherlands could not be replaced or duplicated in Michigan. Old-world styles of dress were also subject to comment and ridicule.	a Dutch habits of dress abandoned.	x
		b American styles of dress immediately adopted.	x
G All members of the family must contribute to their own livelihood.	1. Livelihood activities are family enterprises within which a division of labor is worked out.	a Relatively rapid and thorough development of farms and farm lands.	x
	2. Labor force is easily controlled and highly efficient.	a No unemployment or idleness.	x
H Any job or task undertaken must be done thoroughly and well.	1. Marked preference developed for growing particular crops or for particular types of farming, resulting in specialized agriculture.	a General subsistence farm changed to commercial agriculture.	
		b Emergence of specialized farming types: cash grain, livestock feeding, poultry,	x

TABLE 2. *Continued*

I Cultural components	II Ideology: made spe- cific through ideas, beliefs, attitudes, values, and goals	III Events or circumstances	IV Geographic expres- sion or impact	V CULTURAL APPRAISAL PROCESSES			
				New con- dition	Modi- fied	Reaf- firmed	Aban- doned
			muck farming (onions, celery, potatoes, pepper-ment) and horti-culturists with crop specialties such as blueber-ries, nurseries.	x			
I Productive activ-ity should be sought at all times. Idleness breeds the Devil.		1. Seasonal employ-ment in factories is a profitable way to use energies during slack season.	a Agriculture and industry comple-ment one another. Factories absorb seasonal labor surpluses.	x			
		2. Farming and in-dustrial employ-ment now re-garded as com-plementary on a daily basis in or-der to maximize economic return and make efficient use of available labor.	a Increased farm specialization.	x			
			b Two-shift, two-place work day is both possible and a practical reality.	x			

Works as embodied in constructs, institutions, and instruments, related to ideology

J Use of native tongue: the language their scriptures used, and the "lingua franca."

  1. No universally understood tongue; several Dutch dialects along with Freisian and Low German spoken.

    a Dutch dialects abandoned.   x

    b Adoption of English for communication among themselves and with "Americanized" groups around them.   x

    c Native dialects retained only by older generation, and in archaic forms.   x

K Appreciation of Low Countries' building forms and architectural styles noted in original context for maximizing space and for use of local building materials.

  1. Different needs recognized in pioneer setting.

    a Traditional styles abandoned.   x

  2. Designs modified to suit new conditions and resources.

    a Some Freisian and Nieder Sachsen barns constructed.   x

  3. American-style frame houses and barns adopted.

    a Wood construction with stone foundations adopted.   x

L Residential-village settlement pattern in the homeland.

  1. Dispersed single-family farmstead.

    a Individual farm houses on the land.   x

  2. Nucleated and linear villages seemed impractical and unnecessary in Michigan.

    a Developed only two main centers: Holland and Zeeland, keeping other centers for local use.   x

    b Retained Dutch province names.   x

TABLE 2. Continued

I Cultural components	II Ideology: made specific through ideas, beliefs, attitudes, values, and goals	III Events or circumstances	IV Geographic expression or impact	V CULTURAL APPRAISAL PROCESSES			
				New condition	Modified	Reaffirmed	Abandoned
		3. Cross-roads places well suited for church gathering points.	a Church-dominated communities.				
	M Education must be Christian and learning must be selective.	1. Religion plays a dominant role in education, especially among Christian Reformed people.	a Church operated elementary and high schools.	x			
		2. There is a limited curriculum, circumscribed by religion's dominant role.	a Concentration on traditional subjects, elementary skills, and only limited attention to science.				
			a Both Reformed Church and Christian Reformed Church operate their own college.	x			
		3. Higher education is also church-controlled.					
	N Church must have effective means of keeping in touch with its membership.	1. Church attendance must be regular.	a Large and numerous church facilities and schools.	x			
		2. Religious teachings must be available to all.	a Psalter Hymnal is a prominent and widely used book along with the Holy Bible.			x	

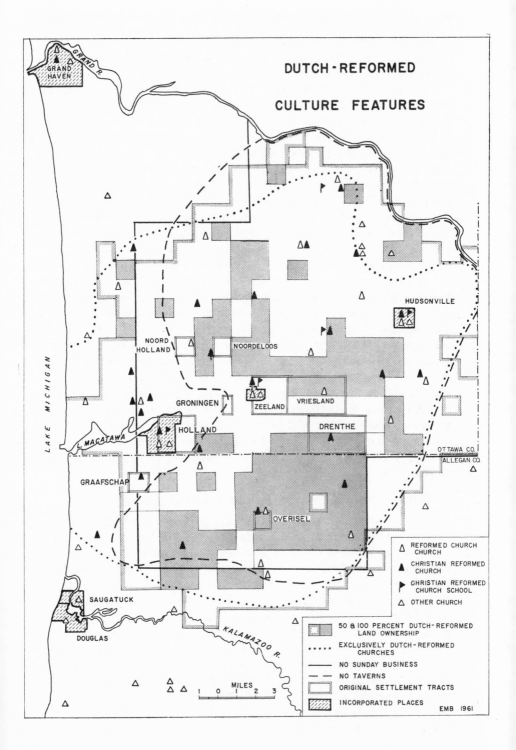

DUTCH-REFORMED

CULTURE FEATURES

GRAND HAVEN

GRAND R.

LAKE MICHIGAN

L. MACATAWA

NOORD HOLLAND

GRONINGEN

HOLLAND

GRAAFSCHAP

SAUGATUCK

DOUGLAS

NOORDELOOS

ZEELAND

VRIESLAND

DRENTHE

OVERISEL

HUDSONVILLE

OTTAWA CO.
ALLEGAN CO.

KALAMAZOO R.

MILES
1 0 1   2   3

△ REFORMED CHURCH
  CHURCH

▲ CHRISTIAN REFORMED
  CHURCH

▶ CHRISTIAN REFORMED
  CHURCH SCHOOL

△ OTHER CHURCH

50 & 100 PERCENT DUTCH-REFORMED
LAND OWNERSHIP

········· EXCLUSIVELY DUTCH-REFORMED
         CHURCHES

―――― NO SUNDAY BUSINESS

― ― ― NO TAVERNS

ORIGINAL SETTLEMENT TRACTS

INCORPORATED PLACES

EMB 1961

263

be presented and discussed in much greater detail, to do so would mask and distract from the essential features of this study, namely, cultural appraisal of ideas by the group and the resultant geographic expression.

The material in column IV identifies the spatial phenomena of the culture group. These are recorded in cartographic form in Figure 1. Eight of the 14 features are mapped and several of the others are indirectly shown. These features indicate the areal extent of the culture as well as some of the spatial relationships that exist among the various elements of culture. The limits of the culture area can be defined by the termination of some of the Dutch-Reformed culture elements on the margins and the presence of some intruding "outside" culture features. The composite pattern shown on the map indicates the relative degree of dominance of this culture, its weak places, and its strongholds. More will be said about the areal pattern on a later page.

The four distinctions under the headings of cultural appraisal (column V) in Table 2 show how the group has assessed ideas, and the features of their culture in relation to the problems they are working out in the face of circumstances confronting them at any given time and place. The results of this continuing appraisal are recorded according to whether they represent innovations or added features of the culture, modifications of older ones, or abandonment of culture features. It must be pointed out that cultural assessment has a particular time-and-place context and, in this study, the range of time is from approximately 1816 to 1960 in the Netherlands and in southwestern Michigan. Wherever possible, both the time and place of changes have been noted. These are shown in column III. In other cases they cannot be marked precisely because record of them was lost, was forgotten, or is now impossible to document.

Dutch-Reformed Culture Evolution and Organization

By reading across the rows in Table 2, it is possible to trace the evolution and organization of specific ideas of Dutch-Reformed culture. For example, the belief in Calvinist ideology was behind the creation of the first Dutch Calvinist church in 1816 (row A, item 1). Since then there have been at least two new institutions stemming from it: the Dutch Reformed Church created in 1834 and the Christian Reformed Church in 1872 (row A, 1; and A, 2, a; and A, 3, a). In each case a conservative group within the sect resented modifications and liberalizations in church practice. Since they insisted on practice being in literal accord with their principles, there has been secession from the parent church as changes occur in practices threatening to alter the ideology. At the present time the two sects are only distinguishable from one another in the application of principle to church practice. The two have separate congregations, although their territories frequently overlap or are coextensive. Neither sect has formal territorial limits, so that church members are free to move from one congregation to another. A total of 61 churches in this Dutch-Reformed community is shown in Figure 1.

Considering items in row B, 1, a; 2, a; 3, a, b; and 4, a in Table 2, the first secession from the state-dominated *Hermvorde Kerk* of the Netherlands in 1834 literally meant a marked schism with the way of life and set of practices that prevailed in the Netherlands at that time. The final break occurred in 1846 when the "seceders," as they were called, migrated to the United States and established a new Dutch-Reformed colony in southwestern Michigan. Their ideas were sufficiently well-developed and carefully considered by their leaders (appointed ministers or *dominies,* as they were called) that they were able to utilize the opportunity to institute new practices compatible with their id logy in accord with the circumstances they found in the new land.

The territory selected for the new colony was virgin forest land so that there was no established commitment or pattern of area organization to contend with, except for the land survey system. This, however, provided a skeletal system for the division of land into usable blocks (sections) and facilitated the orderly allocation of land to individual families (row B, 4 of Table 2).

It cannot be claimed that ideology determines a given set of responses. Rather it is believed that ideology is a framework or guide within which a group acts to determine its future. The Dutch-Reformed ideology is one which demands very rigorous self-discipline, and it is quite consistent that the group established a particular set of forms and procedures to carry out the directives of their conscience. The fact that they so consistently established forms and systems of area organization compatible with their principles, reflects the earnestness with which they held to their ideology and the deep intent on establishing a way of life that would not be subject to "corruptions" and problems known to them earlier in the Netherlands.

By building church-centered communities (B, 3 of Table 2) they did, in effect, restrict or exclude the random and dispersed development of commercial facilities which would compete with the religious purpose of these centers. This purpose was implemented by not allocating space to commercial business except in a few places that they felt possessed particular commercial potential, such as Holland on Lake Macatawa, Hudsonville, and Zeeland. The only non-church-centered establishments in the other communities were mills, blacksmiths, and other farm services. Even these were often separated from the church places around which life revolved. Today the church-centered communities remain largely intact. Gas stations have replaced the blacksmiths and general grocery stores exist in a few places. The present-day settlement pattern is shown in Figure 2.

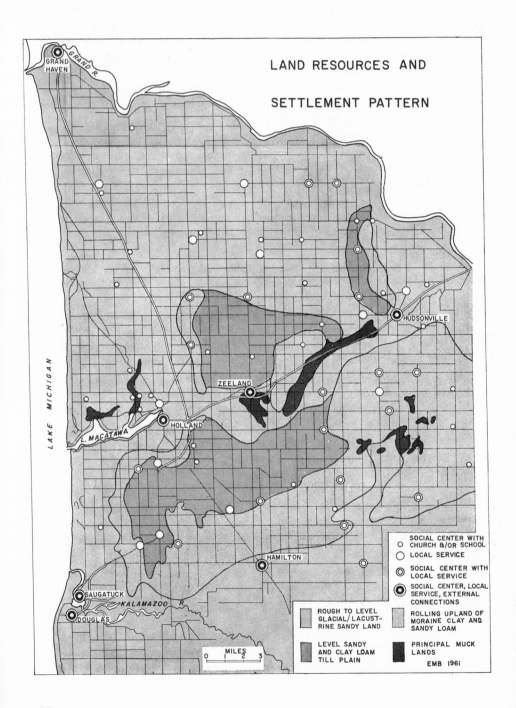

LAND RESOURCES AND

SETTLEMENT PATTERN

GRAND
HAVEN

GRAND R.

LAKE MICHIGAN

HUDSONVILLE

ZEELAND

HOLLAND

L. MACATAWA

HAMILTON

SAUGATUCK

KALAMAZOO R.

DOUGLAS

○ SOCIAL CENTER WITH
  CHURCH &/OR SCHOOL
◯ LOCAL SERVICE
◎ SOCIAL CENTER WITH
  LOCAL SERVICE
◉ SOCIAL CENTER, LOCAL
  SERVICE, EXTERNAL
  CONNECTIONS

ROUGH TO LEVEL
GLACIAL/ LACUST-
RINE SANDY LAND

ROLLING UPLAND OF
MORAINE CLAY AND
SANDY LOAM

LEVEL SANDY
AND CLAY LOAM
TILL PLAIN

PRINCIPAL MUCK
LANDS

MILES
0   1   2   3

EMB 1961

266

In column V of Table 2, only one culture element is shown as having been abandoned (A, 1), namely the state *Hermvorde Kerk*. In its place a new body based on "reformed" doctrines and known in the Netherlands as *Gereformeerde Kerk* was created. This action and the subsequent decision to migrate to the United States led to abandonment of much of their national culture: family, friends, homes, customs, jobs, crafts, and many practices of their localities. Life was never the same for anyone again. Virgin land, undetermined resources, pioneer practices, and hosts of new problems were to confront them. In addition, most of them had not been landowners in the Netherlands, where they were occupied either as tenant farmers or laborers. Some had been craftsmen in the employ of others. These social-economic positions were abandoned when they left the Netherlands and were replaced by the opportunity to become landowners and make their own decisions as primary producers. Never before had they been able to decide what land they would work, how they would work it, or in what kind of farming they would engage.

Since they had suffered for their beliefs in the Netherlands and had decided to locate in an area not already occupied by other people for the privilege of living in accord with uncompromised Calvinist principles, they were anxious to establish control over their new territory. Initially they took up nearly all the government lands in the two southern tiers of townships in Ottawa County and an adjoining portion in Allegan County, Michigan (Table 2, row B, 4).

There were still further ramifications of their departure from the Netherlands in the abandonment of old ways and creation of new ones. It was frequently customary for two or three generations of a family to live under one roof in the homeland. In the new colony there was ample space for everyone to own his own land, and as second and third generations came along there was space for them to make new households on separate holdings of their own. Some properties were subdivided among sons in a family, giving each enough land to enable him to earn a living from it (row C, 1, a).

By possessing land in a compact tract there was little opportunity for non-Dutch-Reformed people to acquire holdings among them. As shown on the map in Figure 1, the pattern of land ownership at present can be described in two categories: the area of more than 50 per cent ownership by people of the Dutch-Reformed community, and the area where they have exclusive control over property. The compact area where more than 50 per cent of the space is occupied by Dutch-Reformed people contains 375 square miles and includes all of the area that was originally taken up by them. There are 106 square miles within this territory which are owned exclusively by the Dutch-Reformed people and, although the pattern is less compact, most of the solid blocks of Dutch-

Reformed ownership are contiguous to the areas in the 50 per cent category. Coupled with this pattern, over the years, the Dutch-Reformed have been very selective of the types of businesses allowed in their community (Table 2, row E, 1). By keeping land ownership among themselves they essentially eliminated the intrusion of outsiders, or at least did nothing to attract them. Both of these devices are used at present, and they remain effective ways of maintaining an ideologically-based society.

Four examples of ways of doing as related to ideology are given in Table 2, rows F, G, H, I. It is apparent that these are primarily concerned with livelihood activities. Again, the implementation of their ideas shows clearly that new practices were favored over older ones. The ways of making a living in virgin pine-covered land were dependent on the abilities of the people to apply past experience to conditions and materials and to work out ways by which their goals could be achieved.

From their past experience they favored clay soils which supported good grass cover when cleared of trees. They recognized two kinds of land and associated conditions in southwestern Michigan: the sandy and clay loam tree-covered uplands, and the lowlands of the Black River and its tributaries covered by fine alluvium and patches of muck land, as shown in Figure 2. Until recently these lowlands were passed by in favor of the upland till and moraine lands with the heavier soils. The till surfaces consist of clay loam soils and are relatively level lands. Sandy and sandy loams are related to the hilly moraines. Early settlers perceived that the heavier clay soil lands produced good grass crops as well as grain when cleared of the timber and were well suited to the grass-grain general subsistence economy of the early stages of settlement. Forty, 80, and 160 acres were common sizes of farm units. These generally prevail today in keeping with the norms established by the American survey system.

Development of new land proceeded relatively rapidly because existing capital was pooled for the acquisition of land, allowing individual families immediate occupancy and the option to: (1) perform community works (such as road building and harbor improvement) as payment for their land, or (2) defer payment until they could earn cash by laboring on farms or in industries outside of their colony. Inasmuch as all members of the family were contributors to the enterprise (row G, 1, a; 2, a), it was not long before farming passed from a subsistence operation to one producing some cash crops and then later developing specializations (row H, 1, a, b).

Individual preferences for particular types of farming had opportunity to be satisfied (row H, 1, a, b). The general subsistence type of farming has now virtually been replaced by a variety of specialized types of commercial agriculture. This shift, of course, also reflects improved farming technology and expanded and diversified markets. The perceptive abilities, work habits, and attitudes of many Dutch-Reformed farmers have enabled them to develop successful specializations in dairying, cash and feed grain growing, livestock or poultry feeding operations, or in one of several types of muck farming: potatoes, onions, celery, or peppermint. In recent years a use has been found for heretofore useless types of sandy soils along the margins of Lake Michigan in the raising of blueberries. On muck and loamy soils many new garden nursery businesses have been created.

The development of an elaborate set of marketing organizations has accompanied this diversity in agricultural activities. Each of the farm specialties has its own marketing organization, processors as well as wholesale distributors, and brokerage firms. The combination of creative and physical energies has brought about the development of a highly successful and diversified agricultural system contributing significantly to the produce required in Detroit and Chicago markets, to say nothing of more local ones.

In response to the idea that there should be continual productive activity, individuals sought non-farm employment during the slack season in winter. Local factory operations were encouraged to utilize the energies and talents of people to produce salable goods. Saw mills, flour mills, and brick making were among the earliest industries they developed; today there are highly successful food processors, metal founding and fabricating companies, and manufacturers of furniture, electrical equipment, boats, tools, dyes, precision instruments, and pharmaceuticals. It is estimated now that 45 per cent of the Dutch-Reformed farmers have more than 100 days of off-farm work per year (row I, 1, a).

Full-time farming shows a marked decline as agricultural specialization and increased productivity advances. Off-the-farm jobs are being taken up even during the normal eight-hour work day. Several of the specialized types of farming can be set up so that the work can be carried on early in the morning and late in the day with perhaps some assistance from members of the family during the day. Poultry raising, horticultural specialty farms, and blueberry plantations can be operated in this manner. All of the various types of farming can now be organized to give the farmer some occasion to take up outside work if even on a seasonal basis (row I, 2, a, b).

Five examples are given of the third component of their culture—works as related to ideology (rows J, K, L, M, N). This set of cultural elements shows the most variety in the kind of cultural assessment that has occurred. The particular elements included under the category "works" are embodied in various institutions, establishments, and instruments. Language, whether written or spoken, when viewed as a cultural element, for geographic purposes, is an instrument by which a multitude of intra- and inter-group relationships are formed. In the case of this Dutch-Reformed group in southwestern Michigan, they did not originally possess a common denominator as far as language was concerned, even though they spoke languages with a common root (row J, 1). The geographic implication of this situation was that Freisians could only operate easily among Freisians, people from Drenthe worked best with others speaking the same dialect, and Zeelanders were unable to communicate effectively with others. Mixing among themselves was difficult, to say nothing of the problems of working with outsiders. As more immigrants arrived and settlement expanded, it became necessary to adopt a common tongue. The English language seemed eminently suited because it made easier communication with outsiders for business purposes, and provided a new basis for provincial groups to communicate with one another. Though some of the native languages survive through use by older generations, they are archaic forms which are difficult for present-day people from the Netherlands to understand. Therefore, the native tongues have been abandoned and have been replaced by English or modified to such an extent that they are barely recognizable as Dutch (row J, 1, a, b, c).

As far as architecture of buildings and their arrangement into a settlement pattern is concerned, the traditional Dutch expressions were abandoned early, leaving only the place names of the communities and some relict barns as reminders of the past culture. Nucleated and linear villages, both common settlement types in the Netherlands, were neither necessary nor desired settlement forms in Michigan. Private ownership of land meant that families preferred dispersal on their individual properties (row K, 1, a; 2, a; 3, a).

Educational facilities are a completely new addition to the culture. Education was regarded, until recently, as consisting of learning the three R's. Only in special cases, when an individual was unable or unsuited to an agricultural occupation, did formal education lead to a career such as the ministry. However, since opportunities and specializations have grown, it has become apparent to an increasingly large part of the Dutch-Reformed community that a longer and fuller education is necessary for young people in order to find employment either inside or outside the community.

Both the Reformed Church and the Christian Reformed Church have established church-supported liberal arts colleges. Hope College, run by the Reformed Church, is the main theological center for the church, comprising a ministerial training center and an undergraduate institution for their membership. Calvin College serves a similar function for the Christian Reformed Church. In addition, this group insists on having its own primary and secondary schools in which religious instruction and a "selective curriculum" are offered (row M, 1, a; 2, a; 3, a).

It is worth pointing out that these cultural elements included under "works" are the ones on which there is customary focus to help distinguish one culture group from another. These are among the most easily observed manifestations of a culture and are frequently assumed to be the culture. In the case of the Dutch-Reformed group several of the works might be overlooked because their visual appearance is not striking. Furthermore, almost none of the present-day works of this culture group are relatable to their national background; rather they are all expressions developed or creations contrived by Dutch-Reformed people in response to conditions and problems which they encountered in southwestern Michigan.

Conclusion

It was expected in the early stages of research on the Dutch-Reformed culture that many of their cultural traits would reflect their European (Dutch) background and represent continuations and modifications of known ways of doing things in the homeland. When the specific ideas, effects, responses, and resultant geographic expressions were examined in the context of group appraisal, most of the identified cultural elements and their geographic expressions were found to be new creations. These have evolved during their occupancy of Michigan and were not known ways or practices followed in the Netherlands. Instead they are innovations designed to support and propagate their ideology.

The role that perception and decision-making have played in shaping Dutch-Reformed culture in southwest Michigan cannot be overemphasized. All of the new creations, or innovations, reflect the ability of these people to perceive new ways in which their ideology might be expressed, enabling them to be part of American culture without compromising the principles on which their way of life stands. One of the reasons Dutch-Reformed culture has been so successful in maintaining its identity is precisely because of the insistence on relating everything to ideology and creating a way of life around it. There has been a constant assessment as to which elements of their earlier culture would be propagated, which abandoned, and which modified to meet new circumstances without basically destroying the culture.

It also can be pointed out that Dutch-Reformed people are conspicuous groups wherever they are found. They may be found in almost all of the states in the United States and comprise prominent groups in Canada and the Republic of South Africa. Those in the latter area which have the same ideology as the group detailed here have established control through their persistence and intense adherence to the Calvinist code and their construction of a system around it. This case gives good evidence to support the idea that there are a variety of ways a given ideology may express itself, and it is out of this diversity that area differentiation is created.

When ideology in culture is viewed on a larger scale, it can be said that as culture groups establish themselves in new surroundings, and include other groups possessing variant concepts, there is heavy emphasis on perception and decision-making, enabling each group to determine its own course based on its specific beliefs. Human traditions constitute major creations of far-reaching significance. Their evolution is relatively slow and faltering to our time-sensitive minds but the changes recorded here were notable in a single generation and their geographical expressions are subject to continual attrition and construction.

According to the hypothesis advanced in this essay, ideology is the heart and core of any culture. It is the intellectual framework for the ways people perceive their environment, the resources they develop from it, and the kinds of area organization they evolve. Therefore, ideology is reflected in the patterns of human occupance. Ideology provides the framework within which decisions and choices are made. In the final analysis the creation, selection, and maintenance of a culture is made possible through the processes of cultural appraisal in a time-and-space setting.

21. Nationalism, Secularism, and the Zoroastrians of Kirman: The Impact of Modern Forces on an Ancient Middle Eastern Minority

Paul Ward English

The influence of Westernization has spread from Western Europe and North America to all corners of the globe. Aspects of Western culture are accepted with varying speed and with differing impact upon traditional cultures. The following article shows how the Western concepts of

> *nationalism and secularism have changed a minority group*
> *and their manner of life in the Iranian city of Kirman.*
> *Similar cultural geographic change has, is, and will*
> *continue to be an important force affecting*
> *communities and areas in many parts of the world.*

This paper proposes to document the impact of two Western concepts, nationalism and secularism, on the Zoroastrians of Kirman. It describes the Zoroastrian community's nineteenth-century rise from the restrictions of Islamic intolerance and its subsequent decline in the liberalized atmosphere of twentieth-century Iran. Elements in the recent history of the Zoroastrians have been shared by other Middle Eastern minorities; thus, their experience is of wider geographical import. It suggests three fundamental changes in the cultural geography of the Islamic world: (1) a reorientation in the structure and organization of Muslim cities, (2) a desegregation and redistribution of Middle Eastern minorities, and (3) a growth of cultural homogeneity in a region noted for its diversity of peoples.

In the nineteenth century, Iranian life was dominated by Shi'ah Islamic thought. Its culture was medieval in character, its society feudal in organization. Religion was the ideological foundation of the state and rejection of orthodoxy was interpreted as subversion. In the cities of Iran, therefore, religious segregation was a principle of town planning and a cornerstone of the political order. Heretical Muslim sects such as the Druze of Lebanon, the Isma'ili of Yemen, and the Kharijites of North Africa retreated to refuges in districts far removed from the seats of urban power. Other minorities sought survival and prosperity in the anonymity of city life. These were the favored peoples—the Jews, Christians, and Zoroastrians—whose religious existence was admitted in Islam because they were the "peoples of the Book" *(dhimmīs)*. Such groups settled on the margins of large Muslim cities where they lived in ghettos, forming geographically united, spiritually coherent enclaves, located within, but living apart from, the mainstream of Muslim life.

In the last fifty years, however, forces of nationalism and secularism reorganized Islamic culture and altered traditional institutions. Allegiance to nation states weakened the bonds of the Islamic community. Civil law replaced religious law as the foundation of society and in theory at least, all men gained equal rights before this new law. Twin concepts of toleration of differences and integration into one society undermined the ghetto system as men's minds and horizons expanded beyond the confines of religious orthodoxy.

SOURCE: Revision of unpublished paper presented at the Annual Meeting of the Association of American Geographers, Columbus, Ohio, 1965. Published with permission of the author, who is associate professor of geography, University of Texas.

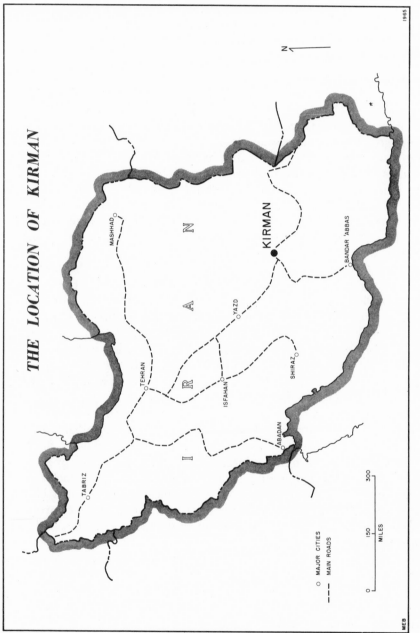

FIGURE 1: Kirman is located on the Central Plateau of Iran at an elevation of 5,680 feet on the old Indian High-way. It is the major political, commercial, and administrative center of southeastern Iran.

274

The impact of these Western concepts was greatest on the urban minorities, the Jews, the Christians, and the Zoroastrians. These groups were liberated from the ghetto, freed from their many restrictions, only to be faced at present with vigorous forces of assimilation which threaten to destroy their religious identities.

The Zoroastrians of Kirman in the Nineteenth Century

In the nineteenth century, Kirman was a traditional, preindustrial Muslim city. The heart of the city was occupied by three institutions aligned on an east-west axis—the Friday-prayer mosque, the bazaar, and the citadel (Fig. 2). The Friday-prayer mosque near the eastern wall of the city was the pivot of social and religious life in Kirman. The bazaar with its covered stalls and associated caravanserais was located adjacent to the mosque and formed the commercial center of the town. The citadel, which was the center of political power in Kirman, was accorded a secondary position in the town plan and was located on the western edge of the city, ringed by walls to protect governmental leaders both from external attacks and internal uprisings.

The remainder of the city was divided into five residential quarters *(mahalleh)* in which the population of Kirman was segregated on the bases of race, religion, and occupation. These quarters were characterized by the pronounced irregularity of their street patterns. Except for the wide avenues which connected the bazaar with the city gates, the lanes in these sections formed a maze of dark, twisting passageways, alleys, and culs-de-sac. Most were less than twelve feet in breadth and were enclosed by the high outer walls of the household compounds. Four of these quarters were Muslim—Kutbabad, Mahalleh Shahr, Maidani Qualeh, and Shah 'Adil—and were occupied by the merchants, gardeners, artisans, and craftsmen of the city. To some degree the preindustrial principle stressing central location was operative and the richest and most powerful people lived near the center of the city, the poorest on the outskirts near the city walls. The fifth quarter was occupied by a small community of Jews, who, by dint of tribute money paid regularly to local officials, were able to achieve a position of relative security inside the walls next to the citadel.

The Zoroastrian quarter of Kirman was located beyond the eastern wall of the city. The precariousness of life in such a location is evidenced by the ruins of the ancient Zoroastrian quarter to the north of the city which was leveled by an Afghan invasion in the eighteenth century. All Zoroastrians lived within their own quarter, and were forbidden to live inside the city walls. As a result, the fire temples, shrines, baths, and

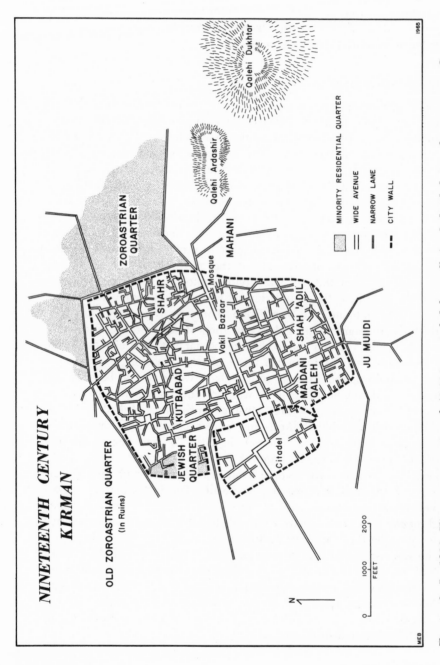

FIGURE 2: In 1900, Kirman was a city of 40,000, encircled by walls, and divided into five quarters. Carpet-weaving, which has since made Kirman famous, was just becoming a major industry.

schools of the Zoroastrians were located here. A community council *(anjuman)* represented members in dealings with the Muslims and as late as 1960 it was still possible to find older Zoroastrian men and women who had never ventured beyond the walls of the ghetto and could not speak the Persian tongue.

Shi'ah Islam was extremely intolerant during the nineteenth century and, because of concern with the ritual impurity of nonbelievers, imposed many restrictions on the Zoroastrians to emphasize their inferior status. First and foremost, as non-Muslims, the Zoroastrians had no legal rights in Muslim courts because law was based on the Muslim religion. Any case brought before the courts, therefore, would automatically be decided against them. Zoroastrians could not ride a horse on the main streets of the city, and if when riding a donkey they met a Muslim of any age or sex, they were forced to dismount and bow. Zoroastrian houses and even their fire temples could not be built taller than one story because Muslims allowed no rivals to the beauty and majesty of their mosques. In addition, Zoroastrians were forced to wear mustard-colored robes, could not wear eyeglasses or stockings nor carry umbrellas, and were not allowed in the city on rainy days. In commercial matters, they were forced to pay higher prices for property, were restricted to a limited number of occupations, and had to conceal their wealth for fear of exciting hostile attacks. Furthermore, there was the constant drain of conversion on the community, particularly after the "law of apostasy" was enforced, and any Zoroastrian newly converted to Islam could claim the property of all of his relatives however distant. Above all, the Zoroastrian community feared the alternatives of enforced conversion to Islam or massacre.

In this atmosphere, the Zoroastrian community developed the characteristics of a closed, introverted, and static society. An endogamous priest class wielded increasing power as religion became the prime focal point of Zoroastrian reality. Unfortunately, many of these priests failed to maintain the theology of their faith, though they continued to tend the sacred fire and practive the ritual. Zoroastrian apartness from the Muslims was emphasized and cherished so that practices such as the exposure of the dead in "towers-of-silence" *(dakhmeh)* located outside the city came to have an exaggerated importance not found in earlier Zoroastrianism. By the end of the nineteenth century, the spiritual decay was so apparent that the Iranian Zoroastrians were forced to look to their coreligionists in India, the Parsis, for religious leaders and leadership.

Nationalism, Secularism, and the Zoroastrians of Kirman in the Twentieth Century

In the first decades of the twentieth century, a new spiritual and intellectual ferment stimulated by the example of the West was at work in Iran. This force emerged in the form of a new nationalism which demanded the establishment of a constitution, a reevaluation of tradition, and the removal of the inept Qajar dynasty. Under the leadership of Riza Shah Pahlavi, elements of a new technology and above all a modern viewpoint were injected into the feudal culture of Iran. Transportation facilities spread and intensified existing patterns of urban-rural communication. Government forces established effective control over tribal areas, shrinking the "land of dissidence" and increasing stability and security. Government involvement in local political affairs, water supply problems, conservation of resources, labor conditions, and other social and economic issues added a new dimension to provincial life. In the cultural sphere, nationalism emphasized everything pre-Arab, pre-Islamic, and in the ancient Iranian tradition. Arabic words were purged from the language, scholars rediscovered the glories of Achaemenid and Sassanian Iran, and Zoroastrian traditions were accorded a place of honor.

Further, the principle of secularization was accepted. Clerical landholdings were confiscated. The judicial system of Iran was overhauled along the lines of the Napoleonic Code and secular law was given primacy over religious law. Government schools replaced mosque schools thereby impairing the major media of religious transmission. In the 1920's, Riza Shah demanded that Iranians dress in Western clothing and outlawed the turbans, hats, coats, and robes which had previously marked a man's race, religion, and class. Also, the Shi'ah ceremonies in the month of Muharram mourning the martyrdom of Imam Husayn, the most widely celebrated religious holidays in Iran, were curtailed.

The impact of nationalism and secularism on the city of Kirman and its Zoroastrian community was immediately felt. The central government ordered that wide avenues be constructed in Kirman and a radial pattern was superimposed on the old city, which shifted its center of gravity to the north and east (Fig. 3). The ancient walls of the city were leveled and many old cemeteries and shrines, which previously had restricted urban expansion, were destroyed. And this expansion was substantial. Kirman's population increased from 40,000 to 60,000 in the first half of the twentieth century, despite a sizable emigration of landlords and traders to Tehran. New suburbs spread beyond the old city walls and in these newly constructed quarters land values were low and houses were less crowded. As a result, the labyrinth of

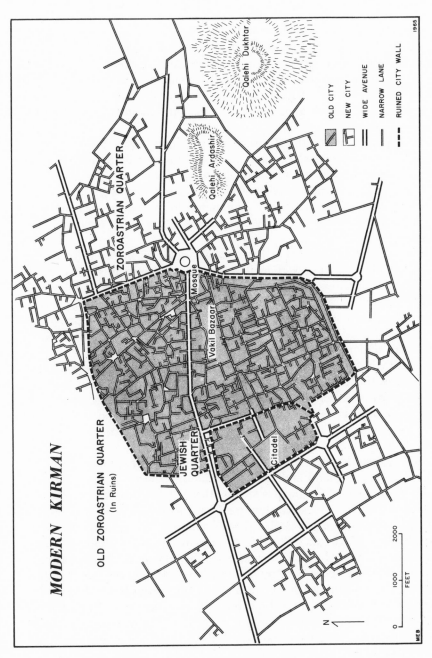

FIGURE 3: At present, Kirman is a city of 60,000 pierced by broad avenues set in a radial pattern. Note particularly the difference in texture between the "old city" and the "new suburbs."

279

twisting lanes so characteristic of preindustrial Islamic cities is not found in the suburbs.

Certain functional changes were also stimulated by these forces. The mosque declined in importance and no longer acted as the focal point of Kirmani social life. Industry, commerce, and crafts were liberated from their previous concentration in the bazaar and new shops sprang up on the new avenues. With increased communication facilities and increased security, location of the upper class at the center of the town was no longer critical, and, one by one, wealthy families moved to the suburbs.

Most important for the Zoroastrian community was the decline in power of the Muslim clergy and their replacement by secular judges, bureaucrats, political leaders, and government teachers. The many restrictions on Zoroastrian activities were eliminated, they were recognized in civil law, one Zoroastrian was appointed to the Iranian Senate, and a general atmosphere of religious tolerance replaced fanaticism in Kirman.

These social changes were immediately reflected in the distribution of Zoroastrians in Iran and in its cities. Zoroastrians in nearby rural settlements migrated to the provincial capital; those in Kirman migrated to Tehran—all searching for areas of increased tolerance and opportunity. The tide of these migrations steadily increased, with the exception of a short period after Riza Shah's abdication in the early 1940's. Now there are no longer any Zoroastrians in villages such as Jupar, Mahan, and Qanaghistan, though ruins of fire temples remain in these places. In Tehran, the Zoroastrian community which numbered in the hundreds in 1930 now numbers in the thousands, and the trend suggested by a count of graves in their cemetery and children in their schools indicates that this community is continuing to grow at the expense of other smaller places.

In the city of Kirman, the impact of secularism was even more definite. The Zoroastrian ghetto and the walls which separated it from the city have disappeared. The map showing the religious affiliation of each household in the Zoroastrian quarter of Kirman documents the degree to which integration has replaced segregation in the urban and social organization of Kirman (Fig. 4). At present families of both religions live side by side. Only 65 percent of the dwellings in the Zoroastrian quarter are still occupied by Zoroastrians; 30 percent are Muslim homes. The remaining houses are unoccupied, representing Zoroastrian families who migrated to Tehran but still own homes in Kirman. Nor have the Zoroastrians moved into a ghetto in Tehran; they are widely scattered throughout the capital and their distribution represents accommodation to land values and economic status, not to religion.

But this physical integration of religions and the movement of the

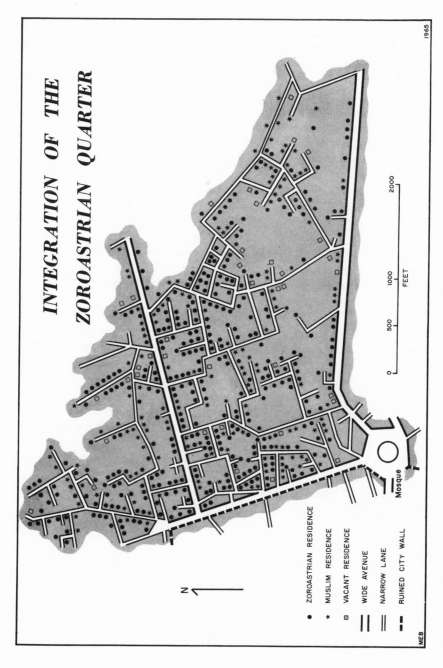

INTEGRATION OF THE ZOROASTRIAN QUARTER

1965

	ZOROASTRIAN RESIDENCE
	MUSLIM RESIDENCE
	VACANT RESIDENCE
	WIDE AVENUE
	NARROW LANE
	RUINED CITY WALL

Mosque

0   500   1000   2000
FEET

N

MEB

FIGURE 4: Nearly one-third of the houses in the Zoroastrian quarter of Kirman are now occupied by Muslims. This would have been impossible in nineteenth-century Iran.

Zoroastrians into the liberalized society of twentieth-century Iran has not been without cost. A Zoroastrian cemetery for example has replaced the traditional Zoastrian "tower-of-silence." This represents a radical departure from Zoroastrian belief and was spurred by modern debates on hygiene. Countless other customs, traditions, and rituals are disappearing as members of the community are assimilated into the mainstream of Iranian life: the "sacred thread," once as important to Zoroastrians as the cross was to Christians, is no longer worn by most modern Zoroastrians; there are fewer ceremonies at the fire temples and fewer people attend; indeed there are few candidates for the priesthood as most young men are drawn into more lucrative pursuits. In the words of their leader "Zoroastrians no longer have time to celebrate their faith," which may well mean that the destruction of Zoroastrian ghettos may be shortly followed by the disappearance of the community.

Conclusion

In conclusion, the data from Kirman suggests that two essentially Western concepts, nationalism and secularism, have (1) revolutionized the structure and organization of traditional Muslim cities, (2) liberated the ancient urban minorities from ghetto existences, and (3) contributed substantially to the assimilation of these people into national societies. As such, the diversity of religious and ethnic communities in the Middle East, one of the hallmarks of this region for centuries, is diminishing. Communities which survived and were probably strengthened by generations of persecution are succumbing to the more subtle forces of assimilation in the newly born, Western-influenced, "open-societies" of the new Middle East. In the case of Zoroastrians, this process is evidenced by the decline of tradition and the priest class, and the adoption of a Western viewpoint. Some authors have applauded the Westernization of Middle Eastern minority groups and others have lamented it; all, however, agree that the process is gaining momentum. It is one of the most fundamental changes that has occurred in this part of the world in centuries.

VI. ECONOMIC
ELEMENTS
AND PROCESSES

All nations constantly seek to improve their economic level of achieve-ment. Since early history, some people have been more successful than others due to such factors as the initiative and ability of the inhabitants, the availability of natural resources, the nature of government restric-tion or encouragement, and location in relation to trade routes. Most regions of the world have long passed from a local subsistence to an ex-change economy of varying degrees of complexity. Competition for the necessary economic elements—raw materials for food, shelter, and man-ufactured products of many kinds—has become highly competitive among nations and individuals.

Agriculture is without question the most important economic process on the earth. Not only is food absolutely essential for maintaining life, but also its production occupies a greater part of the earth's surface and employs a greater number of people than any other activity. In addition, many other agricultural products are the raw materials of industry, and, conversely, rural populations are great consumers of industrial products. Agriculture can be variously classified, but the subsistence and com-mercial categories are most commonly used, with the former occupying by far the greater number of people, whereas the latter provides the great food surpluses necessary to feed the rapidly increasing urban pop-ulations of the world.

The Industrial Revolution which began in lands bordering the North Sea was the starting point of a process that has resulted in the complex societies of western Europe, the eastern United States and Canada, Western USSR, as well as other parts of the world. In some cases the intensity of development has resulted in an industrial "landscape" as in the Ruhr of Germany, the English Midlands; and the New York, Pitts-burgh, and Chicago metropolitan regions of the United States. The im-pact of the Industrial Revolution has been felt to some degree in all corners of the globe. The resultant industrial landscape varies with the culture, political system, and many other factors. Communist coun-tries, for example, can dictate the location of a new steel mill, ignoring at will crucial cost factors which private enterprise carefully considers in terms of profit for the company or individual involved.

Economic geography is highly significant to the organization and

utilization of the earth, because the process includes not only agriculture and industry, but also the movement of products and raw materials along land, sea, and air routes, as well as trade at many points along these routes.

These selections are concerned primarily with various facets and stages of the economic process, but offer insight into a variety of economic activities in many parts of the world.

22. Stages of Technology and Their Impact upon the Physical Environment: A Basic Problem in Cultural Geography

Hans Carol

In this selection, the author establishes five stages of technology, indicating the nature of the economic process within the framework of cultural geography. He points out that in the complex contemporary world all five stages exist in some area of the world. Occasionally, two may exist in the same region, so that a modern plant for heavy industry may be found adjacent to tribal peoples living at Stage 1. This classification and analysis serves as an introduction to the nature of the economic process.

On the assumption that geography may be conceived as the study of the earth shell (geosphere) or any part thereof (geomer), it follows logically that human or cultural geography must focus on the rôle that culture plays within the earth shell. In other words, cultural geography is concerned with the study of mankind's occupation of the earth environment, or, to follow an expression of Preston James, it is concerned with the study of man's "sequent occupance" of the earth shell.[1]

SOURCE: *Canadian Geographer*, VIII 1, (1964), 1–7, with revisions and new illustrations, prepared by the author for this reprinting. The author is professor of geography, York University, Canada.
[1] H. Carol: Geography of the Future. *Prof. Geog.*, XIII, 1, 1961, pp. 14–18; H. Carol: Zur Theorie der Geographie. *Mitteilungen der Geographischen Gesellschaft Wien*, 105, 1963, pp, 23–38 (Festschrift Bobek); R. Hartshorne: *Perspective on the Nature of Geography*. Assoc. Am. Geog., Chicago, 1959; P. E. James and C. F. Jones (eds.): *American Geography: Inventory and Prospect*. Syracuse University Press, Syracuse, N.Y. 1954.

This sequent occupance, according to findings of archaeologists and anthropologists which are recapitulated briefly here, appears to have originated in East Africa about a million years ago. Within this immense time-span man made important technological advances which helped to secure his subsistence and his dispersal over the globe. There are the use of (1) stone implements which helped to overcome the rigours of the physical environment; (2) clothing which enabled him to occupy seasonally cold environments; (3) fire which provided warmth and made it possible for food to be cooked. Such technological inventions enabled *Homo sapiens* of the late Pleistocene period to occupy almost the whole earth shell.

In the Neolithic period, which began some ten thousand years ago, man learned to domesticate wild plants and animals. As a result of this "agricultural revolution," man acquired new and far more dependable modes of food supply based on agriculture and herding.

Some six thousand years ago, the "urban revolution" began. This brought about a differentiation of society into a primary agricultural sector that remained in rural settlements and a secondary industrial and commercial sector concentrated in urban settlements. Such diversification led to increasingly complex socio-economic and technological achievements, which originated and grew in southwest Asia, the eastern Mediterranean, India, China, and Central and South America.

The next distinct thrust of technological evolution, the "industrial revolution," began some two hundred years ago in Europe. This was the first of man's revolutions to have a comparatively rapid worldwide impact, although it occurred in varying degrees of intensity.

In our time, we are witnessing the newest technological revolution characterized by concepts like "automation," "nuclear energy," and "conquest of outer space." This offers man almost limitless opportunities, and space flight even provides him with the possibility of escape from his native environment, the earth shell, at least temporarily.

Through each of these major technological revolutions and accompanying socio-economic organizations man has gained a stronger grasp upon his natural environment with the result that increasingly greater numbers can maintain a safer, longer, and richer life. This evolution is based primarily on one particular aspect of culture, the rational, intellectual capabilities of man which enable him to develop a technological progress. Technological abilities are essentially the measure of man's impact upon his environment, and determine what substance he considers useless, and what substance he considers a valuable resource. Primarily, then, technology and its concomitant socio-economic organization are the cultural attributes through which man exerts his control over his natural and cultural environment.

Historical Perspective

Before embarking upon the core of this paper, a brief historical perspective on the topic of classifying cultural evolution seems desirable. The ideas of authoritative anthropologists and leading geographers are here reviewed.

In the nineteenth century the social sciences were immensely stimulated by Darwinian evolutionary thinking, although sometimes this led to a dead end. The "social evolution" of this period assumed an inevitable, indeed, "natural" development through a series of innate cultural stages, from "savagery" through "barbarism," to "civilization." By the twentieth century, this cultural "evolutionism" based on biological principles was rightly discarded. Frank Boas' anthropological school (Boas, incidentally, was originally a geographer) inaugurated the historical school of anthropological thinking which concentrated on tracing facets of culture to their historical origins. (A similar approach seems to be followed by Carl Sauer's school of geography.)

By the middle of this century a new trend in anthropology can be recognized. Walter Goldschmidt described modern anthropological thinking as a "naturalistic theory of evolution, non-teleological in character. It does not assert a unity in evolutionary sequence; it does not assume an inevitability in development. Rather, it seems the essential process of human interaction operating in such a way as to produce long-run progressive evolution." [2]

Archaeologists and anthropologists such as V. Gordon Childe, Julian H. Steward, Leslie A. White, and Theodosius Dobzhansky are impressive by the depth of their inquiry into the problem of man's changing use of the environment in various stages of his development. The most up-to-date and profound accounts of cultural evolution are presented in the University of Chicago Centennial publication by such significant persons as Kroeber, Leakey, Washburn, Howell, Anderson, Piggott, Bordes, Willey, Braidwood, and Adams. [3]

A summary of some of the current systems of cultural classification used by archaeologists and anthropologists may be listed as follows:

1. On the basis of characteristic materials that are used for tool-making: stone age, bronze age, and iron age. This emphasis on non-perish-

[2] W. Goldschmidt: *Man's Way: A Preface to the Understanding of Human Society.* Holt, Rinehart and Winston, New York, 1959.
[3] V. G. Childe: *Man Makes Himself.* Watts & Co., London, 1936. S. Singer and E. D. Holmyard: *A History of Technology.* Vols. I–V. Oxford University Press, London, 1954. J. H. Steward: *Theory of Culture Change.* University of Illinois Press, Urbana, Ill., 1955; S. Tax (Ed.): *The Evolution of Man.* Vols. II and III, University of Chicago Centennial publ. on "Evolution after Darwin," University of Chicago Press, Chicago, 1960; L. A. White: *The Evolution of Culture.* McGraw-Hill, New York, 1959.

able materials serves the needs of the archaeologists well, but does not satisfy the requirements of a cultural geographer.

2. On the basis of technological evolution: agricultural revolution, urban revolution, and industrial revolution. These classifications of Childe's do designate initial phases of a particular cultural development, but hardly represent an actual status of technological achievement.

3. On the basis of human economic groups: nomadic hunting and food-gathering band and tribal societies; settled hunting and food-gathering tribal societies; horticultural village and tribal societies and herding tribal societies; agricultural-state societies split into peasant community life and urban life; and industrial urban-dominated life. Taxonomy such as Goldschmidt's is the most frequently used in anthropological (and geographic) writing.

In *human geography* outstanding European scholars such as Vidal de la Blache, Alfred Hettner, and recently Hans Bobek, to mention only a few, have concerned themselves with the differentiation and distribution of pertinent aspects of man's culture on the globe.[4] Hettner's posthumous *Die Menschheit* devotes considerable space to cultural stages (Kulturstufen und Kulturformen) of which the following are distinguished both in the text and in the maps: primitive peoples; natural peoples (Naturvölker); semicivilized peoples (Halbkulturvölker); the old cultures, Oriental, Indian, Chinese, Mediterranean, Central American; west and east European culture, their permanent dependencies, their colonial superpositions over large parts of the earth. Bobek in his recent article, "The Main Stages in the Socio-economic Evolution from a Geographical Point of View" sets out the following stages: food gatherers; specialized collectors, hunters, and fishermen; clan-peasantry and nomadic herders; feudally organized agrarian societies; older urban societies characterized by *rent-capitalism; productive capitalism,* industrial society and associated modern urban societies. Bobek's text describes these stages in some detail, and a world map shows their location to the end of the fifteenth century (Fig. 2).

Among recent American introductory textbooks in geography considerable use of the idea of human occupance according to "cultural

[4] Vidal de la Blache: *Principles of Human Geography.* Constable, London, 1926; H. Bobek: Die Hauptstufen der Gesellschafts—und Wirtschaftsentfaltung in geographischer Sicht. *Die Erde,* 90, 1959, pp. 259–98; H. Bobek: Zur Poblematik der unterentwickelten Länder. *Mitteilungen der Oesterreichischen Geographischen Gesellschaft,* 104, 1962, pp. 1–24; A. Hettner: *Der Gang der Kultur über die Erde.* Leipzig, 1920; A. Hettner: *Die Menschheit.* Vol. I of *Allgemeine Geographie des Menschen* (ed. by A. Schmitthenner). Stuttgart, 1947; C. O. Sauer: The Agency of Man on the Earth. In Thomas, W. L., Jr. (ed.): *Man's Role in Changing the Face of the Earth.* University of Chicago Press, Chicago, 1956, pp. 49–69.

development" is to be found.[5] Preston James in his *A Geography of Man* distinguishes the industrial society, the pre-industrial society, and the Soviet society. In *Man and the Earth* J. B. Hoyt introduces stages of human economies, hunting-gathering, pastoralism, simple agriculture, vegetable civilizations, machine civilizations. In a number of introductory textbooks on economic geography authors such as Jones and Darkenwald, Bengtson and Van Royen, Howard Gregor, and particularly John Alexander point to the different socio-economic ways of life and their implications to economic geography, while R. S. Thoman stresses the important difference between technically advanced and underdeveloped societies. Philip L. Wagner in his book *The Human Use of the Earth* wrestles with the same problems as this article tries to encompass.[6]

This brief review, though incomplete, is designed to show that the classification of mankind according to socio-economic development has been widely used in the social sciences, including cultural geography. However, I feel that this area of cultural geography deserves further attention, mainly along the following two lines:

1. Further thought should be given to the recognition of the fundamental problem in cultural geography. For instance, is cultural geography to be defined as the study of *cultures* on the earth surface or as the study of the impact of culture upon the *earth shell?*

2. While there is no doubt that the presently used terminology (as summarized above) is very useful in many respects, a stronger degree of abstraction and generalization could be applied to obtain terms useful to much wider applications. Perhaps such terms could be conceived as "macro-concepts," in contrast to the "micro-concepts" mentioned above.

Stages of Technology

In the five stages of technology outlined below, the principal aspects of culture by which man exerts his control over his environment are envisaged as tools (in the widest sense) and socio-economic organization. Each of the five stages is conceived as a major level of socio-economic

[5] J. Alexander: *Economic Geography.* Prentice-Hall, New York, 1963; N. A. Bengtson and W. Van Royen: *Fundamentals of Economic Geography.* Prentice-Hall, New York, 1957; V. C. Finch, G. T. Trewartha, A. H. Robinson, and E. H. Hammond: *Elements of Geography.* McGraw-Hill, New York, 1957; H. F. Gregor: *Environment and Economic Life.* Van Nostrand, New York, 1963; J. B. Hoyt: *Man and the Earth.* Prentice Hall, New York, 1962; P. E. James: *A Geography of Man.* Ginn and Company, New York, 1959; C. F. Jones, and G. G. Darkenwald: *Economic Geography.* Macmillan, New York, 1957; R. Murphey: *An Introduction to Geography.* Rand McNally, Chicago, 1961; R. S. Thoman: *The Geography of Economic Activity.* McGraw-Hill, Toronto, 1962.
[6] P. Wagner: *The Human Use of the Earth.* Free Press, Glencoe, Ill., 1960.

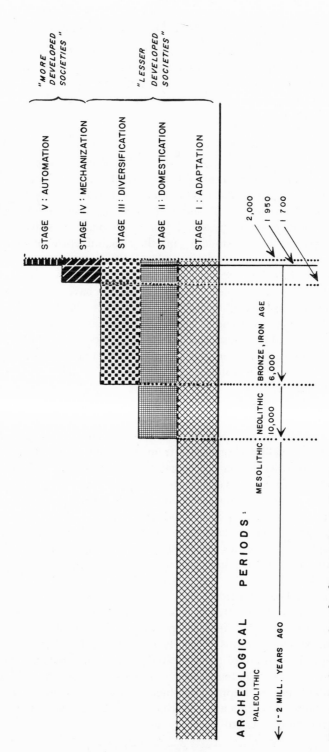

FIGURE 1: Stages of technology in time sequence.

technical achievement and consequently of major potential impact upon the environment, but each is visualized as a distinct, highly generalized type, although it is understood that human groups may in reality occupy any position along the continuum between the technologically least and most developed.

Stage I: Adaptation

In this stage, human groups adapt their way of life to a given natural environment; food is derived directly from wild plants and animals; society is unable to change the environment perceptibly to better supply the basic needs for food and shelter (except that fire is employed as a means of changing certain grasslands); tools are made of materials found in nature (wood, bones, stones) and their manufacture involves only physical but no chemical changes; socio-economic groups are small and comparatively isolated; population density is necessarily low.

Examples of such peoples who still lead, or have led in previous times, a gathering-hunting-fishing way of life are the Bushmen of the Kalahari, the Pygmies of the Congo forest, Eskimos, the pre-Columbian Plains Indians, and the Mesolithic hunters of Europe. As in other stages, various transitions to higher stages occur. This stage is also referred to as "Paleolithic" or "Old Stone Age" society, "hunting and gathering" society, "savagery," etc.

Stage II: Domestication

In this stage, human groups no longer live off wild plants and animals but gain their livelihood primarily from purposely selected and tamed plants and animals; the natural vegetation cover is partly replaced by cultivated crops; man actively creates a cultural environment, indeed a cultural landscape; tools in stone, bone, and wood are of greater variety; new homecrafts include pottery and weaving; there are larger socio-economic groups which exchange products in local markets; much higher population densities are possible. In some Stage II societies, the manufacture of iron tools has been incorporated through cultural diffusion from Stage III.

A large number of African and South American tribal societies are (or have been until recently) at this stage, as were North American Indian cultivators and the Neolithic peoples of Europe. In environments where cultivation of crops is not feasible but the natural vegetation cover is usable, herding of domesticated animals may become the dominant way of life. Contemporary examples include the Masai, the Cattle-Fulani, and the Lapps. This stage is also referred to as "Neolithic" or "New Stone Age" Society, "Barbarism," "Agricultural Revolution," "Hoe Agriculture," "Tribal Society," etc.

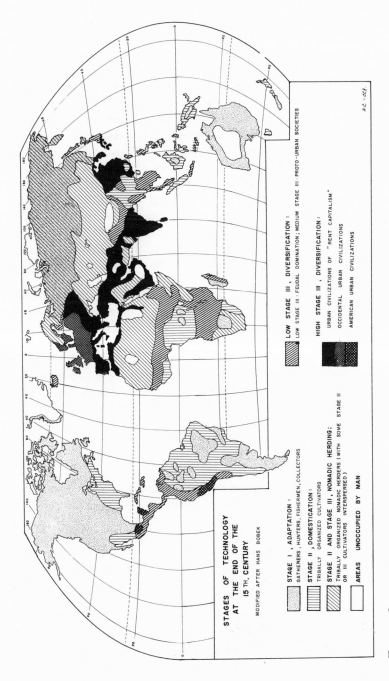

STAGES OF TECHNOLOGY
AT THE END OF THE
15 TH. CENTURY

MODIFIED AFTER HANS BOBEK

STAGE I , ADAPTATION :
GATHERERS, HUNTERS, FISHERMEN, COLLECTORS

STAGE II , DOMESTICATION :
TRIBALLY ORGANIZED CULTIVATORS

STAGE II AND STAGE III , NOMADIC HERDING:
TRIBALLY ORGANIZED NOMADIC HERDERS (WITH SOME STAGE II
OR III CULTIVATORS INTERSPERSED)

AREAS UNOCCUPIED BY MAN

LOW STAGE III , DIVERSIFICATION :
LOW STAGE III : FEUDAL DOMINATION ; MEDIUM STAGE III : PROTO - URBAN SOCIETIES

HIGH STAGE III , DIVERSIFICATION :
URBAN CIVILIZATIONS OF " RENT CAPITALISM "
OCCIDENTAL URBAN CIVILIZATIONS
AMERICAN URBAN CIVILIZATIONS

H.C. - 68

FIGURE 2.

Stage III: Diversification

In this stage, groups are composed of individuals with diverse occupations; however, despite the division of labour and the diversification which exists, the great majority (i.e., over three-quarters) still live directly off agriculture and animal husbandry; better use of the environment is made by the use of more efficient metal tools, animal-drawn ploughs, irrigation, and later on, by utilizing the power of wind and water; there must be, of necessity, an agricultural surplus sufficient to feed a small non-agricultural minority which specializes in governmental, military, commercial, educational, professional, or manufacturing functions; there is communication in space and time through scripts, and at least a small minority are literate; urban settlements (towns and cities) are created by the non-agricultural segment of the peoples in contrast to more traditional forms of settlement of rural way of life; there is a permanent exchange of goods and services between city and rural hinterland, and wide market relations are maintained with more distant parts of the earth; higher population densities over large areas are made possible.

Examples of sedentary peoples who reached this stage are those of ancient Mesopotamia, Egypt, India, China, Greece, Rome, the Mayas, the Aztecs, and Medieval European and Arabian peoples. Among present-day nomadic herders of stage III are the Tuaregs, Arab tribes, and Mongol tribes. This stage is also referred to as "Civilization," "Feudal Society," "Urban Civilization," "Plough Agriculture and Urban Way of Life," "Bronze and Iron Age," etc. Bobek differentiates between: "Occidental urban civilizations" (with citizen's governments), "urban civilizations of the rent capitalist type" (Oriental, Mediterranean, Eastern European) and "urban civilizations of ancient America."

Stage IV: Mechanization

In this stage, productivity is enormously increased by means of machines powered by coal, petroleum, or electricity; an agricultural minority produces enough surplus food on commercial farms for a non-agricultural majority; a large surplus of capital is produced which is invested productively; non-agricultural activities tend to concentrate in urban centres, some of which grow into large and complex cities; communications, market relations, investments, and exploitation of resources are world-wide.

Stage IV technology is based on a symbolic culture which emphasizes an objective, scientific attitude to the environment; it originated in Western Europe and its dependencies in North America, then spread through the rest of Europe, including Russia, and was disseminated throughout the world by means of the colonial impact of Western powers or, in

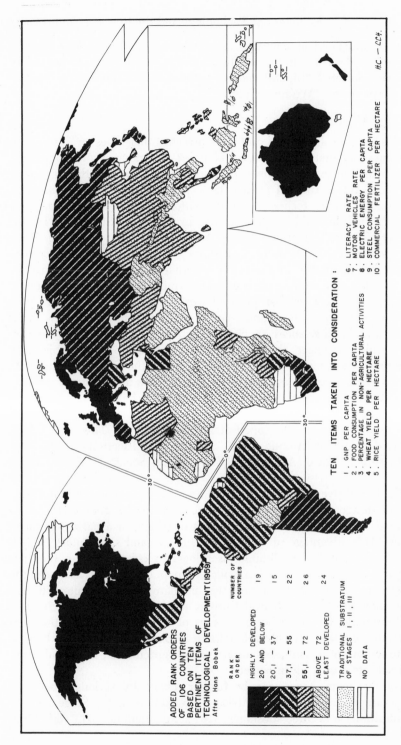

FIGURE 3: World pattern of Stage IV: Mechanization.

ADDED RANK ORDERS
OF 106 COUNTRIES
BASED ON TEN
PERTINENT ITEMS OF
TECHNOLOGICAL DEVELOPMENT (1959)
After Hans Bobek

RANK ORDER		NUMBER OF COUNTRIES
HIGHLY DEVELOPED	20 AND BELOW	19
	20,1 - 37	15
	37,1 - 55	22
	55,1 - 72	26
LEAST DEVELOPED	ABOVE 72	24

TRADITIONAL SUBSTRATUM
OF STAGES I, II, III

NO DATA

TEN ITEMS TAKEN INTO CONSIDERATION :

1 . GNP PER CAPITA
2 . FOOD CONSUMPTION PER CAPITA
3 . PERCENTAGE IN NON-AGRICULTURAL ACTIVITIES
4 . WHEAT YIELD PER HECTARE
5 . RICE YIELD PER HECTARE
6 . LITERACY RATE
7 . MOTOR VEHICLES RATE
8 . ELECTRIC ENERGY PER CAPITA
9 . STEEL CONSUMPTION PER CAPITA
10 . COMMERCIAL FERTILIZER PER HECTARE

HC — CCH

293

part, by independent adoption as in the case of Japan. This stage is also referred to as "Industrial Revolution," "Coal Age," Industrial or Complex Society," "Liberal and/or Authoritarian Capitalism," "Productive Capitalism," "Western Culture," etc.

Stage V: Automation

In this stage, self-guiding and self-correcting machines or systems of machines automatically perform complex programmes of production; human labour mainly devises, produces, and maintains the automatic machines; the mastery of nuclear energy opens new possibilities. Automation, the latest technological revolution, did not gain momentum until the middle of this century so that, in contrast to Stages I to IV, the impact of Stage V at this time can only be tentatively evaluated. However, some significant features of Stage V are already evident or may be predicted: greatly increasing productivity coupled with decreasing working hours; extensive changes in the traditional pattern of farming; changing relations between place of work and place of residence; phenomenal increase in recreational land use all over the world; new forms of research in all sciences, specifically with regard to the earth environment and outer space; the prospect of using hitherto inaccessible earth materials (e.g., mining of the ocean floors) and the use of a multiplicity of new natural resources. The most striking new development is man's capacity to escape temporarily from his native habitat, the earth environment. The fastest upsurge to Stage V is obviously occurring in nations with a highly developed Stage IV technology. This stage is also referred to as the "Atomic Age," "Space Age," "Electronic Age," "Age of Leisure," "Age of Affluence," "The Affluent Society," etc.

The terms given for the five stages are of a very general nature; they do not designate a particular material, a particular period of time, a particular way of life, a particular area of origin, or a particular racial group. This advantage of universality in time and space must be balanced off against their limited usefulness in circumscribing the particular cultural situation of a concrete population. For instance, the nineteenth-century Arab culture was in many respects quite different from the culture of mediaeval Europe, although both were technologically in Stage III. A further advantage of this classification is that it is brief, to the point, and interrelated in a recognizable hierarchical order. More important, it embraces all activities (agricultural, industrial, commercial, etc.) of a given society.

The five main stages may be further refined by various sub-stages. For example, in my work on Africa I have differentiated Stage III (diversification) into three substages: III_1, state kingdoms; III_2, state kingdoms plus specialized craftsmen and merchants; III$_3$, full-fledged diversification as described above.

A Hypothetical Case Study

With the help of this generalized concept the cultural geographer is able to predict the potential impact of man's five major stages of technology upon any type of natural environment. For example, one may choose an arid tropical climate; it is assumed that it has the typical features of vegetation (semi-desert), soils, and water and that landforms are inconspicuous. Now, the generalized Stages I through V may be let play upon the generalized type of natural environment.

Man in a Stage I technology (Adaptation) could make no better use of the vegetation and animal life of the tropical semi-desert than by gathering and hunting. The social organization would consist of small groups that would be economically self-sufficient. These would have to lead a nomadic way of life centred around scattered sources of easily available water. This impact upon the natural environment would be insignificant, and the pre-existing natural landscape would persist.

Man in a Stage II technology (Domestication) would have the potential of either an agricultural or a herding occupation. In the given semi-desert environment, the choice would have to be herding which would be most successfully conducted in small groups. This would necessitate a nomadic way of life because plant and water resources would be quickly exhausted within a specific grazing area. In contrast to Stage I, Stage II technology could provide drinking water for man and beasts procured from considerable depths at many convenient points. The impact upon the natural environment of this technology would be much stronger than the previous one, but the landscape would remain in a quasi-natural state.

In a Stage III technology (Diversification) man would have tools, techniques, and social organizations that would enable the group to cope with the water problem (the major limitation of the arid environment) much more successfully. In favourable areas, the hidden water resources could be mobilized for highly productive oasis agriculture. In addition, the bulk of the semi-desert lands would be used by nomadic herders functionally tied to agricultural oases. Extensive market relations and a network of central places would of necessity develop. The natural landscape would be made into a semi-cultural landscape.

The same environment would be used very differently in Stage IV technology (Mechanization) with the emphasis not on subsistence but on production for a national or world-wide market. Water resources would be tapped very differently so that where necessary throughout the arid land deep drilling, pumping, and piping techniques would be applied to secure drinking or irrigation water. The most favourable areas might be used as irrigated cropland while the rest would be grazing land—although no longer in a nomadic form, but in the form of fenced, sedentary ranches. Ranches would be linked by a network of roads to a hierarchical system of central places that would, in turn, be linked by road, rail, sea, and air transportation to the outside world. Hidden mineral resources not accessible to man in Stages I, II, and III could be exploited. In fact, all potential resources—water, soil, climate, plants, animals, minerals, recreational potentials—would be subject to the inquisitive mind of man in Stage IV. Thus, the impact upon the landscape would be systematic so that it would receive a strong and distinctive cultural imprint throughout.

In a fully developed Stage V technology (Automation), one can only speculate on the innovations that would take place. However, a few potential developments might be suggested. Piped water from far-distant areas could supply moisture for irrigated agriculture if a market demand for such products existed. Ranching most likely would be quite different from that of today's Stage IV. If the example of tropical arid lands cited above might have been previously used by Stage IV technology, in such a case unprofitable ranches might well be converted to a huge nature conservation area populated by scientifically managed wild game. In this event, pleasure hunting by nature-addicted Stage V man could develop as the principal usage. Quite likely hypothetical Mr. Automation would not use a helicopter and atomic shells in his rifle, but would hunt with bow and arrow, albeit elaborate ones, manufactured of synthetic chemicals.

In such a way a man in Stage V technology may choose the same type of land use as man in Stage I technology had adopted, namely, hunting wild game. There is, however, a world of difference between the two. Stage I man in a tropical semi-desert land has no better choice than hunting and gathering; he hunts in order to live. Man endowed with a stage V technology, on the other hand, may use the tropical arid lands in many different ways, one of which may be hunting for sport, for pleasure. The "affluent" hunts no longer to live, but "lives to hunt."

If the stage theory of human occupance postulated in this paper is applied to a *particular* arid tropical environment, the semi-deserts of southern Africa, rather than to a hypothetical case, a number of useful observations can be made. The way of life of the Bushman hunter and gatherers of southern Africa obviously conforms fully to the generalized description of a Stage I technology. Stage II is represented by nomadic herders, the Herero and the Hottentots. However, large portions of the southern Kalahari basin, filled with deep sand deposits, could never be used by these Stage II herders for lack of accessible water resources.

Stage IV technology is represented by European-introduced ranches in the Karroo, along the more accessible borders of the Kalahari, and by deep drilling even in the interior of the sand-filled Kalahari basin. On the other hand, why are there no oases, market towns, established traffic routes as predicted by the stage theory? In vain one may search for causes within the natural environment, but the reason is readily found in the absence of pre-European peoples living in a fully developed Stage III technology. In contrast, the arid lands of northern Africa have been occupied by Berbers and Arabs who could make use of a high Stage III technology in developing their poor resource base.

Thus, by comparing the particular kind of human occupance of a given environment with a theoretically predictable sequence (Stages I to IV) it is possible to gain a fuller insight into some of the central problems of cultural geography.

The Problem in a World-wide Frame

This experiment in geographic thinking should now be carried beyond the example of an arid tropical environment into the natural environments of the whole earth shell. Here, the first problem is to reduce the infinite variety of the physical environment to a small number of generalized types. A lead to the solution of this is provided by the concept of the "generalized continent" which reduces the complex configuration of the earth's land and water bodies to the well-known simple, average shape that disregards all landform differentiations. What must be retained in the "generalized continent" are the pertinent features of the atmosphere near the earth's surface and the causally associated features of the hydrosphere, the pedosphere, and the biosphere that are so essential for the provision of the basic natural resources from which man provides food, clothing, and shelter.

In taking the "generalized continent" and applying the Köppen system of climatic classification to it, one may arrive at as few as fourteen climatic types with differentiations that seem relevant to human occupation (Af, Am, Aw, BSh, BWh, BSk, BWk, Cs, Cfa, Cfb and c, Dfb, Dfc and d, ET, EF). These fourteen types of climate can be taken as causing fourteen types of generalized natural environments, each with a distinct combination of inorganic-organic qualities. These, in turn, may be considered as the scene upon which the five major stages of technology operate. Thus one may formulate a matrix of five cultural by fourteen natural variables which provides seventy potential types of technological impact upon the physical environment. In this way, an intellectually manageable number of highly generalized types is substituted for the infinite, and therefore intellectually unmanageable, variety of real man's occupation of the real environment. What has been gained by this finite set of normative-structural types is a general norm against which infinite reality can be compared, evaluated, and thus comprehended.

It seems that such an approach should lead to the core of cultural geography, making man's occupance of the earth shell intelligible. Also, it would appear that it could displace the outmoded factual descriptive approach which still characterizes to a large degree our present-day geography, and is intellectually unrewarding in that it is unable to provide real insight. Intellectual tension penetrates a science either by relating a known to an unknown by means of the priciple of cause, or by relating a known (an ideal, a general principle, or a model) to an unknown (the complex reality) by means of the normative-structural principle. The normative-structural principle is most appropriate in geography, as postulated clearly by Otto Wernli.[7]

In sum, it is contended here that the basic problem in cultural geography might be tackled at three different levels: (1) by "description" (i.e., a modest generalization working with "micro-concepts"); (2) by strong abstraction and generalization (working with "macro-concepts"); and (3) by theoretical models. In this paper the basic problem in cultural geography has been exposed (but, of course, not solved!) in the light of the second level. The third level may be tried by experts in constructing and using theoretical models.[8]

Some Geographic "Fringe Benefits"

Finally, there are three points of general concern to human or cultural geography that can be derived from this paper. *First*, it is suggested that cultural geography should not be conceived as the study of the distributional aspects of cultural phenomena, rather than that the cultural geographer should make use of the basic findings of the other social sciences in undertaking his major task, the study of "man's role in changing the face of the earth."

Second, it is felt that a useful vantage point from which a general evaluation of man's relation to his physical environment can be formulated is gained. "Environmental determinism" suggests an unawareness

---

[7] O. Wernli: Die neuere Entwicklung des Landschaftsbegriffes. *Geographica Helvetica*, 13, 1958, pp. 1–59.

[8] I. Burton: The Quantitative Revolution and Theoretical Geography. *Can. Geog.*, VII, 4, 1963, pp. 151–62. With Burton, whose article I have read with great interest and approval after completion of this manuscript, I don't see any essential dichotomy in aims between geographers that operate with qualitative terms and theories and geographers that make use of quantitative methods and theoretical models. Coexistence of qualitative and quantitative methods, I would say, is not only possible but imperative for the continuous evolution of scientific geography. Ian Burton's article is, by the way, a perfect example of the good use to which a quantifier can put *qualitative* methods in expressing theoretical ideas and conveying them to others.

of the fundamental rôle that man's cultural differentiation plays in human geography. Determinism has considered "man" as a constant entity, which reacts passively to the active stimuli of the "geographical influences." In my view, "determinism" provides seemingly useful results only under *special* conditions, where one specific culture and its relation to the environment are taken into consideration.[9] Nowadays, a tendency in complete opposition to "environmental determinism" can be sensed; it could be termed "cultural determinism." It assumes that modern man, with the aid of his advanced technology, barely needs to take into consideration the various conditions of the physical environment. Another hypothesis can be related to Febvre's brand of "possibilism." [10] Derived from the views expressed in this paper, man's relation to the physical environment could be stated by the "resource concept" as the impact of man's cultures (through his technologies) in the rôle of *active* variables upon the natural environment in the rôle of *passive* variables.[11]

Third, the difference between "developed" and "underdeveloped" societies can be stated more accurately. "Developed" societies are those which have achieved a full Stage IV technology (Mechanization) or are in transition to Stage V technology (Automation). And through this classification "underdeveloped" societies can be more clearly and precisely characterized: it makes a great difference if a society in a Stage I (Adaptation), II (Domestication), or III (Diversification) aspires to reach a fully fledged Stage IV technology.[12]

[9] G. Taylor: Australia and Canada: A Study of Habitability as Determined by the Environment. *Prof. Geog.*, XIII, 1961, pp. 1–5.
[10] G. Tatham: Environmentalism and Possibilism. In *Geography of the Twentieth Century*, Methuen, London, 1951.
[11] H. L. Hunker, Ed.: *Erich W. Zimmermann's Introduction to World Resources*, Harper and Row, New York, 1964.
[12] W. W. Rostow: *The Stages of Economic Growth*. Cambridge University Press, Cambridge, Eng., 1960. Rostow's five stages designate characteristic economic phases (such as the "take-off" stage) within the transition from our stage III (diversification) to a fully developed stage IV (mechanization).

23. Natural Resources and Economic Development

Norton Ginsburg

Natural resources are the most important economic elements, and their collection, utilization, transformation, and consumption make up the phases of the economic process. The uneven distribution of these resources and the different

*stages of technology in various areas of the world influence
economic development and constitute an important
problem confronting emerging nations.*

The preoccupation of economists and other social scientists with the
phenomenon of economic development, especially in the so-called
underdeveloped countries and increasingly since the end of the Second
World War, has resulted in a spate of literature concerning the developmental process. This literature displays an extraordinary diversity of
interpretations and hypotheses regarding economic growth, suggesting
the deep-seated uncertainty about its character and the causal factors
which together may account for it. Increasingly, moreover, recourse has
been made to economic history for data with which to study and forecast
the course of economic growth in both developed and underdeveloped
countries.

The contributions of geographers to consideration of these problems,
however, have been few. This is all the more surprising since one of the
major factors entering into the course of economic development—natural
resources—is of particular concern to them. Furthermore, the areal
differentiation of economic conditions and prospects has long been at
the heart of economic geography.

This paper presents some reflections on the role natural resources
play in the course of economic growth, especially in the lesser developed
regions of the world. The basic questions it asks are: How important
are natural resources in the course of economic development, and what
relationships do they bear to other factors which enter into the developmental complex? No attempt is made to provide a complete conceptual
framework within which geographic research on development problems
can be pursued more meaningfully, but the conclusions may help prepare the foundations for such a structure.

The Measurement of Development

The terms "developed" and "underdeveloped" have by no means been
defined precisely. If we adopt the broad interpretation of "development"
as meaning the maximization of all available resources (in the economist's sense, whether "natural" in origin or not), then no country can
be termed "developed," since none can demonstrate completely efficient
use of all its assets. The United States, the U.S.S.R., and the western
European countries, as well as Afghanistan, all may be considered
"underdeveloped" in this sense.

Commonly, therefore, the terms are defined on a comparative basis.
The criterion most commonly employed is that of *per capita national*

Source: *Annals of the Association of American Geographers,* XLVII (September,
1957), 196–212. The author is professor of geography, University of Chicago.

product, that is, the value per person in a given country or region of all goods and services produced in one year by its total population. National product (or income) per capita provides an index to the state of an economy and to the position it occupies along the continuum between "development" and "underdevelopment." In this connection, it is important to point out that these two terms refer specifically to economics. They in no sense represent value judgments concerning the non-economic achievements of any society.

Per capita national product clearly is a better indicator of economic conditions than gross national product, which ignores the essential relationships of population to national economies, and tends toward bias in favor of countries with large populations, whatever their demographic characteristics. For example, in 1955 India was estimated to have a gross national product of 27.4 billion dollar-equivalents (slightly more than Canada), which ranked it seventh among the nations of the world. In terms of national product per capita, however, India ranked next to China among the major nations, near the lowest levels of the scale; the figure assigned it ($72) was only about three percent that for the United States. Per capita national product, therefore, is an index to individual levels of living, and these in turn are assumed to reflect the state of economic well-being.

It also is an index particularly applicable to the measurement of *rate* of economic growth and the degree to which economic production is keeping ahead of or following behind population growth. A country's economy may be expanding rapidly, as reflected in a growing gross national product. On the other hand, individual incomes and levels of living may decline if population is increasing more rapidly than gross national product. This point is of crucial importance in the cases of the densely populated underdeveloped regions, such as India or China, where the rate of economic growth must exceed the rate of population increase by a considerable margin if economic difficulties are to be resolved and economic growth is to become self-generating. In other words, the individual worker under such circumstances must be able to "save" (or have put aside in his stead) enough capital to enlarge the productive facilities of the country sufficiently, after his own wants are satisfied, to permit expansion of the means of production at an accelerating rate.

The range of "development" among countries, as measured in these terms, is enormous. In 1955, for example, the United States is reported to have had a per capita national product of $2,343; Sweden, $1,165; the United Kingdom, $998; the U.S.S.R., $682; Italy, $442; Colombia, $330; Japan, $240; Mexico, $187; Egypt, $133; Thailand, $100; the Central African Federation, $61; and China (exclusive of Taiwan), $56.
. . . If we assume quite arbitrarily that a per capita product under

$300 defines "underdevelopment," then we find that the underdeveloped peoples dominate the world, not only in area, but also in numbers. Almost all of Asian Asia, all of Africa except the Union of South Africa, and most of Latin America fall into the underdeveloped category. Included are some 1,780 million people, roughly 68 percent of the world's population.[1]

Problems of Comparing Resources with Product

The preceding discussion is designed to introduce the problem of evaluating the importance of the natural resources factor in the developmental process. If we assume that per capita product is a sound indicator of stages of economic development, then what is required is an analysis of the relationship between the natural resource endowment and per capita product or income in different countries or regions. Unfortunately, for a number of reasons this seemingly practical approach is fraught with difficulties, and indeed may be misleading or impossible.

In the first place, the very concept of national product (or income) per capita is elusive, and its measurement is extremely difficult. The data supplied by ICA are in U.S. dollar-equivalents, converted from local currencies at the official exchange rates. However, the greater purchasing power of the dollar in certain countries may markedly alter the indicated rank-ordering along the continuum between "development" and "underdevelopment." Differences between the real and official value of the dollar also may explain in part the enormous discrepancy in product value between the United States and Canada on the one hand, and certain of the western European countries on the other.

Furthermore, and this may be far more significant, the data assume value systems in non-Western societies which are similar to those in the West and place high monetary value on the same sorts of goods and services.[2] In addition, the data for the lesser developed regions vastly

[1] The distribution of "underdevelopment," or what might be called "economic problemness," presents a fascinating prospect for geographical analysis. Observe the association of the underdeveloped countries for the most part with the lower latitudes; their concentration north of the 30th parallel in the Americas and the 40th parallel in Eurasia; the splendid isolation of Australasia; the fact that, apart from Europe, it is the former "vacant" lands of the New and Australasian worlds which have become most developed economically; the colossal concentration of "underdevelopment" as opposed to the nearly as imposing localization of "development"; and the contrast between the two, the "West" on the one hand and the rest of the world on the other. Some of these observations will be expanded upon in a later paper.

[2] Frankel, *The Economic Impact on Under-Developed Societies* (Oxford: Basil Blackwell, 1953), pp. 31ff. In his discussion, Frankel points out the hidden assumption underlying many universally applied indices to national production and income, such as Colin Clark's, that societal differences "would not affect the purposes for which [an individual] desires or spends income."

understate the importance of goods and services about which we know little, but which may be of great importance to the natives of those regions. This understatement, together with the value-system objection, is exemplified in the case of Pakistan, for example, where the per capita product is estimated at 56 U.S. dollar-equivalents annually. If we assume that the consumption requirements of the Pakistani in any direct way resemble those of Americans, then we also would have to assume that there would have to be many fewer Pakistanis than there now are, since most of them would be dead or dying of starvation and exposure. The actual per capita production in Pakistan, therefore, must, on the one hand, be far greater than it appears to be and, on the other, be of quite a different character than that of the West in order to explain the continued existence of the Pakistanis themselves.

Finally, data concerning national income and production are of the very roughest order for many countries of the world. Indeed, it is only the countries of the West for which reasonably accurate national production and income data are available. The very data upon which the indicator to develop is so often based, therefore, are in themselves highly suspect. Indeed, the degree to which data concerning economic phenomena are available provides almost as useful an indicator to economic development, or lack of it, as the indicator itself.

In spite of these objections, per capita national product provides a rough and useful indicator, probably the best single indicator, of the stage a country has attained on the economic developmental scale. If for the moment we accept it in this light, why cannot we proceed directly to relate natural resources to it? The objections are two. First, as Kuznets makes clear, "comparison requires reduction to a common denominator." In the case of economic development there is an index—per capita capital national product. What comparable index can be used to measure resources? One conceivable measure would be the extent of their utilization per capita and the nature of their exploitation. But utilization is in turn a covariant of the same economic processes for which per capita income is an index. It would be meaningless to compare one aspect of a process with another aspect that varies virtually identically with it. What we probably would be saying is a simple truism: that more highly developed regions (as defined in terms of high per capita production) exploit their natural resource endowments more effectively per capita (or per capita member of the labor force) than those less highly developed. Thus, the "common denominator" of which Kuznets speaks would become the very relationship we are trying to measure. The difficulty, of course, lies in the lack of a suitable alternative index to intensity of natural resource utilization, which can be compared directly with per capita indices to economic development.

Second, any development of indices to the utilization of natural resources presumes a substantial knowledge of the resource base itself, but attainment of this knowledge is circumscribed rigidly by the relative paucity of resource inventory data on a worldwide basis. Such inventories represent one of the primary needs for developmental planning in the lesser regions. Even if such inventories were in existence, however, the problem would remain of developing an index comparable to that for economic development itself. It would mean developing common denominators for such varied resources as hydroelectric energy, soils, drainage, growing season, etc. Since these vary in significance from society to society, from place to place, and from time to time, the development of such indices may prove insurmountably difficult.

This does not mean that we can afford to neglect natural resources in considering the economic realities or potentialities of a given country, despite the example of Switzerland which is called on interminably to illustrate the essential insignificance of the resource endowment to the development of a given region. The fact that orchids technically can be grown in greenhouses in Antarctica does not mean that hothouse agriculture is going to play a significant role in the development of that continent, although under presently unforeseeable circumstances, it might. At our present stage of knowledge, comparisons simply cannot be made between indices to natural resources and per capita indices to attained or potential economic growth, since the former do not yet exist and the latter need to be further refined. All that can be attempted, perhaps, are relatively imprecise and qualitative evaluations of the relations between natural resources available at any one time to any one region and the various other elements which together bear upon the course of economic development. Such evaluations, however, demand some explanation of these several elements and their interrelations.

Major Factors in Economic Development

The classical economists spoke of at least three major factors of production—land, labor, and capital. To these may be added at least two other determinants of economic development—technology and cultural configurations. These factors and determinants will be examined briefly in their reverse order, a reordering which may suggest, but does not define, their significance in the developmental process.

By *cultural configurations* is meant that system of social organization, combined with constellations of values, goals, or objectives, which all societies possess in different combinations. These social systems vary among societies, sometimes only to a modest degree, often sharply. Without resorting to Parsonian terminology, it is clear that some societies are oriented toward goals which emphasize individual initiative and the production of goods and services beyond basic needs. In such a society wants tend to be unlimited, and the entrepreneur becomes a symbol of the means through which these wants may be satisfied and in turn expanded. In other societies, in contrast, material wants may be prescribed within a relatively inelastic cultural configuration to which the entrepreneurial spirit is alien. These model conceptions are, of course, not wholly realistic, but they serve to suggest that in some societies rapid or accelerated economic growth is actively demanded, whereas in others it may not be sought. If a presently underdeveloped country (as measured in terms of very low per capita product) is to develop rapidly, it must have a "will" to develop. That "will" must be possible within the context of its value system, or its value system must be changed, since it lies at the center of institutional barriers to both economic and cultural change. The relations of these observations to natural resource use are direct and clear. Use implies *consciousness* of need and the *will* to invest in the effort required to exploit a given resource. Without them, resource development will not take place, except by outsiders.

Awareness of need, moreover, implies both a knowledge of the uses to which given resources can be put and an understanding of the ways by which those resources can be made available to meet those needs. This knowledge and understanding may be subsumed under the heading of *technology*. All societies, of course, possess a technology, and some of these have made possible the production of surpluses which have introduced economic flexibility into the social system, but historically these technologies have differed conspicuously among themselves. What is meant here, moreover, is a more specifically Western technology, that combination of scientific knowledge and practical engineering which goes by the name "know-how" in the propaganda of American assistance agencies.

Perhaps the most significant aspect of this Western technology is its mobility. All *literate* peoples can *in time* acquire it. Furthermore, it is cheap and rather easily available. Its transfer, however, often may be slow, unless imported in the persons of foreign advisers. These can in turn direct the exploitation of natural resources in ways which probably were not possible by means of indigenous technologies and in directions of use which might not even have been contemplated before.

The fluidity of technology has long acted, in fact, somewhat to the advantage of countries of lesser degrees of development in that they may be able to incorporate into their industrial establishments the latest technical improvements and thereby make these establishments more efficient than the older plants in the already developed countries. It is not unlikely, all other things being equal, that the three new steel plants being constructed in India under British, Russian, and German supervision, respectively, will be among the more efficient in the world, although the differences in organization and tooling among them may in the long run be a national disadvantage rather than advantage. In this connection it also is conceivable that a lesser developed country can practice economies of scale by sizable "crash" programs of development in narrow sectors of its economy, whether they be agricultural or industrial, given suitable availability of other factors of production, especially capital.

If imported skills and services can be purchased relatively inexpensively with the third element of the five—*capital*—other needs for economic growth usually cannot be purchased so cheaply, and large capital accumulations are agreed generally to be necessary if economic development is to be rapid. The accumulation of capital is one of the major difficulties of the lesser developed countries, since many of them are characterized by value systems which place a low premium on saving and a high premium on the allocation of such surpluses as are available to ends that are capital-disseminating rather than accumulating. All, by definition, are characterized by low per capita incomes, which probably mean small surpluses to begin with.

Capital can be acquired and accumulated, however, in several ways— at least in the short run by (1) importation in the form of loans or grants, as in the case of many recipients of aid from the United States or the Colombo Plan countries, for example; (2) the squeezing of living standards to or even below the subsistence level, as was the case in the Soviet Union and may be the case in China; or (3) the rapid creation of surpluses through the application of rapidly acquired technology to given resource endowments.

The third method can take place on one of two levels, either (a) through the improvement of traditional methods of production, as in the case of agriculture and sericulture in immediately post-Meiji Japan, or (b) through the introduction of new technologies directed toward the exploitation of hitherto unused resources, the production of which then can be exported. Here, the examples of Saudi Arabia, Kuwait, Iraq, and Venezuela, and the exploitation of their petroleum resources provide striking examples, as do the mining of gold and diamonds in South Africa. *The role of natural resources in these situations is that of an agent for rapid capital formation,* which may be directed toward ends not directly related to resource utilization, such as improvements in public health and the spread of literacy.

Variations in the quality of public sanitation and medical care or education in turn substantially modify the character of our fourth major factor, *labor.* It is a truism that in order to economically develop, there must be people to develop economically, and their effectiveness as a labor force will vary almost directly with their numbers, health, skills, and discipline. In relatively "new" areas of pioneer settlement, where ratios of people to developable resources are low, every addition to the labor force means a major increment in regional product. This is particularly important when the additions to the labor force are skilled, rather than unskilled. As Hoselitz, Minsky, and others have noted, the rapid economic expansion of the United States from the middle of the nineteenth century on was in no small part due to the massive imports of "capital" in the form of some of Europe's most skilled workmen, although this form of capital does not appear in capital import figures. The recipient country in such cases also is spared the costs of supporting and training the technician until such time as he is able to contribute to the economy; these costs are borne by the "exporting" country.

However, labor not only produces, it consumes; and in many of the great lesser developed regions the effectiveness of the labor force as a means for increasing productivity is hampered by its very numbers and the very high ratio of population to exploited resources. The stagnation which may be associated with these conditions is exaggerated by the wastage of human energy and the discouragement of ambition by seasonal underemployment, ill-health, malnutrition, and a combination of ignorance and poor technology. The vicious circle of stagnation can be broken, it is true, but only by the introduction of new technologies which substantially alter the relations of labor to the natural resources it exploits, at costs of varying dimensions and at the initiative of foreign or indigenous elites which represent a discontinuity with traditional cultural configurations.

It is clear that the course of economic growth is singularly complex and the factors which enter into it are mutually interdependent. It is not correct to say, as some cultural anthropologists might, that indigenous cultural configurations alone determine the nature of economic growth; nor can one support the geographical determinist, if such there be, who would maintain that the nature of the physical environment (or the resource base) directs the course of economic progress. All elements move together, often disjointedly and arhythmically like a man on crutches, but, in sum, in one direction.

Natural Resources: The Fifth Element in Economic Development

If these intimate interrelationships can thus be demonstrated, and if each of these elements in economic growth varies with each of the others, then our fifth variable, *natural resources,* becomes a concept as elusive and dynamic as any of the other four. To the geographer, natural resources in their broadest sense include all the freely given material phenomena of nature within the zone of men's activities, at present a zone extending about twelve miles above the surface of the earth and about four miles below it, plus the additional nonmaterial quality of situation or location. The association of these elements of land, air, sea, and situation in a single area commonly is identified as its "resource base" or "resource endowment."

This definition is misleading, however, in that it assumes a complete knowledge of the ways in which the physical environment may be utilized. This knowledge is in no sense complete, and, in the words of Zimmerman, much of the environment is in fact composed of "neutral stuff" awaiting awareness of its possibilities and the development of technologies which can exploit it effectively. The dimensions of these understandings and the abilities to exploit the resource base, however defined, vary with cultures, with time, and with space. It is necessary, therefore, to distinguish between resource potentialities and a resource endowment both available and understood.

In East Asia, for example, there tends to be a seemingly remarkable neglect of upland areas, that is, of those areas either not suitable for paddy cultivation or convenient for the production of dry crops, even under topographic, climatic, and edaphic conditions which are matched by many productive agricultural areas elsewhere in the world. In large part this condition reflects technologies which are unable to cope with the conditions that exist in the upland areas or which are at least better suited to the physical conditions characteristic of the lowlands. The result is a system of agricultural production geared to the better lands which produce more per unit area at the cost of staggering labor outputs and which, at the expense of seasonal underemployment, suffer labor shortages at the key periods of planting and harvesting.

In the time dimension, resource variations are illustrated by the Great Plains, the rich grassland soils of which were almost entirely neglected by the Plains Indians and which now are one of the great granaries of the world. Another example is the fertile prairies of central Illinois, which at first were neglected by the white settlers from southern Indiana, Kentucky, and Tennessee, who first settled in the more familiar narrow, wooded fluvial lowlands which infrequently scar the smooth prairie surface. Variations in time also may reflect simply the exhaustion of a given resource; witness the ghost mining towns of Colorado or the abandoned farms of western Oklahoma, where the fertile topsoil was partly removed by wind erosion, and drought completed the destruction of what might have been productive grazing lands under careful range management.

Existing resources may remain in the potential category also because of inaccessibility. Inaccessibility may reflect a technical inability to withdraw a material from its matrix of associated elements, as until recently in the case of titanium, one of the new wonder metals. Or it may reflect a simple lack of external economies, as in the case of some ten percent of Japan's forest reserves which remain unexploited because of a lack of transportation facilities.

This point leads to another *caveat* regarding the above definition of natural resources. If a given resource is not accessible, it cannot be described as "freely given," since it cannot be exploited without investment of "capital" in one of its several forms. The qualification may be extended to almost all resources, since they must be acted upon in order to become useful to men. It follows that many resources, as they come into use, are no more "natural" than they are "cultural." Is a long-fertilized, irrigated, and cultivated soil or a planted stand of Japanese cedar "natural?" Only to a degree, of course. We can conceive, therefore, of a classification of resources based upon their degree of "naturalness" in which classification would take place perhaps according to the amount of capital required to make them available.

Two other characteristics of resources remain to be noted. The first is their substitutability, the second their complementarity.

Changes in technology mean changes in resource uses and in a sense competition among resources for given uses. The substitution of certain plastics, some based upon coal, for metals provides one illustration. At one time also the tin can was made of tin plate, that is, sheet steel dipped into molten tin; at a later stage electrolytic tin-plating permitted major savings in tin through much thinner tin coatings over the steel; now many so-called "tin cans" are coated with a fine film of tin only on the outside and are lined with plastic on the inside. In addition, glass containers compete with the "tin can" as a means for packaging foodstuffs. Substitutability has its geographic aspects as well. A given resource in one area that cannot bear the costs of distant transport may be substituted for in another by a more abundant resource. For example, Philippine mahogany or *lauan* and other tropical hardwoods replace genuine mahogany in parts of Asia; and in many Asian countries the ubiquitous bamboo provides an inexpensive scaffolding nearly as efficient and far less costly than the timber, aluminum, or steel scaffoldings used in the middle-latitude West.

Finally, resources tend to complement each other, to be linked in a chain of utilization patterns and of productive processes in which the production of one demands or effects the production or availability of others. The mining and use of iron ore in steel manufacturing demands limestone and coal; the strip-mining of coal destroys valuable farm land in southern Illinois or southeastern Kansas; the clean-cutting of timber in forested areas in Japan is reflected in the silting of reservoirs downstream; and the development of hydroelectric installations in the Columbia River has accelerated the diminution of the salmon fisheries off the coasts of Oregon and Washington. Not only may resources be linked into a complex of productive processes, but also, as

Colby has suggested, the development of facilities for the exploitation of any one resource may make possible the utilization of an entirely unrelated resource. He cites the example of branches of the Southern Pacific Railway from Ogden, Utah, to San Francisco, which were constructed to provide access to the gold, silver, and copper ores of Nevada, but which then made possible the development of a profitable grazing industry centering in oasis-like settlements along the lower flanks of the mountain ranges crossed or paralleled by them.

It is a characteristic of the more highly developed and industrialized economies that they can take into account and integrate complementary resources into systems of production. *In this sense, they are less specialized, less fragmented, and more flexible in terms of resource use than the lesser developed economies in which extreme specialization of resource utilization tends to be practiced* partly because of less highly developed and therefore less flexible technologies. Even the Chinese, advanced as they were a millennium and more ago in the control of water, cleansed the silted channels of their irrigation systems simply by dredging or flushing out the silt periodically; integrated watershed control of water supplies, though known, was not practiced. In effect, the use-possibilities among resources are fewer than in the more highly developed economies.

Economic Development in Relation to Natural Resources

The nature of resource utilization in any society depends upon, and in turn reflects upon, the nature of the economic development that is taking place within it. This development varies, however, with the size and nature of the unit under examination. The question may be phrased: "The economic development of what?" As Kuznets points out, we ordinarily would not seriously discuss the resource development problems of an Andorra or a Monaco. Nevertheless, problems of economic variability arise for minute areas.

For example, Singapore, a British Crown Colony, is well on its way to independence within the Commonwealth. As a politically autonomous unit, Singapore, an island only 26 miles from east to west and 14 miles from south to north, is endowed with a minimum of significant natural resources. It consists of one great metropolis rapidly expanding its urbanized area, surrounded by wasteland and intensively cultivated Chinese market gardens and fishing villages which supply it with only a minute fraction of its food requirements. Its major natural resource, one most difficult to measure quantitatively, is its situation astride the chief maritime gateway between the Indian Ocean and the South China Sea. This situation, combined with certain qualities of British institutions in the area, such as political stability, a sound currency, and an elaborate system of shipping and banking services, plus the entrepreneurial enterprise of its largely Chinese population, make a viable economic future conceivable, much as in the commercial city-states of the Hanseatic League. Even though politically autonomous, Singapore as a great regional commercial center and entrepôt will be economically dependent on political and economic conditions wholly beyond its control. The point here is the relative irrelevance of natural resources other than situation as a positive factor in the economic development of such a city-state. In a negative sense, however, the absence of a resource endowment and a virtually complete dependence upon the outside world for subsistence is a crucial factor in determining Singapore's ability to survive world economic depressions and political transformations over which it has no control.

On the other hand, one can point to a tiny state, such as the Sheikhdom of Kuwait, only 1,930 square miles in size and mostly unproductive desert, which is riding the crest of a rising national income almost entirely from petroleum production alone. Here the significance of a single natural resource is overwhelming.

Nevertheless, under normal circumstances, it is reasonable to postulate that the larger and more varied the resource base of a given state, the more opportunities it will have, *ceteris paribus,* for rapid economic development. All of the major industrialized countries have, or have had, relatively large and diversified resource endowments, and the United States is perhaps the most striking example. But even the United States is far from self-sufficient in natural resources, and lesser political units are even less so.

This being the case, would it not be more productive in the long run to consider the economic development of some supranational unit, such as the British Commonwealth, or western Europe, or the Latin Americas?[3] The prewar Japanese Empire was such a unit and was self-contained to a surprising degree, a degree hidden in part by the fact that Japan's prewar trade statistics did not include her most important trade orientations, those toward her dependencies—Korea, Taiwan, Karafuto, and later Manchuria.

Consideration of such supranational units of economic organization is beyond the scope of this paper, but one major point emerges from a consideration of them, that is, the distinction between the actual possession of a resource endowment *in situ,* and *accessibility* to resources which may be under the control of foreign states. Trade and transportation are the devices by which inequalities among nations in

[3] The productivity referred to here is solely economic. Integration may be practiced on a large scale for non-economic reasons. An example proposed by Munger is that of Portugal and her overseas dependencies for which integration is practiced only "by rigidly controlled departures from the world price system. . . . The values to the Portuguese are political not economic." From a communication to the author.

resource endowments may be minimized; but they can be minimized only at a cost. Every country dependent upon foreign areas for certain of its raw materials must be able to pay for them and for such services as transportation, banking services, and insurance which are necessary in order to make them available.

How can these payments be made? For those countries which already are highly industrialized, capital may be obtained from the production of processed and manufactured materials and services which may be exported in partial payment for needed raw-material imports. In the lesser developed countries, however, this option is unlikely to exist. Payment for imported foodstuffs and raw materials, as well as the manufactured goods which make domestic resource exploitation in part possible, depends in part on the availability of products, usually raw materials, suitable for export. In this context, mineral resources, food surpluses, and forest products tend to play an inordinately important role, at least for short periods of time.[4]

In addition, the exploitation of certain resources and the availability of their products for export often require considerable investment in external services of which transportation may be the most important. Indeed, accessibility means transportation. In the highly developed regions internal transportation systems have long since been developed, and external communications facilities in the form of national merchant marines also may have been created. In the lesser developed regions, however, these types of services often do not exist.[5] As a result, known resources may remain unexploitable, costs of imports will remain high, and raw material exports may be disadvantaged on the world market. Grants and loans from foreign sources provide another source of capital, but grants tend to be few, and loans must be repaid. The importance of loans should not be minimized, but ultimate development depends upon a country's own savings, internally organized, unless it is to become integrated fully into a larger economy as a constant recipient of foreign aid.

Problems of this kind indicate the need for rational planning whereby economic development can be guided. Unfortunately, planning often reflects the erroneous assumption that economic development in lesser developed countries must follow the patterns of development which took place in the new developed regions, and that resources and the nature of their utilization are fixed. However, even in comparing

[4] The export of labor and remittances from nationals abroad are other sources of income, e.g., remittances to China and Lebanon from nationals overseas, or miners from Mozambique employed in the mines of South Africa.

[5] In reality, the dimensions of these facilities vary markedly from country to country. In India, for example, the railway system developed by the British may be regarded as a "freely given, non-natural" resource inherited from its colonial past by a free India.

the patterns of economic growth in the already developed and industrialized countries, significant differences in the developmental process
are apparent. The relatively gradual economic growth characteristic
of Great Britain has not been duplicated since. As Gerschenkron points
out, early British industrialization took place without the large-scale
participation of banking interests or government and was financed
primarily by an accumulation of wealth derived from trade with a
great empire and to a degree with the remainder of the world as well.
In Germany, France, Italy, the U.S.S.R., and Japan, among others,
rapid economic growth took place under the leadership either of giant
banking interests or of the state.

It is apparent that the nature of economic growth will vary within
each unit under consideration and with the time at which accelerated
economic growth begins. Indeed, the rates of growth that are either
possible or desirable also will vary notably with place and time and
with the five major determinants of economic development previously
discussed. The reordering of comparative advantages in resource endowments as a result of new technologies, trade barriers, or intervening
resource discoveries of necessity changes the possibilities and potentialities of resource use and planning.

Recent changes in power technology provide a useful illustration.
According to Hartshorne, not one of the major industrial nations is or
was without access to major sources of energy, particularly the mineral
fuels. Britain acted as the coal mine of the world for a period of time,
and it is worth pointing out as well that at the time it entered upon
its period of modern economic development, Britain was unusually
well-endowed with other resources, such as iron ore, tin, and certain
lesser minerals, and even timber with which to construct a merchant
marine. Germany, France, and Russia also were well-endowed with
energy resources. Other countries, such as Italy, short of energy resources *in situ*, were able, albeit at a cost, to obtain mineral fuels from
outside their boundaries, or they developed hydroelectric potentials to
an exceptional degree. That the availability of energy raw materials
has not induced economic development, however, is illustrated by the
numerous underdeveloped areas well-endowed with such resources—
India is one example; China another.

More important, perhaps, is the future availability to the underdeveloped countries of energy from atomic reactors. At present this
energy is not cheap, especially in the small units which are likely to
be better suited to the needs of most of the lesser developed countries.
However, such energy will become available, if not now, then within
the next several decades. This does not mean that the development
of more traditional energy resources should be delayed; quite the
contrary, since these may remain less costly, given accessibility and

high quality, for a long period of time. It does suggest two important considerations, however: (1) that planning for energy and other natural resource development in the "have" countries must be kept flexible and constantly subject to review, and (2) that the "have-not" countries possess possibilities for economic growth based upon ample supplies of energy that previously were unthinkable.

Case Studies

Many of these various aspects of economic development and of the role of natural resources particularly—the variations that result from differences in the nature of the resource base, from differences in economic and political structure, and from differences in the state of the world economy at given times—may be illustrated by the comparative histories of Japan, Taiwan, Malaya, and to a degree, China and India.

Japan

Japan's modern economic development began late and with a marked socio-economic discontinuity after the fall of the Shogunate and the restoration of the Emperor in 1867. At that time, Japan was a country living right up to its then known and developed resource endowment, and emerging from a 200-year period of virtual isolation. Japan's resource endowment, then and now, is relatively niggardly. Arable land accounts for considerably less than 20 percent of the total land area, as compared with 40 percent in France, and the actual area under cultivation at present is not more than 15 percent of the whole. Soils are of indifferent fertility; growing seasons are long enough in most of the country to permit double-cropping, except in the highlands and in Hokkaido in the north, but they are not long enough to permit the double-cropping of paddy. Forest resources were then relatively abundant, though they now supply about 75 percent of Japan's wood needs only at the cost of their gradual diminution. Mineral resources are abundant in variety, but few are of great commercial significance, and coal, low-quality though it may be, is the single most important mineral resource. Hydroelectric potential, however, is relatively high for a country of its size, about 148,000 square miles, the size of Montana, and the Japanese have developed the larger part of it already.

At the time of the Meiji Restoration, moreover, the press of a population of about 35 millions on these resources under then prevailing technologies was high, and population had remained virtually unchanged for a number of years. Nevertheless, Japan was able to develop economically with enormous rapidity. How was this accomplished?

One thing is certain. The initial stages of the developmental process were financed primarily internally. Foreign loans and capital investment were very small, if strategic. Accumulation of domestic supplies of capital was made possible by the extraordinarily rapid development of the natural resource base and rapid increases in productivity from it. Until after the Sino-Japanese war, Japan's chief source of revenue was raw silk. Quite small investments in sericulture, especially in standardizing the quality of silk output and in increasing silk-reeling capacities, resulted in Japan's displacement of China as the world's prime supplier of raw silk and in the rapid expansion (resulting partly from greater purchasing power in western Europe and the United States) of the world silk market. At the same time, similarly small investments in agriculture through the provision of improved seed varieties, irrigation facilities, better transportation for marketing of agricultural products, and more fertilizers, resulted in agricultural surpluses, the profits of which were siphoned from the countryside by the government through improved tax mechanisms (forced saving), making possible the more massive participation of the state in providing external economies, in investing in alternative productive sectors of the economy, in restricting consumption in the rural areas, and in permitting the rapid growth of large urban complexes with their supplies of labor for modern industrial enterprises. It is even true that the Japanese cotton-textile industry was based originally on Japan-grown cotton, which was in adequate supply until the eighties when a sufficiently modern industry had been developed to require large imports of cotton from abroad. It was the textile industry, first silk and then cotton, that permitted rapid economic growth in Japan. It is safe to say also that the application of easily available improved technologies to the then Japanese resource base so increased its potential as to create surpluses for internal consumption and export. These then permitted the initiation by Japan of a program of heavy-industry development, later financed in part by foreign loans and capital as well as by an expanding export trade.

These assertions may be controversial, especially in light of the substantial inadequacy of Japan's resource base to support the present Japanese economy, but they should be regarded as partial justification for the previous description of natural resources as a means of capital formation and for the admonition that resource planning is a continuing process that varies with the needs and objectives of a given country and the changes in world resource equilibria.

Taiwan

The developmental history of Taiwan has taken place under different circumstances and with different results. Taiwan is a relatively small island about one-fourth the size of Illinois, with an indigenous Chinese population of about 8 millions. Under the Japanese, both gross national product and per capita product rose rapidly. These increases in production also may be said to have been internally financed by more efficient utilization of the island's natural resources, especially agricultural resources. Although only about a fourth of the island is topographically suitable for agriculture, soils are relatively fertile in that fourth, water supplies are relatively abundant, and the growing season permits double-cropping of paddy all over the island, except in the highest highlands. The Japanese invested sizable sums in Taiwan, but at the earliest stages these were designed more to promote political and military stability than not; at a later time, the evidence suggests that investment was far smaller than the value of the surpluses that continued to be produced from Formosan soil. Despite a rising population, agricultural production under the guidance of Japanese technical advisers backed by political authority forged ahead of population increases and permitted the export to Japan of three-quarters of a million tons of rice and a million tons of sugar each year. Some additional development took place in the mining of coal, but especially in the development of hydroelectric resources, which in turn made possible the establishment of aluminum and ferro-metallic processing plants. Consumers' goods, such as textiles, continued to be almost entirely imported.

At the close of the war Taiwan was separated from Japan. It possessed a highly developed agrarian economy which specialized in food crops, was commercially rather than subsistence oriented, and possessed sizable surpluses with which to finance more diversified economic development. Had all other factors remained constant, it is reasonably certain that these surpluses, based upon further improvements in the utilization of agricultural resources, would have permitted the establishment of a viable economy, either as a region of China or as an independent political unit. The great advantage was what we might call a "time-cushion" in the form of surpluses for export by means of which economic planning could have been financed and implemented despite the other limitations of the resource endowment.

Unfortunately, all other things never are equal, and Taiwan's population was swelled by 2,500,000 refugees and troops from China proper, who consume many of the agricultural surpluses and demand capital expenditures on the part of the two governments on the island, which further hamper economic growth. At the same time, the withdrawal of the Japanese agricultural technicians, believed to have numbered up to 20,000, and the diminution of political stability resulted in substantial declines in production which were not overcome until about 1952.

Taiwan still possesses a "time cushion," but its dimensions are much smaller than they were. Economic growth is taking place, and at a rapid rate, but in part by means of major grants-in-aid, which do not require repayment, from the United States. The island's economy is still primarily agrarian, although the reasonable limits of the development of the resource base with given technologies are beginning to be reached, and the significance of other factors is beginning to dominate the scene.

Malaya

The third and quite different example also concerns what might be termed a "colonial" economy, that of Malaya. . . . Unlike the relationship between Japan and Taiwan, that between Britain and Malaya never was so intimate, on either economic or political grounds. Malaya's economy, apart from the commercial functions of Singapore, is clearly dual, and was so from the earliest period of British hegemony. One major sector is Malay, indigenous, primarily agricultural and subsistence, based upon the cultivation of paddy by Malay villagers in restricted areas and secondarily upon Malay fishing activities. The second major sector is basically foreign in that it is managed and manned by non-Malay labor and financed by non-Malay capital, is commercial, and is export-oriented. It in turn is divided into two basic subsectors—one, the production of rubber; the other, the mining of tin. Each of these major sectors displays a notable direct reliance upon the existing resource base of the country. But unlike Taiwan, where there is a time cushion based upon surpluses of foodstuffs, the time cushion in Malaya is of quite a different sort, as is the role of the resource endowment in future development.

Malaya does not feed itself. Indeed, it imports more than half of its food supply. The predominantly food-producing Malay community, 49 percent of the total population, produces enough food only for itself and until very recently existed in relative isolation from the other communities in Malaya. Rubber and tin production have been primarily the result of foreign enterprise and labor—British, Chinese, and Indian. If Malaya were self-sufficient in foodstuffs *and* had the surpluses of tin and rubber for export, there would be an abundance of capital for internal development and for the provision of the increasing social services that are being demanded of the government. These considerations are apart from the huge drains on the Federation budget of the anti-communist campaigns.

Actually, there is capital available from the rubber and tin industries, and Malaya has been the Commonwealth's prime dollar earner, but the need for food imports to meet normal consumer needs means a much more gradual pace of economic development. This pace must vary also with the fluctuating prices for rubber and tin on the world market and the dependence of the colonial export economy upon forces beyond its control. This does not mean that Malaya's resource endowment is poor. Actually, its potentials are poorly understood as yet, and superficially the country is prosperous as compared with most lesser developed regions. But the *nature* of the resource planning and development problem is distinctly different from that in Taiwan where food supplies from domestic agriculture are adequate. In Malaya, a sudden and marked drop in both tin and rubber prices would be disastrous, and levels of living would fall in proportion, with concomitant political unrest. In short, the circumstances surrounding the utilization of the natural resource base are markedly different and require differing measures both of analysis and of policy implementation.

China and India

On quite a different scale China and India possess still other developmental problems relative to their resource endowments.

Each of these countries is characterized by largely agrarian societies, with strong subsistence qualities, and by heavy pressures of population upon known and available resources. There are in effect no food surpluses; indeed there often are deficits. Both are following roughly similar courses of economic growth, though implemented in markedly different ways. Agricultural resources are being developed by the application of technological devices, more so in India it is true than in China, but the need may be greater there. Heavy industry is receiving the greater part of the emphasis in their developmental planning, although lighter industries in both countries have had a rather lengthy history of growth. Both have abundant supplies of energy in the form of coal, China more than India; both have reasonably large nonfuel mineral resources.

They differ substantially in the ways in which economic measures are implemented, as is to be expected when one, India, is essentially democratic, and the other, China, is totalitarian. Their greatest similarity, however, lies in the inflexibility imposed upon their developmental planning and policies by the necessity for increased agricultural production, not as a means for capital accumulation, but simply to prevent starvation, maintain a healthier labor force, and discourage rural (and therefore national) unrest. Both illustrate the degree to which high man-land ratios act as a deterrent to accelerated economic development.

Conclusions

From these preliminary statements concerning the role of natural resources in economic growth follow a few relatively simple generalizations:

1. The possession of a sizable and diversified natural resource endowment is a major advantage to any country embarking upon a period of rapid economic growth. Diversification may be less important than the dimensions of one or more resources, if their reserves are large enough and long-run demand is steady and strong.

2. Resources need not be situated within the confines of the country undergoing development, but they must be accessible. Accessibility implies transportation, and transportation in part implies imports, both of which demand accumulations of capital with which to obtain materials from extra-national or discontinuous resource endowments.

3. One of the major means for capital accumulation is an abundance of easily exploitable natural resources (Saudi Arabia, South Africa, Venezuela).

4. In no sense, however, are natural resources responsible for development and economic growth; they possess no deterministic power. However, "they possess latent utility and are part of an over-all regional capability."

5. They also may set limits upon the approaches to natural resource planning and development. If a given raw material necessary for some phase of industrialization is not located *in situ* and is unavailable due to tariff barriers or high transportation costs, modification of that phase is likely. Or, if rapid rises in agricultural, forest, or mineral production are possible, they may strongly influence the system of priorities and scale of operations which will characterize a total developmental effort or history.

6. Even if abundant, natural resources will not determine the *kinds of uses* to which they will be put. Their availability in agriculture particularly, however, may influence critically the shift from agricultural to non-agricultural employments.

7. The significance and functions of natural resources in economic development will differ markedly with the stages in the developmental process. Under normal circumstances the role of the resource endowment is most important in the earliest stages of economic development, when it acts as a means for capital accumulation and an accelerator for economic growth if abundant, and as a depressant upon that growth if niggardly.

8. Similarly, the significance of indigenous resources is much less to the highly developed countries with their discontinuous world hinterlands and larger supplies of capital, skilled labor, technology, and enterpreneurial experience, than to the relatively lesser developed regions frequently characterized by scarcities of all these factors.

9. Any comprehensive program for economic development demands the development of a sophisticated inventory of resource endowments, an appraisal of present systems of resource utilization, an analysis of

cultural and physical obstacles to resource development, and an estimate of resource potentials, taking into account conflicting uses and demands for given resources and the probable role of technological change over periods of time.

24. The Virgin and Idle Lands of Western Siberia and Northern Kazakhstan: A Geographical Appraisal

W. A. Douglas Jackson

"Khrushchev," as the joke circulated in Moscow, "was a remarkable farmer. He could sow wheat in Siberia and harvest it in Canada!" Without question, one of the important reasons underlying the ouster of Nikita Khrushchev was the failure of the 1963 wheat harvest in the virgin lands of the Soviet Union. Perhaps he should have read the following selection written very soon after the inception of the notorious Virgin Lands Program in 1954. It points out, through very careful analysis of relatively limited available data, the dubious future for this program. Jackson predicted precisely the failure of the program, and, undoubtedly, Soviet geographers must have made similar evaluations and reached the same conclusion, but there were no voices raised against Khrushchev's folly until after the crop failure. Here, scientific analysis by a geographer made accurate prediction possible, the goal of every scientist.

The current project to expand the grain and wheat base of western Siberia and northern Kazakhstan to surpass in production the historically famous Ukrainian granary is the most recent scheme devised by Soviet leaders to transform the agricultural geography of the U.S.S.R. Throughout the steppe and forest steppe east of the Volga millions of acres, de-

Source: *Geographical Review*, XLVI (January, 1956), 1–19. The author is professor of geography, University of Washington.

scribed in Soviet literature as virgin and idle arable land,[1] are to be plowed and sown to wheat and other grains. The organization of large, new state grain farms is planned; and a migration of students, farmers, and workers from the cities and older agricultural regions of the country is being actively promoted on a considerable scale.

The institution of such a program in the spring of 1954 was surprising and somewhat contradictory in view of earlier Soviet pronouncements. The directives of the Nineteenth Party Congress for the Fifth Five-Year Plan, issued in October, 1952, called for an increase of 40–50 per cent in the gross grain crop and 55–65 per cent in the wheat crop, but by far the greater proportion of the increase was to be obtained through higher yields per acre. Moreover, Malenkov, in his report to the congress, stated that "the grain problem, which in the past was regarded as our most acute and gravest problem, has thus been solved, solved definitely and finally." Hence the decision of the February–March, 1954, Plenary Session of the Central Committee of the Communist Party marked a significant change in Soviet grain policy. Instead of stressing the need for higher yields, the plenum directed that in 1954–1955 about 32 million acres of virgin and idle land be plowed for grain throughout the eastern regions of the country. Within a few months the project has assumed enormous proportions. In August, 1954, the amount for 1955 was raised from 32 million acres to 37 million, to which an additional 32 million were to be added in 1956. This goal of some 70 million acres is comparable with the combined grain areas of France, Italy, Spain, Austria, Western Germany, Belgium, and Denmark.

The Soviet Grain Supply

In spite of fluctuations due to weather, the level of grain production in the Soviet Union in recent years has reportedly remained above that in most prewar years. An evaluation of the supply, however, should be weighed against the rapid growth of the population and the increasing demand. Malenkov's optimism notwithstanding, the state grain requirements, as N. S. Khrushchev has pointed out, are constantly growing. The total Soviet population, recent estimates indicate, is now close to 215 million. If correct, this would mean an increase of more than 40 million since 1939, including some 20 million added through the annexation of neighboring territories. Consequently, it is possible that the per capita production of grain is scarcely higher now than before the Bolshevik Revolution. In fact, one writer points out that it may even be less, that the net grain harvest per capita in 1950 was only 430 kilograms, whereas in 1913–1914 it was 490. In addition to meeting the needs of an expand-

[1] No clear distinction is drawn between "virgin" and "idle" lands, nor does any seem possible or necessary. In general, such lands have not been plowed for many years, if at all, and are now utilized as pasture, of apparently low productivity.

ing population, enough grain must be harvested every year to supplement the state grain reserves, to ensure feed for livestock, to meet the requirements of districts specializing in nongrain crops, and to increase grain exports. In view of the serious weaknesses in the livestock situation, to which Khrushchev has publicly confessed, and the apparent desire of the Soviet Union to participate in international trade, it would seem that the danger of demand exceeding supply is real and ever present.

The Sown, Grain, and Wheat Areas of the U.S.S.R.

In 1953 the sown area of the Soviet Union reached a record high of about 388 million acres, or more than 125 million acres above the 1913 total. Kazakhstan and western Siberia together accounted for about a fourth of the increase, and the annexation of border territories during World War II brought an additional 40 million acres into the sown area.

It should be borne in mind, however, that Russian writers of the early Soviet period asserted, without qualification, that the better agricultural land had already been utilized and that any expansion of the sown area would entail greater outlay. It is not unreasonable, therefore, to assume that the increase that has occurred under the Soviets, aside from the incorporation of new territories, has been in less readily assimilable land, requiring much effort and expense to bring into cultivation. Yet, as if to suggest that the economic limits have still not been reached, the current plan is to add another 20 per cent to the sown area by 1956.

In contrast with the enlargement of the sown area, the grain area in 1953 was only 30 million acres larger than in 1913. The greatest increase occurred in the late 1920's, but since then, even with the inclusion of the grain lands of the annexed territories, the general trend has been downward. Similarly, a marked decline in the relative position of grains in the total sowings has taken place: from 90 per cent in 1913, to 73 per cent in 1940, and to 68 per cent in 1953. The decline between 1940 and 1953 reflected a reduction of nearly 10 million acres of grain—primarily feed grain. Much of the reduction occurred in the Ukraine, the central chernozem oblasts, the Povolzh'e, and the Northern Caucasus, but small decreases were also reported in several oblasts in western Siberia and in the Urals. On the other hand, the area sown to grain in Kazakhstan increased by about three million acres.

The sowing of wheat, the principal Soviet grain crop, has been increasing since the early 1920's, and, in spite of a sharp cutback forced by the German invasion, wheat in 1953 constituted 40 per cent of all grains. This ratio indicates an addition of some 40 million acres to the wheat area since the Revolution. In northern Kazakhstan and western Siberia in 1953, wheat—i.e., spring-sown wheat—was sown on about 13 million acres more than in 1913. The new territories brought only slightly more than five million acres to the total wheatland of the Soviet Union. Under the current program, the sowings of wheat will increase during the 1954–1956 period by almost half as much again as the all-Union increase from 1913 to 1953.

Soviet Estimates of Reserves of Arable Land

In contrast with the opinion of the writers of the early Soviet period concerning the utilization of the better agricultural land, writers of the Stalinist period have contended that large reserves of fertile land remain. None of the estimates agree, and little effort is made by the Soviets to clarify the situation. Hence it is difficult to determine with any degree of satisfaction the reliability of the estimates, or to evaluate them. However, there can be no doubt that the Soviet use of the term "arable land" —land suitable for cultivation—is broader than usage in the West and embraces conditions that may be well on the margin for agriculture.

In 1929, Stalin stated that the "free," or arable, land amounted to 25 million acres. A slightly larger figure was given in the prewar edition of the "Agricultural Encyclopedia," which suggested that at least 27 million acres could still be brought under cultivation "within a relatively short period of time"—thus implying that total reserves were even greater. But the most striking estimate of all was made by L. I. Prasolov, a prominent Soviet soil specialist. Writing at a time when gigantic state grain farms were being established in the steppe of northern Kazakhstan, Prasolov estimated that the sown area of the U.S.S.R. could be expanded by some 200 million acres! Of this, at least 74 million acres could be plowed in the chernozem and chestnut-brown soil zones, particularly in the vast forest steppe and steppe east of the Volga.

Unquestionably the initiators of the current scheme are aware of Prasolov's studies. Certainly the 1954–1956 goal of 70 million acres of newly plowed land for the eastern regions compares favorably with Prasolov's estimated 74 million acres. Nevertheless, the Soviets at present assume that as much as 99 million acres of virgin and idle land, suitable for cultivation, are to be found in this immense territory, which includes 8 oblasts in Kazakhstan (exclusive of Semipalatinsk and East Kazakhstan Oblasts) and 1 A.S.S.R., 2 krais, and 11 oblasts in the R.S.F.S.R.

Reserves in Northern Kazakhstan

According to recent data, the northern oblasts of Kazakhstan, including Semipalatinsk and East Kazakhstan Oblasts, contain in all about 68 million acres of fertile land (Table 1). However, in 1953, only 36 per cent of this, or 25 million acres, was actually cultivated. In the northern

TABLE 1. Land Utilization in Northern Kazakhstan, 1953 (*In millions of acres*)

Oblasts	Total Area	Arable Area	Cultivated Area	Idle and Virgin Land		% Uncultivated
Kustanai	48.68	11.61	3.95	2.22	5.43	66
North Kazakhstan	10.38	5.68	2.96	0.99	1.73	52
Kokchetav	19.03	8.65	3.21	1.24	4.20	63
Akmolinsk	37.80	11.12	3.71	1.73	5.68	67
Pavlodar	33.61	8.89	2.72	1.98	4.20	69
Karaganda	99.33	2.69	1.73	0.49	0.47	42
Semipalatinsk	43.24	2.72	1.48	0.99	0.25	46
East Kazakhstan	23.97	2.22	1.48	0.49	0.25	33
West Kazakhstan	38.05	5.19	1.98	1.48	1.73	62
Aktiubinsk	73.64	8.89	1.48	1.98	5.43	76
TOTAL	427.73	67.66	24.70	13.59	29.37	64
In the wheat region		49.16	21.49	9.14	18.53	57
In the livestock region		18.50	3.21	4.45	10.84	83

SOURCE: Total areas from "Administrative-Territorial Division of the Soviet Republics" (Moscow, 1954).

Other figures from Filatov, "The Assimilation of Virgin Lands and the Production of Grain in Kazakhstan," SSK, 1954, No. 7, p. 15. For comparable data for 1941, see Koloskov, Agroclimatic Regions of Kazakhstan, Vol. 1, (Moscow, 1947), pp. 232–233.

half of these oblasts, where wheat culture predominates because of the more favorable climate, about 28 million acres of fertile land reputedly remain uncultivated. In North Kazakhstan Oblast, which lies in part within the forest steppe, more than 50 per cent of the cultivable land is virgin and idle. If large tracts of fertile land do remain, their presence theoretically confirms that the tempo of assimilation in recent years has been slow. In spite of periodic exhortations to speed up the plowing of virgin and idle land, the acreage added to the sown area since the war has not been large. In Kazakhstan, in fact, it has amounted to no more than 700,000 to a million acres a year.

Reserves in Western Siberia

Comparable data are not available for the oblasts of western Siberia. Nevertheless, isolated references in Soviet literature emphasize the existence of large reserves of arable land there also. Indeed, within the existing collective and state farms there are reputed to be about 37 million acres of virgin and idle land, of which at least 5 million acres are attached to the state farms. In Altai Krai and in Omsk, Novosibirsk, Kemerovo, and Tomsk Oblasts idle land is said to constitute between 30 and 60 per cent of the total arable area. In Altai Krai alone, about 15 million acres may still be put to the plow; in Omsk Oblast, about 1.5 million; in Krasnoiarsk Krai and Novosibirsk Oblast, nearly 2 million; and in Tiumen, Kemerovo, Irkutsk, and Chita Oblasts, more than a million.

The directive of February–March, 1954, calling for an increase of 32 million acres in the sown area during 1954–1955, geographically apportioned the acreage as follows: about 15 million acres in northern Kazakhstan; about 10 million in western Siberia; and the remainder in the southern Urals and the Povolzh'e (Table 2). Thus about 78 per cent of

TABLE 2. Original 1954–1955 Plan of Sowing on Virgin and Idle Land (*In millions of acres*)

Oblast or Krai	Collective Farms	State Farms
Northern Kazakhstan		
Kustanai	2.47	1.10
North Kazakhstan	0.86	0.87
Kokchetav	1.73	1.34
Akmolinsk	1.80	1.48
Pavlodar	1.60	0.25
Karaganda	0.18	0.23
Semipalatinsk	0.15	0.04
East Kazakhstan	0.09	. . . .
West Kazakhstan	0.62	0.13
Aktiubinsk	0.62	0.04
TOTAL	10.12	5.48
Western Siberia		
Omsk	1.47	0.34
Novosibirsk	0.95	0.25
Krasnoiarsk	0.99	0.20
Kurgan	0.49	0.12
Tiumen	0.35	. . . .
Kemerovo	0.34	0.27
Altai	4.93	0.76
Chita	0.10	0.01
Irkutsk	0.25	. . . .
TOTAL	9.87	1.95
Urals and Povolzh'e		
Cheliabinsk	0.60	0.40
Chkalov	0.62	1.11
Bashkir A.S.S.R.	0.25	0.26
Saratov	0.20	0.62
Stalingrad	. . . .	0.34
TOTAL	1.67	2.73
TOTAL: R.S.F.S.R. and Northern Kazakhstan	21.66	10.16

SOURCE: Filatov, *op. cit.* p. 17; *Pravda*, Nov. 8, 1954; *Izvestia*, Nov. 10, 1954. The Russian newspapers give data on the fulfillment of the plan up to November 5, 1954, from which the original plan can be deduced.

the expansion was to be in northern Kazakhstan and western Siberia. Much of the increase in 1956 will occur there also, particularly in the Kazakh steppe.

The responsibility for the greater part of the plowing in 1954–1955 was to fall primarily on the collective farms, particularly in Omsk Oblast and Altai Krai in western Siberia, and in Kustanai, Kokchetav, Akmolinsk, and Pavlodar Oblasts in northern Kazakhstan, all of which are reported to have large reserves of virgin and idle land. However, by 1956 the state farms will carry the burden of the additional plowing, as directed in August, 1954. For this purpose, large state grain farms will be created, completely mechanized with new equipment and employing many thousands of immigrants from the older regions of the country. In 1954, about 90 new state farms came into existence in Kazakhstan and more than 30 in the R.S.F.S.R. By 1956 the number of farms will be greatly increased, especially in northern Kazakhstan, which will then have about 450, the largest number of state farms of all regions in the Soviet Union.

Climate

Throughout much of the forest steppe and steppe of western Siberia and northern Kazakhstan climate and soil produce conditions that, in general, cannot be considered the most favorable for the expansion of dry farming. The significant climatic factors affecting the growth of spring wheat in the steppe are given by Koloskov, who states that spring wheat requires a mean temperature of 17° to 24° C. (62.6° to 75.2° F.) during the warmest month, with the sum of the temperatures during the vegetation period (that is, the sum of the average daily temperatures for days with temperatures above 10° C., or 50° F.) rising to 2000° C (3632° F.); enough moisture in the soil at the time of sowing; adequate precipitation during the early period of growth (May to June); and relatively dry weather during the harvest.

The forest steppe and steppe of western Siberia and northern Kazakhstan generally meet the thermal requirements of spring wheat. Average July temperatures range from 65° to 77° F., and the mean July isotherm of 68° F. extends from the middle Volga across northern Kazakhstan to the piedmont of the Dzhungarian Ala-Tau, southeast of Lake Balkhash. Moreover, the sum of the temperatures during the vegetation period rises to 1800° C. and more. In fact, the northern limit of possible wheat cultivation, suggested by Selianinov as the line indicating the sum of temperatures during the vegetation period of 1600° C. (2912° F.), crosses the West Siberian Plain near 60° N., about 4° north of the northern limit of the forest steppe. However, because the valley soils of the lower Irtysh and middle Ob are poorly drained (Vasiugan Swamp), the

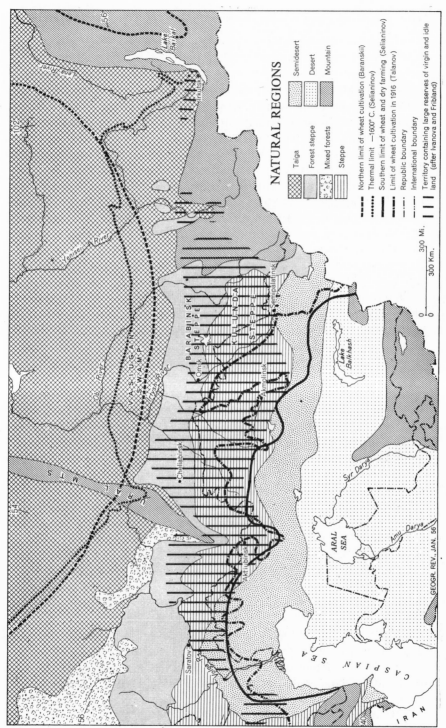

NATURAL REGIONS

Taiga	Semidesert
Forest steppe	Desert
Mixed forests	Mountain
Steppe	

Northern limit of wheat cultivation (Baranskiĭ)
Thermal limit −1600° C. (Selianinov)
Southern limit of wheat and dry farming (Selianinov)
Limit of wheat cultivation in 1916 (Talanov)
Republic boundary
International boundary
Territory containing large reserves of virgin and idle land (after Ivanova and Fribland)

0   300 Mi.
0   300 Km.

GEOGR. REV. JAN. 56

FIGURE 1: Natural regions. (After L. S. Berg: Natural Regions of the U.S.S.R. [New York, 1950].)

327

actual limit of wheat culture, according to Baranskii, does not extend north beyond the 57th parallel (Fig. 1).

Characteristic of the forest steppe and steppe of western Siberia and northern Kazakhstan are extremes of temperature—warm summers and exceedingly cold winters—and a frostless period of 110 to 150 days. If, as Mosolov states, Russian common spring-wheat varieties mature in 85 to 105 days and durum-wheat varieties in 110 to 130 days, then there is some danger of frost, particularly in the northern and eastern reaches of the forest steppe. Although a late frost in spring (mid-May) may not cause too much damage, an early frost in the latter part of August may be critical. Moreover, because sowing and harvesting delays continue to be a feature of Soviet socialized agriculture, the frost hazard will remain; in fact, it may be present even in parts of the steppe where the growing season is longer. Nevertheless, other things being equal, temperature cannot be considered as influential as moisture supply or soil, especially in the southern half of the forest steppe and the steppe.

The southern limit of wheat cultivation, according to both Selianinov and Koloskov, parallels for the most part the southern edge of the steppe, which is climatically represented by the average annual 10-inch isohyet (in Kazakhstan roughly the 46 parallel). Unsuited to wheat culture, therefore, because of insufficient moisture are much of West Kazakhstan Oblast, southern Aktiubinsk, central and southern Kustanai, virtually all of Karaganda except the northeast corner, southwestern Pavlodar, and central and southern Semipalatinsk, in the Kazakh Republic. There is no evidence that under the current project the Soviets plan to push dry farming southward beyond Selianinov's boundary. Yet much of the steppe to the north, though rated suitable for wheat, is climatically problematical, and only in the unpredictable moist years can fairly good yields (at least 10 bushels per acre) be obtained.

Throughout the steppe and much of the forest steppe, precipitation is both insufficient and unreliable. Only in the northwestern parts of the forest steppe, near Cheliabinsk, and in parts of Altai Krai, where about six inches of rain falls on the average from May to July and a lower evaporation rate prevails, is grain growing generally assured of adequate moisture. Elsewhere, the early warm-season precipitation ranges from a mean of 5.5 inches in the southern forest steppe to 3.1 inches in the southern steppe. Toward the south, as precipitation decreases, its variability rises and the hazards to crops are magnified. In addition, the early-summer maximum is characterized by heavy falls, and its effectiveness is greatly reduced. Moisture is thus lost through rapid runoff. Evaporation, too, is rather excessive under rising temperatures, cloudless skies, and low relative humidity.

If drought conditions are characteristic of the steppe and, to a certain degree, of the forest steppe, particularly devastating are the *sukhovei*,

the hot winds that blow from the desert in the Aral basin. In the Kulunda Steppe of Altai Krai, for example, during a recent 10-year period,
the sukhovei lowered the yields of grain by as much as 51 per cent
below average. Even in years when summer precipitation was above
normal (1944 and 1945), a withering drought later in the season reduced
grain harvest by 30 to 50 per cent.

In the cold months light snow falls. The vast, level steppe affords
few natural obstructions to the driving sweep of strong winds; consequently, although snow may cover the ground from November to
April, its depth varies considerably. During the sudden onset of spring,
when average temperatures rise as much as 20° F. in a single month,
melting is rapid and floods are frequent. Thus spring-sown crops do
not receive the full advantage of the winter's moisture, at least not unless
extensive measures are taken to preserve it.

Soils

An analysis of the soils introduces other factors, which, taken with the
climate, underline emphatically the marginal nature of much of the
area of so-called agricultural potential. Although the soil cover of the
territory where the bulk of the fresh plowing will occur may be conveniently reduced to chernozem and chestnut brown (Fig. 2), such a
classification conceals the complex variegation that actually prevails.

Chernozem Soil Zone

There are many acres of uncultivated land in the West Siberian Plain
outside the taiga, but the possibility of extending the sown area through

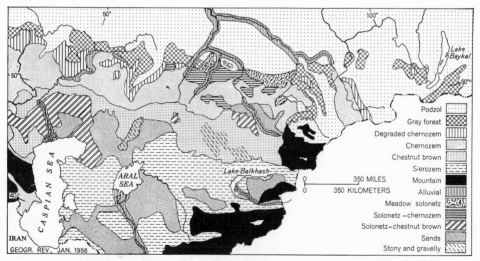

FIGURE 2: Generalized soils map of the region. (After Great Soviet World Atlas.)

much of the chernozem zone [2] is believed by some Soviet specialists to be limited. Indeed, Prasolov stated in 1933 that there was no longer any "free" land—land suitable for plowing—in the chernozem zone. The best Siberian chernozems, he showed, were almost entirely plowed, and expansion of the sown area could proceed only at the cost of fallow land, essential to successful wheat growing. Any increase in production, therefore, could be brought about only by specialization and intensification of methods on land already under cultivation.

However, Prasolov did foresee the possibility of increasing the sown area in some of the chernozem "subgroups," in which in 1933 no more than 50 per cent of the soils were plowed. In this category were about seven million acres of strongly leached and degraded chernozems, about the same acreage of solonetz-chernozems,[3] and about 10 million acres of shallow chernozems in the droughty mountain steppe.

General support for Prasolov's conclusions may be found in an article by Gorshenin,[4] who records at least four areas of possible expansion in the chernozem zone: on leached chernozems; on solonetz-chernozems; on marsh soils; and on southern and ordinary chernozems. According to Gorshenin, no significant increase in the sown area can be expected from the plowing of leached (and degraded) chernozems. The area of virgin and idle land is not large, and additional cultivation would necessitate cutting the trees, which would in turn adversely affect the water supply.

Solonetz-chernozems are generally presumed to be unfit for culture of wheat, which prefers a less alkaline soil. Hitherto solonetz-chernozems in western Siberia have been plowed, and, according to Gorshenin, soils with a deep-columnar structure are satisfactory for grain. However, additional plowing, he suggests, would be done on less valuable soils and present considerable risks. Shallow-columnar soils have been utilized, wherever possible, as pasture, and although their productivity is and has been low, Gorshenin believes they should remain in grass. At the same time, he suggests that improvement of these soils might release more fertile pastureland for grain and wheat. I. V. Iakushkin and several

---

[2] The best Siberian chernozems are in the southern part of the forest steppe, but they occur in pockets and are neither as extensive nor as fertile as the best Ukrainian black earths. Northward the chernozems become increasingly leached; southward into the steppe they become lighter in color and lower in humus. The southern boundary of the chernozem soil zone is irregular, cutting across northern Kustanai Oblast, southern Kokchetav Oblast, and northern Pavlodar Oblast in Kazakhstan.

[3] According to Prasolov, the area of solonetz-chernozems in Siberia amounts to 53 million acres—about 33 per cent of the total area of Siberian chernozems—exclusive of 41 million acres of associated solonetz-meadow.

[4] It is worth noting that the author points out that the most extensive area suitable for agricultural assimilation in western Siberia lies north of the chernozem zone in the podzolic soil zone of the taiga. Here, of course, the extent of uncultivated land is large. K. P. Gorshenin: "On the Assimilation of Virgin and Idle Lands in Siberia," *Pochvovedenie*, 1954, No. 4, pp. 1–10; reference on pp. 1–4.

other Soviet agronomists have opposed the utilization of solonetz-chernozems for wheat, but their opinion has been branded as "excessively
academic" by "realists" in the field. Hence it seems likely that tracts of
solonetz-chernozem soils will be plowed and sown to wheat.

The reclamation of marshland in western Siberia is not contemplated
as part of the current project though it is a feature of the Fifth Five-
Year Plan. Gorshenin stresses that the drainage of marshland, particularly in the forest steppe of western Siberia, would strengthen the forage
base and, indirectly, improve the grain supply. It would not be an easy
undertaking, however. The largest area of marshland in western Siberia,
except for the Vasiugan Swamp, is in the Barabinsk Steppe, between
the Ob and Irtysh Rivers, in Novosibirsk Oblast. It is more than 60 per
cent marsh (including salt marsh). Both drainage and careful management would be required to bring the soils under cultivation, and even
after drainage a strong possibility of secondary salting would remain,
particularly if the marshes lay in saline bottoms. Also, in spite of its
somewhat northern location, Barabinsk is droughty; hence irrigation
would have to be a basic part of reclamation. For these reasons, it is
extremely doubtful whether much improvement could take place there
within the next few years.

The most promising chernozem subgroup is, according to Gorshenin,
the belt of southern and ordinary chernozems found in transition between the forest steppe and the steppe in northern Kazakhstan. Indeed,
he asserts that the reserves of virgin and idle land on these soils are
large, especially in the Ishim-Irtysh basin, in northern Kustanai Oblast,
and in the Kulunda Steppe between the Ob and Irtysh Rivers. He describes the soils as arable and not unlike soils already under cultivation.
However, he adds, significantly, that over large areas these soils are
difficult to manage. In particular, in northern Kustanai and in the Ishim-
Irtysh basin the chernozems possess a heavy clay composition and tend
to become exceedingly hard and dry if proper measures are not taken
to conserve moisture. Rapid exhaustion is another characteristic, to
judge from Soviet experience in Kustanai Oblast in 1934–1935. Elsewhere, for example in the Kulunda Steppe, the soils are very light and
also tend to be dry. In 1916 these areas lay well outside the southern
boundary of spring wheat, though in 1933 Selianinov included them
within the zone of possible dry farming.

Chestnut-Brown Soil Zone

If expansion of the sown area in the chernozem zone seems rather limited, Prasolov and Gorshenin agree that the chestnut-brown soils of the
Kazakh steppe offer wider possibilities. In fact, more than 20 years ago
Prasolov indicated that at least 49 million acres could be added to the
sown area of the U.S.S.R. through the plowing of virgin chestnut-brown

soils, primarily in Kazakhstan. It is well known that wheat sown in dark chestnut-brown soils is often superior to that sown in chernozems, though yields vary enormously from year to year. However, in the chestnut-brown zone precipitation is both lighter and less reliable than in the chernozem zone to the north. Chestnut-brown soils are lower in humus, and continuous plowing rapidly exhausts their fertility and moisture. The degree of alkalinity and the extent of solonetz development are much greater than in the northern steppe. In short, dry farming in the chestnut-brown soil zone involves considerable risk. In view of past Soviet and Tsarist experience, the prospects for successful long-range cultivation do not appear good.

The Prospects

Agricultural specialists attending a conference in Moscow in January, 1954, reported in most cases excellent experimental-field results on virgin and idle land. Yields of wheat as high as 40 and 50 bushels per acre were obtained. The Soviets have indicated, however, that they expect to receive high and steady yields from even the state and collective farms. Lysenko has stated that proper management of virgin and idle land could furnish at least 19.5 bushels of wheat per acre, especially during the first years, though if the land were not cultivated correctly, the yield would be only 13.5 bushels. Lysenko may be vindicated on the most progressive farms, but the yields of wheat in northern Kazakhstan from 1895 to 1914 averaged less than six to nine bushels per acre, and from 1920 to 1934 they were not much higher.

Under dry farming, fallowing is essential. In western Siberia and northern Kazakhstan there is evidence to indicate that a fairly common practice has been to sow wheat year after year on the same land. The Soviets have placed great emphasis, since the end of World War II, on the introduction of proper crop rotations, yet little progress seems to have been made. In fact, crop rotation is said to be only nominally practiced, especially in northern Kazakhstan.

Soviet writers stress that long-range success demands the almost complete application of advanced agronomic principles. Specifically, this means that extensive measures must be taken to conserve moisture; to plow and cultivate the land at the prescribed time; to turn up the sod correctly; to sow effectively, on time, with the best seed obtainable; and, finally, to institute sound crop-rotation systems. Because of the magnitude of the program, it seems doubtful whether all these measures can be uniformly and effectively adopted. Indeed, if advanced agronomic principles had been widely applied to the land already under cultivation, and if tangible results had been obtained, there would, perhaps, be little need to embark with such urgency on so vast a project.

Aside from the serious natural handicaps that will impede the successful execution of the project, there will be other difficulties. Even if the Russians are now better equipped to conquer the steppe than they were, for example, in the 1930's, possessing more experience, a larger body of trained personnel, improved communications, and possibly more machinery and equipment, there remain the complex problems of organization, distribution, and control to which the Soviet system gives rise.

In the autumn and winter of 1954 the Soviet press reported that during the year the quotas for plowing and sowing on virgin and idle land had been exceeded and, thanks to a favorably moist year, a large harvest had been obtained. Yet numerous and serious defects appeared. The housing situation for the thousands of migrants from areas west of the Urals was desperate, supplies of drinking water were inadequate, deliveries of equipment were slow, tractors were left idle and sowing delays were extensive, excessively alkaline soils were plowed, and "organizational difficulties" were pronounced.

Has the Soviet grain problem, then, been truly solved, as Malenkov asserted at the Nineteenth Party Congress? Evidence indicates that it has not. Moreover, there is doubt whether the current project, involving millions of acres of virgin and idle land in a region traditionally noted for its hazards, will greatly improve the situation.

2 5. The Geography of Manure
Eugene Mather and John Fraser Hart

The authors of this unusual study attribute the limited concern for animal manure by geographers and Americans generally to "(1) the 'Chic Sale' tradition in American humor which makes excrement a naughty topic; (2) [the fact that] long-range hazards of cropping without manure are only beginning to be recognized; (3) the American preference for the artificial. Cement, for instance, may be made to look like limestone, flour is 'enriched' with the very vitamins milled from wheat, metal cabinets are made to resemble wood, and 'soil conditioners' are used to maintain soil structure while manure is discarded." Yet in most areas of the world, manure is absolutely essential to effective agricultural production.

SOURCE: *Land Economics,* XXXII (February, 1956), 25–28. Reprinted with permission of the copyright owners, the Regents of the University of Wisconsin. Dr. Mather is professor of geography, University of Minnesota, and Dr. Hart is professor of geography, Indiana University.

The agricultural importance of animal manure was recognized in Europe long before the birth of Christ, and that importance has increased with the passage of time and the development of agriculture. The medieval Flemish proverb: "Point de fourrage, point des betail, point des betail, point de fumier, point de fumier, point de fourrage," has been replaced in modern times by such adages as the English: "Where there's muck, there's luck," or the remark of the Danish farmer that "manure puts the cake on the farmer's table." The European attitude is best summarized by the statement that "farmyard manure . . . . has formed the basis of arable farming throughout the ages. In spite of the great development of fertilisers during the last ninety years, farmyard manure is still the standby of arable farmers; it has been supplemented—not supplanted— by chemical fertilisers." Conversely, in newer societies manure is not given the esteem accorded it in older and more stable agricultural communities. The hazards of continuous cropping with little manure are now beginning to be recognized in newly settled lands, however, and Americans can no longer continue to ignore the importance of manure in the agricultural economy. It is our purpose to discuss the history of manure in agriculture, the characteristics of manure which endow it with such striking agricultural importance, and regional variations in the manner in which manure is used today.

The Agricultural History of Manure

There is little evidence to confirm or deny the use of manure by prehistoric farmers. Clark remarks that "though dung carts may be able to tell more of economic life than chariots or hearses, it is only too evident which would be preferred to accompany chieftains to their graves." He believes that systematic use of manure for agricultural purposes originated when shifting cultivation was replaced by fixed fields during the Bronze Age. It appears that a Late Bronze Age farmer at Jarlshof, in the Shetlands, may have collected manure in his stables, and that the builder of manure carts was a regular member of the village by the end of the prehistoric period. It seems safe to assume that plows used on fixed fields of the early Iron Age required draft animals which were protected in stables and that manure from these stables was used to maintain the fertility of the fields.

Classical literature contains many specific references to the importance and use of manure. Odysseus, for instance, upon his return to Ithaca found his old hound lying on the pile of mule and cattle manure which was to be used to fertilize the fields. One of the Spartan soldiers in *Lysistrata* (411 B.C.) proclaims his desire to stop fighting so that he can go back to his farm and cart manure to the fields. Biblical recognition of the use of manure is evidenced in Christ's parable of the fig tree. In Italy the use of manure had become so well established by the beginning of the Christian era that the Latin authorities on agriculture all stress its importance. Cato recommended folding of sheep on arable land,[1] cautioned the farmer to maintain a large dung heap and suggested that half the manure be used on forage crops, a quarter on the olive orchard, and a quarter on the meadows. Varro, writing about 35 B.C., echoes Cato, and in addition suggests that the servants' privy be placed over the manure pit.[2] In the early days of the Christian era Columella sounds surprisingly modern as he compares the quality of manure produced by various animals and gives instructions for its storage and use.

Medieval agriculture did not reach the high standard set by the Romans, but manure remained important in an age when artificial chemical fertilizers were unknown. Chaucer's plowman, for instance, had hauled many loads of dung. Under the medieval three-field system, however, the commonest method of adding manure to the soil was folding animals on the fallow. Many of the peasants of East Anglia were subject to "fold-soke" (an obligation to graze sheep on the lord's land; the lord realized that the loss of forage was more than compensated by increased fertility) and the custom seems to have been an old one at the time of the *Little Domesday Book* in 1086. Even where free peasants could not be required to render this service, the necessity of manure required that each local area maintain a balance between agriculture and grazing so that fertility would not be lost. Leases often specified the amount of manure to be applied to the farm and categorically forbade, under pain of fine, that any manure be sold off the farm.

The Agricultural Revolution, which brought an end to medieval agriculture, was intimately related to increased production of manure. In Britain, for instance, Smith shows that the new husbandry of the eighteenth century was based on constant tillage, the integration of new crops into the rotation, and the close association of crops and stock. Cattle fattening on crops, crop waste, and oil cake produced vast quantities of manure which was carted back to the fields; sheep were folded, particularly on light soils, where their treading served to consolidate the soil. The integration of crop production and livestock husbandry during the Agricultural Revolution led to the development of various systems of mixed farming which have been transplanted to much of the rest of the world from northwestern Europe. Mixed farming

[1] Folding refers to intensive grazing of small enclosed segments of a field in succession until the entire field has been grazed and manured. The movable fences used in folding are called hurdles, so in parts of the world the practice is known colloquially as "hurdling."

[2] Varro, *Rerum Rusticarum*, I, xiii, 4; I, xxxviii, 2. Twenty centuries later privies are still placed over the farm manure pile in some parts of Europe.

(with the rotation of crops) is particularly conservative of soil fertility, because a large share of the plant nutrients taken from the soil by crops is returned as manure.

The development and widespread dissemination of artificial chemical fertilizers after the fourth decade of the last century has tended to obscure the importance of manure. Ideally, manure should be returned to the soil to maintain its inherent fertility, whereas chemical fertilizers should be used to increase and intensify production and to remedy any deficiencies. In many parts of the world, however, and particularly in the Americas, artificial fertilizers have tended to replace manure completely, instead of serving as a supplement, and the manure has been discarded and wasted. Complete reliance on artificial fertilizers has led to abandonment of livestock in many areas, and frequently has permitted development of monoculture and the undesirable practices associated with monoculture. Plant foods are placed in the soil each spring with the seeds, and removed in the form of crops each harvest. The soil structure suffers from lack of organic matter, and the store of plant foods sinks so low that artificial fertilizer becomes essential to crop production. If this situation is not remedied by growing hay or pasture crops for a number of years, or by providing organic matter through use of manure or green manure crops, resort will have to be made to soil conditioners to save the soil from complete deterioration and erosion.[3]

The Nature of Manure

In terms of manure production, a farm animal may best be described as "a huge tube with thick walls and open ends, one end being the mouth and the other the anus, while the walls form the animal's body." The digestible portions of the animal's food are absorbed through the walls, whereas the indigestible portions pass out in the feces. For the most part, the materials of the solid excrement, which have resisted digestion, are equally resistant to ordinary decay processes in the soil; these materials become available to plants only slowly over a period of several months or even years. The most valuable part of the manure is urine, containing the soluble fraction of the animal's food. Urine, excreted after passing through the blood stream, contains little phosphorus, most of the potash, and over half the nitrogen voided by the animal. Urine is collected directly, or by absorption in various types of litter, such as straw, cornstalks, sawdust, or peat. The terms "stable manure"

[3] We do not advocate the abandonment of artificial fertilizers; in fact, we champion their proper use as a means of intensifying and increasing crop production, but they should be used as *supplements* to manure and not substituted as the sole source of plant food.

and "barnyard manure" thus commonly refer to a mixture of feces and urine-soaked litter.

The composition of fresh manure is directly related to the nature of the animal, but it is only possible to compare the manure of the various types of animals within fairly broad limits (Table 1). A beast which is growing, fattening, or producing milk retains certain portions of the manurial constituents of its food, whereas virtually all of the feed of other mature animals is recoverable as manure. As a general rule, the richest and most concentrated form of manure is dropped by chickens, which void urine with their feces. Cattle and hogs commonly produce more manure than do horses and sheep; the former drink more water, so their feces are more moist and their urine is less concentrated. The dryness of horse and sheep manure is conducive to rapid bacterial change, so these "hot manures" decompose rapidly and must be used with care on certain crops.

The quality of manure is also related to the animal's feed. Although the character of individual livestock feeds varies greatly, as a general rule the richer feeds are more readily digestible and thus produce richer manure. Seven-eighths of the nitrogen of decorticated cotton cake, for instance, is digestible, and thus recoverable in manure; on the other hand, little more than half of the nitrogen in hay is digestible. British farmers frequently give their animals heavy rations of oil cake with the sole purpose of producing adequate supplies of manure.

Fresh manure decomposes rapidly. Microorganisms in the manure attack the urea of the urine and produce ammonium carbonate, which in turn rapidly breaks down into ammonia and carbon dioxide. Both of these gases escape to the atmosphere; it is ammonia gas which gives stables their distinctive odor. As a result of this and other more complex decompositional changes, it is estimated that a loss of about 15 percent of the nitrogen may be expected even under optimum conditions of storage; if the manure is not properly stored, more than a third of the nitrogen may be lost. Various methods have been developed to minimize the loss of nitrogen. Peat litter, for instance, not only absorbs up to ten times in weight in urine but also absorbs ammonia gas which has escaped to the air of the stable. Chemical preservatives, such as gypsum, sulfuric acid, and superphosphate, have been used to stabilize the urea and thus to prevent the formation of ammonium carbonate. All of these preservatives have the added advantage of keeping down the smell, because the manure which smells strongest is losing nitrogen most rapidly. Neither potash nor phosphate on the other hand, is volatile; under normal barnyard or stable conditions they will not be dissipated by vaporization.

TABLE 1. Amount and Composition of Manure Produced by Mature Animals

Type of animal	Average daily production in pounds per 100 liveweight pounds	Percentage of Plant Foods in					
		SOLID MANURE			LIQUID MANURE		
		Nitrogen	Phosphorus	Potassium	Nitrogen	Phosphorus	Potassium
Hogs	9.8	0.6	0.5	0.5	0.4	0.1	1.0
Cows	8.5	0.3	0.2	0.2	1.0	—	1.0
Horses	4.8	0.5	0.3	0.2	1.2	—	1.5
Sheep	4.1	0.7	0.5	0.2	1.7	—	2.1
Poultry	2.3	1.0	0.8	0.4	—	—	—
Humans	1.8	—	—	—	—	—	—

SOURCE: Robert M. Salter and C. J. Schollenberger, *Farm Manure*, Ohio Agricultural Experiment Station Bulletin 605, 1939, p. 7: John Lossing Buck, *Land Utilization in China* (Shanghai: 1937), p. 258.

Agricultural Use of Manure

Manure, which is most commonly used to fertilize arable land, may be collected in stables, barnyards, or feed lots. In parts of Europe the liquid manure is collected in separate tanks, but it is more usual, both there and in other parts of the world, to absorb it in some form of litter. The mixture of solid manure and urine-soaked litter may be removed daily to nearby piles, although it is most efficient to allow manure to accumulate under the feet of animals bedded on sufficient litter to absorb the urine. If manure is removed daily, the manure pile should be protected by shed covers and kept compacted to avoid rapid loss of nitrogen by decomposition and leaching. A feed lot should be provided with a floor of some impervious material, such as concrete, if manure is to be collected efficiently. The manure is commonly hauled directly to the field from the feed lot. Although this avoids double handling, the manure spread in early winter is subject to severe leaching and some decomposition before it can be incorporated in the soil by plowing.

A number of devices facilitate the handling and spreading of manure. Manure may be removed from the barn floor by fork, shovel, broom, or water hose, although the latter method is used only when the value of manure is not appreciated. Many dairy barns are equipped with overhead monorail-and-car to transport manure from the barn to the manure heap. Mechanical loaders attached to the front of tractors scrape manure from the feed lot floor and load it directly into manure spreaders. These spreaders, which distribute manure by means of an endless chain conveyor, can also be used to spread lime and chemical fertilizers. Liquid manure spreaders are relatively uncommon in the United States, but the "honey wagon" is frequently seen in Europe. Hand spreading of manure from wagons, which is a common practice in the less mechanized parts of the world, including the American Southeast, permits more accurate placement of manure in crop rows or hills.

Wherever practical, it is easier to allow the animals to spread their own manure by grazing them in the fields to be fertilized. This may range from intensive folding systems through rotational grazing of improved pastures to ranching systems which are so extensive that manurial effects are not apparent. Folding involves the use of movable fences, or "hurdles," which can be moved successively to each part of the field, and thus ensure intensive grazing and manuring of the entire field. Folding minimizes the danger of parasitic infestation, but necessitates additional expenditure on fencing and labor, so is largely restricted to areas of intensive farming where labor is relatively inexpensive. The American counterpart of the hurdle is the temporary electric fence, which is of increasing importance in those parts of Europe where labor is scarce.

Croplands in mixed farming systems are frequently alternated with improved pastures and thereby receive the benefit of animal manure at least once in the rotation cycle. Rotational grazing involves alternate use of permanently fenced pasture units independently of crops. The pasture units may vary in size from relatively small enclosures to extensive ranges where ranching is dominant. "Halo spots" are a common sight in these pastures and constitute a special management problem. Both cattle and horses relish the rich grass fertilized by their own urine, but assiduously avoid the halos around their own manure. On the other hand, each type of animal relishes the "halo spots" of other animals, so it was the standard practice in Germany to graze one horse with each ten cattle. A number of efforts have been made to eliminate "halo spots" where mixed grazing is impractical, because they may preclude the use of a significant proportion of a permanent pasture. Drag-harrowing breaks up the piles and incorporates the manure into the soil; after a brief period during which animals refuse to graze, the entire pasture is once again usable. Plice has suggested that the phosphonitrogen imbalance in solid manure tends to inhibit sugar formation in plants growing on "halo spots," and has demonstrated that drag-harrowing might be eliminated by treating "halo spots" with molasses or some other sweetening agent.

Non-Agricultural Aspects of Manure

Manure has many non-agricultural manifestations, despite its primary significance as a fertilizer. It is an important fuel in many dry and treeless regions. In writing of an Iranian village, Kernan remarked:

I had seen the most tragic and fatal sign of fuel starvation—fatal to the soil on which village life depends. Manure bricks were drying upon the walls. Their smudgy fires and odoriferous smoke glowed in the little courts that front each house. Iranian farming rarely makes provision for building up humus in the soil. Cover crops and manure are not used for this purpose.

The collection of "cow chips" and "buffalo chips" to heat sod houses was an after-school chore on the Great Plains as late as the turn of the century.

Bird droppings are of importance on the landscape, particularly with regard to the establishment of plant communities. The blue jay has been responsible for many cedar trees along fence rows in eastern United States. Birds are believed responsible for isolated birch-aspen communities in the moorlands of Britain, and the "bird-rocks" of the Canadian Arctic are well known among botanists. Guano, of course, is too well known by geographers to require more than passing reference; no one has ever estimated the expenditure required for removal of guano from buildings, monuments, and even clothing in our large urban centers. Coprolites have provided paleontologists with valuable clues to the life of the past. In a lighter vein, one manifestation of manure is described in the *Saturday Evening Post:*

While I was visiting the assay headquarters, director Bill Mattson picked up a gob of heavy stuff about the size of a pie. It was glossy black and looked like asphalt. It had come air mail, special delivery, from an impatient Kansas City businessman who had been hunting in Colorado. "We get three or four of these a year," Mattson explained. "It just happens that pack rats have an always-in-the-same-place sanitary system, and after several years this is the result. The stuff may be a hundred years old, but I'll tell you, it's a ticklish job to write this man a letter and tell him what his sample is."

The Manure Map of the World

Distributional aspects of the use of manure are depicted on the world map (Fig. 1). Literature for some regions upon which to base such a map is strikingly abundant, whereas for other areas information is quite limited. In view of this, the map is presented as a preliminary effort. Extensive correspondence with agricultural experts in various parts of the world has clarified the mapping of numerous doubtful areas but it is hoped that further research will produce refinements. It has proven impractical to map manurial practices in areas where only small amounts of manure are produced so we have restricted our attention to those areas where manure is produced in significant quantities. It would appear appropriate, as a guide to future research, to summarize our findings concerning the use of manure in the various parts of the world.

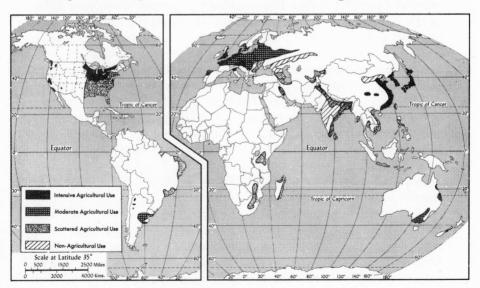

FIGURE 1: Manure map of the world.

Europe and the Mediterranean Basin

Production of farm manure has been a primary concern of European farmers. The loss of livestock in both World Wars has had serious consequences for European agriculture because barnyard manure has been of basic importance as a fertilizer. Manure has been especially prized by gardeners. Thomasson quotes a British lady on the proper techniques of gathering sheep dung in public parks without attracting the attention of romantic young couples, and mentions her misgivings as to whether or not it came under the head of "mineral rights" and as such belonged to the Crown.

In normal times British livestock received "immense quantities of imported feeding stuffs. Every pound of this which they received added to Britain's soil some of the plant food from the land where the cotton or linseed was grown." On the East Lothian plain of Scotland, which is famous for its rich arable farms, bullocks commonly "received a daily ration of 4 lb. linseed cake and 4 lb. undecorticated cotton cake—wasteful feeding, but good dung resulted! . . . . Some farmers reckon that winter court [yard] feeding of cattle does not pay, but the majority are satisfied that the returns from cash cropping justify any deficit from their keep." Lowland arable farmers in eastern England are also willing to take a slight loss on livestock in order to ensure the large supply of manure so necessary to successful arable cropping. Farmers in the East Midland counties rent "yards" to cattle feeders; as compensation for fodder and care of the animals they receive cash and dung. Manure is especially prized in many British market gardening areas; near Edinburgh, for instance, "heavy dressings of purchased organic matter have enriched these soils until they might well be classified as man-made; some go so far as to consider them good samples of manure!"

Scandinavian farmers are also keenly aware of the value of manure. Dairy farms, for instance, depend on manure from cows, pigs, poultry, and horses as the basis of good crops. In southern Scandinavia manure is carefully collected, stored, and spread, so that little of it will be wasted. Lack of adequate fences in Finland prevents complete utilization of croplands for forage, but stable manure is carried to the fields by sled during the winter months and spread by hand during the spring. Perhaps this is why the Lapps call Finns "Lantalainen," which can be translated as "manure spreaders."

Many farmers on loamy soils in the Low Countries, where the Agricultural Revolution began, practiced a rotation of grain, sugar beets, and pasture, and depended upon livestock to maintain soil fertility. Some of these farms switched to sugar beet monoculture, with sole reliance on chemical fertilizers, only to discover that crop yields declined markedly through lack of organic matter in the soil. In consequence, their present trend is toward integrated agriculture once again.

His manure pile is of prime importance to the French farmer.

Le paysan s'intéresse toujours à son fumier, car il sait voir en lui la condition de la fertilité de son sol. Il faut être aussi niais que certains citadins pour s'en gausser et faire la moue. Dans beaucoup de campagnes la dot d'une fille est estimée à l'importance du tas de fumier que produit la ferme de son père.

The banker also estimates the French farmer's net worth by the size of his manure pile.

Horses, cattle, and hogs are relatively scarce around the Mediterranean basin, and the rough hill lands grazed by sheep and goats are unsuitable for crops. Manure is of agricultural significance only in those favored localities where animal husbandry is closely associated with crop production. In the Po valley, for instance, both liquid and solid manures are prized, as the Italian film *Times Gone By* illustrates in a sequence depicting two peasants in a roaring fight over some horse manure. Even in parts of the Mediterranean basin where livestock are of little importance farmers still follow the ancient custom of keeping pigeons to produce manure for their crops.

The use of manure is complicated by a number of environmental factors in the mountain belt which stretches across southern Europe. Grain production, and hence the supply of straw for litter, is rendered difficult by climatic conditions. Scarcity of trees in the alpine zone has led to the use of manure for fuel. The grazed mountain lands are too rugged for crop production, but stall feeding in the valleys produces supplies of manure which are used as fertilizing material.

Manure is of vital agricultural importance in the scarplands of Germany and on the Alpine foreland of Switzerland, Germany, and Austria. Fences are virtually absent; cattle are stall-fed, and agricultural villages are characterized by the strong odor emanating from the manure pile of each farmer in the village. Manure is carefully conserved, carted to the fields, and spread by hand. Night soil is also highly prized in Germany, as in other parts of Europe, but this fact is scarcely mentioned in geographic literature.[4] Nevertheless, the use of night soil poses a problem of public health which must be reckoned with by American tourists and military forces, as well as by the local populace.

The peasant farmers of eastern Europe (including west central Russia) have seldom been able to afford chemical fertilizers so have depended almost entirely on manure. Manure has been absolutely essential to crop production in the non-black-soil belt of European Russia, where peat

---

[4] One might mention, however, Professor Stamp's criticism of "the utter folly of our present waste by town sewage systems which send valuable nitrogenous manures out to sea."

instead of straw is commonly used for litter. The decline in livestock numbers associated with collectivization and war has had such serious effects on crop production that the Soviets have diverted part of their limited supply of chemical fertilizers to this area. Chemical fertilizers are also used extensively in the Uzbekistan cotton-producing areas, where grain production has been sacrificed to provide more cotton land. Although alfalfa is a crop of some considerable importance, and livestock are numerous, there is little litter with which to conserve liquid manure. Prianishnikov notes that it is hardly logical to transport straw for litter 1,500 to 2,000 kilometers from the Siberian grain-producing areas which export grain to Uzbekistan.

Asia and Australia

Livestock are relatively scarce in the Middle East and not all of their manure is used for agricultural purposes although intensive manurial practices characterize some agricultural areas. In Israel, for instance, the supply of manure falls far below the demand, although manure is collected from chickens, dairy cattle, mules, donkeys, horses, sheep, and goats, and the Israeli government is encouraging increased production and use of manure.

In Iraq however, despite the use of manure on cotton fields, gardens, orchards, and pastures, much of the manure produced is used for fuel, as is true throughout the Middle East. Keen actually maintains that it is more economical to use manure for fuel than for fertilizer in areas with dry climates, because of the rapid loss of nitrogen by oxidation. He feels that the heat of oxidation should be obtained in the fireplace, and that the phosphate and potash of the manure will still be reclaimed if the ashes from manure fires are used as fertilizers. In Pakistan, however, where fuel and fertilizer uses are considered competitive, agricultural authorities advocate that as much manure as possible be used as fertilizer.

Livestock play a secondary role in the rice economy of monsoon Asia, and in many areas the rice crop is grown solely with those nutrients derived by natural soil-forming processes. The manure of draft animals is commonly reserved for the rice seed-bed. Nevertheless, it is difficult, with existing farm practices, to collect and use the manure of these animals. The lack of plant foods necessitates unusual practices. Siamese farmers, for instance, dip their seedlings in a paste of bat guano before planting. Silt from ponds, canals, and streams is often used as fertilizer in southeast Asia. Javanese farmers have discovered that the presence of fish in flooded rice paddies acts as a fertilizer, and increases rice yields as much as 10 to 20 percent.

The use of night soil in China, Japan, and Korea has been so emphasized that the importance of animal manure has been over-shadowed.

Shen, for instance, estimates that night soil represents only one-fifth of the manure produced in China, and Trewartha's data indicate that night soil comprises only one-third of the manure used in Japan. Throughout China large numbers of swine are kept as scavengers and manure-producers although the sale of pork no more than covers the cost of their feed. Farm manure provides only one-fourth of the fertilizer required on Japanese farms and much of the so-called manure is actually compost, green manure crops, seaweed, ashes, and other farm refuse; fertilizers are in such short supply that even silkworm excrement is utilized.

Stabling of animals is not necessary in the mild Australian climate, and manure is commonly left in the pastures, although poultry and dairy manure is sometimes collected and sold to city gardeners. Australian farmers consider that wheat production is inadvisable without sheep. Sheep graze wheat stubble, and simultaneously add fertilizer to the land.

Africa

One of the basic agricultural problems of central Africa is the development of a trypanosomiasis-resistant strain of livestock. Until such time the supply of manure will necessarily be limited. Many native tribes in the East African Highlands are ignorant of the fertilizing value of manure. The native in Uganda "is not aware that waste products from cattle, when properly made into manure, have any value whatever as fertilizers for land." Crop residues are burned in Kenya, and the use of cattle manure is just beginning under European tutelage. The Kikuyu actually believe that cattle will become possessed of an evil spirit (thahu) and die if their dung is placed in the soil or removed. "Manure is regarded as useless dirt and its presence in gardens is accidental rather than intentional" in Nyasaland. Manure is used locally in much of southern Africa, primarily for specialized crops. In the Rhodesian tobacco belt, for instance, as much as five to ten tons of kraal manure are applied to each acre of tobacco land. Abandoned kraals are used as tobacco fields; rights to this manure-enriched soil have initiated intratribal conflicts, and pose a serious land tenure problem.

South America

Most of the livestock of South America graze permanent range land, in such areas as Patagonia, Uruguay, southern Brazil, and the Llanos, and little or no effort is made to save their manure. Mild winter temperatures over most of the continent permit year-round grazing so there is little stable manure even in mixed farming areas.[5] The use of manure

[5] Note the analogy to other subtropical areas, such as Australia and the American Southeast, where crops and livestock are also divorced, even on the same holding. Waibel concludes that "the most important thing to do is to end this fatal separa-

in some areas, however, is worthy of note. Many of the livestock of the Pampas graze improved pastures which are rotated with cropland and thus crops receive the benefit of manure. Manure is also used on the vineyards and cane fields of the oases of northwestern Argentina. Many Brazilian orange growers operate dairies with negligible profit in order to obtain manure for their groves. Efforts have been made to rehabilitate exhausted coffee lands in São Paulo by use of chicken manure. Manure from the dry lowlands of northeastern Brazil is transported on mule back in leather bags to the cropped fields of the humid "sierras." Cattle on the Altiplano "are raised primarily to provide fertilizer for the fields under cultivation. Only rarely are cattle marketed."

North America

The most intensive manurial practices in North America are found in an area extending from the eastern Great Plains through the Corn Belt into the Dairy Belt of the United States and Canada. In the Dairy Belt manure is either collected in barns or is dropped as the animals graze rotation or permanent pastures. Considerable quantities accumulate in the barns or sheds during the long winter season when the ground is snow-covered. Manure is distributed to the fields whenever the busy tempo of work on the farm permits, especially during the non-cropping months.

Manure is obtained from a greater variety of animals, and in greater quantities, in the Corn Belt than in any other part of the Western Hemisphere. Cattle, hogs, poultry, and sheep all produce significant amounts of manure here, but the most distinctive manurial aspect of the Corn Belt is associated with the feed lot. Most feed lots exist for the fattening of cattle and hogs. The rich grain and protein supplements fed to the cattle produce rich manure. Grain which passes through the cattle undigested is greedily sought by hogs which consume considerable quantities of feces as they root after the grain. Two to four shoats commonly "follow" each steer. When corn is "cattled down," instead of being fed in the lot, "a sufficient number of hogs should be put into the field to utilize both the corn that the cattle knock to the ground and the undigested corn voided by the cattle in their feces."

Manure is in great demand in market gardening areas along the eastern seaboard of the United States. Some farmers in Lancaster County, Pennsylvania, actually make a practice of feeding cattle under contract in return for the manure they produce. With notable exceptions, such as the Bluegrass region of Kentucky, manure is not highly regarded in the American southeast. In the southern Appalachian burley

---

tion of crop cultivation and stock raising." Leo Waibel, "European Colonization in Southern Brazil," *Geographical Review*, Vol. 40, 1950, pp. 529–547; reference on p. 543.

tobacco region, for instance, all the manure of the farm is reserved for the tobacco field, but in most other parts of the southeast manure is merely tossed into heaps to decompose.[6] The inadequacy of fencing in the southeast prevents rotation of croplands and manured pastures even in those areas where livestock are of increasing importance.

In Cuba, Middle America, and the Great Plains of the United States most manure is dropped on permanent range land. In recent years, however, commercial feedlots which have been established on the Great Plains and in many other parts of the West have proven a valuable source of fertilizer for irrigated cropland. In some irrigated areas farmers have actually begun to keep herds of cattle principally for the manure which they produce. Urban development in the West has been associated with dairying, orchards, and market gardening; manure from the dairy farms has been of considerable value to truck farmers and orchardists.

Many American farmers do not appreciate the true value of manure, as evidenced by wasteful methods of collection, storage, and distribution. American laymen, including many geographers, have also ignored the importance of manure, and have even tended to make it a subject of ridicule and social impropriety. We might all remember that "the value of manure is slightly over $7.50 per ton! This should be of considerable consolation to the man loading manure by hand," just as manure is of considerable importance to anyone interested in maintaining the fertility of our soils and in increasing our food production.

[6] In the northeast Georgia broiler area, for instance, rich chicken manure is given to anyone who will clean the houses, and chicken manure is discarded as a useless by-product at a leading southeastern agricultural experiment station. When they asked a southeastern dairy farmer what use he made of his manure, the authors were offered all they could carry away as the farmer was eager to be rid of it.

26. "Mountain Moonshining" in East Tennessee

Loyal Durand Jr.

The production and consumption of potable alcohol has been and remains an important activity in all stages of man's history. Even in nations at an advanced stage of technological development, elements of a subsistence economy may persist in this economic pursuit. This selection describes a traditional handicraft-type industry with many peculiar

*locational factors. The numbers of this kind of illegal enterprise
may come as a surprise to many "flatland furriners."*

For 160 years or more a regional association has existed between the
Appalachian hill lands and the illicit manufacture of corn whisky—
"mountain moonshine." From the time of the Whisky Rebellion in
western Pennsylvania, in September, 1794, to the present day the federal
and state governments have wrestled with the problem, their concern
stemming primarily from loss of taxes and, in the southern Appalachians,
the existence of large blocks of dry or prohibition territory. How much
of the present illicit manufacture is the result of economic pressure, how
much is a reflection of a traditional pattern of life in which a small still
was as much a part of mountain occupance as the spinning wheel, and
how much is attributable to increased federal and state taxes on legal
beverages is difficult, if not impossible, to determine.

The industry has prevailed in many mountain and hill-country settlements since the earliest days of the pioneer. The Appalachian moun-
taineer, under economic pressure, with a long-established way of life
and a "mountain yeoman" complex, found that one of his crops, corn,
was difficult to transport and of low value; by turning some of it into
a beverage high in value per unit of weight and compact to transport,
he could realize a greater profit. Furthermore, today a ready market
is at hand, both in his home region and among neighboring "flat-
landers." The jokes and cartoons about the Kentucky, Tennessee,
Georgia, and other Appalachian moonshiners, probably regarded as
such by distant persons, have a basis in fact. The *weekly* manufacture
of moonshine in the mountains of Tennessee alone is estimated to be
about 25,000 gallons, and in the state about 32,000. In a single month
(April, 1955) 94 stills were destroyed by state and federal agents in
East Tennessee alone, 23 of them in one day, and raids by county
sheriffs brought the regional total to about 140.

Obviously, geographic distribution of the moonshine industry cannot
be accurately mapped, but only the distribution of destroyed stills.
What percentage these form of the total number is unknown, though
enforcement officials have hazarded a guess. No doubt the percentage
of captured stills is higher today than it was in the past; the airplane
and the helicopter are efficient spotters of stills in the forests and woodlands, and large operations can often be detected by smoke and by
the odor of the mash. Yet movement in difficult terrain is necessary for
the capture of a still, and the agent must maneuver across hills and
creeks, through dense brush, and along dead-end roads. The final rush
may capture the still and the mash, but not the operators.

SOURCE: *Geographical Review*, XLVI (April, 1956), 169–81. The author is professor
of geography, University of Tennessee.

The routes and destinations of the whisky are also matters of conjecture. What percentage is consumed locally, in regional cities, or in distant localities is unknown. The estimated volume of production indicates an outflow of some magnitude. Highway patrols are familiar with some of the carriers, usually "souped up" cars capable of traveling 90 to 100 miles an hour or more. Many of them are caught; others, outdistancing or evading their pursuers, complete their runs and deliver their cargoes into outside channels of trade. The Tennessee State Alcohol Tax Division is aware that some illicit whisky enters incognito into interstate commerce, and it attempts to stop the outflow into Michigan, Ohio, and Illinois.

Estimates of Tennessee Moonshine Production

The moonshine industry of Tennessee is concentrated principally in the eastern third of the state. Although some of the raided stills are purely family enterprises for home consumption, there is not a single county in this Appalachian area without some illicit manufacture of whisky. Commercial production, however, has apparently become the business of a few.

Officials of the Tennessee State Alcohol Tax Division of the Department of Finance and Taxation estimate a state moonshine production of about 1,664,000 gallons a year. If all of it is consumed within the state, the annual state tax loss, based on a tax of $2.00 a gallon, is $3,-300,000. Obviously, much of this is a paper loss, since all but half a dozen counties out of the 95 in the state are dry. With a federal tax rate of $10.50 a gallon, the loss to the federal government is more than five times the state loss.

Federal agents of the Alcohol and Tobacco Tax division of the Internal Revenue Service in the southern Appalachian region place the illicit whisky production in the North Carolina Appalachians at probably five or more times the Tennessee production, in Georgia at three to four times more, in Alabama at three times, and in South Carolina at about the same; the Kentucky production is much smaller. If we assume that

TABLE 1: Whisky Production in the United States *(In tax gallons)*

1946	147,465,000	1951	205,702,000
1947	167,995,000	1952	103,544,000
1948	129,597,000	1953	66,765,449
1949	149,595,000	1954	102,541,246
1950	118,760,000	1955	103,927,044

SOURCE: Internal Revenue Service.

these official estimates are reasonably correct, and that the Tennessee output is a conservative million and a half gallons, we get the astounding total for the southern Appalachians of 21 million gallons or more a year. The economic geographer can hardly afford to overlook this activity! It is "big business," even if engaged in by only a relatively few persons. Compare the outflow with that of legally distilled whisky in the entire United States (Table 1).

Chief Concentrations of Tennessee Moonshining

The state of Tennessee is divided for judicial purposes into three so-called Grand Divisions, East Tennessee, Middle Tennessee, and West Tennessee (Fig. 1), and the inhabitants speak of themselves as being from these areas. Official estimates of weekly moonshine production in these divisions are 24,000 gallons in East Tennessee, 6000 in Middle Tennessee, and 2000 in West Tennessee. Middle Tennessee includes part of the hill lands of the state, particularly the western Cumberland Plateau, and much of the 6000-gallon estimate is for this physiographic region. In other words, most of the whisky is distilled in the eastern, or hilly and mountainous, half of the state, whether or not production is administratively in East Tennessee. West Tennessee's coastal-plain terrain is generally flat; its views are unobstructed by hills or mountains. This is the cotton-producing and "Deep South" part of the state, and the attitudes of its rural inhabitants are quite different from those of the East.

Within the "most productive" East Tennessee region two large centers of moonshine activity stand out, highest both in number of stills raided and in quantity of output. One center lies in the true crystalline-rock mountains of the southern Appalachians, the other on the Cumberland Plateau. Each bears a relationship to market: the first is not far removed from Knoxville, and the second is close to Chattanooga—in fact, an area

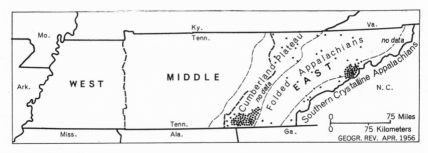

FIGURE 1: Approximate number of stills captured each month in East Tennessee, and their location with respect to the several physiographic provinces of the Southern Appalachian Region. Each dot indicates one still.

on the plateau within 10 miles of Chattanooga is one of the most frequently raided in the state.

The mountains of the southern Appalachians lie along the eastern border of the state. Southern Cocke County (east of Knoxville) has long been recognized as the "capital of moonshining" in Tennessee. Federal and state agents capture an average of about 40 stills a month in the county, and federal agents estimate that some 75 per cent of the illicit whisky of East Tennessee originates there. Stills are large, mostly 500-gallon capacity; occasionally a still of 1000 gallons or more falls to the raiders. Inaccessible coves and valleys, steep mountain slopes, and river and creek sites are desired locations. From this center a large-still region extends northeast and southwest along the face and base of the mountains; thus, although an average of only four stills a month are captured in an adjacent county, they are usually of 500-gallon size; in May, 1955, a 1200-gallon still fell to government agents.

The Great Valley of East Tennessee lies between the southern Appalachians and the Cumberland Plateau. It is the physiographic region of the Folded Appalachians, the ridge-and-valley countryside. Every county in this region has some moonshining activity, based usually on locations along the ridges rather than in the open agricultural valleys. Even Knox County, in which Knoxville is located, has yielded many small stills and an occasional large one, and during 10 months in 1954–1955 the sheriff of Anderson County, in which Oak Ridge is located, captured 35 stills. Stills are small, commonly of 50–100-gallon capacity, and production is for the home market, for home use, or for sale by the drink, in contrast with the true mountain area, where the production is "wholesale." The total number of these stills is unknown. During the preparation of the 59,000 acres of the Oak Ridge Reservation for the townsite and atomic plants, 22 stills were found, left behind by the rural population in the rather rapid evacuation of the area. Stills are hidden in the woodlands on the ridge sides and crests, and in rough karst country in the valleys and on lower slopes. Some of the karst country possesses relief of 200 to 400 feet and sinkhole pockets 200 feet or more in depth. In much of this region county sheriffs raid the stills and are important in the control; the small federal and state forces are compelled by circumstance to concentrate on the large operations in the mountains.

The Cumberland Mountains and Cumberland Plateau exhibit conditions of each of the aforementioned regions. The northern two-thirds is generally small-still country. Two of the roughest and least accessible counties, south of the Kentucky border in the Cumberland Mountains, probably have more stills than fall to the raiding forces; they average only about two "losses" a month. Southward, where the Cumberlands are flat-topped and a true plateau, the size of still apparently increases. The largest are in the part of the plateau adjacent to Chattanooga, cut by the Tennessee River gorge and deep tributary valleys. Blocklike segments of the plateau are almost isolated, heavily wooded, and virtually inaccessible. Hamilton County, in which Chattanooga lies, "loses" some 30 stills a month; the next county to the west, Marion, about 40. In Marion County stills are located at escarpment bases, on slopes, in deep valleys, and on tabular outliers. Suck Creek Mountain, a narrowed stretch of Walden Ridge (the part of the Cumberland Plateau between the Great Valley of East Tennessee and the long, linear Sequatchie Valley), is almost as notorious a moonshine area as southern Cocke County.

Illicit manufacture of corn whisky continues westward on the Cumberland Plateau into Middle Tennessee. This part of the state, however, possesses its own "manufacturing district," apparently based on the Nashville market as well as on the hill-country location. Hickman, a hilly county in the Western Highland Rim, west of the Nashville Basin, is one of the five "most productive" moonshine areas in the state, on the evidence of raids and the experience of government agents. Neighboring counties of the rim share somewhat in the activity.

Economic and Marketing Factors

To what extent is the corn-whisky industry attributable to economic pressure in a region of low income where corn is a leading crop? Certainly the fact that this low-value bulk crop can be readily converted into a more valuable and more easily transported product has been influential, more so in the past than at present. Incomes have been increased, though the figures probably do not show. This circumstance combined with a traditional way of life has led some persons to engage in a more lucrative enterprise without particular trouble to their consciences.

Transportation has invaded the southern Appalachian hill lands rapidly, especially since World War I, and has opened the way to distant markets. Good roads, nearly all of them graveled and many of them paved, have been provided by the respective states. The moonshiner is able to dispose of his product several hundred miles from its region of manufacture, and "specialists" in production have appeared, who devote their full time to the activity. The increasing taxes on legally manufactured alcoholic beverages during recent years and the existence of dry territory throughout much of the adjoining region have provided the moonshiner with a special market situation, in which the customer (or consumer) seeks his goods and services and there is little or no need for him to employ "salesmen." The main problems are secrecy of manufacture in a secluded location, alertness toward the appearance of revenue agents, and transportation of the wares to market.

The Human Element and Dispersion

The Scotch-Irish and American frontiersmen helped "transport" the corn-whisky industry throughout the southern Appalachians during the early days of settlement. Their attitude toward corn whisky was apparently different from that of the early New Englanders. As settlers from New England moved west by way of the northern routes, such as the Mohawk Valley, the whisky still did not appear, at least not in any great numbers. However, literature is replete with references to the problem from central Pennsylvania southward, and history calls it to our attention through the governmental troubles during the Whisky Rebellion. After the period of railroad and highway building, with the resulting improved accessibility of the northern Appalachians, the problem became less acute there; indeed, in many areas it disappeared. Government agents now find the illicit still in the Northeast mainly in urban areas, often in warehouses or dwellings, and operating in an entirely different manner and milieu from those of its southern hill-country counterpart.

How much of the present southern-Appalachian attitude is a carryover from past generations? How much is owing to the lack or difficulty of transportation in the hill and mountain lands? It must be remembered that, as late as 1900–1910, large areas of the southern Appalachians, even in the valleys of East Tennessee, were primarily in a stage of subsistence agriculture except near a few main railroad lines.[1] Undoubtedly there must have been a tradition of local whisky making in certain mountain and hill-country locations, and these have acted as centers of dispersion. When a lumber company in northeastern Wisconsin decided to concentrate on selling its cutover lands to Kentucky mountaineers instead of specializing in immigrants (the usual target of the cutover-land salesman) and succeeded in bringing in large colonies of native Kentuckians, the moonshine still appeared with them. Wisconsin suddenly, and for the first time, found itself confronted with an illegal moonshine industry. In the Cascade foothills of Washington, settlements of Cumberland Mountains people in the Cowlitz Valley introduced a moonshine industry there. Many other such dispersal associations are known to exist.

[1] Before 1870 practically all of East Tennessee had a self-sufficing economy. After this date the Knoxville and Chattanooga areas and a few others developed rapidly as commercial and industrial centers. In 1903 the Tennessee Legislature enacted a no-fence law; this marked the elimination of sheep for homespun woolen clothing. By 1900–1910 the exodus from the farms of East Tennessee to the textile mills of Knoxville and of the Carolinas was in full swing.

Some Reflections on the Future

The recent advent of improved transportation in the hill lands and the increased taxation of legal liquor pose other unanswerable questions. Are groups of outsiders or local "combines" moving in on the age-old corn-whisky industry of the southern Appalachians? Is the hillsman moonshiner being reduced to the status of manufacturer alone, and is his product (aside from that destined for purely local consumption) being distributed by specialists—specialists in transportation, in distribution, and in sales? The evidence from raids indicates that the small moonshiner still grows his corn and produces corn whisky, but many of the largest stills, those in the 500-gallon class and above, use sugar, yeast, and similar ingredients as raw materials, and corn (or other grain) is not significant. Furthermore, the large operators possess no other apparent means of support; after a jail term they go back in "business." If specialization is increasing, in response to a combination of many factors, what will happen to the long-established way of life of the small mountain moonshiner? Subsistence farming in the hills and mountains of the southern Appalachians is on the way out. Each census records fewer true subsistence farms.[2] Perhaps "subsistence" manufacture of corn whisky too is destined to go "commercial."

[2] Partly this is owing to changed census definitions. Partly it is owing to the present-day need for cash and the expansion of the burley-tobacco industry. Partly it is the result of industrialization and the shift of the farm to a "part-time farm" basis, with the operator working in industry but residing on the land.

27. Von Thünen and Urban Sprawl
Robert Sinclair

As was pointed out in an earlier selection, urbanization has been a characteristic development in the later stages of the economic process. Nearly 150 years ago, the German geographer J. Heinrich Von Thünen classified the pattern of development around cities as he observed them in western Europe. His findings have been accepted, almost as law, ever since, and his "concentric ring" idea of 1826 continues to be illustrated in many geography texts. But modern urban, suburban, exurban, and "rurban" developments based on increased individual mobility have brought significant changes in the accepted pattern. Sinclair has analyzed these changes and developed an up-to-date theory, based on

> *differing economic elements and factors and offering a visible
> and understandable explanation of the impact of urbanization
> on land use and land values as a part of the economic process.*

This paper concerns agricultural land use patterns near present-day urban areas, and the forces which determine those patterns. Almost inevitably, the paper starts with the name J. Heinrich Von Thünen, whose celebrated treatise, *Der Isolierte Staat*, specifically dealt with this same topic. Von Thünen's work, one of the first to present a theory of agricultural land use, has been subjected to various interpretations and criticisms through the years. Subsequent workers have taken up his ideas and attempted to introduce elaborations, improvements, or greater precision. Other writers have tended to criticize his ideas because those ideas have little apparent application to modern situations. Nevertheless, Von Thünen's *Isolierte Staat* remains a classic in location theory. The work is still the base from which many agricultural land use studies are developed. The Von Thünen model is still the one against which patterns of agriculture around cities are compared.

The present study is no exception. The writer has based the first part of the study on a consideration of Von Thünen's work and an evaluation of its applicability to modern situations. In doing so, he feels at the outset that it is important to consider the theory's basic purpose, and the simple sequence of operations used in its development.

Von Thünen sought a theory to explain a pattern which he had discovered empirically, as a result of his observations and research. From his findings, he identified the basic forces determining the pattern. These basic forces became the key factors in the formulation of the theory. Essentially, therefore, the applicability of the theory depends upon the correct identification of the basic forces. Where these forces are operating, the theory provides a way of understanding the agricultural pattern, even though specific land uses might differ from those in Von Thünen's example. It is proposed in this study that those basic forces continue to operate in the less-developed parts of the world today, and that application of the theory can still be made in those areas.

On the other hand, where the basic forces identified by Von Thünen are not operating, his theory does not provide a way of understanding the agricultural pattern. This would seem to be the situation today in many advanced, industrialized parts of the world, where the basic agricultural pattern presented by Von Thünen has been outdated by changes in technology and human organization.

At the same time, the writer feels that consistent land use patterns are being formed around urban areas in more industrialized parts of the

SOURCE: *Annals of the Association of American Geographers*, XLVII (March, 1967), 72–87. The author is associate professor of geography, Wayne State University.

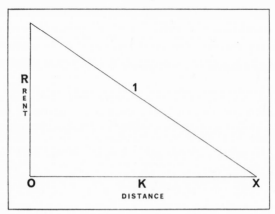

Figure 1: Relationship of Economic Rent and distance from market.

world by forces other than those identified by Von Thünen. This paper identifies one of those new forces and, using it, presents a theoretical framework for understanding agricultural patterns in many present-day urbanized areas. The paper starts by outlining the main facts and logic of Von Thünen's thinking.

Von Thünen's Theory

Von Thünen's primary concern was to discover and examine the laws which governed the pattern of agricultural land use existing in his time and within his experience. He recognized that this land use pattern depended upon competition between various types of agriculture for the use of a particular piece of land. The controlling factor in this competition was Economic Rent, defined here as return from investment in the land. Stated briefly, that form of land use providing the greatest Economic Rent would make the highest bid for the land and displace all others. Von Thünen realized that transport costs were a primary factor determining Economic Rent. Moreover, because transport costs increased with distance, they imparted a spatial variation to Economic Rent. Hence Economic Rent from any one land use can be expressed as a function of distance from the market, as is simply illustrated in Figure 1. As O, the market, is left, increasing transport costs cause the Rent per unit of land R to be diminished for each unit of distance. It is entirely absorbed at the X intercept.

This one land use, however, is competing with other land uses, which, according to their type of production, have different R-slopes. The competition between two types of land use is shown in Figure 2. Here, land use 1 yields a higher Economic Rent R close to the market, but because its slope is steeper than that for land use 2, its advantage ceases at point Z, at a distance of OZ from the market. From this point outward, land use 2 yields a higher Rent R until this is entirely absorbed at X, at a distance OX from the market. The fundamental factor governing the steepness of the R-slope is the relative ease with which the total production of a unit area can be transported. Commodities which yield a large bulk per hectare, e.g., potatoes or firewood, in Von Thünen's time, yield a high Rent close to the market, but because the transport cost per hectare is high, the Rent diminishes rapidly with distance from the market. Commodities which yield a lower bulk per hectare, e.g., grain, do not yield such a high Rent close to the market. However, because transport costs per hectare are relatively low, and the actual value per unit of weight is relatively high, Economic Rent diminishes much more slowly with distance from the market. In Figure 2, therefore, land use 1 might be potatoes, the land use 2 might be grain. One other factor influencing the steepness of the R-slope is the degree of perishability of the produce. Because of rapid deterioration, perishable commodities, e.g., milk, during Von Thünen's time, can only be produced close to the market. Hence their Economic Rent declines very rapidly with distance from the market.

Figure 2 does not only reflect the competition between particular crops. It can also refer to competition between two systems of growing the same crops. The per-hectare production of any crop can be increased by more intense application of labor or fertilizer. At the market, an extremely intensive use of land is desirable,[1] because the resulting in-

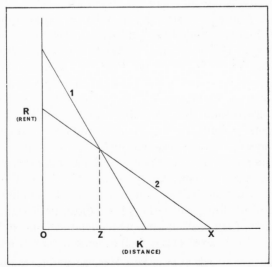

FIGURE 2: Relationship of Economic Rent and distance from market for two competing land uses.

[1] Here, and throughout this paper, the words intensive and extensive are used in the strict, technical sense, and refer to amount of input into the land. Because input is generally related to production, the terms are frequently used quite loosely.

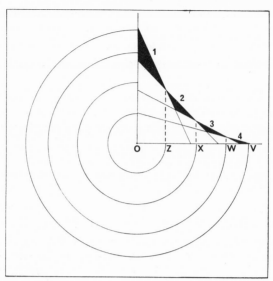

FIGURE 3: Relationship of Economic Rent and distance from market for numerous competing land uses.

creased production pays off in higher Economic Rent. With greater distance from the market, such intensive land use becomes less feasible, because the advantages of increased per-hectare production are offset by increasing transport costs.[2] A less intensive system becomes more desirable. In Figure 2, therefore, land use 1 might be an intensive crop rotation, whereas land use 2 might refer to a rotation system with considerable fallow land. There are two types of exceptions to this general rule. If a nonintensive method results in an extremely high per acre production of a low value product, e.g., wood, in Von Thünen's time, this less intensive land use can exist near the market. Secondly, if a relatively intensive land use results in a product of low bulk but high value, e.g., cheese, this land use can exist far from the market.

It should be noted that the concept of declining agricultural intensity has been the source of considerable controversy, and the concept can be regarded as a Von Thünen law only with the qualifications stated above. Moreover, subsequent writers have illustrated by analytic models that where more than one land use is involved, it is possible for a more extensive land use to exist closer to the market. Nevertheless, the prin-

[2] Two important points should be made here. First, the principle expressed is strengthened by the general operation of the law of diminishing returns. Because each successive input generally yields a smaller increment of output than the last, the desirability of a less intensive system at a distance from the market becomes even greater. Second, the term transport costs refers not only to the costs of transporting products to the market, but also to the overall cost of distance (such as bringing manure and supplies to the farms).

ciple of declining intensity with increasing distance from the market is generally attributed to Von Thünen. The principle corresponded with the observed pattern of agriculture around market centers in Europe and elsewhere, and has come to be regarded as one of the basic contributions of the theory.

The competition between two land uses shown in Figure 2 can be expanded to include a number of land uses (Figure 3). In this case, land use 1 yields a greater Economic Rent in zone *OZ*, land use 2 in zone *ZX*, land use 3 in zone *XW*, and so on. Because *O* is the city, and the various land uses are found on all sides of the city, it is easy to take *O* as center, *OZ*, *OX*, *OW*, etc., as radii, and construct the famous Thünen rings. Such rings are the framework for the well-known pattern of land uses of *Der Isolierte Staat*, which Von Thünen conceived to illustrate the ideas which have been expressed.

Der Isolierte Staat was a finite area of flat, tillable land, uniform in physical characteristics and occupied by farmers who were entirely flexible in their land use practices. The farmers utilized a single form of transportation to carry their products to one market location, a centrally located city with equal access on all sides. Given these propositions, the pattern of land uses which would be found around this city is shown in Figure 4.

Zone 1 in Figure 4 is devoted to the production of vegetables and fresh milk. Such items produced high yields per acre, were perishable under the transport conditions of Von Thünen's time, and city prices for them were so high that no other land use yielded a high Economic Rent.

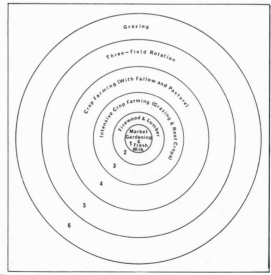

FIGURE 4: Sequence of land uses in *Der Isolierte Staat*.

Zone 2 is forest land, producing firewood and lumber. The per-hectare yield of wood was high, and at the time Von Thünen wrote, city demand was great enough to produce the necessary high Rent. The high costs of transporting wood, however, meant that Economic Rent decreased rapidly with increasing distance from the city, so that the zone did not extend far from the city.

The next three zones are crop farming zones of gradually decreasing intensity. The decline in Economic Rent, owing to increasing transport costs, made it necessary to apply less and less capital and labor, until only the most extensive rotation system was possible. Thus, in zone 3, rye, the most valuable crop, accounted for one-third of the land and was alternated with other crops. There was no fallow land. In zone 4, rye occupied less land and crops were mixed with pasture and fallow land. In zone 5, the three-field system prevailed, with one-third of the land in crops, pasture, and fallow respectively.

In zone 6, distance from the market was too great for crop production, and only the most extensive grazing activities could be carried on profitably.

Von Thünen was consistently aware that the idealized conditions of the *Isolierte Staat* were nowhere duplicated in reality. Indeed, the latter part of his work is devoted to examining how other variables would influence the ideal pattern presented in the first part. For example, he showed diagramatically how the presence of a navigable river and a small town would influence the agricultural pattern. He recognized the variability in soil fertility, in production costs, and in the living standards of farmers. He considered such factors as trade restrictions and taxes. Those considerations modified the idealized land use pattern, but did not affect the basic principles underlying his theory.

Von Thünen's Theory and Reality

Von Thünen's theory has stood the test of time. It was quite applicable to reality throughout his lifetime and for many decades after his death. Indeed, until very recently, the basic pattern of agricultural land use around cities in Europe and North America was in keeping with that in the *Isolierte Staat* and presumably remnants of the pattern still exist in those areas. Moreover, it appears likely that in those parts of the world where transportation is less developed and modern refrigeration techniques nonexistent, Von Thünen principles still apply. Chisholm, in a comprehensive study of the literature on the subject, cites examples of Thünen-like zones near nucleated agricultural settlements in Southern Italy and the Spanish Meseta, agro-towns in Bulgaria, rural parishes in Finland, towns in the Pakistan Punjab, villages in Nigeria and Ghana, and the settlements of shifting cultivators in Africa and South

America.[3] The general conformity of Von Thünen's model with reality, shown in these and other examples, indicates that the basic force upon which the model was based, namely the influence of transport costs (reflecting distance to the market) on agricultural land use, was the determining force for a long period of time in Europe and North America and remains the determining force today in much of the nonindustrialized world.

The situation is quite different today, however, in the highly industrialized parts of the world. The change has been brought about by the revolutionary developments of the last few decades in technology, in human organization, and in living habits. Developments in the field of transportation have had the greatest influence. Improved and more efficient means of transport have displaced former rudimentary methods. Costs of all types of transport have declined greatly in relation to most other agricultural production costs. Moreover, transport costs are not necessarily directly proportional to distance and bulk. Because of refrigeration and air-conditioning techniques, perishable commodities can be carried long distances without spoiling. An increasing amount of agricultural produce is processed before shipment. These new developments help to satiate the changing tastes of the modern city dweller, who demands a more varied and exotic diet than local agriculture can provide.

Related to these transport considerations are three other factors which have profoundly altered the agricultural pattern in modern industrial areas. First, modern organization favors large-scale production and mass transportation of agricultural produce. As a result, physical or other advantages of distant, specialized regions have become more important than in the past. Second, for these same reasons, there is rarely such a thing as a single local market, but rather a nationwide, or worldwide market. Third, the competition for land between various agricultural land uses is complicated by increasing competition from nonagricultural uses. The result of all these factors is that the agricultural land use pattern of Von Thünen's *Isolierte Staat* and the basic forces underlying this pattern, do not conform to the reality of today's industrialized society.

It is important to recognize that the outdating of the agricultural pattern in no way reflects upon the inherent logic and consistency of Von Thünen's theory.[4] What has happened is simply that the empirical ev-

---

[3] Chisholm also indicated how Von Thünen principles can be applied to scales both smaller (on an individual farm) and greater (on a world scale) than that of urban areas.

[4] Indeed, it can be claimed that Von Thünen principles explain agricultural activities on a much broader scale than that of individual cities. As early as 1925, Jonasson characterized the agricultural zones of Europe as being in keeping with Von Thünen principles. Ohlin placed the movements of commodities in international trade within a Thünian framework. Moreover, it is probable that an inherent value of the Thünen model is its applicability to a variety of nonagricultural situations. For

idence collected by Von Thünen concerning the production and distribution of agricultural produce does not resemble the evidence of the present time. More significantly, the basic force upon which he developed his land use theory, namely transport cost to the market, is no longer the primary determining factor in the patterning of agricultural land uses around urban areas.

The questions now arise. Is there any consistency in the agricultural patterns near the more complicated urban areas of the present? If so, are there other basic forces underlying these patterns? Further, can these forces be the foundation of a general theory, which might aid in understanding the contemporary scene?

Urban Expansion

One significant fact differentiates most modern urban areas from the cities of Von Thünen's experience. Whereas Von Thünen envisaged a static city, with set boundaries, in most modern industrialized nations the theme is urban expansion, with population growth and constantly expanding areas of urban land use. The spreading urban region influences rural land use far in advance of the built-up area. This influence, however, has little to do with the market provided by the city, but is the result of the very nature of the expansion process. Although urban expansion is uneven and in many ways chaotic, there is evidence that it creates consistent agricultural land use patterns in the neighborhood of many of our cities. To explain why this is so, certain aspects of the process of urban expansion need to be understood.

The nature of urban expansion is determined by many forces, among which the most basic are

1. urban and rural land price differences,
2. the flexibility offered all land users by modern automobile transportation, and
3. the whims and judgments of human beings.

Of these three, the first is most important in this analysis. Urban land today is much more valuable than rural land, so that where there is direct competition between urban and rural land uses, urban uses generally take over. Further, land where urbanization is expected also is more valuable than rural land. Such land rises in value, and either is purchased from the original owner by developers and speculators, or held by the original owner as a speculation. Finally, land which the owner

example, W. Isard considered the relationship of the Theory to urban land uses. W. Alonso utilized the Thünen model in developing a theory of residential land in *Location and Land Use*. W. Bunge suggests that the Thünen model can be applied to a great variety of human and physical situations where a zonation of phenomena occurs.

thinks might become urban land at some vague future date changes in value. It does not generally change hands, but the owner carries out his activities, or changes his activities, with the feeling that something is going to happen. In short, there is an air of anticipation associated with rural land near modern urbanized areas.

It is worthwhile to digress at this point to make clear that what is taking place is quite in keeping with Von Thünen's theory of Economic Rent. That land use providing the greatest return is making the highest bid for the land and is displacing other land uses. In this case, the land use providing the highest Rent is urban land use, and it is displacing rural land uses. Moreover, if the speculative value of land is taken into consideration, land where urbanization is anticipated provides greater Rent than purely rural land uses. Thus, Economic Rent still declines with distance from the city and the Von Thünen concept illustrated in Figures 1–3 still holds. However, when Economic Rent is translated into patterns of land use, particularly agricultural land use, the conformity with Von Thünen's theory vanishes. This is seen as the analysis of urban expansion continues.

It has been pointed out that land near urban areas is subject to an air of anticipation of urban encroachment. The degree of this anticipation has a direct influence upon agricultural land use practices, particularly upon the intensity of agriculture. For, obviously, the greater the chances of urban land uses taking over, the less practical it becomes

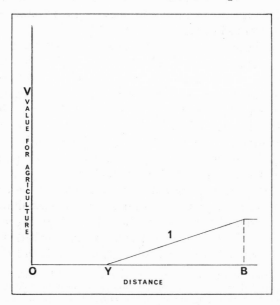

FIGURE 5: Relationship of Value for Agriculture and distance from urban area.

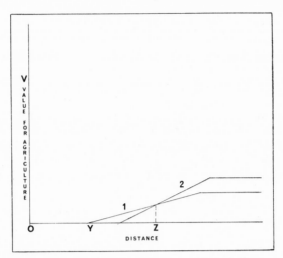

FIGURE 6: Relationship of Value for Agriculture and distance from urban area for two competing land uses.

for the owner to invest highly in capital and labor for agricultural purposes. The degree of anticipation declines with distance from the encroaching city. Hence, distance from the city again becomes the factor which determines the agricultural land use pattern. However, whereas in Von Thünen's *Isolierte Staat* distance was meaningful in terms of transport costs to the market, it is here meaningful in terms of anticipation of urban encroachment.

The effect of distance from the city thus is expressed in the following simple relationship: As the urbanized area is approached from a distance, the degree of anticipation of urbanization increases. As this happens, the ratio of urban to rural land values increases. Hence, although the absolute value of the land increases, the relative value for agricultural utilization decreases. Consequently, the capital and labor investment in agriculture, i.e., the intensity of agricultural land use, decreases. The result of this process is a basic agricultural land use pattern which is the reverse of that found in Von Thünen's time.

This relationship between distance and land use can be expressed in diagrammatical form.[5] In Figure 5, a single type of agricultural land use is measured in terms of V, defined as the value of carrying out this type of agriculture. As O (the urbanized area) is approached, V decreases because the probability of urbanization increases. V is entirely absorbed

[5] It should be made clear that Figures 5, 6, and 7 are not Economic Rent models and that the slope V does not represent the same as slope R in Figures 1, 2, and 3. It is conceivable that this diagram could be correlated with an Economic Rent model of urban and speculative land, as explained above. However, it is felt that the present diagram expresses more directly the operation of urban expansion upon agricultural land use.

at the Y intercept. With increasing distance from O, V increases until it levels off at point B, where there is no more anticipation of urban land prices.

This one land use, however, is competing with other land uses, each with different V-slopes. The competition between two types of land use is shown in Figure 6. Here, land use 1 prevails in zone YZ, but because its V-slope is less steep than that of land use 2, its advantage ceases at point Z. From this point outward, land use 2 takes over. The factor governing the steepness of the V-slope is the intensity of the agricultural investment. Land use 2 is the more intensive type of agriculture, which pays off in greater agricultural returns at a distance from the city. As the city is approached and the likelihood of urbanization increases, the value of such intensive investment in farming declines rapidly. At point Z, it does not pay to carry out this type of farming, al-

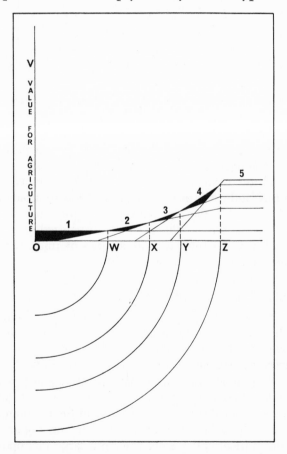

FIGURE 7: Relationship of Value for Agriculture and distance from urban area for numerous competing land uses.

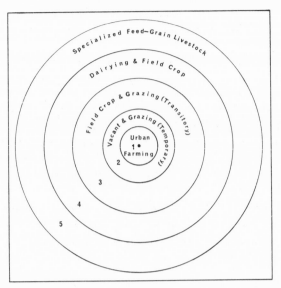

FIGURE 8: Theoretical sequence of land uses around expanding metropolitan area.

though it is still feasible to carry out a type of agriculture which requires a smaller investment (land use 1).

The concept can be extended to include various intensities of land use (Fig. 7). Here land use 1 (the least intensive) will prevail in zone OW, land use 2 (more intensive) in zone WX, land use 3 in zone XY, and so on. Land use 5 extends to an undetermined distance N from the city, because this land use is outside of the area where urban land prices can be anticipated. It is the regional type of agriculture, governed by factors other than the direct influence of the urbanized area. With O as center and OW, OX, OY, etc. as radii, a series of rings, corresponding to Von Thünen rings, can be drawn.

A Theoretical Pattern of Agriculture

Utilizing this theory, let us examine the type of agricultural land use pattern which might evolve today in an area with an advanced industrialized economy. Assume a large agricultural region of specialized feed-grain livestock economy in the United States Midwest. The region is uniform in its productivity, in the type of farming which has developed through time, and in its access to a nationwide market. Assume that the farmers throughout the region are flexible in their farming activities and shrewd enough to take advantage of changing opportunities. At one side of this agricultural region, assume a large metropolitan area, growing in population and steadily engulfing the rural land around it. Assume, finally, that the forces connected with urban expansion influence agricultural practices evenly on all sides of the urbanized area. Given these propositions, the pattern of agricultural land use around the metropolitan edges would be as shown in Figure 8.

In zone 1, at the edges of the built-up area, land is either changing to urban uses, is being subdivided, or is being held by speculators or developers for early development. Some farmers, for various reasons, might not wish to sell their land in spite of the high prices they are offered. They are exceptions, however, and are generally forced out of farming by high urban taxes, zoning practices, or by the nuisance associated with urban living. One or two types of agriculture might still be pursued in an otherwise suburbanized environment. These are activities, such as poultry-keeping, greenhouses, or mushroom growing, which generally take place in buildings, quite often multistoried buildings. Such activities do not correspond to the market-gardening and dairying found in zone 1 of Von Thünen's *Isolierte Staat.* They are, rather, farm factories, and are really industrial, as much as rural, forms of land use. Even these land uses are generally destined for early disappearance.

Zone 2 is mainly a zone of vacant land, where urban subdivision is not yet taking place, but where farming, in general, is no longer carried on. This zone is characterized by broad expanses of barren, unused land, owned by speculators, or farmers who intend to sell the land at the most profitable time. The uncertainty as to when that time will come means that the farmer has no guarantee of continuous farming operation. Generally, he does not farm at all. Sometimes, he rents his land to urban groups for recreational purposes. Any farming activities which do take place in this zone are short-lived and extensive, as where land is leased to some farmer in a more distant zone for the grazing of his animals, or crops of hay are grown with the primary object of keeping down weeds.

Zone 3 is a field crop and grazing zone. It is an area of transitory agriculture, where farming activities are carried on, but with the anticipation of urbanization at some future date. The farmer does not wish to invest capital. Hired labor is too expensive, and it is more profitable for members of his family to find employment in the city than to work on the farm. Frequently, the marketing and supply services so necessary to modern agriculture have moved out of the immediate area, further hampering farming activities. Farming, therefore, tends to be quite extensive. Cash crops have taken over land where more intensive animal husbandry once prevailed. Quite often the land is rented to outside operators who grow winter wheat, corn, or hay, or use the land for pasture. Former goals, such as high productivity per acre, or maintaining land fertility, are no longer present. Over-all, agriculture is steadily becoming less intensive.

Zone 4 is a broad zone of dairying and field crops. At the inner margins of the zone, where there is some anticipation of future urban encroachment, farmers are shifting from dairying to less intensive and less confining cash cropping. Elsewhere, however, the zone is outside the price mechanism of the city in terms of land use being influenced by anticipated urbanization. On the other hand, it is still within the city's influence in a marketing sense because it constitutes the major part of the fresh milkshed of the metropolitan area. Dairying is the main activity, whereas field crops and meat livestock are found near the zone's outer boundary.

Finally, in zone 5 is found the specialized feed-grain livestock of the Corn Belt. The economy is not under the influence of the metropolitan area in any direct way. It continues to serve, and be influenced by, a nationwide market.[6]

In brief, given the stated assumptions of a uniform farming region, flexible farmers, and an orderly influence of the expanding city's price mechanism, the agricultural land use pattern would show zones of gradually increasing intensity from the built-up edges of the metropolitan area to where the city has no direct influence upon agricultural practices.

Factors Which Might Modify the Pattern

It is not surprising that the theoretical pattern presented in this paper is seldom duplicated in reality. The idealized circular pattern of agricultural activities is disrupted by many factors, in some respects more so than the idealized pattern of Von Thünen's *Isolierte Staat* was disrupted by factors present during his lifetime.

First, the stated assumptions of uniformity and simplicity are never found. Agricultural regions are uniform neither in type of farming nor in productivity. Farmers do have individual whims and prejudices. A road and settlement pattern is already in existence. Furthermore, the presence of a single metropolitan area, isolated from other metropolitan areas, is probably the exception rather than the rule.

Second, urban sprawl tends to be somewhat chaotic. Expansion of urban land uses proceeds in an uneven, and often apparently aimless, pattern. It extends along transportation arteries. It develops around certain nodes on these arteries. It concentrates around other nodes (factories or shopping districts) at some distance from the main urbanized area. It leapfrogs over intervening rural areas. It is often affected by, or dominated by, planned public developments (military establishments

---

[6] It will be recognized that in this present example, zone 5 has a less intensive type of agriculture than zone 4. Theoretically, because zone 5 is not directly affected by the urbanized area, it can be either more or less intensive than zone 4, depending upon the general nature of the regional agriculture.

and air bases). Finally, it coalesces with the spread of other cities encroaching from other directions. The pattern of agriculture associated with urban expansion is affected by all the variations and irregularities in the path of this expansion and the concept of a ringed pattern is somewhat unreal. In this respect, however, the model presented in Figure 7, like the model illustrating Von Thünen's theory in Figure 3, need not have been converted into rings. The model could be considered rather as a zonal arrangement, which can extend out from any original shape.

Third, the uneven nature of growth depicted above not only can affect the shape of the agricultural pattern, but can lead to the elimination of zones within the pattern, particularly the outer zones. This happens when urban encroachment from one direction merges with that from another direction, either in the case of two different metropolitan areas, or two sections of the same metropolitan area. The coalescing inner zones can squeeze out the outer zones entirely. An interesting example of this process has been observed by the writer in southern Macomb County, Michigan, an area dominated by two finger-like projections of urbanization, extending from the city of Detroit. The characteristic sequence of agricultural zones extends laterally from both these urbanized arteries into the intervening sector of land. In the period of the author's experience there has not been evidence of zone 5 in this area, but the land uses of zone 4 was once prevalent in the central section, farthest from the two urbanized fingers. Zone 4, however, has disappeared in recent years. It is to be found farther north in the county, where distance from Detroit is greater, and the space between the two fingers is larger. The large areas of vacant land which commonly extends uninterrupted between two cities or between two built-up parts of a metropolitan region, might often indicate that all but zones 1 and 2 of the former agricultural pattern have been eliminated.

Fourth, by reason of its very causation, the pattern of agriculture here presented is a dynamic one. In an area where there is steady urban expansion, therefore, the agricultural zones are constantly shifting outward, the land uses of zone 1 taking over zone 2, those of zone 2 taking over zone 3 and so on. Steady expansion, however, is the exception rather than the rule. Urban expansion fluctuates greatly in space and in time. For various reasons, such as the extension of a water or sewage system, one portion of a suburban region might be rapidly urbanized as an adjacent portion lies stagnant. Similarly, an area might participate in rapid urban growth for a short period, and then wait for a long period before growth again occurs. Often a new growth period never comes. During the nongrowth period, the agricultural pattern may be stabilized for a long period of time.

The stabilization of the agricultural pattern is a phenomenon of great significance and some paradox. For theoretically, because the pattern is brought about by the dynamic quality of the expansion process itself, one might expect the pattern to be disrupted when that process stops. Instead, the pattern tends to be stabilized. This phenomenon reflects the fact that, although urban expansion itself has ceased, the commitments and uncertainties connected with the anticipation of urban expansion remain. Some land is already in the hands of speculators. Other land has begun to deteriorate. Farmers have reduced their overhead. Some may have invested already in other land far from the urban areas. Services for agriculture have gone. The anticipation that another period of urban expansion will take place is maintained. Hence, the pattern remains. Moreover, it is unlikely that an inward shifting of agricultural zones would ever take place, although it is possible that isolated land uses from an outer zone might eventually move into one of the inner zones.

Finally, the general process by which the forces of urbanization influence agricultural land use patterns can be interrupted by various public policies. For example, in many areas, particularly in California, increasing consideration is being given to exclusive agricultural zoning of Class 1 land. In some instances, farmers have even incorporated to protect their land. Whereas it is generally admitted that such measures can have only temporary and limited success, they do cause variations in the land use pattern in and around metropolitan areas.

The variations which have been discussed disrupt substantially the idealized land use model which has been presented, and in some cases allow for striking exceptions to the theoretical pattern. As such, they may be considered distracting variables. These variables do not, however, affect the validity of the principles underlying the theory, which is believed to bring order to agricultural land use patterns near many modern urban areas.

Applicability of the Thesis

Before discussing the applicability of the thesis which has been presented, it is important to point out the bases upon which its main ideas rest. The thesis is not a pure economic model, in that it is not based upon measured economic costs, such as transport costs in the Von Thünen model. It is rather a theoretical construct based upon an analysis of the contemporary urbanization process. This analysis provided insights into the basic forces determining agricultural patterns, and hence allowed the logical derivation of a theoretical pattern. The specific make-up of the model is founded empirically upon observations in the vicinity of urban areas in the Midwest, and more particularly upon field investigations conducted in the Dayton-Cincinnati and Detroit regions. Indeed, the existence of patterns similar to the theoretical one is borne out by observations in the areas of the Midwest with which the writer is most familiar.

If the thesis is valid, however, it should be more widely applicable. For the motivating force of the theory, namely the influence of anticipated urbanization upon the agricultural use of the land, operates in many parts of the Western world. For this reason, the writer has searched the literature for evidence of the processes and patterns outlined in this paper. As might be expected, material is not presented in a manner which precisely documents a theoretical pattern. Moreover, alternative explanations are possible in most cases. However, many studies do provide cases which logically can be associated with the thesis presented here.

One of the most complete discussions of rural land uses in a metropolitan environment is found in Gottman's chapters. Throughout these chapters, a dominant theme is the high proportion of unused, forested land found in Megalopolis. This forested land appears to result from those same factors which account for the large acreages of vacant land characterizing zone 2 (vacant and temporary grazing) of Figure 8. Gottman states the situation as follows:

This predominance of woodland results from the imbalance between expanding urbanization and shrinking agricultural lands. More formerly tilled farm acreage is being abandoned and is reverting to wooded growth than is being consumed by urban and related special uses, and this has been true for some time.

Considerable space in *Megalopolis* also is devoted to discussion of part-time and estate farms operated nonintensively by wealthy owners whose main income is derived from the city. Such farms might be considered a special form of the low-intensity land use found in zones 2 and 3 (vacant and transitory farming zones respectively) of Figure 8. Finally, *Megalopolis* contains many examples of factory farms which were designated the only type of farm able to survive in the Urban Farming zone (zone 1), Figure 8.

A specific study of how suburbanization affects agricultural land use was conducted by Moore and Barlowe in two areas near Lansing, Michigan. Both areas are in a region where dairying has traditionally been the most profitable farm enterprise. Both areas have experienced a shift from dairying to cash crops. Moreover, closer to the suburban area, a preponderance of the cropland was found to be idle or in relatively extensive use through rental to nearby farmers for pasture, hayland, or grain fields. In the same area: "much of the land was planted to wheat, grass, or corn; but not all of it was harvested. Many residents grew a crop on their land to keep down the weeds." Many farmers in both areas felt that advancing suburbanization resulted in poorer farming practices. Fewer livestock were kept. Less attention was paid to good cultural and soil conservation practices. Cash cropping, rather than regular fertility-building rotation, was common. Mining the soil apparently was related to the imminence of platting for nonfarm uses. These practices were in many cases associated with an increase in part-time farming:

The shift from full-time farming has often resulted in less intensive and less efficient farming operations. For most of the farms in the two areas, dairying probably represents the most profitable enterprise. Yet most of the part-time farmers and even some of the full-time operators have shifted to cash crops or to livestock enterprises of a less confining nature than dairying. It is hard to gauge the full effect of this shift in terms of reduced total production. However, it is more or less obvious that much agricultural land is now used somewhat less intensively than it would be if the owners were primarily dependent upon farming for a living.

In a similar study of urban fringe areas near Milwaukee, Wisconsin, Walruth found great variation in the responses to different stages of urbanization. Some areas were changing to less intensive land uses, whereas some dairy farmers were farming more intensively. Walruth, however, found an interesting relationship between the new growth of suburban areas and the acreage of tame hay which seems to reflect the operation of the forces described in this paper:

Hay acreage in some sections was expanded because of the acquisition of farmland by persons whose only interest in farming is to keep weeds down by cutting hay or by selling the standing crop. In other sections, with only a slightly different ownership pattern, these acreages would be untended and considered to be idle.

In the same article, Walruth considered the effect of zoning upon land uses in fringe areas. He concluded that zoning had but slight control over agricultural land use changes.

Grotewald, in a study of changes in land use and agricultural production near Kansas City and St. Louis, noticed: "a general decline in the cultivation of perishable and bulky commodities and a decline in intensive types of farming." Further, Grotewald stated that he found basically the same trends in the Chicago area.

Honzatko, in a statistical survey of agriculture in the Detroit metropolitan area, was surprised to find a prevalence of nonintensive field cropping at the southern edges of the Detroit urbanized area in Monroe County, Michigan.

The studies described thus far, though undertaken in a variety of farming regions, have certain characteristics in common. In general, they took place in regions where agriculture was diversified, involved livestock raising, and was relatively intensive. In these situations, the forces associated with urban expansion led to agricultural practices which were simpler, less confining, and less intensive. Agricultural zones could be identified with those of the model outlined in this paper. It would appear that in such areas the proposed theoretical framework is most directly applicable.

A study involving urban expansion in an entirely different environment is Lessinger's analysis of agriculture in the San Jose area of California. By analyzing the age and bearing conditions of fruit orchards in different zones around the city, he discovered that the amount of deterioration of the orchards was closely related to the degree of anticipation of urban demand as reflected in land prices. Since allowing fruit trees to deteriorate is essentially a way of using the land less intensively, the pattern found by Lessinger would seem to correspond very closely to tenets proposed in this paper.

Krueger found a similar situation in the Niagara fruit belt of Ontario, where "when urban development is approaching, there is reluctance to plant new orchards which would take at least five years to mature." Kruger also discussed how short-term leases (in areas at the urbanized margins) lead to a decrease in farming intensity and farm productivity.

Gregor, in a study of urban pressures on California land, presented evidence which seems to contradict parts of the theory proposed in this paper. It was pointed out, for example, that there is much less vacant land close to urban areas in California than in other parts of the country: "Agricultural productivity, while beginning to decline, is still often comparatively high at the time of urban absorption. If cropping ceases, it is usually of short duration." Gregor also found that small vegetable farms tend to take over cropland nearest the built-up area, crowding out the other farms (fruit farms, and large specialized vegetable farms) which previously had been dominant. It is possible that this zone of market gardening corresponds to zone 1 of the Von Thünen pattern shown in Figure 4. The explanation for this phenomenon, however, could be quite different. Small-scale vegetable farming, intensive as it might be, represents a short-term investment, with relatively quick returns, when compared to the agriculture which is being displaced. In other words, vegetable farming is an interim type of farming which produces relatively large, but short-lived, returns from land vacated by other types of agriculture until urban uses actually take over the land. Viewed in this way, the zone is not out of keeping with the theoretical pattern described in this paper.

These examples from fruit and vegetable areas introduce a concept which might be considered a corollary to the proposed theory. It appears that agricultural activities involving long-term investment are more directly affected by the anticipation of urbanization than those involving short-term investment. Hence, activities with a short-term investment are found closer to the city and those with a long-term investment become more common with distance from the city. Although length of investment time might not always correspond to degree of agricultural intensity, the two are related and the basic principle is the same.

Extensive field observations in still a different agricultural environment indicate that there are farming regions where there is no marked zonation of agriculture at the margins of expanding cities. These are primarily specialized regions of one-crop agriculture (such as parts of the cash grain region) where urbanization brings no noticeable change in the type of agriculture and where indeed "bulldozing often awaits the harvesting of the current crop." The absence of agricultural zonation in such regions is contrary to the concept of pattern assumed throughout this paper. However, the lack of zonation does not necessarily contradict the basic principles which have been advanced. For in these specialized regions, the overall type of agriculture is nonintensive, or involves short-term investment. Hence there is no clearly advantageous, less intensive, or shorter-term adjustment possible, except to stop farming completely. Because of the relatively simple and generally large-scale nature of farm operations, farming can be carried on until the land is taken over for nonagricultural purposes, even though the value and ownership of the land has changed.

This consideration of specialized farming areas introduces a second corollary to the proposed theory. In the case of specialized agricultural activities which are already nonintensive, involve a short-term investment, and require relatively simple farming procedures, urban expansion does not necessarily bring about the distinct zonation of agriculture found in more diversified farming areas.

In total, many studies indicate that the frame of reference presented in this paper can be applied to nonurban land near many urban areas. In certain situations, intensity of land use might better be expressed as length of agricultural investment, quality of farming, or amount of deterioration, but the concept is the same. In specialized farming regions, there is often an absence of agricultural zonation, but this too can be explained within the logic of the theory. In sum, although no study has documented in detail the theory of zonal land use presented here, the concept of agricultural land use increasing in intensity and quality with distance from the encroaching city seems widely applicable. Further, the principles underlying the proposed theory appear to constitute an approximate explanation for this phenomenon.

Conclusion

The concern of this paper has been agricultural patterns near urban areas and the forces which determine these patterns. I suggest that the basic forces identified by Von Thünen are still important in less developed parts of the world, and that in these areas Von Thünen's theory can still be applied as the basic explanation of agricultural land use patterns. In more advanced industrialized parts of the world, however, evidence for Von Thünen's theory no longer appears to dominate the agricultural scene, and the basic forces identified by Von Thünen no longer are the primary determinants of agricultural patterns around cities. The theory presented here is based more firmly upon evidence from the present scene. It incorporates motivating forces which were not of major significance during Von Thünen's time and provides a logical framework of agricultural zonation based upon those forces. It is felt that the theory can be applied to many contemporary conditions and hence provides a meaningful way of looking at agriculture around today's metropolitan centers.

28. Geographical Bases for Industrial Development in Northwestern China
Kuei-sheng Chang

Nearly all development of heavy industry is based on the effective exploitation of minerals. Communist China is making a strenuous effort to catch up industrially with the more technologically advanced nations of the world, yet today remains essentially an agrarian country. The Chinese are attempting to "leapfrog" several stages of the economic process in order to compete effectively and establish their country as a leading world power as soon as possible. It is important to remember when considering the development of the peripheral areas of China that this is a country with approximately the same area as the United States, but having perhaps four times the population. Furthermore, with the growth of the rift between Moscow and Peking, the Chinese

have an additional stake in the development of northwestern
China—their own territorial security.

Since the inauguration of the First Five Year Plan, the ruling authorities
in mainland China have been preoccupied with the rapid industrialization of the country, at any cost. The recent dislocation in the nation's
economy, associated particularly with agriculture, reflects, among other
things, how far the regime has outstretched itself in its drive for industry.
There is no evidence to indicate, however, that once conditions again
permit, the frenzied drive for greater industrial production will not
be resumed.

The Northwest as a Region

Many of the old industrial areas in north, central, and northeastern
China have been restored and even expanded. However, particular
interest attaches to the possibility of large-scale industrial development
in the dry and semi-arid Northwest, where few industrial establishments
have previously existed. If certain favorable conditions exist, as is
claimed, and have emerged as a result of the full-scale surveying and
prospecting of resources in this broad region which have been much
publicized in recent years, then it is appropriate that a geographical
examination should be made.

One of the greatest handicaps in a study of this nature is the lack of
alternative sources of information with which to make comparisons.
The material from official organs, the only source, can be neither readily
verified nor disproved. However, its usefulness can be established, at
least to a certain degree, through checking against closely related
material as it becomes available.

Different Concepts of Industrialization

There are, of course, important differences between the idea of progress
inherent in the communist interpretation of events and some of the
basic concepts of economic growth to which geographers in non-
communist countries have become accustomed. Under free enterprise,
the process of industrialization in a large region usually takes certain
sequential steps which can be clearly recognized: (1) the exploring
of resources; (2) the construction of transportation systems; (3) the
establishment of industrial bases; (4) the undergoing of a series of
economic adjustments until the region reaches a mature stage; and (5)
the evolution of an organic regional industrial entity.

SOURCE: *Economic Geography*, XXXIX (October, 1963), 341–50. The author is
professor of geography, Wayne State University.

Under a communist system, which establishes goals and even date-lines, the industrialization of an undeveloped area will commonly not show the above sequence. In northwestern China, the sequence has been considerably altered. The determination to build up the region into an industrial complex, for strategic and political reasons, has been responsible for a vigorous and broadly based program. This has included the speedy construction of several trunk railroads and numerous highways, the full-scale prospecting of mineral resources, the enforced movement of population, gigantic land-reclamation programs in the desert, and the rapid building of planned urban centers along the main lines of transportation.

Since 1953, thousands of geological workers have been employed in the Northwest in a search for minerals—a scale which is unprecedented in the history of modern China. Several years of both intensive and extensive work have resulted in numerous findings and have apparently laid the groundwork for the changing pattern of development in China's Northwest.

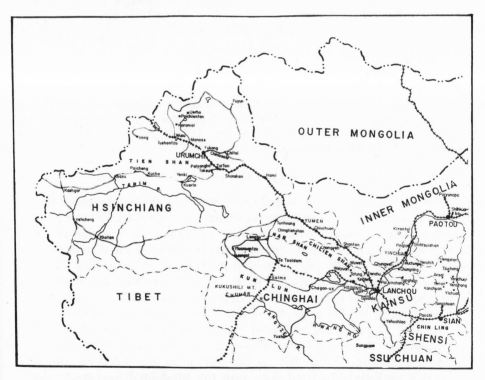

FIGURE 1: Mineral sites and major cities of northwestern China. (The political divisions are based on the Atlas of China, published in Peiping, 1957, and on the Regional Atlas of Communist China, compiled by the Central Intelligence Agency, Washington, D.C., 1958.)

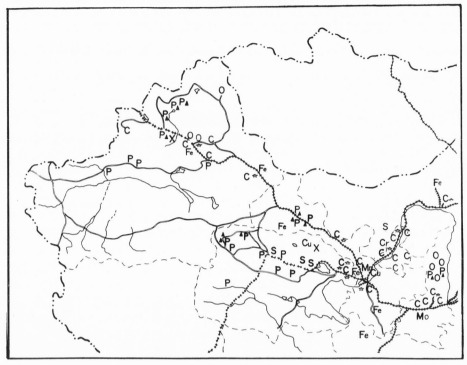

FIGURE 2: Principal mineral resources of northwestern China. Letters and symbols refer as follows: C. coal; Cr. chromium; Cu. copper; Fe. iron ore; Mn. manganese; Mo. molybdenum; O. oil shale; P. petroleum; S. salt; X. Zink, lead, gold, silver, bauxite; ▲ operating oil field; ♔ coal mining center.

Development of the Major Oil Fields

The present regime in mainland China has been greatly concerned that the existence of petroleum reserves should be established. Every finding in this regard, or a discovery of structural formations favorable to the presence of oil, has found a place in the headlines of the official press. Progress has usually been measured in terms of meters drilled rather than the number of wells that have struck oil. However, some worthwhile discoveries have been made. In the Yü-men oil fields, an intensive investigation has led to the belief that the oil reserve may be five times as large as previously estimated. Among them, the Ya-erh-hsia and Pai-yang-ho fields which were discovered in 1957 have been considered most promising. The oil field at Lao-chün-miao has also been considerably expanded. To keep pace with the substantial increase in the production of crude oil in the Kan-su Corridor, the Yü-men oil refinery has been enlarged to a capacity of 400,000 tons per year. The oil wealth of the Dzungarian Basin was well known long before the present period of rule in mainland China. The Tu-shan-tzu oil field was found as early as 1940. Operation in an organized manner began in 1950 when the, so-called, "Sino-Soviet Joint Company for Extracting and Processing Petroleum in Hsin-chiang" was formed. During the first five years, extraction increased fourteen times, at the end of which the ownership of the entire company was said to have been transferred to the government in Peiping. Following upon the transfer, there was the significant discovery of a large oil field at Karamai (which means "Black Oil" in the Uighur language), about 250 miles to the northwest of Urumchi, the leading city of Hsin-chiang. The reserve was initially estimated (in 1956) at about 100 million tons, exceeding all the other reserves then known. Large deposits have also been located at U-erh-ho about 60 miles to the northeast of Karamai and at Pai-chien-t'an which is half way between the two. Extraction in this area began in 1958 and is expected to provide 3 million tons of crude oil yearly by the end of the Second Five Year Plan. The outlook appeared so good that a 92-mile pipeline was constructed to link the oil field with the Tu-shan-tzu refinery, the only one in Hsin-chiang. The pipeline went into operation in 1959. Through it, more than 400,000 tons of crude oil will go to Tu-shan-tzu for refining each year.

Apparently little headway has been made in the Tarim Basin south of the T'ien Shan, except with regard to the possibility of oil strikes under such oases as Bugur, Aqsu, Shache, Kucha and Kashgar. The combined reserve of these oases is estimated at 258,833,000 tons.

No estimate has been given as to the much publicized Tsaidam oil fields, the so-called "Second Baku of China." The basin has been described as a "petroleum sea," stretching from Chagan-us in the east to Dosuk Kul in the west, and from Altyn Tagh in the north to the Kunlun in the south. Within this area, about 100 oil-bearing strata have been found but only some 40 experimental wells have been drilled in Yiu-ch'uan-tzu, Yiu-sha-shan, Leng-hu, and other less known places. The reserve in just the above few places is rich enough to warrant the construction of a refinery at Leng-hu which has a yearly capacity of 300,000 tons. The quality of the petroleum is said to be far above that of the Yü-men fields. Other refineries under construction will be able to process from 100,000 tons to 250,000 tons each. A multiple, oil-bearing structure was also said to have been revealed on both sides of the Ch'ing-hai–Tibet Highway as well as along the banks of the Chumar River. On the southern side of the Kukushili Mountains, seepages of oil and natural gas have reportedly been seen.

The development of the oldest oil field in North Shensi has thus far been given the least publicity. Even the earlier estimated reserve of 2,-343,000 tons, made under the Nationalist Government, has not been emphatically brushed aside. New data suggested that only 40 new oil fields and 60 seepages have been found in a 300,000 square kilometer area, embracing such places as Yi-ch'uan, Yi-ch'ün, An-sai, Kan-ch'üan, Yen-ch'ang, Yen-ch'uan and Yen-an. That the production will probably not be impressive may be evidenced by the fact that construction of a new refinery has not been contemplated for any of these places.

There is little doubt that the Northwest will for a long time play a dominant role in China's oil industry. Except the Nan-ch'ung and P'eng-lai oil fields in the Ssu-ch'uan Basin, nearly all the known oil fields and proven reserves are located in the Northwest; they account for approximately 90 per cent of the total reserve in mainland China, which has been estimated at about 2 billion tons. (A metric ton of crude oil is roughly equal to 7.7 barrels.) It was in this optimistic vein that the giant new Lan-chou refinery was constructed; it is now capable of processing more than 1 million tons per year.

The Untapped Oil Shale Reserve

The outlook could be even brighter when the vast amount of oil shale deposits in this region can be exploited. Of the grand total of 21 billion tons for the entire mainland, 4.5 billion tons, which may be equivalent to about 225 million tons of liquid fuel oil, are situated in the Dzungarian Basin, with 1.5 billion tons at Ya-ma-shan near Urumchi, and the other 3 billion tons near Fu-yün and along the Altai foothills. Those at Ya-ma-shan are reported to have a maximum thickness of several hundred feet and are so close to the surface that they can be extracted by open-cut methods. Added to these, are a half billion tons in the northern Tarim Basin. The oil shale reserve in northern Shensi is considered even greater and is estimated at 4.9 billion tons, or the equivalent of about 273 million tons of liquid fuel. Six oil shale beds with a maximum thickness of 32 meters have been found near Yung-shou and Pin Hsien. Outcrops have also been found at Pai-tzu-k'ou and Tzu-ch'ang. Thus, nearly one half of China's oil shale reserve is located in Shensi and Hsin-chiang.

Newly Discovered Coal Deposits

The next item on the mineral list which also seems in favor of this region is coal. Already, the Northwest has been considered second only in reserves to north China. Many new coal fields have been discovered which have boosted the reserve to more than two-and-a-half times the previous estimate. The most significant of all is the Wei-pei coal field in Shensi. The official estimate of its reserve has been set at the neighborhood of 5 billion tons, "enough to supply the entire Northwest for industrial development." As a start, four mechanized mines have been built at T'ung-ch'uan, 70 miles north of Sian.

By official estimation, practically every province in the Northwest is well endowed with coal deposits. In Hsin-chiang, a large coal district of 3240 million tons, on the northern side of the T'ien Shan, has been said to extend 550 kilometers from Wu-su to Ch'i-t'ai, so covering an area of 120 square kilometers. While most of it is graded as high quality bituminous coal of the Jurrassic Period, there are about 45 deposits of anthracite coal some of which have a thickness of 30 to 60 meters. The coal reserve for Kan-su is given at 2.4 billion tons. Several new coal bases have been added to the list, most of which are near the Lan-chou-Hsin-chiang railway. Of considerable significance are those at A-kan-chen, the oldest in the province, Yao-chieh and Yung-teng with 200 million 'ons, and Ching-t'ai and Shan-tan with coking coal. T'ien-chu and Hsi-ch'eng also have been reported with coal findings. According to incomplete information, Ch'ing-hai has been estimated to have 500 million tons of reserve, principally of the Permian Period, which are concentrated in the northeastern corner of the province, including Hsi-ning, Ta-t'ung (not to be mistaken for the great coal mining center in northern Shansi which coincidentally has the same romanization but is different in Chinese), Hua-lung, and Wei-yuan. Along the foothills of the Kunlun to the west of Meng-ai, seven layers of deposits have recently been found, some of which are a maximum of 25 meters in thickness. The coal field at Wei-yuan covers nearly 525 square miles with a maximum thickness of 66 feet. The target to be attained by these operating fields, by the end of the Second Five Year Plan, has been set at between 13.5 and 20 million tons. Ning-hsia is said to be one of the richest coal regions in China. The largest deposits are found at P'ing-lo and Shih-tsui-shan between the Ho-lan Shan and the Hwang Ho, where a staggering reserve of 10 billion tons has been reported. To the south and the east are some scattered fields at Chung-wei, Chung-ning, T'ung-hsin, and Yen-ch'ih.

Power in the Upper Hwang Ho

Aridity and great changes in temperature will forever hamper the Northwest in large-scale hydroelectric power development. The only station completed thus far is the Urumchi plant with a generating capacity of only 20,000 kilowatts. Attention has naturally been focused upon the potentials of the upper Hwang Ho which cuts through many narrow defiles in eastern Ch'ing-hai and southwestern Kan-su above Lan-chou. The ideal location for power development is the Liu-chia Gorge about 80 kilometers above Lan-chou, where in seven-and-a-half miles the river drops 60 meters. Construction of this dam was initiated in 1958. When completed, it will generate some 1,000,000 kilowatts, enough to supply the new industrial bases around Lan-chou and Hsining. Also under construction are two sizable dams, one in the Yen-kuo Gorge a few miles below Liu-chia, and the other in the Ch'ing-t'ung Gorge. When completed, they will supply an additional 850,000 kilowatts to the area.

Limited but Undetermined Iron Ore Supply

Reports on the occurrence of iron ore in this region are so sketchy that it is not yet possible to determine the true potential of this significant mineral. The few discoveries made so far have not been given as much publicity as the oil and coal findings. A large deposit is said to have been discovered at a place called Ching-t'ieh-shan in the Nan Shan area of western Kan-su, and is estimated at "a good hundred million tons." Three mines on the northern slopes of the T'ien Shan are more certain to be developed, as judged from efforts already made. The hematite deposit near Urumchi is reported to have an iron content of more than 50 per cent. The other two are located at Chabasala and Motousala. South of the T'ien Shan, Ha-mi is producing some magnetite ores. Others mentioned in this respect are a few minor deposits at Chung-wei and Chung-ning in southern Ning-hsia, Min-ho and the Ch'i-lien Shan area in Ch'ing-hai, Yao-chieh in Kan-su, and Shan-shan, Toksun, and Fu-yün in Hsin-chiang.

Incomplete Reports on Ferro-alloy Minerals

On the minor items of the mineral list, reports are far from being complete. Although scores of minerals have been surveyed in a large part of the Northwest, only a few have been reported in any detail. Of ferrous metals, copper and molybdenum deposits have been found in substantial amounts. The large copper-sulfide deposits discovered at Pai-yin-ch'ang near Lan-chou are said to be "equivalent in total reserve to those at Tung-ch'uan in Yün-nan," which have for decades been the chief source of China's copper. Scattered small deposits have also been found at Hami and Kucha in Hsin-chiang, and the Ch'i-lien Shan area in Ch'ing-hai. Molybdenum ores have recently been discovered in the Ch'in-ling Range in Shensi. The Tsaidam Basin and its adjoining Ch'i-lien Shan are believed to be very rich in such minerals as zinc, lead, gold, silver, and bauxite. Some 60 kinds of minerals, according to official sources, have been located in the Ch'i-lien Shan, but no details have been given. Chromium in Ning-hsia is a new discovery. Some manganese in Kan-su and Hsin-chiang, and platinum in Ch'ing-hai and Shensi complete the current list of ferro-alloy minerals.

The Inexhaustible Salt Beds

Numerous vanishing and dried-up lakes have made the Northwest exceedingly rich in salt deposits. The Kirantai salt lake bed has long been the chief source of salt for Ning-hsia and eastern Kan-su. The Tsaidam Basin is regarded by many geologists as formerly a huge inland sea; its name in Mongolian means simply "Salt Marshes" In this basin, within an area 434 miles long and nearly 190 miles wide, are numerous salt deposits which have been estimated at about 26 billion tons. Part of the 216-mile highway across this region has been built on a bed of salt and even the mile-posts are made of salt chunks. These deposits are said to have often a 98 per cent sodium chloride content. There are, in addition, the potash deposits near Ta-erh-han and the boron mines at Ta-tsaidam. Along the T'ien Shan are several places noted for their non-metallic resources, notably gypsum at Pai-yang-ho, limestone at Liu-shu-k'ou a suburb of Urumchi, and quartz crystals and graphite at Ha-mi, Shan-shan, and Pai-ch'eng.

Factors in Favor of Industrial Development

The distribution of these minerals, when plotted on the map, suggests some interesting patterns. It is apparent that the Northwest is not only assured an abundant coal supply, most of which is bituminous, but also has all its major coal fields conveniently situated along or near the railroad trunk lines. Along the Lung-hai railway are the Wei-pei coal field near Sian and the A-kan-chen and Shih-ho-k'ou mines near Lan-chou. The Lan-chou–Hsin-chiang railway links the coal fields of Yao-chieh, T'ien-chu, Ha-mi, Turfan, and Urumchi; and it may in the future also serve the I-ning field. From both sides of this horizontal artery, coal can be also transported from the Ta-ch'ing Shan coal district (including Shih-kuai-k'ou) and the several fields in Ning-hsia by way of the Pao-t'ou–Lan-chou railway, and from the fields in northeastern Ch'ing-hai by way of the Lan-chou–Ch'ing-hai railway. It is a fortunate coincidence that every leading city of the major political sub-divisions is situated on or near a large coal field. With railroad transportation speedily expanded in these areas, the supply of ferro-alloy minerals will encounter no significant difficulties. The primary concern in the development of iron and steel industries lies in the supply of iron ores. Among the proven deposits previously indicated, none seems to be substantial except that near Urumchi and the much publicized deposits at Ching-t'ieh-shan; the latter is somewhere in western Kan-su and presumably not far from the Lan-chou–Hsin-chiang railway. Hsi-ning and Ha-mi have already developed some iron and steel workshops based on local resources, though at the present these are not of great significance. Yet, when the problem is examined in the national perspective, the shortage of iron ore supply, if it does exist, may not be an insurmountable handicap in the large-scale development of a steel industry in the Northwest. At the other end of the Pao-t'ou–Lan-chou railway and further beyond lie the rich deposits at Paiyun-opo near Pao-t'ou, and the Lung-yen iron mines at Hsüan-hua which have already been supplying the steel industry in Peiping. As transportation further develops in southern Kan-su and the northwestern corner of Ssu-ch'uan province, the iron and manganese ores in the Sung-p'an district, which have been surveyed recently and estimated at about 200 million tons, will be more likely to go to Lan-chou than to Chungking. These factors seem strong enough to lead to the selection of Lan-chou as a heavy industrial center in the Northwest. Urumchi appears to be the second best in its location and distribution of basic resources. It is nearly self-sufficient in materials in an area where coal, iron ore, and limestone are all present. Between these two major bases, secondary steel manufacturing centers could be developed, if the demand is sufficiently great, at such places as Ha-mi, Chiu-ch'uan, and Yung-teng. Hsi-ning will be the logical choice for Ch'ing-hai province, and Yin-ch'uan for Ning-hsia.

One of the most significant factors in the industrial development of all arid regions is the limited choice of locations. As with population distribution in a dry land, the distribution of manufacturing establishments tends to be spotty and often results in separate enclaves. Once industries have their roots set, their inertia will be even greater than is the case with those in well-populated humid lands; the degrees of concentration is also proportionately heavier. The terms "ümland" and "hinterland" have no significance in dry lands, especially under a communist type of government. Greatest importance is given to the provision of an adequate transportation system and a large enough laboring force. These yardsticks may be of great value in measuring the degree of urgency and determination shown in planning in the regional industrial expansion of the future.

A study of the rate of population increase and urban expansion of the above mentioned cities also brings out some startling facts. Lan-chou, a city of 190,000 inhabitants in 1949, has already become an industrial giant with no less than one-and-a-quarter million people. With four railroad trunk lines and several major highways now converging on Lan-chou and the construction of the gigantic hydro-electric power installation in the nearby Liu-chia gorge, the tempo of expansion in this urban area may be stepped up, if other conditions permit. The Lan-chou refinery has already been installed and went into operation in 1958. With more than one million tons of refining capacity, it is the largest of its kind in China today. Some rubber, aluminum, and chemical manufacturing plants have been constructed; and seven textile mills are to be transferred here from Shanghai. A locomotive plant is also under construction. It is clearly the intention to set up a large steel industry in this area, which will strengthen by many times the industrial muscle of this fast-growing city, situated at China's geometric center. The urgency of developing the Lan-chou area, in the absence of a steel industry there, appears to have been responsible for the speedy construction of the Pao-t'ou steel plant, the third largest in China, which was completed nearly one year ahead of schedule; it was also responsible for the vital rail link, the Pao-t'ou–Lan-chou line, which was finished well in advance of plan. Pao-t'ou, incidentally, has grown more than twelve times since the inception of the present regime, from a population of 60,000 to one of over 800,000. Both Urumchi and Hsi-ning have experienced an increase of more than five times in less than a decade, and their future roles are easily recognizable. The planning authorities have already let it be known that Urumchi will be a heavy industrial center which will produce railroad cars, diesel engines, automobiles, and electric motors. The substantial increase of skilled workers at Hsi-ning, Yin-ch'uan, Ha-mi, and other projected industrial cities further confirms the general trend in the efforts to turn these ancient oases into industrial sites.

Hindrance to Fast Industrial Expansion

Yet not all the elements will be in favor of the crash program. Against such rapid industrial expansion, there are many other factors which may well be beyond the control and manipulation of even a powerful government. The most hostile factor is the physical setting of this region, which is basically a dry land. West of the Wei Valley, few places have more than 15 inches of annual precipitation. Most places, in fact, receive less than 10 inches. There will be a definite limit to the increase of urban population, beyond which food supply will become an acute problem. Even with the expanded irrigation facilities in the Urumchi district, for instance, the oasis could no longer support an enormous population of over 402,000. Any further expansion could be achieved only by encroaching upon the precious arable land. The mammoth land reclamation project in the Manass Valley was undoubtedly designed to overcome at least part of the problem. But the soils are so alkaline that much of the land cannot withstand more than two or three crops and has often to be abandoned. The fact that the workers in the Karamai and Tsaidam oil fields are earning four times as much as those in eastern China suggests how costly it is for food and other necessities to be sent in from distant places. Continentality in climate makes housing and heating exceedingly expensive, so much so that, taking the Tsaidam for instance, the workers in the oil fields at Yiu-sha-shan, Yiu-ch'uan-tzu, and Leng-hu have to go to Hsi-ning or Lan-chou more than 600 miles away to pass the severe winters. The phenomenal growth of these two cities, as well as that of those previously cited, has already caused great concern to the ruling authorities, both local and at higher levels. The mass migration of population from many parts of central China to Kan-su, the Tsaidam Basin, and Dzungaria has scarcely helped the problem. For dry lands cannot be turned into farms overnight, no matter how much labor is pressed into service. This simple truth, however, is not easily recognized. Since 1959, every farmer in Ch'ing-hai has, by government ordinance, been required to reclaim at least one *mou* of waste land for cultivation every year, in addition to his already overburdened assignments. How long the system of forced labor can be maintained, such as that being practiced in the Manass reclamation project, based largely on the use of captured Nationalist troops, is a question yet to be answered.

The General Outlook

While much of the information cited above could be subject to reassessment hereafter, it now appears certain that some headway has been made in the initial efforts toward industrializing the Northwest. Its success, so far, has been confined to certain localities where essential resources are readily available and where transportation has been improved. Further expansion in the near future will most likely follow a linear pattern, along the railroad trunk lines which traverse the major oases and the more promising coal fields. To achieve this, a number of essential industrial bases must first be established at the most suitable locations, such as Lan-chou, Urumchi, Hsi-ning, and perhaps Yin-ch'uan also. Whatever the cost, the Northwest will be the chief source of oil for mainland China. There is a good base for the chemical industry, but steel production will probably not exceed local needs. The resources in this region are too valuable not to be put into practical use. Strategically, much of the area lies in the heartland of Asia and, by comparison, is less vulnerable than any other region of mainland China. In spite of the current rift between Peiping and Moscow, open hostility along the several thousand miles of Sino-Soviet frontier appears yet too remote to be considered. Beyond the areas of linear growth, however, the limiting factors are so overwhelming that any large-scale development will be extremely difficult and probably not possible, at least in the foreseeable future.

29. Transport Expansion in Underdeveloped Countries: A Comparative Analysis

Edward J. Taaffe, Richard L. Morrill,
and Peter R. Gould

For those nations at early stages in the economic process, the problems of transport of any kind are enormous, so much so that it might be said that the future of these lands depends on the establishment of an effective transportation network. The transportation systems and problems of development for several of the new African states are analyzed in this selection, in which special emphasis is placed on the role of road transport. It is important to recognize that for these areas, trade of raw materials with more advanced areas for machinery and manufactured goods is essential for development, and that for effective overseas trade, adequate ports and port facilities are required as well.

In the economic growth of underdeveloped countries a critical factor has been the improvement of internal accessibility through the expansion of a transportation network. This expansion is from its beginning at once a continuous process of spatial diffusion and an irregular or sporadic process influenced by many specific economic, social, or political forces. In the present paper both processes are examined as they have been evident in the growth of modern transportation facilities in several underdeveloped areas. Certain broad regularities underlying the spatial diffusion process are brought to light, which permit a descriptive generalization of an ideal-typical sequence of transportation development. The relationship between transportation and population is discussed and is used as the basis for examination of such additional factors as the physical environment, rail competition, intermediate location, and commercialization. Throughout the study, Ghana and Nigeria are used as examples.

SOURCE: *Geographical Review*, LIII (October, 1963), 503–29. Dr. Taaffe is professor of geography, Ohio State University; Dr. Morrill, associate professor, University of Washington; and Dr. Gould, associate professor, Pennsylvania State University.

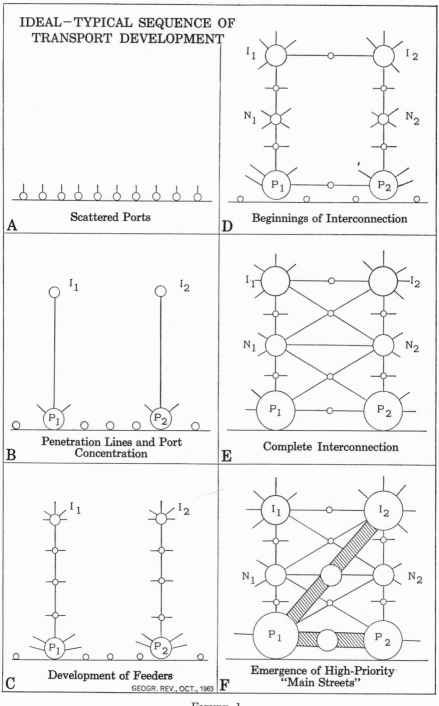

IDEAL–TYPICAL SEQUENCE OF
TRANSPORT DEVELOPMENT

A Scattered Ports

B Penetration Lines and Port Concentration

C Development of Feeders

GEOGR. REV., OCT., 1963

D Beginnings of Interconnection

E Complete Interconnection

F Emergence of High-Priority "Main Streets"

Figure 1.

Sequence of Transportation Development

Figure 1 presents the authors' interpretation of an ideal-typical sequence of transport development. The first phase (A) consists of a scattering of small ports and trading posts along the seacoast. There is little lateral interconnection except for small indigenous fishing craft and irregularly scheduled trading vessels, and each port has an extremely limited hinterland. With the emergence of major lines of penetration (B), hinterland transportation costs are reduced for certain ports. Markets expand both at the port and at the interior center. Port concentration then begins, as illustrated by the circles P_1 and P_2. Feeder routes begin to focus on the major ports and interior centers (C). These feeder routes give rise to a sort of hinterland piracy that permits the major port to enlarge its hinterland at the expense of adjacent smaller ports. Small nodes begin to develop along the main lines of penetration, and as feeder development continues (D), certain of the nodes, exemplified by N_1 and N_2, become focal points for feeder networks of their own. Interior concentration then begins, and N_1 and N_2 pirate the hinterlands of the smaller nodes on each side. As the feeder networks continue to develop around the ports, interior centers, and main on-line nodes, certain of the larger feeders begin to link up (E). Lateral interconnection should theoretically continue until all the ports, interior centers, and main nodes are linked. It is postulated that once this level is reached, or even before, the next phase consists of the development of national trunk-line routes or "main streets" (F). In a sense, this is the process of concentration repeated, but at a higher level. Since certain centers will grow at the expense of the others, the result will be a set of high-priority linkages among the largest. For example, in the diagram the best rail schedules, the widest paved roads, and the densest air traffic would be over the P_1-I_2 and P_1-P_2 routes.

It is probably most realistic to think of the entire sequence as a process rather than as a series of discrete historical stages.[1] Thus at a given point in time a country's total transport pattern may show evidence of all the phases. Lateral interconnection may be going on in one region at the same time that new penetration lines are developing in another.

---

[1] It is interesting to note a few analogies to some of W. W. Rostow's stages of economic development. The scattered, weakly connected ports might be considered evidences of the isolation of Rostow's traditional society; the development of a penetration line might be viewed as a sort of spatial "takeoff"; the lateral-interconnection phase might be a spatial symptom of the internal diffusion of technology; and the impact of the auto on the latter phases of the sequence might be an expression of the emergence of certain aspects of an era of higher mass consumption in underdeveloped countries.

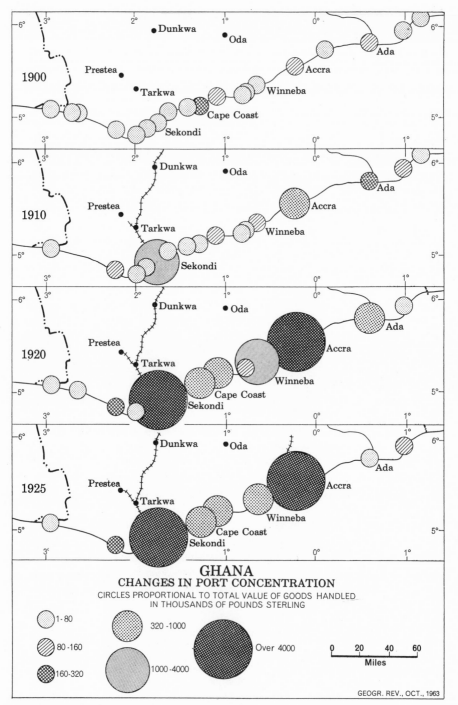

GHANA
CHANGES IN PORT CONCENTRATION
CIRCLES PROPORTIONAL TO TOTAL VALUE OF GOODS HANDLED
IN THOUSANDS OF POUNDS STERLING

1 - 80
320 -1000
Over 4000
80 - 160
1000 - 4000
160 - 320

0   20   40   60
Miles

GEOGR. REV., OCT., 1963

FIGURE 2: Changes in port concentration, Ghana, 1900-1925. Redrawn from map in Gould, *The Development of the Transportation Pattern in Ghana* (see starred footnote in text), p. 45.

390

The First Phase: Scattered Ports

In both Ghana and Nigeria an early period of numerous small, scattered ports and coastal settlements with trading functions may be easily identified (Figs. 2 and 3). These settlements, most of which existed or came into being between the end of the fifteenth century and the end of the nineteenth, were populated by the indigenous people around a European trading station or fort. Many of the people engaged in trade with the Europeans and served as middlemen for trade with the interior, a function jealously guarded for centuries against European encroachment. Penetration lines to the interior were weakly developed, but networks of circuitous bush trails connected the small centers to their restricted hinterlands. River mouths were important, particularly in the Niger delta, but with a few exceptions during the early periods of European encroachment the rivers did not develop as the main lines of thrust when penetration began. Most of these early trading centers have long since disappeared, destroyed by the growth of the main ports, or else they linger on as relict ports, with visits of occasional tramp steamers to remind them of their former trading heyday.

The Second Phase: Penetration Lines and Port Concentration

Perhaps the most important single phase in the transportation history of an underdeveloped country is the emergence of the first major penetration line from the seacoast to the interior. Later phases typically evolve around the penetration lines, and ultimately there is a strong tendency for them to serve as the trunk-line routes for more highly developed transportation networks. Three principal motives for building lines of penetration have been active in the past: (1) the desire to connect an administrative center on the seacoast with an interior area for political and military control; (2) the desire to reach areas of mineral exploitation; (3) the desire to reach areas of potential agricultural export production. In the cases examined, the political motive has been the strongest. Political and military control dominated official thinking of the day in Africa, often as a direct result of extra-African rivalries. The second motive, mineral exploitation, is typically associated with rail penetration. It is today probably the principal motive for the building of railways in Africa, and then only after careful surveys and international agreements have virtually guaranteed the steady haul of a bulk commodity to amortize the loans required for construction.[2]

The development of a penetration line sets in motion a series of spatial processes and readjustments as the comparative locational advantages

[2] For example, the extension of the Uganda railway to Kasese to haul copper ore; the long northward extension of the Cameroon railway from Yaoundé to Garoua to haul manganese; and the new railway from Port-Étienne to Fort Gouraud in Mauritania to haul iron ore.

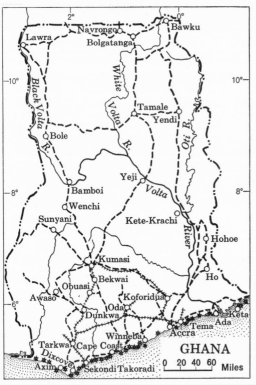

FIGURE 3: Major transport facilities, Ghana. Generalized from several maps in Gould, *The Development of the Transportation Pattern in Ghana* (see starred footnote in text).

FIGURE 4: Major transport facilities, Nigeria. Adapted from Map 1 in "The Economic Development of Nigeria" (International Bank for Reconstruction and Development, Baltimore, 1955).

MAJOR TRANSPORT FACILITIES

+++++++++ Railroads
--------- Main roads
* Former trading posts

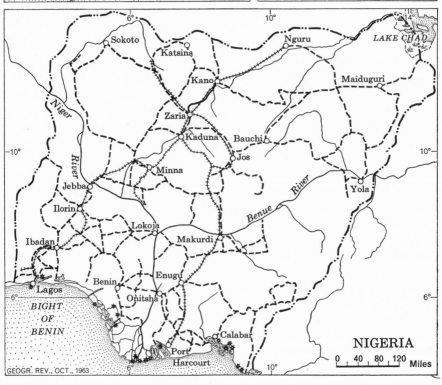

of all centers shift. Concentration of port activity is particularly important, and the ports at the termini of the earliest penetration lines are usually the ones that thrive at the expense of their neighbors (Fig. 2). Typically, one or two ports in a country dominate both import and export traffic, and often the smaller ports have lost their functions in external commerce.

In Ghana several interesting variations on the penetration theme appear (Fig. 3). The desire to reach Kumasi, capital of a then aggressive Ashanti, formed the essentially military-political motive for the first penetration road, which followed an old bush track, sporadically cleared whenever the local people were goaded into activity. The road was built from Cape Coast, and although it is still important as one of Ghana's main north-south links, the port function of Cape Coast declined as Sekondi increased in importance. Sekondi's great impetus came with the building of the rail penetration line to Kumasi at the turn of the century, after which adjacent ports such as Axim, Dixcove, Adjua, Shama, Komena, and Elmina suffered a rapid decline in traffic. The Pra and Ankobra Rivers, east and west of Sekondi, which were formerly of some significance as avenues of penetration, also experienced marked traffic decreases. The initial motive for the western railroad was primarily mineral production (the goldfield at Tarkwa), and secondarily provision of a rapid connection for administration between the seacoast and a troublesome internal center of population.

The eastern railroad penetration line was slower in developing, partly as a result of the interruption of the First World War and of smallpox outbreaks in the railroad camps. The link between Kumasi and Accra was not completed until 1923, twenty years after the Sekondi-Kumasi link. Connection with the rapidly expanding cocoa areas north of Accra was the immediate reason for this line, underlain by the political desire to connect the leading city, Accra, with Kumasi, the main population and distribution center in the interior. As in the case of Sekondi-Takoradi, Accra's importance increased steadily at the expense of adjacent ports as the railroad penetrated inland.

The two penetration lines forming the sides of the rail triangle were now complete, and a considerable amount of subsequent transportation development of the country was based on these two trunk lines. Penetration north of Kumasi was entirely by road, despite grand railroad plans at one time. There were no minerals to provide an economic incentive for railroads, and the barren middle zone, which separated the rail-triangle area from the densely settled north, acted as a deterrent to the continuation of the railroad in short stages.

The Great North Road is the chief line of penetration north of Kumasi, built with a strong political-administrative motive to Tamale, a town deliberately laid out as the capital of the Northern Territories in the early years of this century. Early feeder development focusing on Tamale helped to fix the position of this trunk line and its extension to the northern markets of Bolgatanga, Navrongo, and Bawku. The Western Trunk Road was built with similar motives and grew out of the extensive Kumasi feeder network to link that city with a moderately populated area north of the barren middle zone. In the building of the Eastern Trunk Road political and economic motives were mixed. This road through former British Togoland was originally extended from the Hohoe cocoa area to Yendi for transport of yams to the rapidly growing urban centers of the south, but its extension to the northern border hinged in large part on political motives that were very strong immediately before the United Nations plebiscite and Togo's resultant political affiliation with Ghana. The original road links from the rail triangle and Accra to the Hohoe cocoa area were associated with a political desire to forge a link with British Togoland, and with an economic desire to prevent the diversion of this area's cocoa traffic to the port of Lomé in then-French Togoland.

The process of penetration and port concentration in Nigeria (Fig. 4) was markedly similar to that in Ghana; the main difference lay in the greater emphasis on long-haul rail development and the subsequent higher level of economic development in the north. Again the initial motives were somewhat more political than economic; for even the early penetration to the north via the Niger River by the Royal Niger Company had imperialistic as well as economic motives. In a sense, Kano might be regarded as analogous to Kumasi. Both are important interior centers which predate European settlement and which were later connected to the main ports by rail penetration lines. The chief differences, of course, are the vastly greater distance between Kano and the coast and the greater width of Nigeria's relatively barren middle zone. Mineral exploitation was also a major motive for the building of rail penetration lines in Nigeria, particularly the eastern railroad. The line from Port Harcourt was started in 1913 and was connected with the important Enugu coalfields three years later. This port serves also as the principal outlet for the tin output of the Jos Plateau. The connecting of agricultural regions to the coast, though not a strong initial penetration motive, was apparently associated with the actual linking of the northern and southern lines.

As in Ghana, the rail penetration lines form the basis for the entire transportation network. The only area of extensive road penetration is in the northeast, from the railroad at Jos and Nguru to Maiduguri. The main motive for establishing tarred roads and large-scale trucking services was the attraction of the Lake Chad region to the northeast. However, the Maiduguri region is now being connected by rail to the main network, despite the recommendation of a mission of the International Bank for Reconstruction and Development, which felt that roads could more efficiently accommodate the expected increase in traffic. In the southeast there is no effective road or rail penetration line.

Port concentration has been marked. The decline of the delta ports began with the building of the rail penetration line from Lagos and was accentuated by the building of the eastern line and the concomitant growth of Port Harcourt. In 1958 these two major ports accounted for more than three-quarters of Nigeria's export and import trade.

The Third Phase: Feeders and Lateral Interconnections

Penetration is followed by lateral interconnection as feeder lines begin to move out both from the ports and from the nodes along the penetration lines. The process of concentration among the nodes is analogous to the process of port concentration; it results when the feeder networks of certain centers reach out and tap the hinterlands of their neighbors. As feeder networks become stronger at the interior centers and intermediate nodes some of them link and thereby interconnect the original penetration lines.

Figures 5, 6, and 7 present a sequence of road development in Ghana from 1922 to 1958. The shading represents road-mileage density as recorded in a series of grid cells of 283 square miles superimposed on a highway map. In 1922 Ghana had just entered the phase of lateral interconnection, with east-west linkages both in the south, along the coast, and among the centers of the north, and with an extensive feeder network steadily drawing more and more of the smaller population centers into the orbit of Kumasi. Development in the southwest was weak, owing to railroad competition and to a deliberate policy of maintaining an economic road gap between Sekondi-Takoradi and Kumasi. This gap was finally filled in 1958, and only now is the southwest beginning to realize its great potential in cocoa and timber. By 1937 lateral interconnection had become more marked. The connections east and west of Tamale provide a good example of links between intermediate nodes. The 1–20-mile shading, for example, now reaches west from the Tamale node on the Great North Road to the node at Bole, which was just developing on the Western Trunk Road in 1922; Yendi on the Eastern Trunk has been similarly linked. Lateral interconnection has become intensified in the north, and the 21–40-mile shading now covers the entire zone between Bawku and Lawra. In the Kumasi area feeder development has continued, and the 21–40-mile shading blankets the Wenchi-Sunyani area to provide a fairly good network of interconnections between the Western Trunk and the Great North Road in the zone where both converge on Kumasi. Urban geographers will note the strong analogy to the process of interstitial

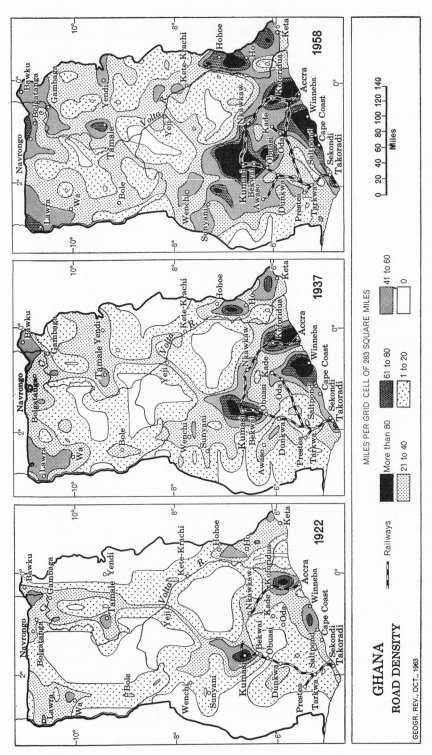

FIGURES 5-7: Road density in Ghana, 1922, 1937, and 1958. Redrawn from maps in Gould, *The Development of the Transportation Pattern in Ghana* (see starred footnote in text), pp. 104, 107, and 109.

filling between major radial roads converging on a central business district.

In 1958 the lateral interconnection process is fairly well developed. Only a few areas are still without road links, formerly inaccessible areas having been tapped by the expanding road network. A new series of high-density nodes have developed since 1937 and already are reaching out toward one another. Marked examples occur in the north between Tamale, Yendi, and other northern population centers, and in the south in the developing and extending nodes around Kumasi and east of the Volta River.

It is clear from the regularity of the progression of the highway-density patterns that extrapolation of the density maps to some future date would be reasonable. In a sense the map sequence is a crude predictive device. For instance, the probability of an increase in road miles for any area between two nodes is greater than that for a comparable area elsewhere.

In Nigeria a basically similar pattern had developed by 1953 (Fig. 8), with many of the earlier nodes of high accessibility in the south linking laterally to form an almost continuous high-density strip, broken only by the Niger River near Onitsha. Lines of penetration linking the north and the south across the barren middle zone, a feature clearly brought out by the map, are relatively weakly developed, and the degree of lateral linkage is well below that of northern Ghana. Only the Kano and Zaria nodes, in areas of high agricultural production and at the center of strong administrative webs, and the Jos node, at the center of the tin and columbium mineral complex, stand out as exceptions. Heavy rail competition, which resulted in severe restraints on long-haul trucking for many years, has clearly weakened the western road penetration lines, and the similarity to southwestern Ghana is strong. Areas totally inaccessible by road are still numerous, particularly in the barren middle zone and along the periphery of the country. To the political geographer the general weakness of the linkages between the Eastern, Western, and Northern regions will be of particular interest. There is, in fact, a clear visual impression that the general pattern of accessibility by road in Nigeria in 1953 is similar to that of Ghana in 1937—hardly surprising in view of the much larger size of Nigeria, the longer distances, and the lower per capita tax base from which the greater part of road development funds must come.

The Fourth Phase: High-Priority Linkages

The phase following the development of a fairly complete and coherent network is difficult to identify, and a variety of labels might be applied to it. Certainly the most marked characteristic of the most recent phase in the cases studied is the dominance of road over railroad. A common theme throughout the evolution of the transportation system in Ghana and Nigeria, and also in the other examples studied, has been the steady rise in the importance of road traffic, which first complements the railroad, then competes with it, and finally overwhelms it. However, the evidence available seems to indicate that this occurs irrespective of the stage of transport development, and it is possible that a greater number of road penetration lines are now being built in areas which would have required rail penetration lines in the past.

The idea of a phase of high-priority linkages is based, somewhat weakly, on a logical extrapolation of the concentration processes noted in the earlier stages of transport development in Ghana and Nigeria, and is supported in part by highly generalized evidence from areas with well-developed transportation systems.

Interior centers, intermediate nodes, and ports do not develop at

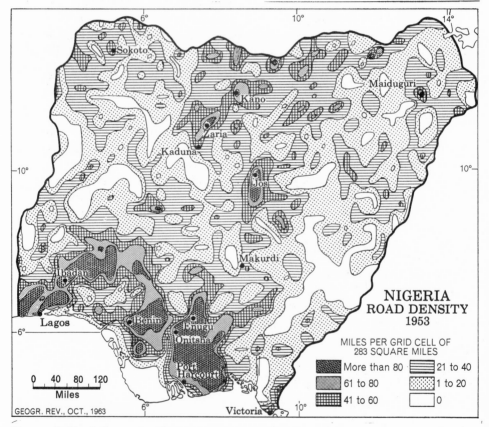

FIGURE 8: Road density in Nigeria, 1953. Compiled from sheets of the 1:250,000 map series published by the Federal Survey Department, Lagos.

precisely the same rate. As some of these centers grow more rapidly than others, their feeder networks become intensified and reach into the hinterlands of nearby centers. Ultimately certain interior centers and ports assert a geographic dominance over the entire country. This creates a disproportionately large demand for transportation between them, and since some transport facilities already exist, the new demand may take such forms as the widening of roads or the introduction of jet aircraft. In general, transport innovations are first applied to these trunk routes. For example, in the United States the best passenger rates, schedules, and equipment are usually initiated over high-density routes such as New York–Chicago. In underdeveloped countries high-priority linkages would seem to be less likely to develop along an export trunk line than along a route connecting two centers concerned in internal exchange. There is some weak evidence that high-priority links may be developing in the two study countries. High-density, short-haul traffic in the vicinity of Lagos may be the forerunner of a "main street" between cities of the western part of the rail bifurcation. In Ghana the heavy traffic flows focusing on Accra (flows that have tripled every five years since the war) have virtually forced the authorities to bring the basic road triangle up to firstclass standards of alignment and surface.

VII. THE POLITICAL PROCESS

"Man is not born free, he is born national." The national state system as it exists almost throughout the world is an end product of the political process as well as one of the great geographic realities. The state occupies space—usually carefully defined and protected space—on the surface of the earth, and is an expression of political regionalization. Nearly all of the wars of the last centuries have had as underlying causes differences between national states. These differences were not only in physical characteristics such as size and resources, or in population, but were also differences in attitudes, ideologies, and desires. A study of the differences that exist both within a national state and between national states constitutes the core of political geography and its somewhat more dynamic associate, geopolitics.

Since the Second World War, Americans have become acutely aware of the world around them, and of American responsibility in world affairs. As a result, concern for the political process as a geographic expression often is an integral part of introductory geography courses. In a world deeply torn by conflict between nations, it is essential that every student and every citizen increase their understanding of the geographic realities underlying the affairs of nations.

3 0. The Functional Approach in Political Geography
Richard Hartshorne

The political process as an element of cultural geography lends itself to analysis and classification similar to the economic process in that there are stages of development and essential elements. The functional approach recognizes that a national state or other political unit has internal and external functions which set it apart as an entity in space. One important advantage of the functional approach is that it

may be applied to political units and thir problems—
whether minor civil divisions within a country, or
supranational organizations such as NATO
or the European Common Market.

. . . The fundamental purpose of any state, as an organization of a section of land and a section of people, as Ratzel first put it, is to bring all the varied territorial parts, the diverse regions of the state-area, into a single organized area.

What does the state attempt to organize, in all regions of the state-area?

In all cases, it attempts to establish complete and exclusive control over internal political relations—in simplest terms, the creation and maintenance of law and order. Local political institutions must conform with the concepts and institutions of the central, overall, political organization.

In many social aspects—class structure, family organization, religion, and education—a state may tolerate considerable variation in its different regions. But because of the significance of these factors to political life, there is a tendency—in some states a very marked effort—to exert unifying control even over these institutions.

In the economic field, every modern state tends to develop some degree of unity of economic organization. At the minimum, it establishes uniform currency, some uniformity in economic institutions, and some degree of control over external economic relations. Beyond that, states of course vary greatly in the degree to which all aspects of production and trade—price and wage levels, etc.—are placed under uniform control.

Finally, and most importantly, because we live in a world in which the continued existence of every state-unit is subject to the threat of destruction by other states, every state must strive to secure the supreme loyalty of the people in all its regions, in competition with any local or provincial loyalties, and in definite opposition to any outside state-unit.

Throughout this statement of the organization of the state-area as a unit, the geographer is primarily concerned with emphasis on regional differences. The state of course is no less concerned to establish unity of control over all classes of population at a single place. In political geography, our interest is in the problem of unification of diverse regions into a single whole; the degree of vertical unification within any horizontal segment concerns us only as a factor aiding or handicapping regional unification.

SOURCE: *Annals of the Association of American Geographers,* XL, 2 (1950), 95–130. The author is professor of geography, University of Wisconsin.

Parenthetically, we may also note the ways in which this primary function of the state affects the general field of geography. Land-use, industrial development, trade, and a countless list of social aspects of human geography in any region will differ in greater or less degree as a result of the efforts of the state in which it is included to control its development as part of a single whole. Only the peculiarity of geographic study in such a large country as the United States, where we are usually forced to do most of our work within the territory of our single state, has permitted us to study geography as though we could ignore political geography.

Our analysis of the primary function of any state leads directly to the primary problem of political geography. For no state-area constitutes by the nature of its land and people a natural unit for a state, in which one merely needs to create a government which shall proceed to operate it as a unit. The primary and continuing problem of every state is how to bind together more or less separate and diverse areas into an effective whole.

For the political geographer, this presents a wide range of specific problems for analysis. In every state area, larger than such anomalies as Andorra or Liechtenstein, the geographer finds: (1) regions that are more or less separated from each other by physical or human barriers; (2) regions that in greater or lesser degree diverge in their relations with outside states; and (3) regions that differ among themselves in character of population, economic interests, and political attitudes. Let us look briefly at each of these types of problems.

Centrifugal Forces

Geographers are familiar with the effect of particular types of physical features in handicapping communication between regions. Semple and others have described for our own early history the political consequences of the forested Appalachians and later of the mountain and desert barrier of the west. Whittlesey's study of the Val d'Aran depicts in detail the problem in that bit of Spain north of the Pyrenees. In most modern states, however, these problems have largely been overcome by the development of the telegraph and the railroad. They continue of importance, however, in parts of the Balkans, in the highland states of Latin America, and in China.

Since state organization requires communication not only from one region to the next, but from a central point to each peripheral region, distance itself is a centrifugal factor. Obviously, distance within a state depends on its size and shape. Size and shape are significant to the state in other, quite different respects, but I suggest we wait until we have determined that in our analysis, rather than attempt to proceed deductively from size and shape to consequences.

Of human barriers, the most common is the absence of humans. Un-inhabited or sparsely inhabited areas were, until recently, difficult and dangerous to cross. It was primarily on this account that relatively low mountains, in central Europe or the Appalachians, long functioned as dividing zones. Even in the Alps, the problem of surmounting high elevations was less serious, in the Middle Ages, than the difficulty of securing supplies along the way and the ever-present danger of attack from "robber barons."

Further, the presence of such relatively empty areas created, and still creates, a feeling of separation in the regions on either side. Both on this account and because of distance, oceans continue to function as the strongest separating factors, other than Arctic ice, even though they have long been crossed with relative ease.

France has first inaugurated the interesting experiment of incorporat-ing trans-oceanic areas into the organization of its state. Its West Indian islands and the island of Réunion in the Indian Ocean are now depart-ments of metropolitan France, sending delegates to its national assembly. We may be about to do the same with Hawaii [now accomplished].

Perhaps the most difficult barrier to overcome is separation by a zone populated by a different people, especially an unfriendly people. The Germans have apparently convinced the world that the separation of East Prussia by the Polish Corridor was an experiment that is never to be repeated. (They overlooked the fact that there were not one but two alternatives to that device.)

Serious difficulties may arise for a state, if any of its regions have closer relations with regions of outside states than with those within the state. This is commonly the case where a boundary has been changed so that it now cuts across an area formerly within a single state. The partition of Upper Silesia, in 1922, presented a particularly intense case. But there are many cases, not dependent on boundary changes, in which a region has closer connections, particularly economic connections, with regions of other countries than with regions of its own state. We are familiar with the political importance of this factor in each of the major regions of Canada, each more closely related in certain respects with the adjacent areas of the United States than with the other regions within the Dominion. In some cases, mutual interdependence among the regions of the state area is less than the dependence of individual regions on remote, overseas countries. This is a major problem of the Australian Commonwealth, in which each state unit is primarily depen-dent on separate trade with Great Britain. In Western Australia, this factor, together with notable physical and human separation, has led at times to demand for secession from the Commonwealth. Northeastern Brazil offers a somewhat similar problem for study.

The geographer, however, must beware of drawing conclusions from the physical map, or, on the other hand, of assuming that an economic situation to which we are accustomed represents a "normal" development in economic geography, independent of a particular political framework. Consider southern California, separated by thousands of miles of desert and mountain from the main body of the United States, facing the Pacific highway to densely populated lands of the Orient. And yet which region of the United States is more completely bound into the economy of the country as a whole?

All the previous examples are relatively extreme cases. In most instances, the potentialities are highly flexible. The plain of Alsace, separated from the rest of France by the rugged heights of the Vosges, facing southern Germany across the narrow band of the Rhine floodplain and easily connected with northern Germany by that navigable river—with which state does it fit in terms of economic geography? Surely the answer must be that in terms of modern technology, all these features are of minor importance, and in terms of economic potentialities of the area, it can be associated almost equally well in either the French or the German economic unit.

Separation of regions by barriers or by divergence of outside connections is commonly less important than the centrifugal forces that result from diversity of character of the population. To secure voluntary acceptance of a single common organization requires some degree of mutual understanding; obviously this is easier in a population homogeneous in character. Further, where regions differ in social character, the tendency of the state to force some degree of uniformity of social life meets with resistance. Thus the very attempt to produce unity may intensify disunity. Hungary, before 1918, was the classic example; since then, Yugoslavia has perhaps been the leading, among several successors.

What particular social characteristics may be important depends on the particular state. Everyone thinks of language and religion. I suggest, also, education and standards of living, types of economic attitudes and institutions, attitudes toward class and racial distinctions, and, especially, political philosophy.

For materials on these topics, we look to that branch of geography that has been least developed—social geography. In most cases, what materials we have provide only the raw data, the facts about the distribution of, say, religions or races, rather than the regional differences in social attitudes toward these facts; it is the latter that we need.

Thus, the fact that Alsace was predominantly Roman Catholic, like France but unlike most of Germany, was less important than the fact that its attitude toward the relation of church and state was similar to that in the German Empire of 1871-1918, and was in conflict with the anticlerical attitude of the French Republic.

Racial differences, in the terms studied by the physical anthropologist, may be of no relevance to our problem. The distribution, percentage-wise, in the different countries of Europe, of blondes and brunettes, dolichocephalic versus brachycephalic—what does it matter? These facts have no reflection in social or political attitudes in those countries. Though standard material in most geographies of Europe, I submit that they have no significance to political geography, or for that matter, to geography in general.

In contrast, the United States is a country in which regional differences in attitudes of people toward the racial components of the regional group—as indicated by skin color—are of tremendous importance in social, economic, and political life. We have mapped and studied the underlying differences in racial composition, but we have not studied the phenomenon itself—namely the differences in attitudes. We need a map, a series of maps, portraying different kinds and degrees of Jim Crowism in the United States. These I would rate as a first requirement for an understanding of the internal political geography of the United States, for in no other factor do we find such marked regional cleavages, such disruption to the national unity of our state. For geography in general, in one quarter of our country, these attitudes are fundamental factors in every aspect of the human geography and are significantly related to its physical geography.

Geographers are more familiar with differences in economic interests, since these are more closely bound to the land. But these are seldom seriously disrupting to national unity. It is true that almost every modern state has experienced marked political tension between the divergent-interests of highly industrialized regions and those of primarily agricultural areas. But these very differences tend to lead to interlocking, rather than competing, interests. Even when competing, economic differences, Marx to the contrary notwithstanding, are easier to compromise than differences in social and political attitudes.

Furthermore, the state is only in partial degree an economic unit. Since it is basically a political unit, the state necessarily imposes the greatest degree of uniformity in political life. Political attitudes are peculiarly inflexible. If a region is accustomed to one set of political concepts, ideals, and institutions—most especially if its people feel that they have fought in the past to establish those political values—it may be extremely difficult to bring them under the common cloak of a quite different system. Even where regions formerly in separate states have voluntarily joined together to form a state, on the basis of common ethnic character—for example, the three Polish areas in 1918 or the

Czech and Slovak areas—the marked difference in past political education led to difficult problems.

In times and areas of relatively primitive political development, such factors were no doubt of minor importance. In long-settled areas of relatively mature political development, they may be of first importance. The classic example is, again, Alsace. Thanks particularly to the French Revolution, the people of that province had become strong supporters of political concepts, ideals, and institutions that could not be harmonized within the semi-feudal, authoritarian monarchy of Hohenzollern Germany.

Conversely, one may understand on this basis the negative reaction of the Swiss in 1919 to the proposal that the adjacent Austrian province of Vorarlberg should be added to their state.

Centripetal Forces

The preceding discussion of political attitudes points to an essential ingredient that has been lacking in the discussion up to this point. We have been considering a variety of centrifugal factors in the regional geography of a state area, which make it difficult to bind those regions together into an effective unit. In considering how such difficulties may be overcome, we have not asked whether there was any force working to overcome the difficulties, anything tending to pull these regions together into a state.

This omission, I suggest, has been the single greatest weakness in our thinking in political geography. If we see an area marked clearly on both physical and ethnic maps as suitable for a state, but which for many centuries was not integrated as a state—as in the Spanish peninsula, the Italian peninsula, or the German area—we cudgel our heads to find factors in its internal geography that will explain the failure. We forget that before we speak of failure, we must ask what was attempted.

The Italian peninsula, together with the northern plain attached to the mainland but isolated by the Alps, with a settled population speaking approximately a common tongue since the Middle Ages, has offered one of the most obvious geographic units of Europe for the development of a state. Yet Italy, as an Austrian minister jeered, was only a geographic expression; there was nothing that could be called even the beginnings of a state of Italy. For no one of importance had any idea of producing an Italian state, and, had anyone tried, his purpose would have shattered in conflict with two opposing ideas: one, the concept of the Papal States, the secular control of mid-Italy by the Pope in order to secure his undivided domination of Rome as the spiritual capital of Western Christendom; the other, the concept of a single great empire in the heart of Europe, extending from northern Germany to northern Italy. Only after the power of these centuries-old ideas had been irrevocably destroyed by the ferment of the French Revolution, was it possible for any Italian leader to consider seriously the unification of Italy.

One of the concepts that prevented integration in Italy is likewise the key to the failure of medieval Germany to develop a unified state, at the time when the kingdoms of France and England were being effectively established. For centuries, the persons holding the title of King of Germany, and whatever opportunity that might give, were far more affected by the higher title of Emperor. Inspired by the grander idea of reincarnating the empire of Rome, they fought to build up a state straddling the Alps, uniting many different peoples. The sacrifices made in the vain attempt to accomplish the greater idea destroyed the possibility of achieving the lesser, when later emperors finally were reduced to considering German unity.

The fact that a country has a name and a government, that an international treaty recognizes its existence as a state and defines its territorial limits—all that does not produce a state. To accomplish that, it is necessary to establish centripetal forces that will bind together the regions of that state, in spite of centrifugal forces that are always present.

The State Idea

The basic centripetal force must be some concept or idea justifying the existence of this particular state incorporating these particular regions; the state must have a *raison d'être*—reason for existing.

Although ignored in much of the literature of political geography, this is not a new thought. Ratzel defined the state as a section of land and a section of humanity, organized as a single unit in terms of a particular, distinctive idea. Maull, among other German geographers, has discussed the concept at some length. It was presented to [the] Association of [American Geographers] a decade ago.

At the primitive level, Ratzel explained, this idea may be no more than the will of a ruler, to which, for whatever reasons, all the regional parts through their local leaders grant their loyalty. In such a case, as in the empire of Charlemagne or that of Genghis Khan, the state may endure hardly longer than the lifetime of the individual ruler. In the attempt to perpetuate the binding idea of loyalty to a personal ruler, there evolved the concept of hereditary monarchy. Where that succeeded, however, we find there was always something more—politically minded people in the various parts of the kingdom came to regard the state, for reasons independent of the monarch, as representing something of value to them. Today the monarchical institution is safe only in those states in which the monarch has exchanged the active power to rule for the passive role of personification of the national heritage.

To be sure, a state in which the original idea has lost its validity will not fall apart at once. The forces of inertia, vested interests, and fear of the consequences of change may keep it going more or less effectively for some time. But inevitably a structure that has lost its original *raison d'être*, without evolving a new one, cannot hope to stand the storms of external strife or internal revolt that sooner or later will attack it. For when that day comes, the state, to survive, must be able to count on the loyalty, even to the death, of the population of all its regions.

It is not mere coincidence that the terms I have been using came to me from a Viennese geographer, in his analysis of the failure of the Hapsburg monarch. Unless Austria-Hungary, Hassinger wrote after the First World War, had been able to discover and establish a *raison d'être*, a justification for existence, even without the calamity of the war, it could not long have continued to exist.

Those states are strongest, Ratzel had concluded, "in which the political idea of the state fills the entire body of the state, extends to all its parts."

What does this mean for our study of the political geography of a state? It means, I am convinced, that before we can begin to study the problems presented by the centrifugal forces I have previously outlined, we must first discover the motivating centripetal force, the basic political idea of the state. Under what concept, for what purposes, are these particular regions to be bound together into one political unit, absolutely separated from every other political territory?

Does this seem too remote from geography? Too much like political science? The student of geography of climates must understand the nature of air-masses, as analyzed by the meteorologist. We cannot intelligently study the geography of soils, until we have grasped the soil scientist's analysis of soil types. In agricultural geography, it is not sufficient, we now know, to study crops and animals; we are concerned with the farm unit of organization of crops from fields, livestock in barns and pasture, all directed toward ultimate production of food for the farmer and products to be sold from his farms. We are not ready to begin the study of farm geography until we have analyzed the farmer's purpose—the idea under which his piece of land is organized.

Geographers generally know quite a bit about farming, so they may know beforehand what is in the farmer's mind, or perhaps they can infer that from observation of the visible facts—the fields, silo, corncrib, or cow-barn. But to know for certain, you must ask the farmer.

Whom shall we ask concerning the idea of a particular state? Obviously, one must go to those who actually operate the state in question.

This is not so easy as in the case of the farm or factory. A modern state is an organization operated, in greater or less degree, by all the politically minded people included in it—ideally its entire adult population.

One might logically suppose that geographers should be able to find the answer to this question in studies in political science. Unfortunately, from our point of view, political scientists seem to have concerned themselves solely with the idea and purpose of the generic state—the purposes, that is, that are common to all states. This ignores the very thing that is of direct concern to the geographer—namely, the idea that is distinct for the particular state in contrast with that of other states, that which makes for significant differences from country to country. Perhaps that means that it is logically a problem for the geographer.

In any case, unless we can find the answer to this fundamental question in the works of other students—perhaps of the historians, if not the political scientists—we are apparently forced to work it out for ourselves. We must discover and establish the unique distinctive idea under which a particular section of area and of humanity is organized into a unit state.

I realize that the problem is remote from the geographer's training and knowledge. But years of stumbling effort have convinced me that there is no circumventing it. Until we can determine for any particular state the idea under which it is organized, we shall have no basis on which to analyze its political geography; we shall not have started on the significant contribution that geography can make to the study of states.

Perhaps we exaggerate the difficulty of the problem because it is unfamiliar. To pin down precisely the particular idea on which any state is based is certainly very difficult, but study of the essential historical documents may enable one to come fairly quickly to a rough statement sufficiently close to the mark to be usable.

Let me give you a case in which one of my advanced graduate students had particular difficulty—the state of Iraq. He finally arrived at something like this: the idea of an Iraqi state sprang from two factors: (1) the recognition by the Great Powers of the strategic and economic significance of the Mesopotamian region, and (2) the need to provide a *pied à terre* for Arab nationalism banished from Syria. On the basis of these two considerations, there was established a territory embracing the settled Arab region of the Tigris-Euphrates plain, together with adjacent but dissimilar regions of mountain and desert tribes, the whole to be developed as a separate Arab state.

You note that the idea of this state was a compound of purposes, and those external: foreign diplomacy and transported nationalist fire. That was the case in 1919. One would need to determine whether the Iraqi have since evolved a truly native concept.

In much older states, we may expect to find that an indigenous *raison d'être* has evolved that may have little or no relation to the original genesis. To determine the distinctive idea of such a state, therefore, we must study the current situation, rather than the remote past. In the well-developed modern state, politically minded people in all regions of the state area are conscious of their loyalty to the state, and have some common understanding, even though not clearly phrased, of what that state means to them. In such a case, we may recognize, I think, the existence of a *nation*—as something distinct from the state itself. . . .

The Application of the State Idea in Political Geography

Whatever is found to be the *raison d'être*, the underlying idea, of the state, it is with this concept, I submit, that the geographer should start in his analysis of the state area. What use is he then to make of it? His first concern is to determine the area to which the idea applies; then the degree to which it operates in the different regions, and finally the extent of correspondence of those regions to the territory actually included within the state.

On this basis, we may approach the most elementary problem in political geography—namely, that of distinguishing within the legal confines of its territory those regions that form integral parts of the state area in terms of its basic idea, and those parts that must be recognized as held under control, in the face of either indifference or of opposition on the part of the regional population.

The vast areas of the subarctic lands, whether in Alaska, Canada, Sweden, or the Soviet Union, sparsely populated by primitive tribes, with a few scattered settlements of civilized peoples, are organized politically as though they were colonies of an outside state, even where there is no break in the extent of territory under the same flag. The same is true of tropical lowland areas, in almost all the Latin American countries. In most of the latter, these essentially unorganized territories constitute over half the total area officially credited to the country.

A more difficult question for definition is raised in examining the areas of long-settled Indian population in the highlands of tropical America—both in Central American states and in the Andes. Are these areas of native languages and culture to be considered as integral parts of states, or are they not still colonial areas subject to outside control, even though the center of control is not in Spain, but in the neighboring districts of Spanish-American culture?

A similar situation may be found in more highly developed countries. Thus during the centuries in which all of Ireland was recognized in international law as part of the United Kingdom, its greater part was certainly operated in fact as a subject area, distinct from the controlling state. Much the same may be true today of certain portions of the Soviet Union, notably the so-called republics of Central Asia—but the difficulty of determining the actual operations of the Soviet government make definite statement impossible. On the other hand, we have in the United States clearcut though tiny relics of internal colonialism in the Indian reservations.

If the idea of the state is based on the recognition of the existence of a nation, then the major geographic question to consider is whether there is close correspondence between that area of the nation and that of the state. Are there regions within the state whose population do not feel themselves part of the nation? Are there regions of the nation that are not included within the state—the issue of irredentism?

It is not easy to measure the area to be included in a particular national group. In many cases, we must approach the question indirectly. If we can determine the essential factors involved in the particular nationality, we may be able to measure the area over which each of these factors exists. On this basis, we may establish certain areas that are clearly included in the given nation, and other areas that adhere in terms of some factors, but not in terms of others.

The entire area over which the nation extends, but in varying degree of intensity, may then be compared with the area presently included in the state. We have thus determined not only the areal correspondence of state and nation, but also the regions in which the national character is partial rather than complete. We shall thereby have presented, in part in map form, the basic factors and relationships involved in the primary problem of political geography—the analysis of the degree to which the diverse regions of the state constitute a unity.

Internal Organization

At this point, we reach one other problem for analysis—the relation of the internal territorial organization of the state-area to the regional diversities we have analyzed. Though all the regions of a state are clearly included under the state idea and have complete loyalty to the overall concepts of the national unit, regional differences inevitably cause some differences in interpretation and implementation of those concepts.

If those differences are relatively minor, as in most of France or, I presume, in Uruguay, the regions may accept unitary government from a single central authority. If the differences are great, the attempt to impose such a uniform system may provoke opposition endangering the national unity. Since such regional differences are important in most countries, but most states attempt to operate under a uniform, centralized government, the number of examples of this type of problem is very large. Spain, at the moment, provides one of the most striking.

Certain states recognize openly the need to permit diverging interpretations of the overall concepts of that state, and hence significant differences in the institutions and law thereunder. This is the system of the federal state, of which Switzerland provides the oldest example, the United States the largest. In both cases, a notable degree of regional heterogeneity is guaranteed by the constitutional division of powers.

In this country, we are at the moment engaged in one of our periodic crises in determining just how much social and political autonomy is to be permitted the regions that are crudely represented by our so-called States. This crisis, incidentally, causes the Congress of the United States to work for the social and political geographer, producing raw material useful to us in measuring differences in intensity of regional attitudes toward the facts of racial composition.

The possible ways of organizing the state area are not limited to the unitary and the federal systems. The United Kingdom, for example, has evolved in the course of its long history a most complicated system, under which Wales, Scotland, Northern Ireland, the Isle of Man, and the Channel Islands each has a different degree of autonomy adjusted to its particular linguistic, religious, economic, and political geography.

In determining the method of state organization of a country, the student must study the actual method of government, not merely the words written into a constitution. He will recognize that while the constitution of the Soviet Union grants on paper more independence to its member republics than is true of the individual states of this country, and even though it encourages and exploits a great variety of languages and folk cultures, in every other respect of economic and political life, it operates its vast area of radically different regions as a highly centralized monolithic state.

Analysis of External Functions

In a functional approach to the analysis of the political geography of a state, our first half was concerned with the internal problems of the state area. The second half is concerned with the external relations of the state area to the other areas of the world, whether those are also organized as states, controlled by outside states, or unorganized. For convenience, we may group these relations as territorial, economic, political, and strategic.

Territorial Relations

Under territorial relations, we are of course concerned in the first instance with the degree to which adjacent states are in agreement concerning the extent of territory which each includes. Whether the area in question is large or small, agreement ultimately requires the determination of a precise boundary.

Of all the problems of international relations, those concerning the allocation of territories and hence the determination of boundaries are the most obviously geographic. . . .

If we start with what we are studying—the state areas—we can recognize the essential function of the boundary from its name: it is that line which is to be accepted by all concerned as *bounding* the area in which everything is under the jurisdiction of one state, as against areas under different jurisdiction. (Consideration of the functions of a boundary zone, as an element of military defense, for example, is a separate question to be considered elsewhere.)

The first thing to know about an international boundary, therefore, is the degree to which it is accepted by all the parties concerned—i.e., the adjacent states and the population whose statehood is determined by the location of the boundary.

Consider the following cases of international boundaries: the boundary between Great Britain and France (including the Channel Islands with Great Britain); that between France and Spain; that between Switzerland and Italy (including the Ticino boundary that reaches far down the Alpine slopes almost to the Po Plain); and, finally, the boundary between the United States and Mexico both east and west of El Paso. These run through radically different types of physical zones. Some correspond closely with ethnic divisions, others do not. But from the point of view of the primary function of an international boundary, all are in the same category, namely that of boundaries completely accepted as final by the states themselves and the people of the border areas.

In a different category is the Franco-German boundary (considered as of 1930). Though this was fully accepted by France and officially so by Germany in the Treaty of Locarno, one could not assume that the German leaders intended that acceptance to be final, and by imprisoning some of the local leaders in Alsace, the French government demonstrated its lack of faith in the complete acceptance by the Alsatian people of their inclusion in the French state.

Still different is the case of the German-Polish boundary of the inter-war period, which neither state accepted as more than a temporary division of territory claimed by both sides.

Where boundaries run through primitive, essentially colonial, regions which at present have very slight productive value, but offer possibilities for future importance, we may need to recognize a different set of categories. Thus we may find cases in which for a time the states concerned, while not committing themselves to an ultimate boundary, raise no question concerning the line lost in the wilderness, but may at any moment challenge, with the force of arms, the line that had apparently been accepted. . . .

The second question concerning any international boundary (whether or not it is fully accepted) is the degree to which its bounding function is maintained by the bordering states; the degree, that is, to which all movements of goods and persons across the line are effectively controlled by the boundary officials. In examining that, the geographer will of course observe the ways in which the control is made easier or more difficult by the character of the zone through which the boundary line is drawn.

A special aspect of boundary problems emerges where the territory of a state reaches to the sea. Though open to use by all, the seas are in fact little used by anyone. Hence, it is sufficient for most purposes to define the boundary simply as following the coast, as most treaties do. But for certain purposes, notably fishing, border control, and naval warfare, the exact determination of the line in the waters may be critical. There is no overall agreement in international law, either as to the width of territorial waters—the zone of sea included as part of the possession of the bordering state—or as to the manner in which the off-shore line bounding those waters follows the indentations of the coast. . . .

The use of territorial waters by merchant ships of a foreign state, commonly for the purpose of entering the ports of the country concerned, represents the most common occurrence of use of territory of one state for the purposes of another state. In this case, the purpose is mutual. In other, more special cases, problems arise from the desire or need of the people of one state to utilize the territory of a foreign country in order to have access to still other countries, or in some cases to a different part of their own state. Both Canada and the United States have permitted the construction of railroads across portions of their territories, whose major purpose was to connect regions of the other country—e.g., the Michigan Central across Ontario from Detroit to Buffalo, or the Canadian Pacific across the State of Maine from Montreal to St. John, New Brunswick. European countries commonly will not tolerate foreign railroads across their territories, but the Polish railroads in the inter-war period operated, for Germany, through trains between East Prussia and the main part of Germany.

Nearly all states recognize the need of providing transit service for trade across their territories between states on either side, though this involves a multiplicity of minor problems of control. Most important are provisions for transit from an inland state to the seacoast, in order to have access to the countries of the world accessible by sea routes. The Grand Trunk Railroad of Canada, now a part of the Canadian National Railways, not only crosses New Hampshire and Maine to reach the sea, but, when the winter ice closes the St. Lawrence, uses the harbor of Portland, Maine, as its port of shipment for foreign trade of interior Canada, which constitutes most of the total traffic of that American port. In certain European cases more specific arrangements seem necessary: a section of a port, as at Trieste or Hamburg, may be allocated exclusively to handle the transit trade of a foreign country.

Economic Relations

. . . In the analysis of a state area, the need to consider its economic relations with outside areas arises from the fact that in many respects, a state operates, must operate, as a unit economy in relation with other unit economies in the world. The difficulties arise because, while it must operate completely as a political unit, a state area operates only partially as an economic unit.

The first problem is to determine to what extent the economy of one state area is dependent on that of others, though the mere analysis of self-sufficiency is only a beginning. If one says that the United States produces a surplus of coal and iron, but is dependent on foreign countries for much of its supply of tin, nickel, and manganese, of sugar and rubber—such a statement, even in precise percentage figures, tells us directly little of importance. If a country has plenty of coal and iron, it can normally secure the other metals mentioned from wherever in the world they are produced. Under abnormal conditions of war, or threat of war, it is essential to know that the manganese normally comes from the Transcaucasus in the Soviet Union, the tin from British Malaya (but can be obtained from Bolivia), whereas the nickel comes from adjacent Canada. Natural rubber supplies are available in adequate amounts only in one remote region—Malaya-East Indies—but nearby Cuba can supply most of our sugar needs.

In general, the geographer will analyze the economic dependence of one state area in terms of the specific countries concerned, and their location and political association in relation to the state he is studying.

Since all sound trading is of mutual advantage to both parties, to say that one state is economically dependent on any other necessarily implies also the converse. But the degree to which any particular commodity trade, shipping service, or investment is critically important varies in terms of the total economy of each of the two states concerned. It is only in this sense that the common question, "Is a particular state economically viable?" has any validity, since every state above the most primitive level is in some respects critically dependent on others.

The problem is far from simple, but perhaps we can suggest two generalizations. As between two countries that differ greatly in the size of their total national economy, the economic relationships between them are more critically important for the lesser country (though this might not be true under war conditions). This is true because these economic relationships, which may be taken as equalized through international balance of payments, will form a larger proportion of the total economy of the lesser state. An obvious example is found in the relation of Eire to Great Britain, of Cuba to the United States.

The second generalization rests on the fact that the critical significance of the trade depends on the possibility of alternatives, of finding other sources for needed supplies or other markets for products which must be sold to maintain the national economy. Most popular discussions tend to think only of the former, whereas under the capitalist profit-system under which most international trade operates, it is the latter that is more significant. The reason for this is that for most commodities of world production, there are alternate sources of supply at moderate increase in cost; there may not be alternative markets even at greatly reduced selling prices.

Finally, we may note that relatively few areas of the world now produce a surplus of manufactured goods requiring a high degree of technological development, and these constitute therefore a relatively limited market for the surplus of primary products of farm, forest, and mine, which can be produced widely over the world. Consequently, the countries producing primary products, even the very necessities of life, may find it more difficult to find alternative markets for their products than the industrial countries producing articles less essential to life. With wider spread of industrialization over the world, this situation would of course be altered, conceivably reversed.

It should not be assumed, however, that these rough generalizations will provide the answer in any given case. Consider the problem posed by the independence of Austria after the dissolution of the Hapsburg empire—a problem which Austria still faces. To survive as a viable economic unit, Austria needed to maintain with the adjacent regions, re-organized as independent states, a high degree of economic relationship. Its position in competition with otherwise more favored regions of industrial Europe made it peculiarly dependent on markets immediately to the east. For these eastern neighbors, such relationships were also necessary for the maximum economic progress, but were not vitally necessary to economic life. If, for political reasons, and to develop their own industries at greater cost, they preferred not to trade freely with Austria, they had the choice of the less profitable plan, whereas for Austria the alternative was economic collapse.

In the nineteenth century, international economic relations, though both supported and retarded by state action, were generally operated as the private business of individuals and corporations. With the depression of the 1930's, the rise of totalitarian states, and the last war, there has been an increasing tendency for the state itself to direct the operations of international trade and investment. In these respects, states function increasingly as economic units, so that the economic relations among them become increasingly important in the politico-geographic analysis of the state.

Political Relations

The most obvious form of political relation of a state to any outside territory is that of effective political control—as a colony, possession, dependency, or "protectorate." Commonly, we recognize only a small number of states as colonial, or imperial, powers: eight or nine in western Europe, together with the United States, Japan, Australia, and New Zealand (the latter two functioning in islands of the Southwest Pacific). Germany was eliminated from the list by the First World War, Japan by the Second. If, however, we recognize the colonial reality of areas adjacent to a state and legally included in its territory, but actually not forming an integral part of that state (as discussed earlier in this paper), the list is far longer—including Canada, Norway, Sweden, the Soviet Union, China, the Union of South Africa, and most of the Latin American states. A newcomer to this list is the Indonesian Republic, with large territories subject to it, in the primitive areas of Borneo, Celebes, etc.

The legal forms of colonial relationship vary widely—even within a single empire, such as that of Great Britain. Further, these legal forms may or may not express the reality of the relationship, the degrees to which political organization is imposed and operated by the outside state. It is the latter, I presume, that is our concern in political geography.

One characteristic of colonial areas that is of particular concern from our present point of view is the degree to which the governmental system of the home state is extended over the colonial territory. France is in the process of fully incorporating certain formerly colonial areas into metropolitan France, but others only partially. Many imperial powers have always extended their legal systems into colonial areas, so far as citizens from the home country are concerned, so that within any colonial area there may be an overlapping of two authorities—one having jurisdiction over citizens of the home state, the other over native people.

Many countries recognized by treaty as independent states, and functioning in large degree as such, are nonetheless under some particular degree of political control by an outside power. This may be limited to utilization of small fractions of the territory of one state by the government, usually the armed services, of the other—e.g., Great Britain in military control of the Canal Zone of Egypt, the United States Navy at Guantanamo Bay. The most important, relatively, is the American control, for essentially an indefinite period, of the Panama Canal Zone, across the most populous part of the Republic of Panama. In other cases, the outside country may control directly no part of the territory, but rather exercise limited control, as through an adviser, over major aspects of government, especially foreign relations, customs, or the national budget. The United States has in the past exercized such control for limited periods over small states in the Caribbean area; a group of outside powers for years operated the tariff customs of China to raise money to pay the Chinese foreign debts. The clearest case of political domination of supposedly independent states by an outside state today is found in the obvious control by the Soviet Union over the internal policies as well as foreign policy of the "satellite" states on its west, from Poland to Bulgaria, even though this relationship is expressed in no formal treaties.

Generally speaking, recognition of independent sovereignty of a state by the other states of the world presumes that that state will maintain similar political relations with all friendly states, will not be bound by special political associations with any particular states. Numerous exceptions, however, are widely recognized. Thus the dominions of the British Commonwealth are recognized as having emerged from colonial to independent status, even though they continue to be held together in continuously voluntary confederation with the United Kingdom, extending to one another numerous political and economic privileges not extended to other states. Likewise outside states have long recognized the special political concern of the United States for the Latin American republics, a concern now finally expressed in treaty as a mutual policy of association.

Likewise they have recognized the longstanding political interest of the United States in the Negro state of Liberia. The . . . North Atlantic Pact, though intended primarily for military purposes, contains political clauses which, if implemented, would tend to create a special political association of the United States, Canada, and the states of western Europe.

Finally, of course, nearly all the states of the world have accepted certain political commitments in joining the United Nations; insofar as this applies to all states, such commitments are universal, rather than geographically distinctive. . . .

31. Core-Areas and the Development of the European States System

Norman J. G. Pounds and Sue Simons Ball

Most of our ideas of political structure and organization, including the concept of the state as an entity, have been developed in or derived from Europe. The European state models have been widely imitated elsewhere and for several centuries the nations of Europe have been a dominant force almost throughout the world. As a result, with the exception of some of the newly established states, most nations have had a developmental process starting with a core-area, the germinal center from which the larger political entity was derived. As a result, the core-area concept is a fundamental part of the political process and a useful tool for geopolitical analysis.

"There is no little provincial state," wrote Lucien Febvre in 1932, "which has not had its germinal, its geographical startingpoint." Among the 130 or so sovereign states which today decorate the political map of the world, it is perhaps legitimate to distinguish two broad categories: those which have been created arbitrarily to fill some preconceived geographical frame, and those which have grown slowly and over a long period of time from some nuclear, germinal, or core-area. This division is not rigid or absolute. Some states, such as France, which are commonly thought of as growing by a process of accretion around a core-area, nevertheless came to think of themselves as filling out a prescribed physical framework. To these two generalized categories we have given the names of "arbitrary" and "organic" states. If they may be typified by their extremes, perhaps Jordan and Tsarist Russia may serve as examples. The purpose of this paper is to examine the physical nature of and the geographical role performed by the core-area in the formation of a particular group of states, namely those of Europe.

The geographical pattern of the states of Europe had, in general,

SOURCE: *Annals of the Association of American Geographers,* LIV (February, 1964), 24–40. Dr. Pounds is professor of geography, Indiana University, and Dr. Ball (Mrs. James Wallace) is assistant professor, Eastern Michigan University.

taken shape before the age of modern nationalism, and it is difficult to discover among the forces which brought the states into being during the Middle Ages those same forces which gave impetus to their policies and shaped the boundaries in the nineteenth and twentieth centuries. It cannot be denied, however, that a state system, once established, profoundly influenced the emergence of national feeling within the political boundaries already drawn. There are several instances—the Netherlands is an example—of national feeling coming within a very short span of years to fill out the geographical framework that had been defined arbitrarily, like new wine poured into an old bottle. Examples are no less numerous of the territorial expansion of neighboring states into the political no-man's land which once separated them, and of the competition of neighboring national ideologies for the adherence and loyalty of the peoples who inhabit it. However profoundly they may have been modified and their expansion influenced by the forces which make up modern nationalism, most European states grew in fact by a process of accretion from germinal areas which have come, after Derwent Whittlesey, to be called "core-areas."

A core-area must have considerable advantages in order to permit it to perform this role. Simply put, it must have within itself the elements of viability. It must be able to defend itself against encroachment and conquest from neighboring core-areas, and it must have been capable at an early date of generating a surplus income above the subsistence level, necessary to equip armies and to play the role in contemporary power politics that territorial expansion necessarily predicates. In terms of the Middle Ages, with which we are primarily concerned in this paper, this means a fertile soil, well cultivated within the limits of contemporary technology, a population dense enough to derive the maximum advantage from local resources, and, generally, a long-distance commerce to enable it to obtain materials not locally available.

The question has been raised whether those who initiated the process of state expansion had any clear concept of the future geographical limits of the state, and whether they strove consciously to reach them. In nineteenth-century France, a school of historians, led by Albert Sorel, argued that from the first the French kings conceived of a France bounded by its "historic" or "natural frontiers." It is difficult to accept such a view either for France or for any other country. Geographical concepts of space, distance, and direction were in general indefinite and unrefined. Maps were in some degree schematic, and rarely gave even an approximation to a true picture of the land. When the sons of the Emperor Louis the Pious met at Verdun in 843 to divide their father's lands between them, they discovered, not without some sense of shock, that they did not know what it was that they were dividing. In the words of the contemporary chronicler, Nithard:

And when those who had been sent by Ludwig and Charles to divide the kingdom had arrived, it was asked whether any among them had any conception of the extent of the whole empire. When no one was found with this knowledge, it was suggested that messengers should be sent to all parts to record what was there.

It is inconceivable that, when the states system of Europe began to take shape, people could have had any clear concept of the geographical ends to which their expansion might be directed. Until the eighteenth or even the nineteenth century the territorial expansion of states was contingent and empirical, and only when the process of growth had made considerable progress did ideas both of nationalism and of a kind of geographical predestination enter in and attempt to impose a final shape upon the boundaries of states.

The medieval Kingdom of Hungary, it has recently been claimed by Andrew Burghardt, is an exception to the generalization that the state, in Europe at least, was never preordained and given, complete and clearly defined by the hand of nature. "The state idea bequeathed to his nation by King Stephen," he wrote, "was at that time unique in Europe, in that it dealt with a territorially completed state. In terms of area, the Kingdom of Hungary was fully grown when it was born. . . . In Hungary no growth from a central, vital core was necessary. . . . The great contribution of the Magyars to Europe was the organization of the Carpathian Basin, and this was possible as an entirety, or not at all."

This echoes the traditional Hungarian argument, which has always asserted the basic physical and historical unity of the Pannonian Basin, and denied the validity of the contrary claim that the Hungarian Kingdom grew from a relatively small core-area near the Danube until it had embraced unrelated ethnic groups in the surrounding region of hills and mountains. To quote Burghardt again, "In Hungary no growth from a central vital core was necessary. The Kingdom had been established within an area eminently suitable to the creation of one state." Without examining at this point the historical validity of this claim (see below page 435), some doubt may nevertheless be expressed whether King Stephen (A.D. 977–1038) had any clear concept either of the geographical extent or of the physical unity of the Pannonian Basin, nor is it at all clear that he made any attempt to dominate and control it.

France the Prototype

France is so often cited as the type case of the expansion of a state by territorial accretion around a nucleus or core-area, that it is worthwhile to examine this process somewhat more closely. Some unity was given to the area now known as France by the Roman Conquest in the first century B.C. Its boundary was established along the Rhine, as a result in large measure of the contingencies of war. Its administrative focus lay in the middle Rhône valley, at Lugdunum (Lyon), from which the Roman road system radiated over the country. Roman authority was either withdrawn or overthrown in the course of the Germanic invasions, and a congeries of small states emerged in its place, changing shape in a kaleidoscopic fashion until they were again united under the Carolingian rulers. Under the later Carolingians not only was the territory over which they ruled fragmented politically, but political authority itself became so attenuated that the local regions of France—the counties and duchies—became, under their counts and dukes, for practical purposes independent of the central authority.

The theoretical unity of most of what is today France was perhaps never in question, but this purely national unity ceased to be translated into the practical terms of political authority and control. The so-called unification of France consisted not in the extension over the whole area of the titular authority of a king of France—that was already admitted—but rather of the extension of the practical power of a government whose seat was in the country's capital. This could only be done by replacing the quasi-regal power which local dukes and counts had assumed, by the royal power itself. It was a question of the French king stepping into the place of the local territorial lord, and of adding to his own titular authority the latter's practical power. It is evident that the French kings succeeded by the end of the Middle Ages in doing just this. It is no less evident that this is what the Holy Roman emperors failed to do in either Germany or Italy. The French kings annexed to themselves the power of the local aristocracy by a variety of means: marrying their heiresses, overthrowing them in war, or even buying out their pretensions.

How it was done is, in the present context, less important than the definition of the nuclear area *from* which it was done. The Paris region was of no exceptional importance under the Romans, and provided a permanent residence for none of the later Merovingian and Carolingian rulers. The Carolingians more often made their home in northern France, the Low Countries, or the Rhineland. Charlemagne's favorite residence was Aachen, and the last of his successors in France made his home in the hilltop city of Laon, in Champagne. The rise of Paris to preeminence would seem to have owed little to environment or to tradition, and everything to the personality of its local rulers, the Counts of Paris of the Capet family. The enfeeblement of the last Carolingians, the personal strength and vigor of the early rulers of the House of Capet, and the success with which they held their small island in the Seine against the Norsemen, all led in 987 to Hugh Capet attaining the empty honor of being elected king of France. His real power was as wide, and

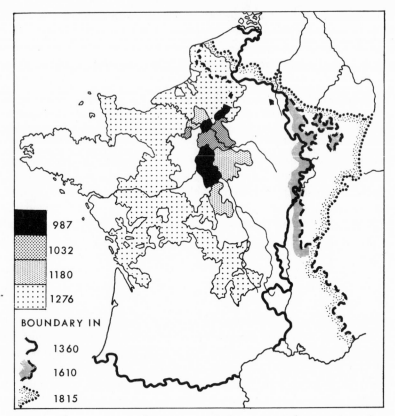

FIGURE 1: The core-area of France, and the territorial expansion of royal authority.

no wider than the lands which he personally controlled. These lands surrounded Paris, and extended, with interruptions, beyond Senlis to the northeast and southward beyond the Loire. This was the *domaine royale,* and the royal power was later extended only by accessions to this area of direct royal control (Fig. 1).

It was entirely accidental that this *domaine royale,* the nucleus around which the Kingdom of France, as distinct from the geographical concept of France, was built, lay, for the greater part, in the fertile soils of Beauce and Brie. The Polyptiques [1] of the ninth and tenth centuries are evidence of the prosperity and dense population of these areas. Irminon's Polyptique demonstrates the high degree of organization of the manors, and Ferdinand Lot has argued that its population in the ninth century was greater than the rural population of the same area in the nineteenth. It is highly probable that it was the greater

[1] Surveys or inventories of estates, which normally included lists of manors and the numbers of their inhabitants.

wealth and population of this nuclear area that gave the early Capets the influence and the material power which allowed them to extend their authority. This expansion was neither continuous nor regular; nor can it be related to the facts of physical geography, such as the convergence of rivers on the Paris region. Its course was at every stage contingent upon the exigencies of birth and death, succession and war.

The French example is far from typical of the territorial accretion of a state from a nuclear or core region. Expansion was not continuously outward, and it consisted not in the extension of the limits of the state *per se,* but rather of a particular kind of governmental control over it. Nevertheless, the boundary of France remained at the end of the Middle Ages approximately where it had theoretically been for centuries, along the lines of the rivers Scheldt, Meuse, Saône, and Rhône, with some local departures from this line. Between the sixteenth century and the period of the French Revolution, the limits of the state were physically advanced to the Alps, the Jura, and the Upper Rhine. This latter expansion accords more closely with the generalized concept outlined at the beginning of this paper, of the territorial expansion of a state by the extension of its authority into areas which it had not hitherto possessed either in theory or in practice.

Northwest Europe

Fifteen of the major political units which at present make up Europe may be said to have expanded to their present limits from a clearly conceived core-area, and in most of them the political capital remains today in the nuclear area from which expansion took place. The most clear-cut examples are:

United Kingdom

The Roman occupation of the British Isles stopped short of the Scottish Border and faded out along the Marches of Wales and in the Celtic Southwest. The states of the Saxon Heptarchy had each a small nucleus for its own tribal territory, but wars between them and the invasion and settlement of Norsemen and Danes in the northern and eastern parts of Britain led in time to the emergence of Wessex which during the last two centuries of Anglo-Saxon history became the dominant power in Britain, extending its authority northward and northeastward. It was to the ancient Kingdom of Wessex that the Norman rulers in effect succeeded in 1066, and they were obliged to reconquer much of the north of England themselves. Their core-area, the material base from which expansion and reconquest took place, was the Thames Valley. Here, Domesday Book shows us, was a region of relatively dense population, intensive agriculture, and high land values. There

OVER 8 RECORDED
PERSONS PER SQUARE
MILE 1085 – 1100

LIMiT OF AREA
SURVEYED IN
DOMESDAY BOOK

THE
PALE

VERULAMIUM
LONDON
CANTERBURY

0   50   100

FIGURE 2: The core-area of Great Britain and the expansion of sovereignty.

were isolated areas of greater wealth and prosperity outside this
nuclear-area, as there were also areas of small population density within
it, but the former were isolated, and the latter easily circumvented.
Foremost among the outlying areas of high population was East Anglia,
broadly the counties of Norfolk and Suffolk. If one asks why this area
never became the core-area from which an English state was built, the
answer—the contingencies of history aside—may lie in its high degree
of physical isolation, with the Fenland to the west and the forested,
lightly settled London clays to the south. The limit of Anglo-Norman
power is roughly defined by the boundary of the territory surveyed in
Domesday Book.

Wales was slowly penetrated by Anglo-Norman influences, and at the
end of the thirteenth century was conquered, though not formally
absorbed into the Kingdom of Britain until the sixteenth. The map (Fig.
2) shows the chief lines of Anglo-Norman penetration into the Highland
Zone of the British Isles. Scotland was subjected to a number of abortive
invasions, before it in 1603 came to share its king with the rest of
Britain, and in 1707 was joined with England in a parliamentary union.

Scandinavia

Both Sweden and Denmark developed from core-areas which differentiated themselves at an early date, while Norway presents a special case which is discussed below. For Sweden the archeological evidence shows a dense population even in the Middle and Late Iron Age (about A.D. 400–800) in the lowland region which encloses Lake Malaren. Almost all the important Late Iron Age finds are from the area of Uppsala, or Uppland; the seat of the earliest recognizable Swedish state was at Old Uppsala, and from this area one can trace at least the broad lines of a political expansion. This core-area, defined in Figure 3 in terms of Late Iron Age settlement, was not outstandingly fertile, though far more productive than the hilly regions to north and south. The branching waterway of Lake Malaren became a commercial focus relatively early, and

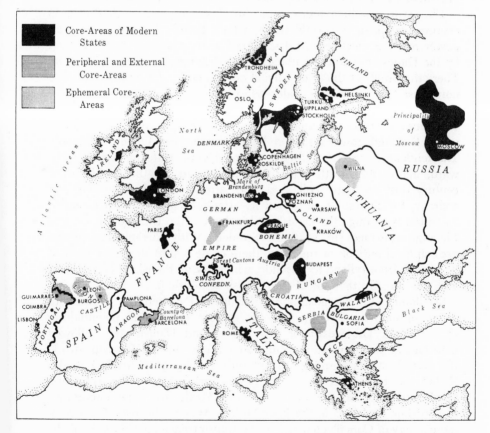

FIGURE 3: Core-areas of modern European states. (Boundaries are shown as of the late 15th century.)

the Uppland region, furthermore, enjoyed some degree of physical protection during the period of the *Völkerwanderung*. In the pre-Viking age
(seventh century and earlier) Swedish rule had probably been extended
from this area southward into the hills of Gothland, and throughout
the medieval period it was slowly extended northwestward and northward into the thinly peopled forest region of Norrland. In the early
Viking age, the maritime connections of the Uppland region led to
Swedish settlement along the eastern shore of the Baltic Sea and to
the penetration of Swedes into and even across the territory that was
later to become Russia. This expansion and settlement were not, however, followed by the establishment of political control from the core-
area itself until the early years of the seventeenth century. The hills
of Gothland formed a southern frontier to the Swedish state, and not
until 1660 was Swedish rule extended to the southern and southwestern
provinces of modern Sweden, Skane, Blekinge, and Halland.

The territory which today comprises Denmark was until the tenth
century occupied by several tribes, whose boundaries shifted as their
power rose and declined. At first a kind of paramountcy was exercised
by the Danes of southern Jutland, in what is today Schleswig-Holstein.
There the profits of the trade carried on by Danes and Frisians between
northwest Europe and the Baltic contributed to the wealth and power
of the local rulers. But the hegemony of this area was not permanent.
The country was in fact united in the tenth century by a ruling family
whose seat and power rested at Jelling in northern Jylland (Jutland).
The tendency was at first for the young Danish state to expand westward, across the North Sea, to Great Britain. In the mid-eleventh
century this "sea-state" collapsed, and, after a period of division and
anarchy, the Danish state turned its attention eastward and extended
its authority through the Danish archipelago to the Halland, Skane, and
Blekinge provinces of southern Sweden. With this change in the
geographical outlook of the state, there came a shift in the location of
its capital, from Jylland to Roskilde, which lay on the island of Sjaelland
and was already the seat of the Danish archbishop.

Sjaelland, with the neighboring island of Fyn and the territory of
Skane in southern Sweden, had far greater agricultural potentialities
than Jylland. The wealth of this, the second Danish state, allowed
it to engage in extensive maritime adventures, and its location astride
the Danish straits permitted it not only to engage in trade but also
to tax the trade carried on by others, primarily by the Hanseatic
merchants, between the Baltic and the North seas. The importance
of maritime trade led in the later Middle Ages to the rise of the commercial city of Copenhagen and to the transferrence there in 1445 of the
seat of the Danish kings.

Despite the shifts in the center of Danish rule, it is difficult not to see in Sjaelland and neighboring Fyn and Skane, the core-area of the modern Danish state.

Switzerland

Switzerland, though clearly growing by a process of accretion around a core-area, departs in one important respect from the general pattern of states which grew in this way. The Confederation originated in 1291, when the Four Forest Cantons of Uri, Schwyz, and Ob and Nidwalden united in opposition to the feudal restrictions from which they suffered. The success of their cause attracted other areas which became in turn cantons in the confederation. The difference between the core-area of Switzerland—the original cantons—and that of other states examined thus far lies in the fact that, whereas the latter were fertile, prosperous, and relatively densely peopled, the Swiss area was essentially poor. The documents show, in the area of the Forest Cantons, a sparse and primitive population, whose ideas of political organization were rudimentary in the extreme. The paradox is explained by the fact that, whereas other core-areas derived their political power and their capacity to expand in part at least from their productive agriculture and relatively dense population, the core-area of Switzerland derived both wealth and political ideas from the trade and the merchants who came from Italy to Germany by the newly opened St. Gotthard route.

East and Southeast Europe

The Slav countries present what are perhaps the clearest examples of territorial expansion from nuclear areas. Indeed, it is possible to discover more incipient core-areas than were able ultimately to expand and to become nuclei of separate states. Some, especially in the Danube basin and Balkan peninsula, after serving for a time as the core-areas of primitive or tribal states, lost their primacy or were extinguished by invasion and conquest. It thus became the role of historical forces to choose from among the several areas of increment in this area those which were to develop as the foci of their respective states. Curiously most of these core-areas had appeared by the end of the tenth century as centers of relatively dense population, foci of trade, and centers of some form of political power.

The Polish and the Russian cases are the simplest, along with the non-Slav Hungarian state. The Czech example is somewhat more complex and those of the Balkans are of a degree of complexity which excludes them from this category of states growing from simple core-areas.

Poland

The Polish state emerged a thousand years ago in the area of relatively good soil and early settlement (Fig. 1) which is bounded on the three sides by the River Warta and its tributary, the Notec. The intrinsic advantages of soil were reinforced by the commerce between the Baltic region and southern Europe, which followed the lakes and navigable rivers characterizing this region. The seat of the earliest Polish kings as well as of the first archbishop was Gniezno. The political capital was later shifted to Poznan, still within the core-area, and later to Kraków and in 1596 to Warsaw, which lay a short distance outside it. Gniezno remained the ecclesiastical capital until this function was also taken over by Warsaw.

This Polish core-area was protected by the flat, wide, and marshy valleys of the rivers which enclosed it on most sides. The surplus which derived from its agriculture and commerce was in part invested in the Romanesque churches which still distinguish this region, and in part furnished the armies with which the early kings extended their rule westward approximately to the line of the lower Odra (Oder) River and eastwards to the Prypec marshes and the "cities" of Ruthenia. During the following centuries, the Polish state lost territory on the west, and expanded farther to the east. Its original core-area became eccentric without however ceasing to be part of prepartition Poland. One is, however, still reminded of the early primacy of the Gniezno-Poznan region by its name: Wielkopolska, or Great Poland.

Russia

The Russian case is too familiar to require, or to deserve, any extended discussion. The first Russian state had its focus in the Steppes, where it had every advantage except that of natural protection. The second grew up amid the mixed forest of the Muscovy region, around the headwaters of the Volga and Oka rivers, and here it enjoyed some degree of natural protection, without, however, the sources of agricultural and commercial wealth which had distinguished the Kievan state.

Muscovy spread outwards from the Moscow region with the same apparent constancy cf purpose which characterized the extension of royal power in France from the Paris region, And, like the "expansion" of France, that of Muscovy has also been attributed to a kind of grand design, a compulsion to expand outward until the sea set a limit to expansion. Although it is as erroneous to see such a *Leitmotiv* in Russian history as it is in that of France, the formation of the Russian state is marked by an almost continuous outward movement from the sixteenth to the nineteenth centuries. It was not "an insatiable thirst for salt water," as has been convincingly discussed by John Morrison, but local and immediate contingencies which led to the phenomenon of Russian expansion to the seas. The Russian core-area of Muscovy had the advantages of protection from the raiders of the Steppe; it lay at a focus of routes which tended to follow the Russian rivers, and it possessed a natural fertility which, though less than that of the Steppe region to the south, was probably as high as that of the Polish core-area.

The Danube Valley

The valley of the middle and lower Danube, together with the Czech lands of Bohemia and Moravia, is made up of a series of basins, generally level and relatively fertile, ringed by hills or mountains. One can distinguish the plains of northern Bohemia and of Moravia, the small basins along the Danube, especially those between Melk and Tulln, and below Vienna; the larger plain between the Leitha-Little Carpathian ridge and the Bakony Forest; the Transdanubian region, or Dunántúl, and the Sava valley in Slovenia and Croatia. Here, as in Poland and Russia, lived a number of tribes, many of which were listed and briefly described by the anonymous Bavarian geographer of

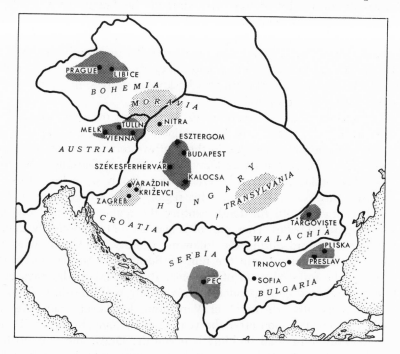

FIGURE 4: Core-areas in the middle Danube valley; for key to symbols see Figure 3.

the ninth century and by the Arab traveler and merchant, Ibrahim Ibn Jakub. We do not know how primacy among these tribes was achieved, but it is tempting to attribute it to the area, the agricultural productivity, the population density, and the commercial relations of those core-areas which came to be dominant. Unquestionably such environmental factors were little more than permissive; the contingencies of history played the major role in this process of selection.

If we exclude the nebulous state of Samo of the seventh century, the earliest Danubian state to emerge was "Great Moravia," to which the missionaries, Cyril and Methodius, were sent in the ninth century. Its core was made up of the plains of southern Moravia and southwestern Slovakia, and its capital may have been the city of Nitra, 45 miles to the northwest of Bratislava. The Moravian state was extinguished in the late ninth and early tenth century by the Magyar invaders, and its core-area became a disputed borderland between Germans, Czechs, and Hungarians.

The valley of the River Elbe in northern Bohemia was more fortunate in its history. Two separate political units, perhaps tribal in origin, developed here, based respectively in the western and eastern parts of the region. Whatever their origin, the conflict between them came to be focused in the rivalry of the Premyslids of the Prague area and the Slavniks of the area lying to the east around Libice (Fig. 4). In the course of this conflict the Premyslids were victorious, and united first the lowlands around Prague, and later extended their authority first to all Bohemia and then to Moravia and Silesia. It is from this Czech state of greater Bohemia that modern Czechoslovakia derives, in part at least, its boundaries and traditions.

Austria constitutes an exception to this pattern of state building in east-central Europe, and will be examined below. In the meanwhile, another state began to emerge in the southwestern corner of the Pannonian Basin. There the rivers Drava and Sava, discharging from the Alps of Carinthia and Carniola, are separated only by a low, broken, and easily traversed divide. Into this region Croat tribes came in the seventh century. Until the tenth century the region remained one of loosely organized tribes. Then part of it became united politically under King Tomislav, and during the following century the Croat state expanded to the Adriatic, into the hills of Bosnia and Serbia, and eastward into the forested plain of Slavonia. Its core lay in the Sava and Drava valleys, and corresponded approximately with the three *Zhupaniya* (administrative districts) of Varazhdin, Krizhevats, and Zagreb, which were created soon after the year 1100 by King Koloman. There was reputedly some road building between the Drava and Sava to the east of Zagreb at this time, and a bishopric was established in Zagreb. But already Croatia was beginning to fall under the control of the

Hungarian state, and a Croat state based upon this core-area failed to maintain itself.

Hungary

The Hungarians, or Magyars, had entered the plain that has since borne their name about the year 896. They were made up of a number of tribes, of which that of Arpad seems to have been dominant and may have been the largest. Arpad's horde crossed the Danube and settled the region still known as Transdanubia, or Dunántúl. The center of his power was near Székesfehérvár, which was the Hungarian capital until, in 1247, this was moved to the hill of Buda, overlooking the Danube, 40 miles to the northeast. The Hungarian tribes, which seem to have spread widely over the plain, were a loosely organized group, over which the authority of Arpad and of his successors was gradually established. The core-area of this state was the land which Arpad settled in Dunántúl, though it probably extended across the ridge of the Bakony Forest to the Little Alföld, where it embraced part of the area of the former Great Moravian state. Within this area the two archiepiscopal sees, Esztergom and Kalocsa, not to mention a number of monasteries, were established.

It may be suggested that the early Hungarian kings had no concept of the unity of the great plain, and did not identify themselves with it. They may, however, have visualized some unity among the Magyar and related tribes, and thus have gradually established their own authority over the plain. But it was not until the end of the eleventh century that they established their rule over the southwestern or Croatian parts of the plain. Their authority over the surrounding hills and mountains came much later, and Hungary, like its neighbors, seems to fall into the category of states which grew by a process of accretion around a core-area.

Romania

Romania is perhaps the marginal example of a state that has been derived by a process of accretion from a nuclear-area. Romanian historians claim a historical continuity from the province of Dacia, which the Romans held in the second and third centuries A.D. The future state of Romania emerged, however, outside the limits of the Roman province, in the plains of Walachia and Moldavia, which lay beyond the curving line of the Carpathian Mountains and Transylvanian Alps. It is difficult to say whether its Romance-speaking, or Vlach, population came from beyond the Danube to the south or from beyond the mountains to the north and west. Walachia emerged under the dominance in turn of Hungarians, Bulgars, and Turks; Moldavia, under that of Turks, Tatars, and Poles. The focus of power in the Walachian

principality lay in the loess-covered plains of the center, where Târgo-
viste became its capital during the Middle Ages, and was subsequently
replaced by the city of Bucharest, 45 miles away. Moldavia was in
general poorer because more exposed to the raiding Tatars from the
Russian steppe. The best soil and the densest settlement lay toward the
north of the province, amid the loess-covered hills around Iasi. This
focus of political power in Moldavia was separated by a distance of
some 200 miles, as well as by the marshes along the lower Pruth,
Siret, and Danube, from the Walachian core-area. It may be that political power did, in fact, extend outward from each of these core-areas
to cover their respective provinces during the Middle Ages, but of
this process there is no unambiguous record. The boundaries of the
provinces themselves were the result of wars and treaties between
the Turks (who retained a jurisdiction that was at times only nominal
until 1858) and their northern neighbors. The Romanian state was
created in 1859, when these two provinces were merged under a
single ruler, and it increased its territory during the following half
century, with the incorporation of southern Dobrodgea, Transylvania,
the eastern border of the Hungarian Plain, and Bessarabia.

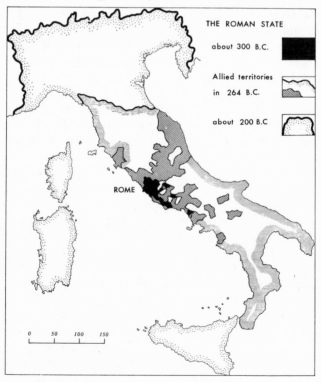

FIGURE 5: The core-area and expansion of Roman authority in Italy.

Southern Europe

The modern states of Italy and Greece were established during the nineteenth century. They were shaped by the current spirit of nationalism, but their boundaries had in some degree been influenced by memories of the *Italia* and *Hellas* of classical times.

Italy

A lasting shape was given to the concept of Italy by the expansion of the Roman Republic to cover the whole peninsula. Its nucleus was the city of Rome and the surrounding Campagna (Fig. 5). The record of the invasion and conquest of the hill country to the east and southeast and of Etruria to the northwest is a matter of legend rather than of history. It was followed by the conquest of southern Italy from the Greeks and Carthaginians, and of the Po Valley, or Cisalpine Gaul. The unity of Italy in the geographical sense was thus effected in classical times. The Germanic invasions undid this work and the Middle Ages perpetuated the chaotic political pattern which then evolved. Commercially, Florence, Venice, and Genoa came to surpass the city of Rome, but in an ideological sense Rome never lost its primacy; nor the concept of a united Italy, its fascination for at least an educated minority of Italians. The events of 1860–1918 restored by a series of quick strokes the geographical pattern of the late classical period.

Greece

Greece achieved unity in ancient times, but not through the efforts of the Greeks themselves. Though the commercial primacy of Athens was as clear-cut as its cultural dominance, its sovereignty was restricted to Attica, and the "Athenian Empire," even when its control by Athens was least disputed, remained something of a misnomer. Political unity was imposed on the Greek peninsula from outside, in turn by the Macedonians, Romans, Byzantines, and Turks. Whatever the rulers, the primacy of Attica was undisputed, and it remained the seat of a local government until it became in 1832 the capital of an independent Greece. The boundaries of Greece were extended by stages to enclose the whole peninsula, the northern littoral of the Aegean Sea, and the Aegean islands. Greece is, like Romania, a marginal case, where the focus of economic and political power had long been apparent, but around which the state was not built by a process of accretion.

Core-Areas of Dependent Territories

At least four states of the European states system began as dependent territories which developed nevertheless around a definite and clearly defined core-area. Only after expansion from this nucleus was almost complete, did the territory thus unified, become politically independent.

Republic of Ireland

The unity of the island of Ireland was achieved from the late twelfth century onwards, by conquering immigrants from England, who made the Dublin region the basis of their activities. The core-area from which English authority spread out over the island may be roughly equated with the so-called "Pale," an area of some 1,200 square miles, forming the hinterland of Dublin (Fig. 2). The political and economic dominance of this area became so secure, that no attempt was ever made by independent Eire to move it. In the meanwhile, however, English and Scottish settlement in the seventeenth century had created in the northeast of the island a second core-area in the lowlands that surround Lough Neagh and extend down the Lagan valley to Belfast. Today, and probably for the last three centuries, the Belfast and Dublin areas have been the most densely peopled areas in Ireland. But the marked difference between the Protestant tradition and the industrial economy of Belfast and its hinterland, and the Catholic and rural traditions of the Dublin hinterland led in 1922 to the partition of the island into the Irish Free State (now the Republic of Ireland) and Northern Ireland, which has since remained an integral part of the United Kingdom, with its political and economic focus in Belfast.

Finland

The Finnish case fits the model closely. Political unity was imposed on the area by Swedish settlers who occupied the southwestern littoral, where the climate is less severe than in other parts of the state and agricultural land is more extensive and of a higher quality than elsewhere in the country. The making of the later Finnish state came about, not so much by conquest, as by the process of pioneer settlement in almost virgin country. The core-area of Finland is roughly the hinterlands of Helsinki and Turku, today the largest cities, and in the early Middle Ages probably the only area with a settled population.

Austria

The Republic of Austria began its political history as a frontier dependency of the Duchy of Bavaria, to which it stood as the Ostmark, the Eastern Borderland. Its political center moved gradually down the Danube valley, as Austria fulfilled its historic function of protecting south Germany from invasion and then extended its authority eastward into the Pannonian plain. The capital of the Ostmark was established first on the Danube at Melk. About 1100, the capital was moved to Tulln, and later in the twelfth century to Vienna. At about the same time the Ostmark terminated its dependence on Bavaria, and became —what it remained until 1806—the Duchy of Austria. In this instance the filling out of the territorial limits of the state was completed after Austria had ceased to be a dependency of Bavaria, but the process had begun while it was still a "colony."

Norway

During the early Middle Ages, a group of tribal kingdoms came gradually to be dominated by the one which centered in the Trondheim area. The growing population of this fjord coast sought, like the early Danes, adventure, wealth, and new lands to settle westward beyond the sea, in the British Isles, Iceland, and even Greenland. Trondheim remained the Norwegian capital and the seat of the archbishop until 1380. Thereafter, Norway was ruled by Danish kings; the functions of capital were transferred to Denmark, and no attempt was made to built a cohesive state around the Trondheim core-area.

In 1814, rule over Norway was transferred to the king of Sweden, and the Oslo region, which in the early Middle Ages had constituted the important tribal kingdom of Vestfold, now began to assume the role formerly played by Trondheim. Oslo lay close to the Swedish boundary, and had easy communications with Stockholm, which other areas more traditionally Norwegian did not have. In 1906 the union between Sweden and Norway was terminated. By this date the governmental functions were so well established in Oslo, that no attempt was made to transfer them to any site more closely identified with Norwegian history and culture. Instead, the name of the capital was, in 1925, changed from the Danish name of Christiania, to the now familiar Norwegian name of Oslo.

Summary

In the previous pages we have examined fifteen European states which can be said in some sense to have grown by a process of accretion around a core-area. We have also mentioned some areas, which during the early Middle Ages had some of the characteristics of core-areas, but whose independent existence was terminated by the growth of others. With the exception only of that of modern Switzerland, these core-areas have certain features in common. All are regions of good soil and, in early times, of relatively high agricultural productivity. They were, in Fleure's phrase, "regions of increment." Most were centers of prehistoric population and culture and archeological evidence, dating in some instances from as far back as the Neolithic, shows them to have been relatively densely populated. Several were colonized by various of the Neolithic Danubian cultures. This is especially true of the Paris region, central Poland, and the various core-areas already in existence along the middle and lower Danube valley. Attica and the Roman Campagna came to be intensively settled and cultivated in early classical times. All showed during their formative period in the early Middle Ages—roughly from the eight to the twelfth centuries—a very heavy investment in art and architecture, itself an indication of the surplus which these areas yielded, and most became the seat, not only of civil administration, but also of ecclesiastical.

Most of these core-areas lay also at the focus of routes. Relatively little is known about the volume or even of the direction of the trade carried on by the core-areas which emerged during the ninth and tenth centuries. The scanty finds, in central Poland, in Bohemia and Moravia, in the neighborhood of Paris, in southeastern England, in Muscovy, and in central Sweden, taken together with the literary sources, are evidence that it was, for its age, both vigorous and important. The wealth gained from trade must in every instance have contributed to the political power of the core-area, and, in the case of Switzerland, provided the chief source of income for the incipient state.

Lastly, most core-areas possessed in some degree a natural means of defense which gave them some protection during this early, formative period. In some instances the core-area lay away from contemporary invasion routes. In others a physical barrier was provided by forest, such as gave some protection to the Paris and London regions, or of wide, marshy valleys such as enclosed the core-area of Poland, or of mountain and waste such as enclosed the core-areas of Sweden and Switzerland.

Eccentric and External Core-Areas

The political geography of the Balkan countries and of Spain and Portugal differs from that of the European countries already discussed, insofar as the original core-areas from which they grew either lapsed into relative insignificance or were later abandoned. In other words, expansion was in these instances a one-sided or unidirectional movement, and the focus of political power moved with the advance of the boundary. The core-area today is thus marginal to, or even outside the boundaries of, the state.

Spain and Portugal

The Iberian Peninsula had been part of Roman Empire, and its political and economic foci had been along the shore of the Mediterranean Sea. Most of the peninsula succumbed to the Moorish invaders in the eighth century, but remnants of the local population maintained themselves in the northern mountains, where, in quasi-independence, they perpetuated a system of petty states of their own. From the valleys of the Cantabrian Mountains and the Pyrenees they spread southward, creating at one time a tier of no less than half a dozen small states. As these states expanded southward into a region of more genial climate and, in general, of better soil, their capitals were also moved south. Portugal severed its connection with the Galician mountains from which it had sprung, and its capital city was first Guimaraes, then Coimbra, and finally, after 1256, Lisbon.

In the Spanish part of the peninsula the city of Madrid, chosen in 1561 by Philip II to epitomize the new-found unity of the peninsula, succeeded to the functions formerly performed by a group of more northerly capital cities of the "Five Kingdoms": Burgos, Leon, Pampluna, Saragossa, and Barcelona. Castile, indeed, had never had a fixed seat of government, "the capital being," in typical medieval fashion, "wherever a peripatetic court happened to find itself, with Valladolid and Toledo as preferred centers in the two previous reigns." The several core-areas from which modern Spain derived, unlike that of Portugal, still lie wholly within the boundaries of the state but are today peripheral to it.

Balkan Peninsula

The comparable development in the Balkan countries has been complicated and interrupted by war, invasion, and conquest. Yugoslavia Bulgaria, and even Romania were represented during the Middle Ages by states, each having a distinct core-area, which it retained for centuries, however much its peripheral regions may have fluctuated with the vicissitudes of war. The medieval Serb state thus had its nucleus in the basins (polja) of what is today Kosovo-Metohija and neighboring areas. Here the flat-floored *polja,* with their covering of residual clays, provided a region of modest increment. Today it is distinguished by a rich legacy of early medieval churches, built in a Byzantine style well adapted to local materials and needs. One of them, the church of Pec, became the seat of the Serb archbishop and patriarch. It was within this, its own core-area, that the medieval Serb state, in 1389, suffered the disastrous defeat of Kosovo, which led to its extinction early in the following century.

When early in the nineteenth century a Serb state again emerged, its nucleus lay in the forested Sumadija region, in northern Serbia, where the successful revolt against Turkish rule first broke out. It was not until 1913 that the Serb state again came to embrace its original core-area, now largely deprived by migration of its Serb inhabitants, and settled by Albanians.

Bulgaria

The Bulgarian state was created by an invading Ural-Altaic people, who entered the Balkan peninsula from the South Russian Steppe. They crossed the lower Danube and settled in the open loess-covered region between the Balkan Mountains and the Danube. Their number, and the rapidity with which they were assimilated by the local Slav population, are a matter of dispute. There is no question, however, that the Bulgarian Empire continued to be ruled from the area where they first settled. Here were their earliest capitals, Pliska and Preslav, and in this area recent excavations have revealed extensive remains of the earliest Bulgarian Empire. From this nuclear region, the first Bulgarian state spread south across the Stara Planina and even to Serbia and Macedonia, and beyond the Danube into Walachia and even the Hungarian Plain.

After a period of eclipse and conquest by the Byzantine emperors, the Second Bulgarian Empire arose from the ashes of the first. Its core-area was again on the fertile platform which slopes down from the Stara Planina to the Danube, and its capital was established at Trnovo, about 60 miles west of the sites of the earlier capitals. From this area the Tsars of the second Bulgarian Empire (1185–1393) extended their rule to cover an area similar to that held by the First Empire.

The third Bulgaria did not appear until 1877–1878, when the Turkish Empire suffered military defeat and was obliged to recognize the Bulgarian state. Although this new Bulgarian state embraced the Danubian platform and had pretensions no less extensive than either of its predecessors, its capital was established at Sofia, south of the Stara Planina. This choice demonstrated a new orientation in Bulgarian politics. Bulgaria no longer linked itself with the region from which the Bulgars had come; instead, it looked for territorial advancement to the south, at the expense of the Turk. The site of the capital of Bulgaria, like those of Portugal and Spain, moved south with the territorial expansion of the state.

States without Core-Areas

The survey of the states of modern Europe leaves only three major states unmentioned: Germany, the Netherlands, and Belgium. The formation and growth of each of these differed in certain respects from that of other European states. The Netherlands and Belgium were formed, not in response to the urgings of nationalism, but as a result of war and the European power balance. The Netherlands were created almost overnight by the successful revolt against Spain of some of the Hapsburg possessions in the Low Countries. In the words of G. J. Renier, the Dutch people "found themselves overnight where it had taken the people of other national states centuries to arrive." Once the state had been created, its focus of political and economic power came to be established in the Province of Holland, where it has since remained, but the state did not grow up around this nucleus.

Belgium is a yet more arbitrary creation. It remains substantially what was left of the Spanish Low Countries after the Dutch revolt, trimmed and modified in detail by subsequent treaties and agreements. From the late Middle Ages until 1815 it was a dependency first of Spain and then of Austria. Linked with the Netherlands in 1815, it broke away in 1831, and became the Kingdom of Belgium. It remains divided between two culture groups, the Flemings and the Walloons, each with a sort of core-area in respectively the cities of Flanders and the rolling plains of central Belgium, but in neither instance did this focus of power serve as a nucleus around which a state was built.

To this list should be added six other states: Albania, an arbitrary creation of the London Conference of 1912–1913, which, though justified by its ethnic composition, owed both its origin and its boundaries to the complex power balance in Europe at that time; and Luxemburg, Liechtenstein, Monaco, San Marino, and Andorra, feudal units which are individually too small to have had distinct nuclei from which they developed.

The German Case

It is impossible to fit Germany into any one of the categories previously discussed in this paper. Its ultimate unity was not the result of a gradual expansion from any recognizable core-area, nor was it arbitrarily imposed from without. It was achieved almost suddenly by the strongest of the many small states which made up nineteenth-century Germany, acting in the name of German nationalism. "The internal physical structure of Urdeutschland is inimical to unity," wrote Derwent Whittlesey, attributing to nature what was essentially the result of the contingencies of history. The original Germany of the early Middle Ages was made up of a number of tribal dutchies. "The tribes did not set in the mold of stem dutchies because of tribal coherence, but because each group settled down in a core of arable lowland separated from its neighbors by wooded hills, marshy lowlands, or sandy heaths and forests." There were, in other words, some half dozen core-areas, not one of which "possessed clear superiority of power based on either agricultural or commercial resources." A kind of balance was preserved between them, and the imperial title was tossed from Saxon to Swabian, to Franconian, to Bavarian dukes. The nuclear-region of Lorraine, consisting of the fertile plains of the upper Meuse and Moselle, was too close to France and too exposed to French territorial claims and to invasion by French armies for it ever to have had a good chance of becoming a nucleus of a German state. The same is true of Burgundy whose political and economic focus lay in the Saône valley. The four remaining German duchies, Swabia, Bavaria, Franconia, and Saxony, had a greater potential. Swabia centered in the fertile loess-covered plains that lie amid the rolling hills of the upper Neckar and upper Danube valleys. Bavaria had as its core-area the scattered areas of good farmland which lay on each side of the Danube from Donauwörth down to Passau, separated by more extensive areas of forest and marsh. Franconia, which included the Rhine plain from Bingen up to Heidelberg, as well as the Wetterau and the loess lands along the middle Main valley, was potentially richer in its agricultural resources, was a focus of early commercial activity, and was almost centrally placed in medieval Germany. If one could conceive of the German emperors of the Franconian dynasty (Conrad II, 1024, to Henry V, d. 1125) as playing a role similar to that performed in France by the House of Capet, a progressive unification of Germany might have been achieved. Franconia was the economic focus of the medieval German Reich; it was probably the most densely peopled; it contained many of the larger commercial centers, and its leading cities: Frankfurt, Mainz, Worms, and Speyer were by far the most frequent meeting places of the medieval German Diet of the Holy Roman Empire.

The most significant rival to Franconia would have been Saxony, whose core-area spread over the loess belt, between the hills of central Germany and the marshy and thinly peopled northern plain. Throughout most of the tenth century and into the eleventh the German Empire had the Saxon dukes as its titular head. But the Saxons, like the Lorrainers, lay on the border of medieval Germany and eastward conquest and settlement in the Slav lands occupied their energies, just as expansion down the Danube valley did that of the Bavarian dukes.

Yet it was around none of these nuclei that Germany was in the end united, but instead around a relatively poor and backward area which was even outside the limits of the early German Empire. The rise of Brandenburg, first to an equality with the older power centers of Germany, and then to a position of supremacy was achieved in defiance of the factors of physical geography. It was, in the words of A. J. Toynbee, "an unprepossessing country . . . with its starveling pine-plantations and its sandy fields," and he attributed the rise of Brandenburg-Prussia into its position of supremacy to the stimulus of this "hard country." The fact is that the Hohenzollerns of Brandenburg proved to be able to organize and develop the modest resources of their realm and to build so efficient a military machine, that they acquired the power to extend it by conquest and ultimately to draw the whole of Germany into an empire ruled by themselves.

There thus proved to be in Germany two separate core-areas, the middle Rhineland and Brandenburg. As late as the mid-nineteenth century the historical, cultural, and economic dominance of the middle Rhineland was still apparent. The "Parliament," which reflected the strivings of Germans for political unity in the early nineteenth century, met in 1848 in Frankfurt. Only with the political failure of this movement, did the ultimate triumph of the more easterly core-area become assured. It is not without significance that, with the division of Germany into East and West, their respective capitals are Berlin, in Brandenburg, and Bonn, only about 85 miles downstream from Mainz, and thus on the fringes of the more westerly core-area.

Conclusions

In this paper the territorial growth of about 25 European states has been reviewed. Fifteen of them have achieved their present limits by a process of accretion around a nuclear- or core-area. In every instance, the core-area was itself a region of increment; they were foci of trade routes and, with the exception only of Switzerland, were regions of some agricultural surplus during the early periods of this territorial growth. In most instances also—since territorial expansion began during the Middle Ages—the seat of the archbishop or patriarch lay also in the core-area. Lastly, the core-area is usually distinguished by its medieval architecture, itself a consequence of the surplus production of the region.

A second group of states grew from core-areas which are today peripheral or even outside their present territory. The reasons for the abandonment of the initial core-area vary from one state to another. In the case of the states of the Iberian Peninsula, the original centers were strongholds and refuges from the Moslem invaders, offering little advantage beyond a degree of military security, and were abandoned as soon as the Moslems weakened and withdrew. In the case of the Balkan examples—Serbia (Yugoslavia) and Bulgaria, there was a long hiatus, marked by foreign conquest, between the medieval state and its reappearance in modern times. The new state emerged with a new center for its political activities, determined by the political and military exigencies of the time.

Lastly, we have the small number of states which were established, as it were, at a blow, by a sudden creative act, either of external powers, as in the cases of Belgium, Luxemburg, and Albania, or of internal forces suddenly mustered to resist external pressures, as in the case of the Netherlands.

It remains to examine the significance of this argument to the conditions of today, and to ask whether the different ways in which the territory of each of the European states was put together has any relevance to their coherence and viability. The territorial evolution of a state is only one among many factors in national unity, but it would appear from an examination of list A in Table 1 that those states which

TABLE 1

A Distinct core-area	B Peripheral or external core-area	C No distinct core-area
England	Spain	Netherlands
Ireland [1]	Portugal	Belgium
France	Yugoslavia	Albania
Switzerland	Bulgaria	Luxembourg
Sweden		Germany
Norway [1]		
Finland [1]		
Denmark		
Czechoslovakia		
Austria [1]		
Hungary		
Russia		
Romania		
Italy		
Greece		

[1] The core-area in these instances emerged when the state possessed some form of dependent or colonial status.

grew by a process of accretion around a central, or eccentric but none-theless internal core-area, have a higher degree of unity and cohesion than the others. France, the United Kingdom, Switzerland, Sweden, and Denmark clearly belong to this category of highly cohesive and politically and socially united countries.

In most of the states in list A, the cohesiveness or sense of unity diminishes outward from the core-area toward the borders of the state, as might, of course, be anticipated from a theoretical model of their formation. The actual degree of cohesiveness depends to a large degree on whether the actual boundaries have been cut back, as in Hungary, to eliminate areas and peoples not fully attuned to the ideals of the country, or, as in Czechoslovakia, expanded to embrace peoples who could not be expected fully to share these ideals within a measurable period of time.

In general, a much smaller degree of unity and cohesion characterizes both states with peripheral or external core-areas and also those which were created arbitrarily without ever having experienced a process of territorial growth. Of both it may be said that they lack a specific focus, epitomizing national values and perpetuating the earliest memories of the nation. Yet generalization is difficult. A state, created arbitrarily by an act of war and its concluding truce, such as the Netherlands, may nevertheless develop the most intimate sense of cohesion, and another, like Italy, which first acquired unity by a steady outward expansion from the plains of the lower Tiber, may still today, mainly for social and economic reasons, lack such cohesion and unity.

32. The Bases of Support for Political Parties in Burgenland
Andrew F. Burghardt

In societies accepting a popular franchise, the individual's vote directly affects the political process. As is well known, voting behavior varies widely, and although polls have established a reputation for a fair degree of accuracy, the use of the geographical analytical tool—the map—reveals more precisely the differences and frequently the real bases of voting behavior. This study of a small area of Austria demonstrates the method and effectiveness of this type of analysis.

Of all the Habsburg areas that were transferred so readily by the Entente powers after the First World War, Burgenland is the one in which the political consequences of the transfer can be most freely studied. Probably only in Burgenland can an outside observer ask pertinent questions of officials and peasants without incurring distrust, engendering fears, or without receiving noncommittal answers. Burgenland has largely been spared the virulent nationalisms, population transfers, complete state centralization, and one-party rule, which have in all the other transferred areas destroyed any possibility of drawing valid conclusions from the development of the local political life.

Burgenland is the easternmost province of Austria. It extends roughly 100 miles north-south and bears the entire boundary between Austria and Hungary. It is nothing more than a thin slice of territory; nowhere is it more than 20 miles wide, and over 90 per cent of its inhabitants live within ten miles of the "Iron Curtain." Its population, which was 276,136

SOURCE: *Annals of the Association of American Geographers*, LIV (September, 1964), 372–90. The author is associate professor of geography, McMaster University, Canada.

in 1951, has been steadily declining since 1934.[1] Because it is long and narrow and crossed by the easternmost reaches of the Alps, Burgenland falls into several distinct local areas which had, until World War II, very little contact with each other. The northern three *Bezirke* (districts) contain the lowland corridors between the Hungarian Basin and the Vienna Basin, but the four more southerly *Bezirke* are subdivided into alternating bands of forest and tilled land by the alternation of gravel terraces and flat-bottomed valleys. Burgenland is also the least German (87 per cent), the most Protestant (14 per cent), and the most rural of the Austrian provinces.

The purpose of this study is to attempt to determine which groups of people in what areas of Burgenland support the various Austrian political parties, and why they do so. In order to delimit the area patterns of voting allegiance, the results of every *Gemeinde* (commune) were plotted on a map of the province for every federal election since 1922. From a comparison of these maps the areas that have adhered consistently to one party, or that have vacillated from one party to another, were determined. To obtain more precise statistical information, the results for each party in every *Gemeinde* were averaged for the federal elections of 1949, 1953, 1956, and 1959. The interpretation of the patterns and statistics was based largely on the information and insights gained from numerous interviews within Burgenland and in Vienna in 1956–1957 and 1960–1961.[2]

It must be stressed at the outset, therefore, that this is not a study of the political parties in themselves, nor of their ideologies, their platforms, or their candidates. No attempt will be made to trace the origins or development of party organizations or political theories. Similarly, the issues that were stressed in each election will be ignored, since it is felt that in overall terms these issues have had only a scant impact on the voting results, and very little effect on the development of individual political identifications.

Political History

When the transfer from Hungary was finally effected in November, 1921, Burgenland was established as a distinct and semiautonomous province within Federal Austria. This was in itself a change of some

[1] The population in 1934 was 299,447. The unofficial totals of the census of 1961 list 270,875 inhabitants. Throughout this study the figures for 1951 will be used in preference to the 1961 totals, because the 1951 statistics fall within the decade 1949–1959 which includes the elections used to calculate the average votes of the individual *Gemeinden*.

[2] This study was made possible by a grant in 1956–1957 from the Division of Earth Sciences, National Academy of Sciences–National Research Council under its Foreign Field Research Program, financed by the Geography Branch, Office of Naval Research, and by a United States Government (Fulbright) Research Grant in 1960–1961.

magnitude, for two reasons: first, Austria was federalized, whereas Hungary had been relatively centralized, and second, there had never existed previously a governmental unit even approximating the new province. The few politically experienced persons living in this strip were hardly capable of assuming the reins of political leadership, since their experience had been within the context of the Magyar language and legal code, and the Budapest parliament; in addition, many bore the onus of having been pro-Hungarian during the three years of strife which preceded the transfer. Many of these men left the area as soon as it was occupied by the Austrian gendarmerie. The few who remained were handicapped further by the fractured nature of the terrain and the previous complete lack of ties between the north and south of the new Burgenland.

In 1921, therefore, Burgenland appeared to be a political vacuum. Because of the almost complete dearth of party leaders and civil servants, crowds of bureaucrats, who had become unemployed by the destruction of the empire, entered the territory. Except for a few of the leaders of the *Christlichsoziale Partei,* almost all the party leaders and many of the candidates themselves were imported into this virgin territory from Vienna to participate in the first election.

1922–1930

THE ELECTIONS / The first election was held on June 18, 1922, and was contested by four parties, the *Christlichsoziale Partei* (*CS*, Christian Party), the Sozialdemokratische Partei (*SD*, Socialist Party), the *Bauernbund* (*BB*, Peasants' Party), and the *Grossdeutsche Partei* (*GD*, Great German Party).[3] The Christian (Catholic) and Socialist parties were the two principal parties of Austria and mutually antagonistic. The Christian Party looked forward to an increase of its mandate in the federal parliament, since it was assumed that the Burgenland peasants would vote for the traditional party of the peasantry. The Socialist Party based its strength on the men who, though living in Burgenland, were employed in factories and construction work in Vienna. The Peasants' Party competed with the Christian Party for the support of the peasantry but held little appeal for the merchant and professional groups. The Great German Party was frankly nationalistic. In the critical years 1918–1921 the members of this party had made the most strenuous efforts to gain Burgenland for Austria, and the *GD* looked forward confidently to a large vote as a reward for its efforts.

To everyone's surprise the Socialists gained a plurality of the votes cast, *SD* 39 per cent, *CS* 31 per cent, *BB* 15 per cent, and *GD* 13 per cent. Because of the political inexperience of the province, the village

[3] Yet a fifth party, the *Burger und Bauern,* contested the first election, but it made so poor a showing that I have chosen to ignore it. It never ran again.

results probably owed more to the efforts of a few interested persons than to any established loyalties.[4] It is clear that in the initial introduction of the party apparatus into the province, the Socialists had been far more successful than had been their competitors. The men who commuted to jobs in Vienna formed a solid core of Socialist strength, whereas the agricultural peasants, living in less accessible villages, divided their votes among the three other parties.

Only one year later, on October 21, 1923, another federal election was held. The *Grossdeutsche Partei* virtually disappeared with this election. The sole aim of this party seemed to be the conclusion of an *Anschluss* of Austria with Germany, and this had been made impossible by the Entente powers. A new unique party, the *Kroatische Partei* (Croatian Party), made its lone appearance in the ballot at this time. The result was another mild victory for the Socialists, although the Christian Party had made significant gains: *SD* 39 per cent, *CS* 37 per cent, *BB* 19 per cent, *GD* 3 per cent, *Croatian* 2 per cent.

Te election of April 24, 1927, was the simplest of all the interwar campaigns, since only three parties were involved. The *Grossdeutsche Partei* combined with the Christian Party to form the *Einheitsliste*. With this added support, the Christian Party obtained for the first time a plurality of the votes cast, *CS* (*Einheits*) 43 per cent, *SD* 41 per cent, *BB* (*Landbund für Österreich*) 16 per cent. In the election of November 9, 1930, the last to be held before the war, the Great German Party disappeared entirely, but its place was taken by three new, extremist parties; the *Heimatblock*, the Nazis, and the Communists. The Christian Party again won a plurality of the votes cast, *CS* 41 per cent, *SD* 38 per cent, *BB* (*Nationaler Wirtschaftsblock und Landbund*) 16 per cent, others 5 per cent.

MINOR PARTY SUPPORT, 1922–1930 / At the close of eight years of party life, Burgenland appeared to be tending to conform to the Austrian version of a two-party system; in the final two elections the majority of the *Gemeinden* had chosen one of the two major parties. Yet, the Peasants' Party continued to receive approximately one-sixth of the ballots cast. Since the *Bauernbund* [5] and the *Grossdeutsche Partei* did not reappear after the Second World War, it is fitting to examine at this time the bases of their support. Figure 1 indicates the parts of Burgenland which gave strong support to these two minor parties.

[4] A good example of this lack of a pattern is given by the lower Pinka Valley in easternmost Güssing Bezirk. This lowland had no road connections with the rest of the province or Austria and hence formed a definite local unit. Yet, the ten *Gemeinden* voted (in sequence north to south), *GD, SD, CS, SD, CS, BB, GD, GD, CS,* and *BB.*

[5] This party ran under a slightly different name in each election; the name *Bauernbund* is used throughout this study for the sake of clarity and simplicity. The changes in name did not cause any changes in its bases of support.

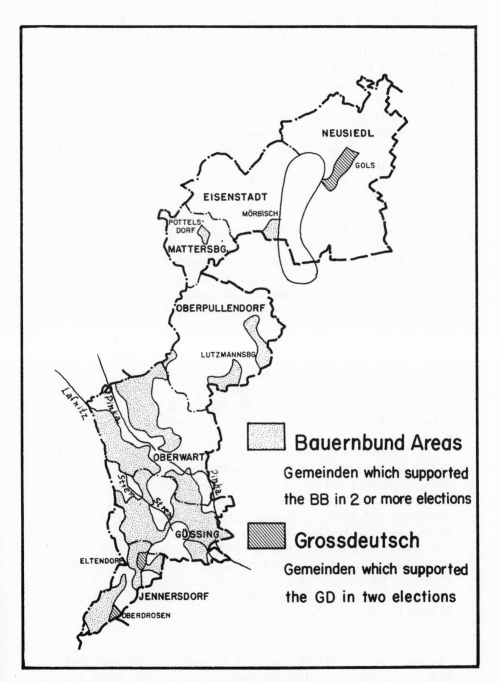

FIGURE 1: Areas of minor party strength, 1922-1930.

As is evident from the map, most of the *Bauernbund* strength lay in southern Burgenland; in the elections of 1922 and 1923 this party gained a plurality of the votes cast in both Oberwart and Güssing Bezirke. However, by 1927 the party had lost its preeminence and was outpolled by the Christian Party in both of these districts. Whereas the *Gemeinden* located amid the forests of the gravel terraces and the Lutheran villages, no matter where located, continued to vote *Bauernbund*, the Catholic villages in the Pinka and Strem valleys transferred their support from the *BB* to the *CS* between 1923 and 1927.

The decline in power of the Peasants' Party between 1923 and 1927 appears to have been brought about by the introduction in 1926 of effective ties with the outside world. In November, 1926, a railroad connection was completed between Oberwart Bezirk and Vienna. As soon as this railroad began operating, bus lines were established to join the valleys of Güssing Bezirk to the railroad and hence to Austria. As soon as these remote valleys were given contact with the rest of the province and country, they changed over from the *Bauernbund* to the Christian Party. Perhaps the closer connection with the national economic life suggested a tie to a more important political party; perhaps the *Christlich* party organization was itself dependent upon established lines of communication for its effectiveness.

Thus one may conclude that the *Bauernbund* had two bases of support, the Lutherans and the more isolated Catholic peasants. The Lutherans supported this party strongly and faithfully, since for them the *Bauernbund* was a solution to their problem of wishing to vote neither Catholic nor Marxist. In contrast, the support of the isolated Catholic peasantry proved to be strongly affected by improvements in accessibility.

The *Grossdeutsche Partei* ran separately in only the first two elections. Only three *Gemeinden* (Gols, Eltendorf, and Oberdrosen) supported this party in 1923, and two of the three are Lutheran. In the 1922 election over half of the villages to give the Great German Party a plurality or majority were Lutheran, so that again one may note a correlation between religion and support for a minor party.

It is clear from Figure 1 that northern Burgenland from the first ignored the minor parties and cast its support for the Socialists and the Christians. Since well before 1918 northern Burgenland had enjoyed close ties with Vienna; evidently the minor parties could prosper only in areas of relative isolation.

1945-1959

THE ELECTIONS / The first postwar election, held on November 25, 1945, was contested by only three political parties. The Allied occupation powers had decreed that only one non-Marxist party would be permitted, whereas both the Socialist (*SPÖ*) and the Communist (*KPÖ*) parties could campaign. The result of this edict was an enforced amalgamation of all the non-Marxist elements into a new party, the *Österreichische Volkspartei* (*ÖVP*, People's Party). Although the *ÖVP* was technically a union of all the *Bürgerlich* elements, it was considered by Burgenlanders to be a continuation of the *Christlichsoziale Partei*.

The election of 1945 was unusual then, in that it gave the voters (especially the Lutherans) no choice but to vote either "Catholic" or Marxist. In addition, this election was unusual in that two-thirds of the voters were women; many of the men were still in prison camps, or otherwise away from home. The result was a complete victory for the *ÖVP* the first party ever to gain a majority in Burgenland (see Table 1).

TABLE 1. Election Results, Burgenland, 1945–1959

	ÖVP	SPÖ	FPÖ	
1945	52%	45%		3%
1949	52%	40%	4%	3%
1953	48%	45%	4%	3%
1956	49%	46%	3%	2%
1959	47.2%	46.6%	5%	1%

The election of October 9, 1949, is the first postwar vote that may be considered to be normal. The men had returned home, and consequently the number of ballots cast increased by a full 25 per cent over the previous campaign. Furthermore, a new rightist minor party, the *Freiheitliche Partei Österreichs* (*FPÖ*, Freedom Party), appeared on the ballot.

The election of 1949 was the last to give an absolute majority to any party. Beginning with the election of February 22, 1953, the Socialist Party steadily whittled down the *ÖVP* lead until, in the election of May 10, 1959, the two principal parties were separated by only 1,201 votes.

As is obvious from Table 1 the minor parties have enjoyed far less success after the Second World War than before it. The *Bauernbund* of the 1920's had no counterpart in the 1950's. Since 1945 neither of the minor parties has ever gained a plurality in any of the 320 *Gemeinden* of Burgenland.

Figure 2 depicts the regions of support for the two principal parties. Instead of a random scattering of Socialist or *ÖVP Gemeinden*, clustering is the rule; within any region exceptions are surprisingly rare. Within region 2 every village has given the Socialist Party at least a

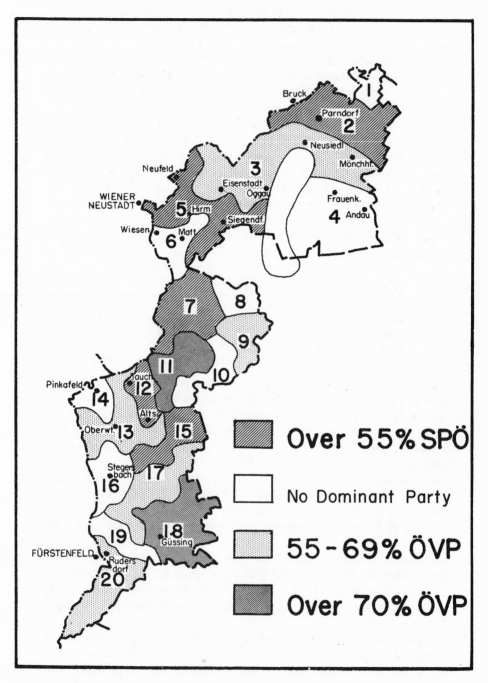

FIGURE 2: The voting regions of Burgenland, 1949-1959.

plurality, and all but one an absolute majority, whereas in the neighboring region 3 all 19 *Gemeinden* have given the *ÖVP* a plurality, and all but two a majority.[6]

		PERCENTAGE OF VOTES CAST	
Region	Population (1951)	*ÖVP*	*SPö*
1	4,437	52	46
2	12,325	34	55
3	38,170	57	36
4	18,918	52	40
5	35,640	31	62
6	15,641	52	43
7	15,407	36	60
8	7,488	53	45
9	8,956	62	35
10	7,616	53	42
11	7,677	72	25
12	5,591	33	57
13	15,635	55	38
14	7,738	42	51
15	10,951	39	55
16	13,979	46	52
17	12,853	60	37
18	13,483	72	24
19	5,779	40	49
20	17,850	58	31

Economic Groups

Industry and Commuting

Although Burgenland contains very few factories, 27 per cent of the population is listed as being dependent on *Industrie und Gewerbe* for its livelihood.[7] The largest industries are a sugar refinery at Siegendorf (region 5), textile mills at Neufeld (region 5), and textile mills at Pinkafeld (region 14). Siegendorf and Neufeld are among the strongest Socialist villages of the province, with average votes of 71 per cent and 73 per cent *SPÖ*, respectively. In addition they have voted 10 and 8 per cent Communist so that the total of their Marxist votes exceeds 80 per cent. The villages surrounding Pinkafeld also vote heavily Socialist but Pinkafeld itself is an anomaly in that it has given the *ÖVP* a slight plurality. Villages involved in mining follow the same tendency; Altschlaining (region 12, antimony) has voted 52 per cent Socialist and 13 per cent Communist, and Tauchen (region 12, coal) has voted 60 per cent Socialist and 5 per cent Communist. Strong Marxist voting also

[6] For a short discussion of these twenty regions, as regions, see, Burghardt, "Regions of Political Party Support in Burgenland (Austria)," *Canadian Geographer*, Vol. VII, No. 2 (1963), pp. 91–98. Their population and voting percentages are as follows:
[7] The basis of economic support is used rather than the number of workers because the latter includes farmers' wives as workers if they help their husbands on the land.

has occurred in those *Gemeinden* which formerly contained factories or operating mines.

These mines and factories account for only a minority of the industrial workers of Burgenland; most of the *Arbeiter* are employed outside the province. Since well before World War I commuting to the nearby Austrian cities has been an important part of the local way of life; its magnitude can scarcely be overestimated. In Schattendorf, at the eastern end (farthest from Vienna) of region 5, of the 1,100 persons of working age, over 600 are employed outside the *Gemeinde*, almost 300 in Vienna alone. Even from the south crowds of workers travel to jobs in the cities of the Vienna Basin. In Kemeten (northern part of region 16) some 300 of the 900 persons of working age are employed outside the *Gemeinde*, 100 in Vienna alone.

From most of Burgenland commuting to the cities is not an easy task. Only in the north (regions 2 and 5) is it possible for a worker to come home every evening, and even then the journey requires well over an hour each way. For at least half of the Burgenlanders who work outside the province, commuting is on a weekly basis. The men are home only on weekends; the rest of the week they share cheap rented rooms in the less fashionable sections of Vienna. These men remain legal residents of Burgenland and hence vote within the province.

Despite its inconvenience, commuting is obviously the free choice of most of the men engaged in it. The factory worker has security and extensive social benefits; he usually enjoys a better income than the agricultural peasant and is assured of a pension when he retires. His weekends at home, short though they be, are free. In addition, the worker feels that he has advanced to a slightly higher social plane simply by leaving the land. For such reasons young men are drawn towards the cities to the west, and once these men leave the land they never return to it. A peasant may with fair ease change from agriculture to factory work, but the reverse almost never occurs.

The principal goal of the commuter is the national metropolis, Vienna, which is located within 50 miles of much of northern Burgenland. For the Burgenlander, Vienna is a city of factories, building work, and railroad yards. The tens of thousands of office jobs require some higher education or training and the commuter from Burgenland has had none of this. Only the more presentable girls can find more pleasant work, usually as clerks in the many small stores of the city. Consequently, the man who commutes to Vienna almost invariably becomes an *Arbeiter* and a voter for the Socialist Party.

Urban employment is so attractive to the peasants of Burgenland that unless they are engaged in a highly lucrative form of agriculture or are far from the main lines of transportation, great numbers of them will choose to commute. Consequently, location in relation to transport lines

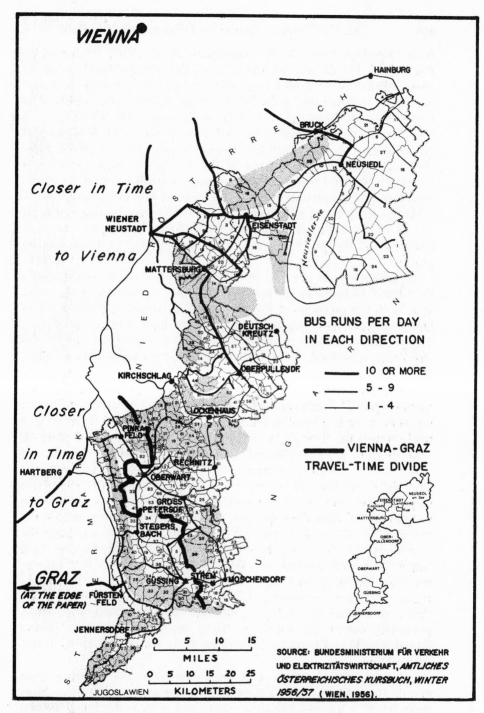

FIGURE 3: The frequency of bus service in Burgenland, 1956.

455

is an important factor in the regionalization of voting tendencies in Burgenland. The *Gemeinden* located along the principal transport routes almost always vote Socialist (e.g., regions 2 and 5), whereas those that are remote usually vote for the People's Party. Often regions of balanced voting occur in the peripheries of the main commuting areas. In these transitional zones the journey to work outside the province is possible but so tedious that the quality of the soil appears to be a factor in the choice of occupation and hence of the voting; the men on rich soil remain on the land whereas those on poor or small holdings commute. Such transitional areas may be noted in Figure 2 as regions 8, 10, and 16.

Within Burgenland four types of commuting may be distinguished: (1) to employment within the province, (2) to Vienna, (3) to other cities outside the province, and (4) to agricultural work outside the province.

Approximately 29 per cent of the Burgenlanders who work outside their home *Gemeinden* are employed in other communes of the province. With the exception of the governmental centers of Eisenstadt and Oberwart, commuting distance is everywhere limited to ten kilometers. The capital, Eisenstadt, employs some 1,500 persons from outside the city limits, who reside in at least 60 different *Gemeinden* in all parts of the province.

Within Burgenland it seems clear that the local governmental centers extend a pro-*ÖVP* influence into their surrounding areas. Most of their commuters are employed in office work or in shops, and these persons tend towards the People's Party. In contrast, most of the other centers, since they are usually industrial, exert a strong pro-*SPÖ* influence.

In terms of numbers involved and in its political implications, the most significant form of commuting is that to Vienna. The metropolis employs over half of all the persons who work outside their home *Gemeinde*, and over three-quarters of those who commute outside the province. In regions 2, 5, and 7 Vienna may be said to dominate the election results. In the north commuting to Vienna often makes local employment seem insignificant; Wulkaprodersdorf is only four kilometers from the Siegendorf sugar refinery but has only 19 persons working in Siegendorf compared to 130 in Vienna. The proximity of Vienna thus may be said to result in a strongly Socialist atmosphere, which permeates almost the entire province; where transportation to the capital is rapid and frequent the Socialist Party almost always dominates the balloting.

Approximately 15 per cent of the commuters work in other cities outside Burgenland. By far the most important of these is Wiener Neustadt, which is a major industrial center and is located immediately on the provincial boundary. Yet, despite its 1,100 commuters, the dominance of Wiener Neustadt extends only ten kilometers into the prov-

TABLE 2. Goals of Commuters, 1956 *

Outside Burgenland		Within Burgenland	
Vienna	8,670	Eisenstadt	1,485
		Oberwart	600
Wiener Neustadt	1,093	Pinkafeld	411
Bruck a/d Leitha	400	Tauchen	317
Fürstenfeld	276	Mattersburg	235
Graz	110	Siegendorf	186
Neudau	100	Stegersbach	127
		Frauenkirchen	114
Leoben	88	Oberpullendorf	108
Tribuswinkel	73	Jennersdorf	107
Neuhofen a/d Krems	61		
Weigelsdorf	58	Neufeld	98
Hainburg	53	Güssing	93
		Lockenhaus	90
		Rudersdorf	82
		Neudörfl	69
		Stadtschlaining	61

* These figures are only approximate and in most cases are too low. In copying down the figures the very low numbers in any *Gemeinde* were ignored, so that a few commuters to each of these centers may have been missed. However, the error affects all the places equally and can scarcely have affected the relative standing of the various centers. The figures are from Osterreichisches Statistisches Zentralamt (*Beiträge zür Osterreichischen Statistik*) *Wohnort–Arbeitsort der Unselbständig Berufstätigen* (Wien: 1956).

ince; beyond that distance the majority of commuters tend towards Vienna even though they must pass through Wiener Neustadt to reach the capital.

All the border cities of Lower Austria act as bases of Marxist strength within Burgenland. The influence of the Bruck a/d Leitha sugar mill may even be traced eastward as a gradually diminishing Communist vote: Bruckneudorf 10 per cent, Parndorf 5 per cent, Neudorf 2 per cent. In contrast the border cities of Styria appear to exert an influence in favor of the *ÖVP*. Exceptions to this rule occur, but generally the major Styrian centers near the boundary are accompanied by strong *ÖVP* voting in the neighboring Burgenland *Gemeinden*. Eastern Styria is a region of *ÖVP* dominance, and its largest centers (Fürstenfeld, Hartberg, and Feldbach) are commercial centers. The strongly conservative non-Marxist influence of these towns may help account for the *ÖVP* voting in the industrial *Gemeinden* of Pinkafeld and Rudersdorf, both of which lie on the border.

The fourth type of commuting differs from the others in that it consists of agricultural rather than industrial workers. Only some 4 per cent of the commuters are included in this grouping, but they form a majority of those commuters who live on the upland terraces of the southern two *Bezirke*. They are especially numerous in the *Gemeinden* flanking the Strem valleys of Güssing Bezirk.

Despite the fact that they are employed in agriculture, these contracted laborers evidently do not feel a strong tie to the *ÖVP*. Their home villages vote far more strongly for the *SPÖ* than do the other agricultural villages nearby. However, one cannot conclude that the agricultural commuter is attracted by Marxism; rather, it would be more accurate to say that he is not attached to either party, and that the vote of his village may depend on factors other than occupation. The relative location of his village appears to have a strong bearing on its vote. Along the terrace surface north of the Strem valley all the *Gemeinden* are similar in that they have poor soils, are surrounded by forests, and are the homes of numerous agricultural commuters. Despite their similarity a clear progression is notable from west to east; successive *Gemeinden* have voted Socialist in descending order: 61 per cent, 41 per cent, 29 per cent, 23 per cent, 10 per cent. In this case accessibility to the rest of Austria seems, of itself, to have increased the Socialist voting whereas isolation, of itself, has strengthened the *ÖVP* voting.

Agriculture

Within Burgenland it is universally believed that the *Bauer*, the agricultural peasant, automatically supports the *ÖVP*, and that he will vote against that party only because of personal opposition to some local leader or clique, or because of close ties with a Socialist candidate. Clearly, this is an oversimplification. The Lutherans form a great exception to this "rule" since they continue to hesitate to vote "Catholic." (The special case of the Lutherans will be dealt with later.) But even among the Catholics distinctions must be made.

For purposes of this study, one may divide the Catholic agricultural peasants into five categories:

1. those engaged in a profitable form of commercial agriculture,
2. those with good land who are relatively isolated,
3. those on poorer, gravelly land,
4. those who do not own their own land but perform agricultural work,
5. the contracted laborers housed in work camps on the large land holdings of the northeast.

CATEGORY 1 / The peasants engaged in a prosperous type of commercial agriculture vote solidly for the *ÖVP*. This group, located almost entirely in the north, includes the vintners, the fruit growers, and the few peasants raising vegetables for the Viennese market. In the typical vineyard or fruit village all except the landless laborers vote strongly and consistently for the *ÖVP*. Thus one finds figures uniquely high for northern Burgenland, such as 73 per cent *ÖVP* in Wiesen (region 6, fruit), and 77 per cent in St. Georgen, 66 per cent in Mönchhof, 65 per cent in Oggau, 63 per cent in Weiden, and 62 per cent in Donnerskir-chen (all vineyard villages within region 3).

CATEGORY 2 / In terms of percentages, the strongest support for the *ÖVP* occurs not in the*Weingemeinden,* but in the small remote villages which are located on the rich alluvial soils of the south. The typical peasant in these villages lives off his own land and sells calves, pigs, poultry, and eggs to the Viennese meat dealers who drive their trucks into the remote villages. For such peasants Vienna is so far away that commuting is beyond serious consideration.

Population pressure and the desire for a "better" life do induce many persons to seek their livelihood elsewhere; these persons do not com-mute, but emigrate. Those people who move to Vienna may well change to the Socialist Party but they then cast their votes in Vienna and not in Burgenland. This heavy emigration, especially of young people, tends to increase the *ÖVP* vote even beyond what might be expected from a "typical" peasant area. The more radically minded elements leave, the more conservative, rooted elements remain, and it is these latter who feel the most strongly the identification of their way of life with the People's Party.

Thus isolation has become an important factor in the development and maintenance of *ÖVP* strength. The most notable region of this type is the remote southeastern corner of Güssing Bezirk (region 18) where the *ÖVP* percentage increases steadily the farther east one travels. There Deutsch Bieling in the four elections between 1949 and 1959 gave the Socialist Party just one vote, and its *ÖVP* percentage stands at 99.8. The two other villages in this Austrian salient have voted 97.2 and 94.3 per cent *ÖVP*, respectively. Similarly in the isolated separate world of the Zöbern Valley (the southern half of region 11), five of the eight *Gemeinden* have given the *ÖVP* more than 90 per cent of their votes. Thus the factor of isolation, which between the wars led toward the occurrence of pockets of *Bauernbund* support, now tends to induce the highest examples of *ÖVP* support.

In these remote areas the smallness in population of a *Gemeinde* also increases the dominance of the *ÖVP*. The smaller the village, the more unlikely it is that Socialist influences will enter it, and the more likely it is that a uniformity of opinion can be created and maintained by village leadership. This is well demonstrated in region 18 (eastern Güssing Bezirk). In that region 13 *Gemeinden* each have a population of over 300 and 15 each number under 300. Of the 13 larger than 300 only one has had an *ÖVP* percentage *higher than 78 per cent,* and that one is in the extreme southeastern corner previously mentioned; of the 15 smaller than 300 only one *Gemeinde* has had an *ÖVP* percentage *below 78 per cent,* and that one is integrally joined to a larger *Gemeinde.*

CATEGORY 3 / The third type of agricultural peasant, the one trying to wrest a living from poor land, is less predictable than the two types already mentioned. Such poor peasants often feel a strong dissatisfaction with their situation and are apt to vote erratically or even Marxist as a form of protest. The relative location of the individual *Gemeinden* appears to be highly important in the understanding of their voting records; those surrounded by *ÖVP Gemeinden* (area 18) vote strongly *ÖVP,* whereas some of those near Socialist *Gemeinden* have voted Socialist. What does seem clear is that these peasants on their patches of dry soil bounded by the forest feel little identification with the reputed party of the peasantry.

CATEGORY 4 / The agricultural peasant who must commute to work outside his home *Gemeinde* has already been discussed. A more common type of landless agricultural peasant is the man who works on the vineyards and orchards of his wealthier neighbors. The landholder who possesses more than about two hectares of vineyards requires manual help with their care, unless his family is large and all its members are available for work. Consequently, many landless field hands are employed in the *Gemeinden* of northern Burgenland. These workers feel no ties whatsoever with the *ÖVP* and show instead a strong tendency to vote Marxist. In some of the *Weingemeinden* the Socialist vote is surprisingly high considering the reputation of vintners for conservatism. Most impressive, however, have been the Communist votes in some of the vineyard villages (Rust 19 per cent, Gols 9 per cent, and Breitenbrunn 6 per cent). The total Marxist vote has reached 55 per cent in Rust, 47 per cent in Jois, 42 per cent in Breitenbrunn, and 40 per cent in Gols, and all of them are famed for their wine.

CATEGORY 5 / The agricultural laborer on the large land holdings of the north is also landless, but he is unique in that he lives in isolation from normal provincial life in a work camp, a *Meierhof* or *puszta.* When Burgenland was transferred to Austria, the flat northeast contained many of the holdings so common to Hungary. These estates were tilled by contracted laborers who were housed in specially constructed work camps located far from the village centers. Although some of these large holdings have been sold and subdivided since 1921, many still exist, especially in the vicinity of Frauenkirchen (region 4).

When the Soviet forces entered this area late in 1944 they made a special effort to attract the votes of these discontented, socially isolated field hands. The Eszterházy lands were taken over on the pretext that they had been *Deutsches Eigentum,* and were worked by the Soviet occupation forces for the benefit of the peasants on the land. Eszterházy himself was in a Hungarian prison. These *USIA Betriebe,* as the expropriated holdings were called, became cells of Marxist strength. Thus within a thoroughly agricultural region, Frauenkirchen has voted 46 per cent Socialist and 10 per cent Communist, Andau has voted 51 per cent Socialist and 3 per cent Communist, and Wallern 38 per cent Socialist and 6 per cent Communist.

This support for the Communist Party has, however, proven to be ephemeral. The Soviet forces left the area in 1955 and during the Hungarian Revolution Eszterházy escaped to Austria; the Communist vote dropped sharply. In Loretto, site of an Eszterházy holding, the *KPÖ* vote dropped from 12 per cent in 1956 to 2 per cent in 1959. Although the landless laborers have been leaving the Communist ranks, they have not transferred their votes to the *ÖVP;* rather they have chosen to support the Socialist Party or the newer and stronger minor party, the *FPÖ.*

It is evident that the *ÖVP* can depend on the allegiance of only two groups from among the agricultural peasants, those for whom agriculture is a highly profitable way of life, and those who are especially isolated from the rest of the country. The *ÖVP* can also hope for a very slight majority of the votes of the peasants working the poorer soils. The last two types (those peasants who do not own their own land) remain largely outside the fold of the *ÖVP;* most of them vote Marxist, and most gave the Communist Party relatively strong support until 1956. It seems clear that only the contented Catholic peasants feel a strong identification with that political party which is generally considered in Austria to be closely tied to the peasant way of life. Within Burgenland the peasantry appears to be a rather fragile base for the political hopes of the *ÖVP.*

Other Occupations

Some 11 per cent of the inhabitants of Burgenland are dependent for their livelihood upon commerce, governmental service, and the professions.[8] Included in this grouping are the merchants, the civil servants and other office clerks, and a small number of lawyers, teachers, doctors,

---

[8] Unfortunately, the Austrian census classification *Handel und Verkehr* includes transportation workers with merchants and bankers. *Handel und Verkehr* supported 5.2 per cent of the population, *Freie Berufe* 2.0 per cent, and *Öffentliche Dienst* 3.3 per cent. If one arbitrarily assumes that half of the *H.u.V.* total is in transportation (and hence probably voting Socialist), then the remaining total for the three categories would be 7.9 per cent.

dentists, and clergymen. Whereas the population of the province has been declining steadily, the number of persons listed in these categories has been increasing slowly.

Although a few of the teachers and civil servants support the Socialist Party (or even the Freedom Party) on ideological grounds, the vast majority of the office workers and professionals, and virtually all the merchants, support the ÖVP. In two of the four interwar elections Eisenstadt voted Socialist, but since 1945 it has always voted for the ÖVP. In a similar fashion Oberwart has become an ÖVP center in the midst of the Socialist upper Pinka valley. Consequently the continual decline in ÖVP-voting peasants through emigration and commuting is being partially compensated for by a continual increase in the number of ÖVP-motivated office workers and professionals.

Minority Groups

The Croats

The Croats include, officially, 11.1 per cent of the inhabitants of Burgenland and are the largest (30,599) of the ethnic minority groups (see Fig. 4). The Croats are also the only minority group that has presented cultural demands to the provincial and federal governments. The Croatian Culture Society has campaigned for the preservation of the Croatian language and culture in Burgenland, and for increased representation of the Croats in the provincial government.[9]

To further the aims of the Culture Society, the Croatian Party was organized in 1922 in Grosswarasdorf (region 9), Oberpullendorf Bezirk. This party ran in the election of 1923 but received only 2,557 votes (2.1 per cent of the provincial total), 80 per cent of which were cast within Oberpullendorf Bezirk. Following this poor showing the Croatian Party amalgamated with the *Christlichsoziale Partei*.

In the elections of 1922 and 1923 the Croats of the northern three *Bezirke* voted strongly Socialist whereas those of the southern four *Bezirke* divided their votes among the Christian and Peasant parties and, in 1923, the Croatian Party. Following the amalgamation of the Croatian with the Christian Party, the Croatian vote became divided between the Socialists in the north, and the Christian (later ÖVP) in the south. In the more remote areas of the south a few *Gemeinden* continued to support

[9] The number of Croats is much disputed. A more accurate, though unofficial, figure would be 34,427 (12.6 per cent) since many of the bilingual Croats were listed in the German column in the census. Even this latter figure is a decline from the 14.1 per cent of the population which the Croats constituted in 1923. For a brief discussion of this problem of determining the numbers in the two ethnic minorities see the book, Burghardt, *Borderland, A Historical and Geographic Study of Burgenland (Austria)* (Madison, Wisconsin: 1962), p. 247. Pages 253–66 include a discussion of the cultural efforts of the Croatian Culture Society.

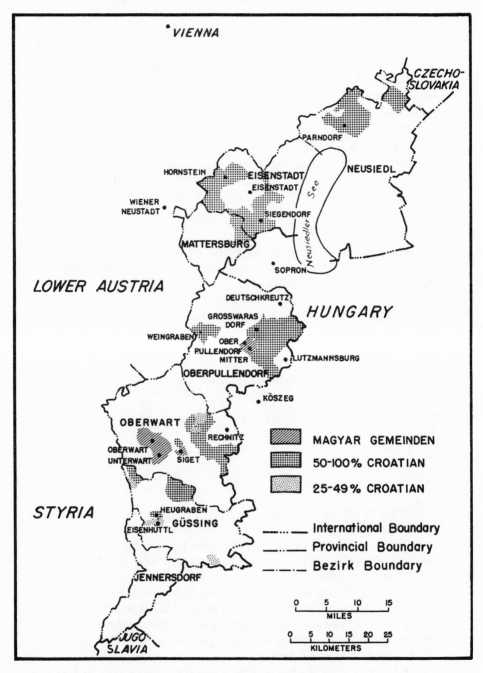

FIGURE 4: The non-German *Gemeinden* of Burgenland, 1951.

the *Bauernbund* in 1927 and 1930, but these have supported the *ÖVP* since 1945.

It is, of course, impossible to determine the exact number of votes that have been cast by Croats for each of the political parties. The closest that one can come to ascertaining the Croatian voting patterns is to calculate the averages of those *Gemeinden* which have a Croatian majority. Such a calculation indicates a clear majority for the Socialist Party (see Table 3).

TABLE 3. Croatian Voting, Elections of 1949–1959

	ÖVP	*SPÖ*	*FPÖ*	*KPÖ*
Croatian *Gemeinden*	43.4%	52.4%	1.1%	3.0%
Burgenland total	49.3%	44.4%	3.9%	2.3%

However, a breakdown of the totals by districts (Table 4) reveals that the heavy Socialist vote is concentrated in the north rather than throughout all the Croatian areas.

TABLE 4. Croatian Voting by Bezirke, Elections of 1949–1959

		SPÖ vote, per cent	
Bezirk	*Total votes of the* *Croatian* Gemeinden	*Croatian*	*Entire* *Bezirk*
Neusiedl	10,881	56	43
Eisenstadt	34,846	60	48
Mattersburg	10,809	68	53
Oberpullendorf	23,336	41	44
Oberwart	9,143	43	45
Güssing	9,748	40	38

Therefore, the majority given by the Croats to the *SPÖ* cannot be attributed either to an inherent tendency of the Croats to vote Socialist or to the minority status of the ethnic group. Instead, the relative location of the Croatian settlements appears to offer the best explanation for these results.

In Neusiedl Bezirk most of the Croats live in two large *Gemeinden* astride the commuter railroad and highway to Bruck and Vienna. These villages vote no more heavily Socialist than do the neighboring German villages on the same transport routes (region 2). In Mattersburg and Eisenstadt Bezirke the Croatian communes are almost all located in the lowland traversed by the two railroads and three highways which lead to Vienna and Wiener Neustadt. This lowland is the heaviest area of commuting in the province and the fact that it is Croatian is coincidental. In addition, the sugar refinery at Siegendorf is located in a Croatian *Gemeinde*. On the other hand, the vineyard and fruit areas which flank this lowland are principally German; only one of the *Weingemeinden* is Croatian and that one, Oggau, has voted heavily *ÖVP*.

Most of the Croatian *Gemeinden* of Oberpullendorf and Oberwart districts are located in remote areas and have voted heavily *ÖVP* much as have their German neighbors. The presence of the Croatian Culture Society leadership has probably increased the strength of the *ÖVP* in Oberpullendorf Bezirk but it seems probable that region 9 would have voted for the People's Party even if the area were German rather than Croatian. In Güssing Bezirk the Croatian *Gemeinden* are located in the western, more Socialist, half of the district.

Thus, it appears that among the Croats ethnic, cultural, or linguistic factors have had little discernible political significance. It seems evident that the voting responses of the Croats may be explained on the same bases as those of the Germans, that is, on economic, occupational grounds, which are based ultimately on the relative location of the villages.

The Magyars and Gypsies

In 1951, the Magyars numbered officially 5,251 or only 1.9 per cent of the population of the province.[10] They are virtually limited to five *Gemeinden*: Oberpullendorf and its satellite village, Mitterpullendorf, and Oberwart and its neighboring villages of Unterwart, and Siget in der Wart. Since there are so few Magyars it is difficult to make any meaningful generalizations as to their voting responses. The small linguistic minority is divided among three religions, Catholic, Calvinist, and Lutheran, which further complicates any attempts at generalization. Oberwart and Oberpullendorf are important governmental and transportational centers and show no strong tendency for either party. Oberwart is the larger of the two and has voted consistently, though weakly, *ÖVP*. Oberpullendorf is the less important of the two and is situated at the southern end of a belt of heavy commuting (region 7); it has given the *SPÖ* a slight plurality. Unterwart is Catholic and agricultural and has voted strongly *ÖVP*; Siget is agricultural but Lutheran and has voted Socialist. There has been no strong support for any minor party. All that one can conclude is that again the ethnic factor by itself has had no discernible significance in the voting responses of the Magyars.

The Gypsies are too few and scattered to make any impact on the voting. However, the local belief is that the Gypsies have tended to vote

---

[10] The addition of those bilingual Magyars whom the census listed in the "German" column would raise the percentage to 2.8 per cent. Even this latter figure is a great decline from the 1923 figure of 5.2 per cent.

Communist because of the assistance they have received from the *KPÖ* in obtaining monetary compensation for their persecution under the Nazis.

The Lutherans

The Lutherans number approximately 37,500 (14 per cent of the total)[11] and are located in all seven *Bezirke,* although their greatest concentrations are in the hills and terraces of the south (see Fig. 5).

Throughout the interwar years the Lutherans refused to support the *Christlichsoziale Partei* because of its obvious ties to the Catholic Church. The *CS* party based its social program on Papal teachings, spoke often of "Catholic Austria," and was led during the 1920's by a Catholic priest, Msgr. Ignaz Seipel. The Burgenland Lutherans were keenly aware of their minority status within Austria and claimed that they suffered from religious discrimination in that none of their members could hope to obtain a high governmental position. In those villages within which both the Catholics and Lutherans had parish churches, relations between the two faiths were often severely strained. There are still *Gemeinden* in Burgenland where the two communions tend to form separate communities with their own *Gasthäuser* and stores, as well as churches and schools.

Within the Lutheran villages located in regions of heavy commuting, religious tensions had little obvious effect on the voting; the Lutheran commuters voted Socialist much as did their Catholic neighbors, since the Socialist Party was clearly non-Catholic. However, most of the Lutheran villages are located in relatively remote areas, away from the principal commuter routes, or in the vineyard belts. The inhabitants of these *Gemeinden* preferred to avoid the Socialist as well as the Christian Party on ideological grounds. Hence the Lutherans were in the interwar years the most consistent supporters of the *Bauernbund.* The composite totals of the four interwar elections in the 48 *Gemeinden* with a Lutheran majority were: *Bauernbund*—112, *Sozialist*—37, *Grossdeutsch* —29, *Heimatblock*—6, and *Christlich*—6.[12] Since the *Grossdeutsche Partei* ran only in the first two elections and the *Heimatblock* only in the last, the poor showing of the *Christlichsoziale Partei* is truly remarkable.

In the election of 1945, the Lutherans were forced to choose among three parties, each of which was either "Catholic" or Marxist. The Peo-

[11] The exact number of Lutherans is impossible to determine for 1951 since the census included all Protestants within one total of 38,995. The only non-Lutheran Protestant group in Burgenland is the Calvinist parish in the Magyar quarter of Oberwart City. This parish includes some 1,500 persons; therefore, an estimate of 37,500 Lutherans must fall within 100 persons of the correct total. (The 1934 census did make distinctions and listed 1,552 Calvinists and 38,830 Lutherans.)
[12] The results of two *Gemeinden* are missing from the 1922 election.

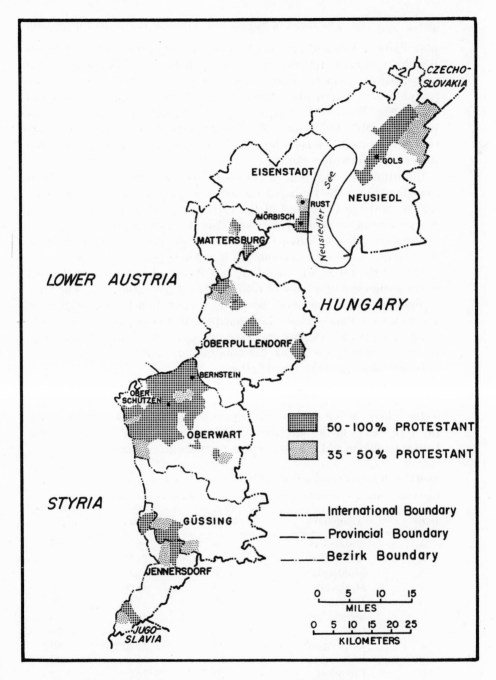

FIGURE 5: The non-Catholic *Gemeinden* of Burgenland, 1951.

468   32. The Bases of Support for Political Parties in Burgenland

ple's Party *(ÖVP)* had no official connection with the Catholic Church but the Lutherans felt that it was nevertheless a continuation of the prewar *Christlichsoziale Partei.* However, in the election of 1949 a new party, which was neither Marxist nor "Catholic," appeared on the ballot. The *WdU (VdU),* later to be transformed into the *FPÖ,* was strongly rightist and favored the development of closer ties with West Germany; it could be considered to be in some ways a successor to the prewar *Grossdeutsche Partei.*

Unfortunately, the *WdU–FPÖ* could not be taken seriously. Even though some of the Lutheran *Gemeinden* displayed a rush of support for this party in 1949, most of the voters recognized that the Freedom Party could never aspire to be more than a very minor party with only a nuisance value in national or provicial politics, especially so since the two major parties had combined to act as a governing coalition.

Most of the Lutherans, therefore, cast their ballots for one of the two major parties out of a sense of realism even if not enthusiasm. The anti-Catholic bias has remained, however, even if muted. The composite results for the four elections between 1949 and 1959 are: Socialist—109, People's Party—83. Despite their peasant character many of those *Gemeinden* which had voted for the *Bauernbund* must have supported the Socialist rather than the People's Party.

Even though no Burgenland *Gemeinde* has given the Freedom Party a plurality, Lutheran backing for the minor party has been noteworthy. Table 5 lists the ten *Gemeinden* with the highest voting percentage for the *WdU–FPÖ* in the elections of 1949 through 1959. The correlation between religion and support for this party seems obvious.

TABLE 5. Support for the *WdU–FPÖ*

Rank	Gemeinde	Region (location)	FPÖ, per cent	Lutheran, per cent
1.	Pöttelsdorf	6	28.4	87
2.	Kalkgruben	7	24.7	72
3.	Mühlgraben	20	18.9	67
4.	Mörbisch	5	18.3	78
5.	Kukmirn	19	17.9	78
6.	Schmiedrait	13	16.6	86
7.	Gols	3	15.6	80
8.	Loipersbach	5	15.6	89
9.	Willersdorf	13	14.8	92
10.	Eltendorf	20	14.3	70

However, it must not be assumed that a Lutheran *Gemeinde* will automatically vote strongly for the *FPÖ;* considerable variation occurs among the villages and regions. It seems clear that before the Protestants of a village will decide to vote strongly for the *FPÖ* some element of ideologically motivated leadership must be present. Such leadership is usually supplied by the pastor, and hence the strength of the *FPÖ* varies considerably from parish to parish, and from those villages with a resident pastor to those without one.

Remote in the hills of northern Oberwart Bezirk are four small villages, only one of which can boast of a paved road leading out of its valley. This is the most Protestant part of Austria; all four *Gemeinden* are over 95 per cent Lutheran, and one is 100 per cent. However, in none of these villages does the *FPÖ* average exceed 4 per cent; rather the vote has gone heavily for the *ÖVP* (87, 77, 66, and 64 per cent). These *Gemeinden* are evidently beyond the reach of their own parish centers and in their isolation these villagers vote much as do their Catholic counterparts.

In the more accessible portions of the southern hills, only a few of the *Gemeinden* are large enough to support a resident pastor; the surrounding Lutheran villages are labeled as *Filiale*, that is, they are considered to fall under the spiritual jurisdiction of the centrally located pastor. Usually a clear correlation can be noted between the presence of the pastor and a high vote for the *FPÖ*; almost in every case the parish center has had a higher *FPÖ* vote than have had the *Filiale* around it.

Thus the impact of religion is felt in many ways in the political life of Burgenland.

The Bases of Party Strength— Summation and Conclusions

Osterreichische Volkspartei

Those members of the Catholic peasantry who own and work their own land and are relatively content with their way of life remain the principal base of support for the *ÖVP*. The landless laborers are largely lost to this party, as are also many (perhaps half) of the peasants tilling the poorer soils. Except in the most remote villages the Lutheran peasants give only mild support to the People's Party.

The Catholic peasants who vote heavily for this party may be divided into two differing groups, the more isolated peasants of the south, and the prosperous wine, fruit, or vegetable farmers of the north. The former group is the larger but is declining steadily in numbers. Except in the fruit and vineyard regions, the isolation and the smallness of a village augment its tendencies to vote strongly *ÖVP*.

The second, less important, base of support for the People's Party consists of the persons engaged in office work, commerce, or the professions. Their numbers are very small, but the office staffs of the governmental agencies are steadily increasing in size. Since this portion of the ÖVP vote is increasing while the peasant portion is decreasing, the core of party strength and power is shifting steadily from the south to the north, from Güssing to Eisenstadt Bezirk.

Sozialistische Partei Österreichs

The workers in industry, construction, mining, and the railroads continue to form the base of support for the Socialist Party. A minority of the *Arbeiter* are employed within Burgenland, but the majority commute to work in nearby cities, principally Vienna and Wiener Neustadt. Hence the areas of Socialist strength in Burgenland form bands or zones along the major rail and bus lines into and across the province. Except for the prosperous wine and fruit-growing areas, the *Gemeinden* which enjoy the closest contact with Vienna tend heavily to vote Socialist.

The landless agricultural laborers form a second, although far less important, source of support for the SPÖ. In addition, perhaps half of the peasants tilling the poorer soils have voted for this party. The Lutherans have given the Socialists a majority, but much of this majority has come from the Protestant villages which are located in the mining and commuting area.

Freiheitliche Partei Österreichs

The strongest support for the FPÖ has been in those Lutheran *Gemeinden* which have resident pastors. The Lutheran *Filiale* villages have given somewhat less support to this party. A scattering of votes for the FPÖ has come from governmental employees, and from the noncommuting landless agricultural workers.

Kommunistische Partei Österreichs

The Communist Party has been, despite the support it received from the Soviet occupation forces, the weakest party of Burgenland and is now almost extinct.[13] Its principal support has come from the workers in the sugar refineries and in the mines currently or recently in operation.

From 1949 through 1956 the landless laborers of the northern estates and vineyards formed a second source of votes for the Communist Party, but since 1956 most of this vote has been lost to the Socialist or Freedom parties. In Burgenland it is believed that many of the Gypsies vote Communist, but there are so few Gypsies left in the province that this source of votes is of only negligible importance.

[13] In the most recent election, that of November 18, 1962, the Communist Party (KLS) received a total of only 1,715 votes in Burgenland (0.97 per cent).

Conclusions

From the foregoing discussion it becomes clear that location and religion are the principal factors influencing the patterns of voting in Burgenland. Ethnic factors, although they have been highly publicized, have had almost no observable bearing on the voting results. The typical Croat or Magyar does not identify his language or even his minority status with any political party; rather he tends to vote on the basis of his occupation.

In contrast to language, religion is very important. The reluctance of the Lutherans to vote for a party they associate with the Catholic Church resulted in strong and consistent support for the *Bauernbund* between the wars, and above average support for the Socialist and Freedom parties since 1945.

However, six-sevenths of the Burgenlanders are not Lutheran, but Catholic; therefore, it is the relative location of the *Gemeinden* which gives the fullest explanation of the voting results. Although it is true that the vote of the individual citizen remains unpredictable, and that local voting often seems to be strongly affected by the presence of village cliques and feuds, yet the overall results of these *Gemeinden,* when mapped, fall into distinct areal patterns which may be interpreted as follows:

1. The *Gemeinden* located along the south-facing slopes conducive to viticulture have remained the homes of prosperous peasants who have ignored the opportunities to commute to work elsewhere and have voted strongly and consistently for the *ÖVP*.

2. Those *Gemeinden* which are not involved in prosperous commercial agriculture and which are located close to rapid transportation to the Vienna Basin have become the homes of hundreds of commuters who have strongly and consistently voted Socialist.

3. The *Gemeinden* located near mines presently or recently in operation, or large local industries, have voted Socialist.

4. The *Gemeinden* located the farthest from the Vienna Basin in terms of travel time have voted overwhelmingly for the *ÖVP*.

5. The *Gemeinden* located in a transitional zone between the commuting regions and the isolated regions have voted slightly for the *ÖVP*, but with considerable variations from village to village. The *Gemeinden* with good land have voted for the *ÖVP*, whereas the *Gemeinden* on poor land have voted for the *SPÖ*.

Finally, it should be pointed out that Burgenland since its establishment has remained uniquely open to outside influences. The cadres, the ideologies, even the candidates of the political parties were introduced into the new province from outside in 1921. Although the parties are now locally organized, outside influences still have a great bearing on the voting results. The majority of the Socialist voters in Burgenland may be said to be casting their ballots within a predominantly rural area on the basis of a political identification they have acquired outside the province. Although it is the influence of Vienna which seems to permeate the province, lesser influences can be said to emanate from other Austrian cities as well. From the cities of Lower Austria this political influence is always Marxist, that is, Socialist or Communist, but from the Styrian towns it is usually conservative, that is, in favor of the People's Party.

The dominance of Vienna in the political life of Burgenland is facilitated by the ever-increasing ease of travel to the capital. The closeness of the metropolis hinders the growth of a local commercial life which could be expected to increase the strength and the effectiveness of the ÖVP; and yet the closeness of the capital allows for a continuing depopulation of the remote agricultural areas, while supplying an ever-increasing labor market for the commuter. Thus the proximity of Vienna has in a twofold manner worked towards the increasing strength of the Socialist Party in Burgenland: by supplying industrial jobs for a peasantry eager to desert agriculture, and by preventing the development of that truly indigenous political life which could be expected to form a core of strength for the ÖVP.

33. Sovereignty of the Sea
G. Etzel Pearcy

More than 70 per cent of the surface of the earth is covered by the sea. This vast area, uninhabited by man, might be thought to be free of his political maneuverings. But as is well known, man not only makes considerable use of the sea; he also, in recent times, is extending political control over the sea and seeking ways of controlling even more parts of the sea depths and floors. As a result, the global sea is becoming increasingly important to the political process.

The Single Ocean Concept
The sea covers some 140 million square miles, or 70.8 percent of the world's surface. It is possible to be in the ocean on a ship 1,600 miles from the nearest land. At one point in midocean a ship can be more

SOURCE: Geographic Bulletin No. 3, April, 1965. Department of State, Washington, D.C. The author is The Geographer of the Department of State.

than 3,500 miles from the nearest continental landmass. Ocean areas run into statistical values of enormous proportions, far exceeding land areas of national and even continental extent. The Pacific Ocean with some 64 million square miles and the Atlantic and Indian Oceans together with another 60 million square miles constitute the bulk of the total hydrosphere.

That the oceans of the world, in addition to their vastness, are joined one to another by wide passages leads some oceanographers to speak of *The Global Sea*. This concept is indeed well adapted to the modern trend of a world shrinking in travel time and in which states come ever closer in their interspatial relations. Colossal expanses of water off their shores have long intrigued land dwellers. Many have turned to the sea to earn their living in one way or another while countless others have crossed oceans bound from one land area to another. Nevertheless, the sea to date has failed to receive attention commensurate with its dimensions or with the careful examination given to the development of land surface.

As recently as a decade and a half ago little hope was held for the oceans as a reservoir of resources which might help to feed or otherwise reduce the specter of a hungry and rapidly expanding world population. Ships have long sailed the seven seas and world fisheries for years have yielded an annual catch on the order of 15 to 25 million tons, but new startling innovations and discoveries in marine science have largely taken place only since World War II began to fade into history as another great episode in world affairs. In this new era, however, and with accelerating momentum, oceanography has been sharply enlivened by recognition of a new and vast fishing potential, by offshore oil wells in deeper and deeper water, by the analysis of mineral globules from the bottom of the sea holding untold wealth, by the successes of nuclear-powered submarines, and by the advances in desalination of sea water. Some enthusiastic scientists declare that indirectly the production of fish meal alone could substantially augment the world's food supply. New methods of travel, fishing, extracting minerals, and making depth soundings exemplify some of the techniques which further advance development of oceanography and direct our interest toward offshore problems.

The U.S. Coast and Geodetic Survey probes deeply into oceanographic research testifying to our concern with offshore claims and their resource potential. This Bureau operates seven oceanographic vessels, equipped with laboratories, for scientific investigation over all parts of the global sea. One, the *Pioneer*, has recently returned from the Indian Ocean where it has engaged in the United Nations-sponsored cooperative Indian Ocean Survey.

Growing nationalism in a world fraught with tensions also causes many nations to look seaward, whether apprehensive as to securing their domain or to extending it. In fact, strong nationalism by its very nature serves as the incipient forerunner to offshore claims—always increasing, never decreasing. Not uncommonly a state will make greater offshore claims in response to similar claims on the part of a neighboring state.

The emergence of 54 newly independent states since December 1943, each with a fresh consciousness as to its national domain, has accentuated attention given to sovereign territory and its bounds. As one naval officer expressed the question of claims at a Law of the Sea Conference, ". . . international negotiations here are little more than 'diplomacy of the grab.' " Unfortunately these trends are in direct opposition to policies strongly upheld by the United States and other nations believing in freedom of the seas as a means of engendering world commerce and promoting international cooperation in an effort to insure peace. A paradox appears when a nation that advocates advancing space exploration and utilization by opening the skies to all nations at the same time seeks to restrict movement in the seas. An examination of proceedings in U.N. conferences will show that this incongruous situation has not been uncommon. All the more ironic is the situation when one traces through past centuries the long uphill pull to render the seas free from limitations of mobility in order to facilitate an exchange of goods on a worldwide scale. Highlighting this crusade was Hugo Grotius' much publicized support in the early 17th century of *mare liberum*. The maritime states, centering along the periphery of the North Atlantic, must again champion the right to keep the world's shipping lanes open in accordance with geographic logic rather than the prejudiced dictates of statesmen.

That the U.S. Government has an intense interest in the new look at the sea, and in pressing for freedom of movement upon it, has ample evidence in the literature of the day and in official writings. An especially graphic document is the text of the "Advancement of Marine Sciences—Marine Sciences and Research Act of 1961." [1] In it President Kennedy is quoted as having written, "Knowledge of the oceans is more than a matter of curiosity. Our very survival may hinge on it." In pursuit of this worthy objective it becomes imperative at the outset to distinguish the rights (or lack of rights) of the several sovereign states of the world in the exploration and exploitation of the seas.

Question of Offshore Jurisdiction

Every part of the global sea, whether a segment in mid-Pacific or a fragment along an irregular coast such as that of Norway, should in

[1] Calendar No. 399, 87th Cong., 1st sess., Senate Report No. 426.

theory at least fit into a worldwide jurisdictional pattern. In other words, every square mile of sea surface and seabed and every gallon of sea water should be accounted for—who controls any given point on, over, or under the surface of the sea and to what degree should be a matter of record. Accord among the states of the world in these matters not only contributes toward stability in international relations but facilitates cooperation in the use of the oceans' resources as well as spatial advantages which their broad expanses have to offer.

No less than 99 sovereign states have coastlines bordering the sea, including insular (Iceland, Philippines) as well as mainland territory (France, Thailand). Another 26 states are landlocked, yet they justifiably demand certain rights with respect to the sea. These figures do not include some 15 dependencies and areas of associated sovereignty along the coasts of continental mainlands as well as a highly diverse assortment of islands, parts of islands, and exclaves of varying sovereignty which also face or are surrounded by the sea.

Obviously the landward margin of the sea adjacent to a coastal state demands the preponderant amount of attention from the state—the more immediate the zone offshore the more intense the concern. At the other extreme, all states have interests which stretch across the widest of oceans so that they may engage in maritime commerce with any part of the world or otherwise utilize such broad expanses of emptiness in the interests of science.

Unfortunately offshore claims vary from state to state. Too, there are gaps or vagaries relative to precise definitions and means of identification within the scope of any given claim. At the same time abuses abound in the observance of those acts which have been established as conventional law of the sea rules and procedures. With respect to the geographic situation along the world's seacoasts it must be granted that distribution of land and water and shoreline configuration produce a pattern which in no place is a duplicate to that of any other place. It is little wonder, therefore, that the application of an effective jurisdictional pattern to so complicated a physical setting encourages biased interpretations and meets with so much controversy.

Breadth of the territorial sea has long caused serious controversy among the world's states but only in 1958 at the first Law of the Sea Convention at Geneva did it take on ominous overtones. Claims vary from 3 miles by the United States and most maritime nations of Europe and the Commonwealth, through 12 miles by the Soviet Union and countries of Eastern Europe, to 200 miles by some of the west coast countries of Latin America. Again, fishing interests widely overlap the issue, creating bitter feelings which have on occasion bounded out of the international courtroom and onto the decks of war vessels convoying fishing craft. Normally, however, fishing agreements take form over the conference table. In recent months frequent talks at high levels between the United States and other countries over fishing rights indicate the concern with which this matter is viewed.

Navigation rights along the periphery of the oceans where shipping lanes narrow to traverse constricted straits and channels likewise signal conflict of national interests. Here converge ocean routes through physical bottlenecks or at the approaches of the world's seaports. Commerce depends entirely upon egress from and ingress to the loading dock, for the millions of square miles of "open seas" are not at all open without accessibility to the terminals.

Less flexible than regulations for water transit, air rights for commercial aviation rigidly restrict air routes to jurisdictional rather than geographic patterns. Aircraft may not fly over the territorial sea of any state unless they have the right to also fly over that state's sovereign land area. Thus, no "right of innocent passage" exists as with surface craft. Rights of a state to overfly the territory of other states are exclusively by agreements among states. The bilateral agreement is the common basis upon which the world's international air route structure hinges. Military aircraft, obviously, cannot fly with impunity over foreign territory, including the territorial seas, without risk of diplomatic note or antiaircraft fire.

The itinerary of any naval vessel close along a foreign coast or through strategic waters may be tantamount to creating tension and precipitating crises, even among otherwise relatively friendly states. Visibility may come into play to further complicate the situation. Ships only 3 miles offshore may easily be seen, adding to the emotional factor in the case of naval craft rights. The most peaceful coastal patrol may loom as a war scare if alarm is generated to an uninformed and gullible citizenry. In direct contrast, the presence of war vessels offshore may have a stabilizing influence, a technique at times used by the U.S. Navy in looking after "brush fires."

Visibility further enters the picture in the case of surface craft versus submarines. A submarine may glide through the territorial sea (assuming sufficient depth) unobserved, while a destroyer or cruiser must carefully respect the outer limit of the territorial sea to avoid possibility of an international incident. Here the difference between a 3- and a 12-mile territorial sea makes a tremendous impact, for the offshore zone between mile 3 and mile 12 constitutes an area where undersea craft can act unobserved and with cunning and at the same time be immune from surface vessels in pursuit. Surface ships in this zone have no such advantage and may not pursue submarines within the territorial waters of other states.

Stated succinctly, the problems of offshore sovereignty amount to a single, though complex, question: "What state holds jurisdiction over what part of the seas and to what degree?" Even where there may be fairly precise guidelines by which to measure jurisdictional limits, the highly irregular coastal pattern in many areas handicaps any uniform application of them from one part of the world to another. In response to such an overwhelming problem of legal delineation a worldwide framework of jurisdiction may for reference purposes be constructed from a combination of legal documents and hydrographic charts. The resulting zonation of the sea, vague or conflicting though it be in places, establishes the basis for a system of offshore compartition whereby the potential of the world's major water bodies may be utilized in the most effective manner by the community of nations.

Offshore Pattern of Zones

Lines of jurisdiction, easily fixed and demarcated on land, do not lend themselves to ready identification on the surface of water bodies. A network of buoys could conceivably serve this purpose though for the most part hydrographic charts are used for discerning various zones and their limits. National mapping agencies seldom issue material upon which jurisdictional limits are shown, but charts officially published form the basis for plotting offshore claims. The zonal pattern over the global sea, as discussed below, may not be regarded as constituting a system of political entities such as might commonly be found over land areas. Rather, the zones are delineated according to textual specifications and represent a point of departure, or frame of reference, for carrying on offshore activities and from which procedures may be projected. In many instances these specifications fail to encompass detailed data, thus requiring some objectivity in their interpretation relative to actual coastal or bathymetric situations.

Offshore zones near the continental margins or major islands are normally small and tightly fitting segments, particularly in areas of fringing islands and along irregular coastlines. Lines of contact between jurisdiction of neighboring sovereign states also occasion complexities in the pattern. As distance from a shoreline increases so decreases the interest and concern of the coastal state in offshore matters. In turn, the stringency of jurisdiction also decreases. In the high seas sovereign jurisdiction may theoretically approach zero. An exception would be aboard ship where the sovereignty of the flag flown prevails.

Within the idealized zonal pattern under discussion five basic zones, roughly parallel to the coast, may be distinguished: internal waters, territorial sea, contiguous zone, continental shelf, and high seas. In all instances offshore zones are alined in relation to a baseline, which is the legal version of the coast. The following paragraphs present the highlights of each of the offshore zones as distinguished by jurisdictional function.

Internal waters are those along a coast inside the baseline. They consist of water areas in bays and mouths of rivers or estuaries as well as certain other hydrographic features fringing the shores. In contrast, "inland waters," a somewhat similar sounding term, usually refers to such features of the landscape as lakes, rivers, and canals. The Great Lakes, for example, are inland rather than internal waters. Along coastal stretches where the straight baseline is applied, areas of internal waters may lie seaward of what normally would be the baseline of measurement. Sovereignty over these waters is identical to the land area of the coastal state along which they lie.

The *territorial sea,* or *territorial waters,* comprises a zone of water off the coast of a state, which may vary in breadth from 3 to 12 or more miles. The United States recognizes the territorial sea as being no more than 3 miles in breadth. Complete sovereignty is maintained over this zone by the coastal state, but in most circumstances with the right of innocent passage to ships of other states.

The *contiguous zone* comprises a band of water outside, or beyond, the territorial sea in which the coastal state may exercise controls such as those over customs and sanitation. The contiguous zone is measured from the same baseline as the territorial sea, and may extend no more than 12 miles seaward from it. In all cases the contiguous zone is coextensive with the landward margin of the high seas. It also may, and usually does, extend over part of the continental shelf. Since this zone exists for specific purposes, the overlapping of zones creates no particular conflicts in jurisdiction.

Since the Law of the Sea Conferences in Geneva in 1958 and 1960, one frequently sees reference to *fishing zones*. In theory, these zones in many respects correspond to the principles of the contiguous zone, but in practice have no status in Law of the Sea documentation.

Continental shelf refers to the seabed area beyond the outer limits of the territorial sea. The term has both physical and legal connotations but in Law of the Sea matters the latter are usually implied. Briefly, this zone may be exploited exclusively by the coastal state for mineral and certain other resources. Waters of the contiguous zone, as mentioned above, may either wholly or in part lie over the continental shelf without any conflict in claims because of duplicate legal zonation. Neither are fishing rights affected by any legal aspects of the continental shelf. The rights of the coastal state apply to the water in the case of the contiguous zone and to the seabed below in the case of the continental shelf, thus introducing a third dimension to offshore jurisdiction.

High seas refer to all water beyond the outer limit of the territorial sea. Here are the vast ocean areas of the world, for the most part subject to a minimum of control as denoted by the freedom of the seas concept. Surface navigation, aerial navigation, laying of cables, and laying of pipelines exemplify those activities which may be carried on by any state in any part of the high seas. Although the high seas are in part coextensive with the waters of the contiguous zone and those over the continental shelf, freedom of the seas is not invalidated by the zonal overlap. Only specific activities, as disposal of waste materials and collection of customs, fall within the category of the high seas (nearest their landward margins) and at the same time come under control of a state's jurisdiction.

Horizontal Stratification of Jurisdictional Limits

On and below the surface of the sea offshore claims run into three dimensions where jurisdiction over the seabed differs from that of the superjacent water. For example, a coastal state may have the right to drill for petroleum in a submarine area for which no fishing rights obtain to that state. In turn, the vertical dimension of offshore rights above sea level may differ from those on and below the surface of the sea. Here *airspace* must be added to a full inventory of offshore zones, superimposed as it is over the entire surface pattern.

Rights in airspace offer none of the flexibility found on and below the water surface. Overflight of foreign aircraft may not take place over the territorial sea of any state without bilateral (or multilateral) agreement. Nor does there exist in the atmosphere a counterpart to the contiguous zone, or any other special purpose rights of transit. Thus, no right of innocent passage prevails as for surface craft, a situation giving rise to the possibility of hostile action against planes counter to regulations in marginal sea areas where tension exists.

Breadth of the Territorial Sea

No state or statesman will deny the fact that there *is* a territorial sea (or territorial waters) and that it extends along all coastlines of all countries. Such a zone of offshore water lends itself quite logically as that margin of the sea where a state may without interference carry on littoral functions essential to national welfare. The meeting of land and water, two violently contrasting types of physical environments, must necessarily require numerous activities not normally associated with the land alone. Modern methods of transportation and commerce and the consequent easy accessibility of a coastal state create a sense of apprehension on the part of some states to the degree that from a defense point of view the territorial sea may be regarded as a cushion of protection. To other states the opportunity to engage in commerce relegates territorial waters to avenues of ingress and egress and without aspirations of broad exclusive claims of sovereignty.

A major problem of high international concern involves the breadth of the territorial sea—how far seaward should a state's sovereignty extend? This specific question, simple though it may appear, has stirred up animosities in the world community, especially plaguing those states seeking to uphold the freedom of the seas concept. Planes and ships may be fired on, and international incidents over coastal fishing operations may result from conflicting views on this score. Full-scale international conferences in 1958 and 1960 at Geneva under the auspices of the United Nations on the Law of the Sea failed to resolve this issue or bring about any agreement among nations.

The primary basis for recognizing any given breadth of the territorial sea as an international norm lies in guidelines provided by the International Law Commission.[2] Pertinent statements in the documentation reveal the lack of any precise attempt to pin down a fixed breadth. The result has been interpretation by individual states of the rather inclusively worded premises to support national politics and aspirations. The drafted statements in question are contained in Article 3 of the International Law Commission's report as follows:

The Commission recognizes that the international practice is not uniform as regards the delimitation of the territorial sea.

The Commission considers that international law does not permit an extension of the territorial sea beyond twelve miles.

The Commission, without taking any decision as to the breadth of the territorial sea up to that limit, notes on the one hand, that many States have fixed a breadth greater than three miles and on the other hand, that many States do not recognize such a breadth when that of their own territorial sea is less.

The Commission, without taking any decision as to the breadth of the territorial sea fixed by international conference.

The spirit of the above statements seems to imply 3 miles as the conventional breadth by the phrase, ". . . many states have fixed a breadth greater than three miles . . ." Three nautical miles has long been the distance generally accepted by those states upholding the concept of the freedom of the seas.[3] Conversely, other states have set the breadth of their territorial seas at 12 miles, claiming it to be within the limits of the Article. A number of states have also decreed breadths more than 3 and less than 12 miles, while still others have exceeded 12 miles.

Several countries, along the west coast of Latin America facing the unlimited vista of the Pacific, reached the extreme of settling on a terri-

[2] Report of the International Law Commission, General Assembly, Official Records: 11th sess., Supplement No. 9 (A/3159), United Nations, New York, 1956.
[3] Three nautical miles corresponds to 1 league, a former unit of measurement used in marine science. Also, a commonly accepted but not necessarily irrefutable statement attributes the 3-mile breadth to the distance a cannonball could be fired.

torial sea of no less than 200 miles in breadth. Such decrees reflect a desire to retain exclusive fishing rights offshore for this distance, but nonetheless they impinge on the concept of the freedom of the seas. The resulting pattern of claims thus varies from the coast of one political entity to another.

In recent years more and more states have unilaterally extended their territorial waters, usually to 12 miles. Several of the newly independent states of Africa have acted in this fashion. According to one estimate, if all countries were to extend their territorial waters to this distance some 3 million square miles would be lost to the regime of the high seas. Even more important, many of the world's strategic straits and narrow water channels along continental margins and between islands in archipelagoes would be converted from high seas to territorial waters. Examples include the Strait of Dover, Strait of Hormuz, entrance to the Gulf of Bothnia, entrance to the Gulf of Finland, Strait of Gibraltar, Straits of Bab-el-Mandeb, and passages in the chain of Indonesian islands.

During the 1960 Law of the Sea Conference in Geneva the United States, together with Canada, proposed as a compromise a 6-mile territorial sea plus a 6-mile fishing zone. Although the measure failed passage (narrowly) by the necessary two-thirds majority, the concept of greater control on the part of coastal states remains active as evidenced by recent claims. States in seeking to extend their offshore claims in this manner have so far favored reasonably modest distances. Despite the above-mentioned proposal, which entailed a 6-mile territorial sea, the U.S. policy since the Geneva Conference of 1960 continued to adhere strictly to a 3-mile territorial sea.

Double Continental Shelf

In contrast to offshore zones of planimetric design, the continental shelf definitely involves three physical dimensions. In addition to length and breadth, the floor of the sea varies in bathymetric elevation. Unfortunately, yet a "fourth" dimension comes into the picture, for the legal definition of the continental shelf differs markedly from that pertaining to the physical feature itself. Each of the two concepts needs careful attention in order to properly distinguish between the physical and the legal versions.

In a literal sense the continental shelf refers to that part of the ocean floor immediately peripheral to the continental landmasses of the world. In scientific literature one usually sees reference to a depth of either 100 fathoms (600 feet) or 200 meters as being the outer edge of the continental shelf, where on the average there tends to be a definite steepening of slope to greater depths. Maps conveniently show submarine contours of these values to illustrate the limits. Actually, 100 fathoms equal only about 183 meters, but the location of the break in the slope is so indefinite that it cannot be precisely identified by a fixed mathematical value. In fact, the criterion of 100 fathoms tends to be somewhat high since available data show the average depth of the break in slope to lie between the 60- and 80-fathom submarine contours. On the other hand there is positive evidence of continental shelves at much greater depths, the most extreme being 550 meters for the Sahul Shelf off the coast of northern Australia.

The actual angle of slope on a true continental shelf is incredibly small, only about 2 fathoms per mile, or 0.085 degree. The human eye cannot detect a slope of even double this inclination. In many instances, however, the surface of the shelf is not smooth, but forms terraces, ridges, hills, depressions, and canyons. Uneven submarine topography of this type obviously makes the physical shelf difficult to delineate, especially where its outer periphery is fractured and defies generalization.

On the average the continental shelf extends seaward for about 30 miles. But the average width is not very meaningful because of the great variation to be found from place to place. Along the west coast of South America, for example, where mountains rise sharply from the coast, the submarine surface in turn plunges to great depths with very little trace of a ledge which could be construed as a continental shelf. At the opposite extreme, the entire Bering Strait area, extending 800 miles north of the north coast of Siberia, is less than 100 fathoms in depth. At other places, also, the width of the shelf is measured in hundreds of miles, including the Atlantic Ocean off the southern coast of Argentina and the South China Sea off the eastern coast of the Malay Peninsula. The Persian Gulf, some 600 miles long by 230 miles wide is nowhere deeper than 50 fathoms. Its seabed qualifies in its entirety as continental shelf.

In view of current international interest in—and conflict over—Law of the Sea matters the continental shelf has strong legal connotations as well as physical import. There must be means of identifying jurisdictionally that zone of water along any coast relative to the resources of its seabed, particularly minerals. Increasingly it becomes necessary to clarify the rights of sovereign states to exploit offshore resources. Regardless of its location, any given offshore resource must legally appertain to one sovereign state or another, or be subject to the regime of the high seas and thus accessible to any sovereign state.

Guided by reference to the Report of the International Law Commission of 1956, a legal definition of the continental shelf was promulgated at Geneva in 1958 by the following wording:

. . . the sea-bed and subsoil of the submarine areas adjacent to the coast but outside the area of the territorial sea, to a depth of 200 meters or, beyond that limit, to where the depth of the superjacent waters admits of the exploitation of the natural resources of the said areas.

Continuing, the definition went beyond the former Report in that it applies to islands as well as continental mainland:

... the sea-bed and subsoil of similar submarine areas adjacent to the coasts of islands.

Supplementary to the definition of the continental shelf, the rights of exploitation were expressly specified:

The coastal State exercises over the continental shelf sovereign rights for the purpose of exploring it and exploiting its natural resources.

In light of the above excerpts cited from the Articles adopted by the Conference at Geneva, a coastal state has sovereign rights for the purpose of exploring and exploiting resources on or under the seabed of the shelf.

Thus the zone of territorial waters differs in concept from that of a continental shelf as conceived by international jurists. Territorial waters, including their seabed, are part of the sovereign territory of the state, so that no question arises which might challenge the rights to exploit resources within these limits. It is beyond the outer limit of the territorial sea of any state that the definition of the continental shelf becomes critical.

Full sovereignty of both water and seabed extends from the shoreline (or baseline) to the outer limit of the territorial sea. Seaward from this limit the water falls into the region of the high seas, of free access to all states. But with respect to the seabed and its resources certain sovereign rights exclusive to the coastal state exist, thus bringing the third dimension into play. In short, beyond the outer limit of the territorial sea any distant state may navigate freely on the surface of the water, may engage in fishing (assuming there are no other restrictions by definition or agreement), but may not exploit minerals and certain other natural resources from the seabed of the continental shelf.

High Seas and High Flying

All water beyond the outer limit of the territorial sea qualifies as high seas. Here stretch the vast ocean areas of the world, void of sovereignty and subject to the doctrine known as *freedom of the seas*. Over, on, or through this part of the sea any nation may operate aircraft, surface vessels, or submarines. Neither are there restrictions in the high seas to such activities as laying cables or pipelines or, if not in violation of international agreements, to fishing.

The landward margins of the high seas may in part be coextensive with the waters of the contiguous zone and over the continental shelf (but coextensive with only a portion of those over the physical version of the continental shelf). The establishment of any fishing zone as projected by some states must necessarily be in the high seas. However, the freedom of the seas concept as it applies over the high seas does not conflict with the right of the coastal state in any of the zones seaward from the outer limit of the territorial sea or with the continental shelf.

Although the high seas represent the ultimate in opportunities for mobility on an extensive scale, their use for world commerce may be greatly hampered by legal limitation of movement along the margins. A zone of territorial water compounds the restrictive effect of coastal configuration in the narrow seas and along irregular shorelines. Any increase in the width of the territorial sea decreases, out of all proportion to the area involved, high seas maneuverability along the coast. For example, any straits more than 6 but less than 12 miles in width will have a continuous zone of high seas extending through them with a 3-mile but not a 6-mile territorial sea (Strait of Gibraltar, Straits of Malacca).

Air Space

Unlike ships that ply the seas, aircraft have no "right of innocent passage" over territorial waters—only above the high seas is there an absence of any restrictions pertaining to sovereign rights. The complicated structure of international airways with their technical requirements must in all cases conform to the sovereign pattern of land and the marginal seas. Each mile in the air denied to commercial aircraft, as by greater breadth of the territorial sea, offsets just that much the great advances made by the aeronautical industry. Planes of one state may fly over the territorial sea of another state only by bilateral or multilateral agreements, and such accord is by no means always assured in the present-day world. In frequent instances aircraft must fly many extra miles to avoid overflight of certain sovereign territory. For example, a jet aircraft bound from Tehran to Tel Aviv, to avoid flying over Iraq and Syria, will require an additional 245 miles, or approximately an additional 30 minutes of flying time. Flight of military aircraft must adhere strictly to practices incorporated in Law of the Sea conventions. In fact, the shooting down of military planes which "stray" over the territorial waters as well as land territory of an unfriendly state is by no means unknown.

Crises Ahead

Accord and agreement prevail in many aspects of Law of the Sea matters. Those functions pertaining to offshore administrative routine, such as collection of customs and sanitation entail very few controversial points. Also, the manner of establishing offshore zones and the degree of control within them find widespread approval from country to country. The international community, however, runs headlong into serious problems over certain specific aspects of marginal sea complexities—commonly in the form of legal impasses. Major attention is focused upon two specific issues and their attendant ramifications in the economic, political, and defense fields: (1) Breadth of the territorial sea and (2) question of zones with exclusive rights.

The U.S. position holds traditionally to a 3-mile territorial sea, falling into classification as "narrow." Arguments in favor also conform with American policies and attitudes toward international cooperation and progress. In brief the U.S. position:

1. Supports maritime activities and international trade with a minimum of restriction on traffic.

2. Prevents many straits and channels from being closed as high seas passages.

3. Proves advantageous for defense measures, hence facilitates world order.

4. Favors exploration and investigation of offshore areas by oceanographers and other scientists with a minimum of restrictions against freedom of movement.

5. Reduces expenses for patrolling.

6. Allows a flexibility by enabling special-purpose zones to extend beyond territorial waters.

The United States does not recognize any unilateral extension of either the territorial sea or zones of exclusive fishing rights. In the matter of fisheries, however, agreements between or among interested sovereign participants are recognized. In recent months American delegations have participated in conferences designed to properly consider feasible fishing rights off coasts where there have been problems and claimed infractions of international procedure.

Because of growing interest on the part of most countries in oceanography in general and offshore waters in particular the entire subject of the Law of the Sea appears open to expansion. Unfortunately nationalistic aspirations on the part of many states as well as international tension throughout the world augurs badly for harmonious accord over the global sea in the foreseeable future. Alined with these ills is the wide and ofttimes bitter competition for the resources and serviceable uses in, under, and over the sea. Recognition and understanding of the problems and adherence to international justice appears to be the path ahead, with the hope that a more cooperative spirit will evolve and prevail.

VIII. THE REGION AS A CULTURAL ENTITY

The concept of "region" has long been a tool of geographers and other scientists in setting apart areas with a high degree of homogeneity of one or more criteria. In recent years the term "cultural region" has been heard frequently, as a new criterion for differentiating areas large and small was found useful for spatial analysis. "Culture realms" and "culture worlds" have been used to distinguish very large areas with a high degree of commonality if not homogeneity. We frequently speak of such units as the "Arab world," the "Western world," the "communist realm," recognizing as we do that these terms are massive generalizations, yet indicating in areal shorthand that similarities exist, despite differences, within the immense areas to which we refer.

At more intimate scales we find a diversity of culture regions—agricultural regions with a dominant crop pattern, religious culture regions, and many others—each, having unique cultural environments readily visible to the geographer in the field, and perhaps even more evident when plotted on a map.

The following selections indicate some of the factors, conditions, and influences that lead to the development of cultural regions and give examples of such regions.

34. How Does an Agricultural Region Originate?

J. E. Spencer and Ronald J. Horvath

Although "agricultural region" is constantly used by geographers as an analytical description, and maps of agricultural regions are found in nearly all geography texts, relatively little attention has been paid to the genesis and evolution of such regions. Yet knowing origins and change are essential to a full understanding of the current landscape. In answering this very basic question, the authors consider three greatly different agricultural areas where regionalization either has taken place or is in process. Each analyzes a unique agricultural pattern and culture.

In the descriptive and analytical literature of agricultural geography there still exists a significant gap concerning the processes by which a particular region of the earth becomes the agricultural region it later is described to be. This gap is most notable with reference to the original development of an agricultural region out of what essentially is a lightly modified wild landscape, but it also is present where an established agricultural region is transformed into a different kind of agricultural region. In writings on the geography of agriculture there are many papers that demonstrate the regional dominance of a particular crop or crop combination, once that crop or crop series becomes well accepted in the region. Similarly, there are recently available excellent studies that demonstrate changes, once those changes have been initiated or have taken place. The techniques and methodology of recognition and demonstration of dominance and significant change are developing effectively, but too little attention is paid to the intrinsic processes by which dominance and change take place.

This article is a tentative and speculative inquiry into cultural causation, centering its attention on the issue of processes in origination and in change. No attempt is made to crystallize theory, but the issue is raised in the hope of focusing attention on the problems involved.

The question of treatment in a speculative article emerges as a first consideration. It seems to us that the basic nature of this article ought to be exploratory, and that any tentative conclusions suggested here should be verified, rejected, or modified by substantive research carried out on specific agricultural regions. A second question logically follows: How many regions should be examined for potential conclusions, one or more? Should one region be studied in depth or should we extend our survey to include different kinds of regions? The exploratory nature of the article makes a multiregional survey highly desirable and, in order that the peculiarities of one culture realm may be avoided, cross-cultural regional analysis should form the basis of the tentative conclusions. With this in mind we have surveyed one occidental and two oriental examples, beginning with the American Corn Belt, and followed by the Philippine coconut landscape and the Malayan rubber landscape. The American Corn Belt has been clearly identified as an agricultural region, whereas the coconut-producing sector of the Philippines and the rubber-producing zone of the Federation of Malaya have

SOURCE: *Annals Association of American Geographers,* LIII (March, 1963), 74–92. Dr. Spencer is professor of geography, University of California, Los Angeles; Dr. Horvath is a member of the same department.

not yet been clearly recognized and labelled as agricultural regions of a mature sort. The article will not inquire into and demonstrate fully the origin and evolution of three regions, in part because of the limitations of space. A preliminary survey will be presented, which will necessarily preclude the consideration of all aspects exhaustively.

The Origin and Evolution of the American Corn Belt

First of all it may be asked: What is the Corn Belt or what are its basic characteristics? Viewed as an agricultural complex the Corn Belt is a crop and animal assemblage primarily producing corn (mainly used as an animal feed), hogs, and cattle, and secondarily yielding several minor products. A considerable variation is encountered within the region. For example, predominantly cash grain areas with few animals are found as well as permanent pasture areas with many animals. Besides areal variation the Corn Belt has changed significantly through time. Weaver has demonstrated beyond all doubt that the Corn Belt has been changing internally and no longer is so clearly the Corn Belt. Many geographers, the writers included, have informally dubbed it something else, but its formal name appears to be shifting to the Corn-Soy Belt. Weaver has suggested in fair detail the process by which the soybean intruded itself into one portion of the region, though he has not fully elaborated the story.

Comment on Corn Belt beginnings is not entirely absent from the literature. As early as 1925 J. Russell Smith offered an explanation of how the Corn Belt began.

The Corn Belt is a gift of the gods—the rain god, the sun god, the ice god, and the gods of geology. In the middle of the North American continent the gods of geology made a wide expanse of land where the rock layers are nearly horizontal. The ice gods leveled the surface with their glaciers, making it ready for the plow and also making it rich. The rain god gives summer showers. The sun god gives summer heat. All this is nature's conspiracy to make man grow corn. Having corn, man feeds it to cattle and hogs, and thereby becomes a producer of meat.

Though we may admire the poetic tenor of the explanation, we can only query: Who told man to raise corn, and to have cattle and pig breeding stock handy? If the explanation were true, why had not the first man to live here, the American Indian, originated the Corn Belt hundreds, if not thousands, of years before the white man finally produced it?

The following statement is also pertinent to the problem of origins:

Only gradually have the present agricultural patterns of eastern North America made their appearance. At first there was very little difference between one place and another. The European grains were tried, but very quickly the colonists adopted both Indian crops and Indian methods. In the course of time, however, certain areas became differentiated from other areas in terms of agriculture.

In the same paragraph thirteen crop regions were enumerated, but there is no suggestion of the specific processes by which these separate regions originated and became differentiated.

It is not our purpose to criticize two outstanding works, but rather to show two earlier statements which are somewhat symbolic of a variety of views on geographic causation. A third and more recent statement is given in the following section on colonial antecedents.

Colonial Antecedents

The pattern of early colonial agriculture was a blend of American Indian and European crops and practices. After European crops and cropping methods failed, Indian crops and methods were borrowed. Most notable among the Indian crops was corn. The initial agricultural contribution of the Indians to the colonists was great, for it included not only a number of crops which were well suited to the local environment, but it also included methods and techniques, such as clearing land and fertilizing fields. To the aboriginal agricultural complex, the settlers added livestock, especially cattle and hogs. The hog found excellent conditions in the forest and multiplied rapidly. They foraged for themselves and required only a little of the farmer's attention. At harvest time they might be fed some corn to fatten them before slaughter. Cattle were also important in the early subsistence stage.

In the Colonial Period commercial agriculture emerged slowly in favored localities. One of the earliest pork packing centers was the Connecticut Valley, where as early as 1660 hogs were fattened with corn for market. Later Virginia and North Carolina came to be the outstanding pork-producing areas of the Colonies. As for cattle, an early division of grazing and feeder areas occurred. The Connecticut Valley was an early feeder area and was the center in which cattle were collected from grazing areas as far afield as Vermont. The western portions of the Carolinas and, to a lesser degree, western Virginia and Pennsylvania were the most important colonial grazing areas. These areas contributed to the evolution of the grazing and droving practices that later characterized the humid prairies and finally the semi-arid West. Cattle and some hogs were driven from these early feeder areas to the markets in New York and Philadelphia.

One outstanding area can be identified in which another feature of the Corn Belt complex was further evolved—southeastern Pennsylvania. Higbee has described this area as the cradle of the Corn Belt, tracing the Corn Belt almost intact to a Colonial start in southeastern Pennsylvania.[1] Higbee has pointed out one of the truly outstanding areas in American agricultural history and the evolution of some Corn Belt characteristics can be traced back to southeastern Pennsylvania. However, it appears an oversimplification to deduce the whole complex from this one source. The first and most important difficulty is that the dominance of corn is not explained. A second important difficulty is that the hog never assumed a primary position among livestock in southeastern Pennsylvania.

Perhaps the two most important areas bridging the gap between the Eastern seaboard and the classical Corn Belt are the Kentucky Bluegrass area and the Nashville basin. During the 1790's these areas apparently had a rudimentary Corn Belt economy, but later became centers, respectively, for breeding fast horses and growing tobacco. It seems that these two areas may have been the most significant areas in the evolution of the Corn Belt system lying outside the classical Corn Belt.

In summary, there occurred a significant development of Corn Belt traits in Colonial America; the European settler's contact with the American Indian resulted in an agricultural metamorphosis. During the subsequent development several favored localities can be identified as significant centers in the evolution of the Corn Belt system: the Connecticut Valley, southeastern Pennsylvania, the Kentucky Bluegrass area, and the Nashville Basin. In the Corn Belt the major traits were combined, modified, and further evolved. The story that follows will attempt to indicate the steps by which American farmers developed this agricultural scheme and fitted it to the forested and grassland landscapes of the Middle West.

The Landscapes of the Middle West and Their Settlement

Within the area to become the Corn Belt pioneer settlers encountered two major landscape types: first, the woodlands, and second, the grasslands of the prairie and Great Plains. In general the forested area cov-

---

[1] Higbee has closely approached the issue of origins in some of the chapters of a recent volume, and his chapter on the Corn Belt deals specifically with the issue. Though less dramatic than Smith's description, Higbee's description covers the same ground in discussing physical origins of the region. He says, in part, in his section on cultural origins: "Early in the eighteenth century an industrious group of immigrants from the German and Swiss Rhineland came to settle in the shale and limestone lowlands of what are now the counties of Chester, Lancaster, and York. These people built fine barns, bred high-grade livestock, and were adept at maintaining soil fertility by the use of ground limestone, gypsum, and animal manures. They were successful at clover culture, and practiced crop rotations which generally included corn, wheat, barley, oats, and clover-grass meadows. They were good dairymen as well as cheese and butter makers and kept hogs to dispose of such dairy wastes as skim milk, buttermilk, and whey . . . The crop and animal husbandry practices of these farmers of early Pennsylvania set the style for the modern Corn Belt." Edward Higbee, *American Agriculture: Geography Resources, Conservation* (New York: John Wiley, 1958), p. 233.

ered almost all of the eastern portion of the region, but the percentage of woodland decreased towards the west, finally occurring only in narrowing belts associated with the rivers. The grasslands, conversely, increased in area towards the west, though they occurred only in small areas in central Ohio and Indiana.

Two types of woodland can be distinguished: those which were well drained and those which had excessive water. The latter occurred in the flood zones adjacent to rivers and low lying swamps. The grasslands of the prairie are commonly divided into wet and dry prairie, depending on drainage. In general the sectors of prairie and woodlands having poor drainage were settled later than were the areas which were well drained.

From the geographic point of view, the settling of the Midwest and the evolution of the Corn Belt can be divided into two periods related to the collective interaction of farmers with the two landscapes. The first period lasted roughly until 1850 and was characterized by the restriction of farming to the forested areas or grasslands adjacent to the woodland. The Corn Belt began in several places within the forested landscape. The techniques necessary to subsist in this environment were long a part of the colonial farming culture in the seaboard zone. The outstanding characteristic of the second period was the dispersal of farmers into the grasslands of the prairie and great plains, which at first presented a significant hindrance to the farmer whose technology and crop mentality had developed in the forested landscape. Before the modern Corn Belt could take its present outline there had to occur a major transformation in the abilities and understandings of American farmers to deal with the new prairie landscapes.

The typical sequent economic utilization of the two landscapes is difficult to determine. A Corn Belt economy was reached in different parts of the present Corn Belt at different times. For example, the Scioto River basin of Ohio had the beginnings of a Corn Belt economy in 1805, whereas large scale wet prairie cultivation did not occur until the 1880's. Further difficulty arises because the typical sequent utilization of the grasslands differs from that of the forest landscapes. In the drier forested areas subsistence farming developed first and was followed by commercial farming, and then by Corn Belt farming. The grasslands proceeded from livestock grazing to subsistence farming to commercial farming and, finally, to Corn Belt farming. In the woodlands as well as the grasslands there were differences in the cropping sequence owing to good or poor drainage.

The Forested Landscape

Near the end of the eighteenth century, American pioneers began settling the forested river courses west of the Appalachian Mountains. The

Ohio River valley and the valleys of its tributaries were the early focus of this activity. The forested environment was well suited to the economy of the earliest pioneers since they derived the greater part of their sustenance from hunting, fishing, and gathering. The early pioneers often engaged in a small amount of agriculture, copying Indian methods and cultivating Indian crops. Their main crop was corn.

Characteristically, a more farming-minded group of settlers followed, causing the neighbor-shunning pioneers to move on to virgin country. At first the newcomers' economies differed little from those of the earlier pioneers; however, subsistence agriculture played an ever-increasing role. The settlers clung tenaciously but not exclusively to the wooded land, which required many years of toil to clear. Beginning in western Ohio the treeless prairie often was available, but such areas were either avoided or only their margins were cultivated. For two centuries American farming had taken place in a wooded landscape and the livelihood of the early farmers depended on this kind of environment. The river supplied domestic water, a means of transportation, and some fish. The forest supplied logs for fences, cabins, and domestic fuel, and the good soils, once cleared, were easy to cultivate with simple tools, and provided bountiful yields. Corn continued to be the chief crop in the cropping patterns of the subsistence farmers, though additional new crops were grown, including wheat and several kinds of vegetables. The farm diet included the ever-present hog.

The evolution of a commercial economy proceeded very slowly at first. A small surplus of corn or wheat might be produced which could be sold to settlers passing through or to new settlers in the area. The hogs brought in by settlers found excellent conditions and multiplied rapidly by foraging in the forest. One of the qualities of the razorback which made it a successful animal in the woodlands was its ability to elude predators. Most pork was bound for home consumption, though some could be transported to another settlement down river.

Within the classical Corn Belt the emergence of the Corn Belt system can be traced back to several scattered areas in the forested landscape. Four areas are noteworthy: the Scioto Valley, the Miami Valley, the Indianapolis-Middle Wabash, and the Sangamon valley. The Scioto River basin may well be the earliest Corn Belt nucleus, dating back to 1805, when the first herd of corn-fattened cattle were driven to the eastern market from the area which was to become a part of the Corn Belt.

Corn very early assumed a dominant position among the commercial crops grown in the forested landscape. One reason for the popularity of corn was that many of the settlers came from an area which had a well-established corn-cropping tradition. Added to this was the corn-growing tradition of the Indians who inhabited the area. Since corn proved to be the most useful and reliable crop for a subsistence economy, its ascendance to dominance as a commercial crop came rather easily.

One of the most important qualities of corn was its reliability. Time and time again the agricultural literature and pioneer letters point out this quality. For example, Solon Robinson notes in passing, while describing a harvest, "Corn was good, as usual." The varieties of wheat grown, on the other hand, were plagued by rust. The ecological superiority of corn was a very important consideration to the subsistence-oriented farmer, but soon more corn could be grown than could be eaten by the local population. As the farmer began to think of outlets for this surplus, the ways of disposing of corn seemed to be a primary consideration, and agriculture began its trend toward the commercial pattern.

Wheat was the only crop that came near challenging the dominance of corn. Many western pioneers understandably wanted to grow wheat, since wheat has traditionally been an excellent frontier cash crop, and it had a history of use in Colonial seaboard or European cropping. Wheat had a number of drawbacks, of which the most important were that it was not as reliable a crop as corn and transportation during the pre-railroad era was difficult and costly. The Miami valley is an excellent example of an area which produced wheat until 1820 and turned to corn, hogs, and cattle after repeated troubles with wheat. Solon Robinson said in 1850, after many years of advocating wheat as the crop for the prairies, "Is it not time for you (prairie farmers) to begin to think that wheat is not the most natural and profitable staple crop . . . Does any land in the world produce better beef than the prairies . . . Indian corn, the best crop in the world for making beef, rarely, if ever, fails."

A major problem associated with the commercial production of corn was its bulkiness. Corn could be shipped down the Ohio and Mississippi rivers to New Orleans but this was never satisfactory. Transportation was so difficult that even when market prices were favorable, transport cost often proved to be the limiting factor. An early solution was to turn the corn into a more compact and valuable product. Converting corn into whiskey, pork, or beef satisfied this need. Hogs and cattle could be raised without being fed corn, but it was soon found that corn-fed livestock commanded much higher prices. Another aspect of the utility of livestock was that they could be turned onto a field of corn, hence eliminating the need to harvest, a practice which fit well into the prevailing farming philosophy that "land is cheap but labor is dear." An added advantage to fattening hogs and cattle was that they could transport themselves to market. The golden age of droving was between 1810 and 1840, although droving began well before 1800 and continued up to the Civil War, when herds of cattle, horses, sheep, hogs, and sometimes even turkeys were driven across the Appalachian Mountains to the eastern seaboard.

After 1817 the steamboat became a significant stimulant to the production of hogs. Pork could be satisfactorily salted and shipped in barrels down the Mississippi River. The limited market for salted beef explains the continuance of cattle droving. Hogs in smaller numbers were still driven with the cattle, since they added no extra expense.

The emergence of a Corn Belt economy can be seen in the years preceding 1850. The scattered zones were in many respects miniature forerunners of the modern Corn Belt. The farmers primarily grew corn which they fed to hogs and cattle. The evolution of the present extent of the Corn Belt is the result of the spread of this agricultural system into the grasslands from the forested zones.

The Grasslands of the Prairie and Great Plains

No precise date can be given for the farmers' emancipation from the forested landscape. First, the oak openings in Ohio were cultivated and during the 1840's a small number of farmers began moving out onto the edge of the prairie. As a result of the development of successful prairie cultivation techniques, the late 1850's, the 60's, and the 70's saw the rapid populating of the prairie. The complete exploitation of the wet prairie awaited tiling and ditching which became popular in the 1880's. Development of the steel plow during the 1830's had made the breaking up of the tough sod a far easier task than before.[2] The corn crop was limited by the acreage the farmer could cultivate; consequently, introduction of the horse-drawn cultivator contributed to rapid expansion of the area of production. Well-drilling equipment and the windmill provided a means of securing water and removed the necessity of living near a stream; barbed wire solved the fencing problem. A subsistence farming economy did not fare well on the prairie, but commercial farming did and the settlement of the prairie was made possible by the technological advances that came in this era.

The extension of railroads to the Midwest during the 1850's had a significant influence on the extension of a Corn Belt economy. The railroad removed the dependence on river transportation for exporting Midwest products. It hauled in lumber for the construction of houses and fences, and made access to the West much easier from the eastern United States. The end of droving must be attributed to the railroad, but this did not occur at once. Farmers were reluctant to change because they considered the cost too high and some believed at first that the animals lost more poundage in a moving car than in walking to market.

[2] The mould board plow had been developed earlier, but the sticky prairie soils adhered to its rough wood or cast iron mould board. The steel plow carried a smoothly polished mould board that cut smoothly through all types of soils.

Grains rather than livestock were affected by the railroad in the early years and an increased percentage of corn was sold as a cash crop. The railroad companies sold their lands to settlers and were vitally concerned about farm production. As a result, the railroad companies engaged in crop experimentation, promoted agricultural fairs, and made other efforts to promote prosperity. In other words, the influence of the railroad, unlike other transportational developments, was far more than just another improvement in transportation.

Corn was the leading crop on the prairie almost from the beginning. Early trial and error found that other crops were not well suited to prairie conditions and that corn was the best first crop to plant on the rich prairie soils, because it was a quick maturing, highly versatile crop that seldom failed. Corn was an important constituent of the "hog and hominy" diet of the pioneer farmers in addition to being a cash grain crop or livestock feed crop. Other assets of corn were: first, planting corn cost only one-fourth to one-half the cost of planting wheat; second, corn was an easier crop to grow; and third, corn did not need to be harvested within a short period, eliminating the need for additional labor.

Wheat, the second most logical crop from the viewpoint of cultural acquaintance patterns, was rarely successful on the prairie soils. Repeated wheat failures caused many advocates of wheat to abandon it. However, wheat remained a crop in the Corn Belt until the 1870's, when wheat produced in the more arid parts of the Great Plains permanently lowered the market price of wheat, making it an uneconomical crop on the increasingly expensive Corn Belt land.

The bulkiness of corn remained a hindrance to its sale and the limited consumer-industrial demand left the prairie farmer with the choice of turning to a new crop or finding a use for corn. Feeding corn to hogs and cattle was apparently not obvious to the prairie farmers at first. Local newspapers and agricultural newspapers were hardly in accord on the crop for the prairie, and Ross lauds the foresight of a writer in 1859 who advised: "Raise Corn always in preference to Wheat. Learn to convert Corn into Pork, Beef, and Wool by the cheapest and most economical modes."

The hog fitted nicely into the prairie farming pattern. The reason for the popularity of the hog was summed up by British agriculturalists visiting the Middle West: "The hog . . . met the requirements of the middle western farmer more perfectly than any other animal because of its omnivorous character, its hardiness, and the great abundance of cheap food."

Cattle retained an important position in the grassland portion of the Corn Belt. The expansion of corn-growing onto the prairie displaced the livestock-raising economy from the humid prairie to the semi-arid portions of the Great Plains. However, the same functional relationship between stock-raising areas and stock-fattening areas was retained. Many Corn Belt farmers kept dairy cattle, especially in areas which had a great deal of land in permanent pasture.

Sheep raising was short-lived in the Corn Belt. Wild dogs, diseases, price decline, and, perhaps most important, the unwillingness of farmers to give sheep the necessary care contributed to the rapid decline of sheep raising.

When all things were considered over a long period of time, the most reasonable utilization of corn was as a feed to livestock in both forest and grass landscapes.

The suitability of corn, hogs, and cattle to frontier life and to the natural environment was an important consideration, but this alone does not explain production of any of these products. The role of the market in forming the character of the Corn Belt is indisputable. Thus, as the early reason for feeding corn to livestock, "to walk corn to market," declined as a factor, hogs and cattle remained because of increased market demand. Price continued to be an important determinant in the corn-hog-cattle economy and the relative amount of each commodity sold depended on its price. However, the lesson had to be learned slowly, because objective data were not originally available.

Elements of a Farming "Mentality"

Up to this point the inquiry has emphasized the economic, technologic, and agronomic aspects of the origin of the Corn Belt; although scattered remarks have pointed to the role of the social and psychological elements of culture. The myths, beliefs, or mental set of a particular group may or may not have any basis in fact; nevertheless a belief or mental set may be the cause of a particular pattern. The decline of sheep as an important animal can not be fully explained by disease and wild dogs, for these were minor problems. The Corn Belt farmers have surmounted more formidable obstacles, i.e., the draining of the Black Swamp and the wet prairie, and the up-breeding of livestock. Rather the decline of sheep is better explained by considering the psychological factors and cultural traditions of a society. The farmers' unwillingness to give sheep the necessary care, and, perhaps even more important, the general dislike for sheep were the causes for the decline of sheep on Corn Belt farms.

The probings of rural sociologists into the question of how farmers accept new ideas have indicated the workings of an involved cultural process. The regularity with which an innovation comes into a farming region and diffuses through it has led to a classification of individuals according to the speed with which they accept new ideas. According to this classification a given farming population is composed of innovators, adopters, and nonadopters. One study indicates that this process was operating during the settlement of the Corn Belt. Thus, the interaction of neighbor with neighbor and of individual with community regarding agricultural matters represents the working of this cultural process at the grass roots. The process involves individual and collective diagnosis of an environment, selection of a suitable crop from acquaintance patterns, and observation of the reaction of the crop to the environment and to the market. The argument of two neighbors over some cropping technique or the advice given to new arrivals in the area by older residents can have far-reaching consequences, in view of the fact that this same scene is taking place throughout an area about to become an agricultural region settled by an immigrating population.[3]

Several institutions, such as the general agricultural newspaper, the local newspaper, and the agricultural fair, magnify or modify this basic cultural process. In a sense the newspaper magnified the basic neighbor-to-neighbor discussion by printing the points of view of local farmers on the merits of some agricultural issue. The agricultural fair allowed farmers from a wide area to get together to see agricultural developments. However, "the evaluation of the fair as a composite educational institution apart from other educational or semi-educational organizations . . . is impossible."

The agricultural experiment station and the government agricultural literature may also have influenced the crop pattern. But Bardolph states that "Illinois farmers in the years before 1870 shared an almost pathological aversion to book farming that characterized the rural class throughout the nation."

Taken from the point of view of psychological aspects, social processes, and cultural traditions of the settlers, the Corn Belt can be regarded as the landscape expression of a farming "mentality." A farming "mentality" in this context refers to the totality of the beliefs of the farmers over a region regarding the most suitable use of land in an area.

The Maturing of an Agricultural Region

Another issue which can be raised, but not here completely resolved, is: When does an agricultural landscape become an agricultural region, or when did the Corn Belt become the Corn Belt? The seemingly crucial

[3] The experience of the senior author's father illustrates the role of the neighbor in the development of an agricultural region. In 1891 he bought a piece of unimproved farmland in Iowa, in a sector not yet fully occupied. Having come from a northern Ohio farm originally, he was unfamiliar with the local Iowa croping practices. Since he had a limited economic stake behind him, and could not afford to engage in unproven experimentation, he canvassed the local farmers for advice. He planted nothing but corn and handled his land as did his neighbors. In accepting the local traditions, he succeeded and also moved with the trends, acting as one more agent to mature an agricultural region.

element in this question is some form of recognition. It may well be that the kind of recognition that is chosen must be arbitrary. In the case of the Corn Belt, one might ask, when was the term Corn Belt first used? The earliest date that Warntz found in popular sources was 1882. The crystallizing of the concept of the Corn Belt appeared in print in 1903. The date by which a Corn Belt economy was achieved varied from one part of the region to another. Western Ohio had a Corn Belt economy decades before eastern Nebraska. An inclusive date might be between 1890 and 1900. The outline of the Corn Belt took its present form around the turn of the twentieth century. The basic distribution of corn and hogs has remained rather similar to the distribution in 1900 athough minor changes have occurred. By 1925 the maximum acres in corn had been achieved and since then there has been a decline.

In summary the Corn Belt system is the result of a long evolutionary process. The seaboard area of the Colonial period contributed significantly to the development of the primary traits of the region. Later scattered Corn Belt nuclei can be identified in the forested landscape near rivers. By about 1850 a new technology plus experience with the prairie resulted in a dispersal of settlers and the Corn Belt system into grasslands of the dry prairie and later into the wet prairie. This inquiry into the origin and evolution of the Corn Belt points to the working of a cultural process, in an evolutionary way, rather than to a gift from a pantheon of gods or to a widespread and purposeful copying of an efficient model known to all settlers.

The Philippine Coconut Landscape

May we turn now to southeastern Asia for an interesting variation in the development of agricultural regionalism. One of the distinctive landscapes of the Philippines is the coconut landscape.[4] There are about 2,800,000 acres of coconut palms in the Philippines today, and the area is expanding steadily. Coconut trees can be found growing throughout the archipelago, entering into home domestic economy or commercial agriculture, but there are several environmental factors that have motivated a regional concentration in planting coconut trees. The most significant environmental factor is the seasonal distribution of the typhoon, whose strong winds damage the crowns of the trees, blow off the fruits, or break off the trunks and blow down lightly anchored trees. Another factor is temperature, since the tree does not produce well in the lower temperatures found at high altitudes. Lesser factors are local occurrences of poor drainage or very low quality in soils. For the Philippines, environmental factors help set the northern boundaries of

---

[4] Coconut landscape and rubber landscape are used simply as descriptive terms, uncapitalized, since neither can be equated to the Corn Belt as a formal agricultural region at its present stage of development.

the coconut-producing region, and also affect its localized expression. The southward boundaries of the region find no such environmental limitation and recent expansion of coconut plantings has been in this direction.

In major terms the coconut palm becomes really significant in the landscape south of Manila, and the chief concentration of trees in 1962 is in central southern Luzon, south of the Laguna de Bay. Here millions of trees are found in almost solid plantings, in spaced plantation patterns, and in the more crowded irregular plantings of the traditional type; coconut trees are so dominant in the landscape that the term coconut landscape has real meaning.

The Background of Coconut Cultivation

The coconut palm has been grown for a great many centuries in the Philippines as a basic crop plant, since the tree and its fruit have extremely wide-ranging utility as construction material, handicraft raw material, tool and utensil material, and as food and beverage. Earlier the oil was the primary lighting fluid in Philippine homes. Almost every Filipino is familiar with coconut in most of its ramifications, as a crop tree and as a product of almost infinite use in Filipino culture. He is well aware that in the southern Philippines, in the lower hill country and on the lowlands, the coconut is very dependable as a crop. Colloquially the coconut often is referred to as the "lazy man's crop" for, once the tree is well started, the owner may, figuratively, recline under it the rest of his life with coconuts falling in his lap. The coconut palm has a very long productive life, with a maximum not clearly determined but appearing to approach one hundred years. Familiarity with, confidence in, and liking for the coconut seem to resemble the feeling of earlier American occupants of the central midwest for corn.

Since at least the tenth century whole coconuts have been a commodity purchased by Chinese traders, and from the fifteenth to the nineteenth centuries China was the chief buyer of such coconut products as were exported from the Philippines. European interest in coconut products was satisfied by India, Ceylon, or the Indies, and exports to Europe from the Philippines were insignificant until the very end of the nineteenth century. The utility of the coconut to the native economy of an increasing population during Spanish times was the real reason for expansion of plantings from the fifteenth to the late nineteenth centuries. As Spanish prohibitions on general foreign trade with the Philippines were relaxed during the latter half of the nineteenth century, sugar, manila hemp from abacá, and tobacco became items sought after and, as agriculture changed, these three products attracted the attention of farmers to the possibilities of commercial agriculture. In 1870 a geographical study of the islands treated the production and export of each of the three crop products at length, but almost ignored coconut, even though it must have been widely distributed and basic among crop plants of the islands.

Factors Contributing to Change

During the late decades of the nineteenth century the European demand for edible fats began to outrun mid-latitude supplies, and the coconut began its rise as an item of export agriculture in the Asiatic tropics. By 1890 the Philippine export figure still stood at only 4,654 tons of copra, but by 1897 it had climbed to 50,714 tons, and the Philippines were about to become important as a world source of coconut products. Already the south-central Luzon region was notable for its coconut plantings, for this region had long supplied most of the domestic volume of lighting oil and the slowly rising volume of coconut exports. Here already were centered the small undertakings in coir manufacture, the making of small volumes of dessicated coconut, and such other industrial operations as related to coconut. Manila and the central plain of Luzon formed the chief markets. Elsewhere in the islands only Cebu was a significant contributor to foreign markets. Had the world demand for coconut leveled off near the 1897 level, the southern Luzon area could have continued to supply the Philippine export volume, plantings elsewhere would not have increased greatly, and those local surpluses would have gone to waste as they had done for centuries. But the world demand continued to rise, and free trade patterns between the United States and the Philippines became operative in 1909. These changes stimulated the market for Philippine coconut products, and produced a marked increase in palm plantings in southern Luzon. Filipinos became aware that the coconut was becoming a salable product, adding still another utility to the already long list of its uses.

After 1910 increasing acreage of coconut were planted in various southern sectors of the Philippines, both as small holdings and as plantations. Filipinos have controlled almost all small holdings, and Filipinos, Chinese, and Americans have participated in plantation development. However, the total amount of land that is devoted to plantation-sized holdings is relatively small, and coconut production from such holdings is only about 10 per cent of the total Philippine production.[5]

The share of coconut land today owned by non-Philippine citizens is very small, and coconut production primarily is on small Filipino-operated farms. About half the farms south of Manila today grow coconut palms, and only rice is grown on more farms than grow coconut.

[5] Elsewhere in southeastern Asia 100 acres normally is the holding used to distinguish between the "small-holder" and the "plantation" or "estate" operator. This is the criterion used here.

Sugar cane, abacá, and tobacco, by contrast, are chiefly specialist crops grown by relatively few farmers. The former concentration of coconut plantings in south-central Luzon today amounts to less than one-fifth the total coconut plantings of the islands. The coconut landscape of the Philippines forms a positive and dynamic regionalism today which is occupying an ever-larger proportion of crop land and is extending farther southward.

The mechanics of extending the coconut landscape are varied. Some new farms now are being planted to coconut by operators who are commercially minded at the outset, and who can afford to plant a given acreage fully. There are also the dooryard or field margin plantings by farmers who are primarily growers of rice, sweet potatoes, abacá, or corn, in a diversified cropping pattern which envisions the coconut only as a portion of a cropping complex. And there are farmers who plant rice, corn, abacá, bananas, sweet potatoes, or manioc as short-run cropping patterns, but who annually interplant coconut seedlings until the time when the palms cover the whole of the farm, and the farm then becomes a commercial coconut producer. Since coconut plantings are almost invariably a part of any of the specific techniques, the coconut landscape is being extended. The ultimate extent and shape of the coconut-producing region cannot now be clearly predicted.

In the years since 1910 the price for coconut products on the world market has fluctuated widely. During periods of war, prices have been high, but there also have been periods during which coconut product prices have been low. However, prices of other agricultural commodities flowing into international trade also have fluctuated, and coconut production has maintained its "lazy man's crop" advantage in the popular mind. The rate of expansion in plantings of coconut palms has fluctuated over the decades but planting has never ceased.

The Psychology of Coconut Planting

Coconut planting occupies a prominent place in the minds of most farmers in the southern Philippines. This psychological mind-set is a strong force in the evolution of the coconut landscape. It is a culturally habituated predisposition toward a particular crop providing a stable return which helped to start an agricultural regionalism and continues to expand that regionalism at present. The regionalism was begun under circumstances of international economics, and is continuing and expanding in consequence of the long life of the palm, its long-term utility, and its simple technology regardless of short-term factors of international economics. To most Filipino coconut farmers the world price and competitive volume of coconut products do not now figure very prominently in their thinking, since the "lazy man's crop" psychology has strengthened. If coconut continues to be a marketable crop, even at low prices, if no epidemic of disease wipes out plantings wholesale, or if no other crops enter the picture with psychologically strong competitive attractions, the Philippine coconut landscape will continue its expansion. Coconut farming, as a way of life, pleases the Filipino and he persists in it despite periodic low prices. Agricultural agents in the Philippines often despair at this persistence and at the refusal of farmers to experiment with other potentially more profitable crops, but in the mind of the Filipino farmer changes in the way of life are involved in such crops, in addition to the risk of experiment.

In summary, a coconut landscape in the Philippines has come about somewhat differently from the way in which the Corn Belt developed in the United States. In a region in which coconut has long been grown as a subordinate subsistence crop, its comprehensive utility made it known to all inhabitants throughout the Philippines, and younger generations grew up thoroughly indoctrinated. The basic technologies for processing the harvested coconut matured in the small core area of south-central Luzon. A sudden change in the expression of world commodity demand provided a set of circumstances by which subsistence coconut farmers could become commercial coconut farmers, in their own home area and on their own terms. Had the world demand arisen in 1700, Filipinos might then have capitalized upon it, or had the demand not appeared when it did, the crystallization of the region would have been delayed. Increasingly Filipinos have capitalized upon the opportunity, and they now consume a very small percentage of their total coconut production. In what has been a home area of the coconut palm for many centuries a strong agricultural regionalism has crystallized. At this point there are gaps that remain still uncultivated or that contain a complex of other crops in the landscape. The dynamics of change still are in process toward a mono-crop regional landscape, an agricultural pattern satisfying the way of life preferred by many Filipinos.

The Malayan Rubber Landscape

As a last example of the way in which cultural elements impinge upon the issues of agricultural regionalism, we may review the case of the Malayan rubber landscape. The crop creating the chief agricultural regionalism was entirely alien, and the chief creators of the regionalism also were alien to the country. Though at one point a clear regionalism showed itself, recent developments have moved in the direction of diffusion of the rubber landscape to all parts of Malaya.

Nineteenth Century Malaya

In the early nineteenth century Malaya was a country with a small population, with only localized expressions of agricultural landscapes, with a large expanse of lightly altered tropical forest, and with only the beginnings of the plural culture and economy that became so characteristic of the early twentieth century. Malays participated to a small extent in the nineteenth century forest extraction of various of the rubbery gums that were becoming of interest to Europe, but they preferred their riverine and coastal village kampong life, in which fishing and jungle gardening were combined in a distinctive pattern that made little areal impact upon the landscape. During the century Europeans and Chinese actively pursued tin mining, chiefly in a zone inland from the west coast. During the last half of the century Europeans interested in agriculture or in trade in agricultural commodities could not interest Malays in participating in the production of items which interested Europe. As British efforts to establish plantations for growing sugar, cacao, coffee, and pepper persisted, the Malays declined to work as wage earners on the plantations, and the British imported Indian laborers, thus contributing a significant element to the population. Had the Malays been willing to engage in wage earning in agriculture, thus altering their own living patterns, the social history of Malaya might well have taken a different course, and the rubber landscape might have presented a different appearance today.

The Introduction of Rubber

None of the efforts at growing sugar, cacao, or coffee succeeded, and the growing of spices was almost a lost art when British efforts at agricultural production in Malaya reached major proportions. Between 1870 and 1895 there was considerable experimental growing of several of the rubbery gum-producing trees. Brazilian *hevea* rubber seedlings were first grown in the Singapore Botanical Gardens in 1877. By 1895 experiments in Malaya concluded that Brazilian *hevea* rubber trees were the most satisfactory of the several possibilities, and there were numerous interplantings of *hevea* rubber trees with young coffee plantings near Kuala Lumpur. Coffee prices slumped in the last years of the century, whereas the price of rubber rose, and by 1901 all the European-owned coffee plantations had been interplanted with rubber trees. In 1905 the total area of rubber trees was about 50,000 acres, and the price was about two Malayan dollars a pound, but most of the trees still were too young to tap, and the Malayan export was but 105 tons. Falling coffee and cacao prices, booming rubber prices, and the successful growing of *hevea* rubber trees turned the tide of opinion rapidly to favor rubber growing, in itself clearly a case of economic motivation.

By 1909 the acreage of young rubber trees was 290,000 and the 1910 price of over five Malayan dollars a pound produced a crisis, boom reaction in Malaya. British plantation companies were rapidly formed,

Chinese interests greatly expanded, and in the states of Selangor and Negri Sembilan even Malays planted rubber trees in their kampong gardens or converted a few of their rice fields to smallholdings of rubber. The ease of securing land on which to plant rubber was a significant factor in the whole operation. By 1921 plantings had expanded to just over 1,500,000 acres, the Malayan production totalled 181,000 metric tons, and the price of rubber went down to thirty-three Malayan cents. Malaya produced nearly half the world supply of rubber in what amounted to a crisis-depression. About half the rubber plantings were in smallholdings of under 100 acres each, the plantations of over 100 acres being owned by Chinese and British interests. The larger smallholdings were Chinese or Indian, and Malay holdings were in the very small acreage category.

The crisis-depression was clearly an economic matter of supply and demand, but it had few objective guide lines by which to determine the proper levels of development of agriculture, and the reactions of the participants varied. The Malays went back to their traditional living patterns, not much affected by an interesting gamble that had not paid off very well. Europeans and Chinese, however, floundered in the depression, and put into effect governmental restrictions on tapping, planting, and the alienation of land for rubber planting purposes. The Europeans and Chinese saw the Indonesians greatly expand Indonesian plantings, production, and exports, and then they slowly eased Malayan restrictions and increased their own plantings. Some kind of restriction on alienation of land to rubber planting, in the various Malay states, remained in effect until 1947. By 1940, however, the acreage under rubber had increased to 3,481,000 of which 2,107,000 acres were on plantations for which land had been alienated before the restrictions had been imposed. The increase in smallholder acreage came chiefly through the diversion of lands alienated for other purposes, and was chiefly effected by Chinese and by Indians.

By 1940 the expansion of rubber planting had created a "rubber belt" regionalism in Malaya. Though there were scattered plantings elsewhere, by far the largest share of the acreage was found in a forty-mile wide belt, inland from the west coast, stretching some 500 miles north-south between Singapore and Penang. Throughout much of the rubber belt there was a marked tendency to mono-crop patterns, the result of the large acreages of plantations and the larger units in the smallholdings which were planted in the European pattern. As an often repeated colloquialism put it: "Years ago the monotony of driving through Malaya was the endless miles of jungle. Now the monotony of touring in Malaya is the endless miles of rubber plantings." Only the southern Selangor and Negri Sembilan zone of Malay smallholdings broke the mono-crop regionalism, wherein small patches of rubber, rice fields, and kampong gardens of jungle-like mixture produced one of the most attractive land-scapes of Malaya.

Change in Malay Attitudes

In the mid and late 1930's considerable numbers of Malays began to accept the wage-earning outlet and to work on rubber plantations or the larger smallholdings of Chinese and Indians. They then discovered anew the comparative advantages of rubber as a cash crop, and the comparative values of different daily work schedules for a tropical environment. Rice field labor patterns involve much arduous work during the heat of the day, whereas the daily routine of rubber gathering is done early in the day during the cooler hours and involves less work in the open sun. Though Malays in one part of Malaya had participated in 'the early boom gamble, and had suffered the ups and downs of the market price structure, the experience of the 1930's gave Malays in other parts of the country a comparative taste of a good daily work schedule. The experiments made an impression, and by 1940 rubber planting had begun to interest the Malays as a satisfactory kampong garden crop which could be worked when money was needed and the trees rested with a beneficial effect at other times. This change in attitude on the part of the Malays can be documented and dated, but the basic causes for such change have not been explored. Whether or not the course of development may be ascribed ultimately to simple economic motivation, the psychological change among the Malays themselves is significant in bringing about the recent areal changes in the nature and limits of the rubber landscape.

Recent Developments in Rubber Planting

By 1953 the total rubber plantings of Malaya stood at 3,727,000 acres by official record, of which 2,029,000 acres were operated as plantations, and 1,698,000 acres were classified as smallholdings of under 100 acres each. All four ethnic elements participated in plantation production, with European plantations totalling 1,412,000 acres, Chinese plantations 462,000 acres, Indian plantations 113,000 acres, and Malays operating the smallest total of 41,950 acres. In the smallholder pattern the Chinese are dominant in acreage units that range from 25 to 99 acres, and the Malays clearly are dominant in the smallholdings of under 25 acres. Two-thirds of the holdings under 25 acres in 1953 were held by Malays, with over 200,000 holdings totalling over 675,000 acres and probably yielding an arithmetic mean of about 3.2 acres per smallholder. However, the 1953 statistics are somewhat fictitious, for they are derived from official Land Office records of alienation of land to rubber planting. For the plantations the figures are relatively sound, but for the Malay smallholders in particular the official data do not reveal the actual rate at which Malays have turned their previously alienated land into rubber planting, nor do they suggest the patterns of interplanting kampong gardens with rubber trees.[6] Only about 200,000 Malay smallholdings were represented in the 1953 data itemized above, and it is thought that rubber tree plantings are to be found on far more Malay homesteads and other landholdings than the official record indicates.

Chinese and Indian smallholder plantings, particularly those in the 25–99 acre category, tend to be aligned within and around the margins of the former "rubber belt," whereas many Malay rubber plantings fall outside the main rubber zone and are diffused over Malaya at the present time.

The late 1950's, for all of Malaya, brings still another issue of change to the picture of agricultural regionalism. The rise of synthetic rubber in the industrial West might seem to pose a threat to the continuance of agriculturally produced natural rubber, or at least to the expansion of such planting. Many throughout the Malayan rubber industry are aware of this threat, and there is a strong pressure for diversification of agriculture among the rubber growers which could eventually break the dominance of rubber in the rubber belt as the dominance of corn has been broken in the American Corn Belt. However, the great advances made in rubber tree breeding, producing strains of very high-yielding trees, offsets this industrial threat in the minds of the Malayan plantation operators. Concern over the threat lies behind the whole replanting program that is going on among European, Chinese, and Indian plantation operators, and also among Chinese and Indian smallholders of the 25–99 acre group. Despite the industrial threat new plantings of rubber, in all acreage patterns, are actively in process throughout Malaya, in which process government programs of rural agricultural development are taking an active role. This latest trend is to extend the former "rubber belt" widely over Malaya as a result of what seems to be almost a "rubber planting fever" gripping Malaya.

The kampong garden and small patch of low-yielding seedling rubber create a new and serious question for the Malay. Government replanting subsidies and technological procedures are not really applicable to the small Malay holdings, many of which are not registered as rubber lands. The Malays now find themselves potentially in the position of marginal and uneconomic producers, for their low-yielding seedling stock is aging

---

[6] The official data obviously cannot reflect a total acreage with accuracy, because the traditional Malay procedure in a kampong garden is to mix many species of small plants, vines, shrubs, and trees together in a "jungle garden" combination, and rubber trees have been added to this already rich complex as one more element. But Malays also have been turning old rice fields and other lands toward rubber in an increasing trend, adding new rice fields and other types of planting patterns to compensate for the loss of rice lands. Seldom is this done in mono-crop field patterns, so that accurate acreage data are almost impossible to derive.

rapidly past the productive age. Kampong rubber fitted the Malay way of life and, by its very volume and distribution, affected both the re-gionalism of the rubber landscape and the annual production of Malayan rubber. Will the Malay abandon his kampong plantings for the larger holdings of mono-cropping that make feasible government subsidy and provision of new plantings? Will he drop out of rubber production again because he does not choose basically to alter his way of life? Or will the Malay gradually find a way to secure new planting stock of im-proved quality and continue to lead his traditional life centered around the kampong garden? In any case the resultant cultural choice will affect the distribution of rubber plantings and hence impinge upon the re-gionalism of agriculture in Malaya.[7]

In Malaya today government experiment station trials of many differ-ent crops in new strains and varieties find successful opportunities for diversification, and though many pressures exist toward diversification, no other crop has captured the minds of Malayans (be they Malay, Chinese, Indian, or British) comparable to the psychological mind-set toward rubber. In 1957–1962 more land has gone into high-yield grafted rubber plantings than into any other crop.[8] Not only is the Malay small-holder making efforts to find a way to remain a rubber grower but Chinese and Indian farmers are planting smallholdings of rubber, and almost every government land settlement project has devoted a major share of its land to rubber trees.

Between the large planter and the smallholder, rubber is coming to dominate the agricultural landscape of increasing portions of Malaya, despite the continuance of a narrow coconut belt along the west coastal fringe and despite local successes with coffee, palm oil, pineapple, and other crops. The former easily delineated "rubber belt" remains on the Malayan landscape as a core region, but eastward the rubber landscape is spreading steadily, in ribbons, block units, and patches. The Malayan rubber landscape has been created in little more than a half century by aliens, using an alien plant. The cultural refusal, or reluctance, of the Malays to participate in the development of an alien system of agricul-ture in the early stages of the evolution of the agricultural system and

[7] This discussion is pointed at the issue of regionalism, and not at the issue of pro-duction economics. However, it can be said that the Malay kampong garden, with its mixed plantings, is ecologically sound for the tropical environment, and that the addition of rubber trees to the jungle garden was a valuable addition. The Malay kampong rubber producer was a low-cost producer whose practices approached the most economical technology of producing natural rubber, and if the Malay can secure new high-yield planting stocks the continuance of the system is ecologically and eco-nomically sound for the kind of life that many rural Malays have so far preferred.
[8] Nursery grown seedlings now are field-planted and grafted with material from a highly selected parent (clone), whereas older plantings were of unselected seedlings allowed to mature into trees of tapping age.

the rubber landscape was a strong element in its early distinctiveness. The later acceptance of rubber planting began to change the nature of the rubber landscape. The recent marked expansion of rubber planting by all ethnic elements resident in Malaya again is altering the composition of the rubber landscape and is rapidly spreading it across Malaya.

Summing Up

Three agricultural patterns have been presented which represent three different-type examples. They are similar in that a commercial production results in each case, but there are dissimilarities in the other characteristics of the three regions. The diversity involves many aspects, the more notable of which follow:

1. Regarding crop origins rubber is alien, coconut is native or practically so, and the corn-animal assemblage is of mixed ancestry.

2. In age the Corn Belt is the oldest, its regional aspects taking shape during a span of decades ranging from about 1810 through 1900; the coconut zone began to develop regional characteristics during the decades from 1890 through 1910; and the rubber zone is the youngest, with its regional expression taking shape only during the decades 1900 through 1920.

3. The coconut and rubber areas are beginning to approach a monocrop pattern, whereas a multiple crop-product complex has developed in the American area.

4. In maturity the Corn Belt has passed a zenith as a climatic agricultural region and is undergoing change of a secondary nature, whereas both the coconut and rubber landscapes are still in states of growth and expansion that do not yet justify the specific term "agricultural region" in either case.

5. The landscape of the Corn Belt now is a strongly developed cultural landscape created from mid-latitude grassland and forest regions, the coconut landscape contains important sectors of still lightly modified wild subtropical forest not yet incorporated into the cultural landscape, and the rubber landscape contains an older core of "rubber tree forests" surrounded by a large zone of lightly altered tropical forest upon which the rubber landscape is advancing.

6. In human occupance the coconut region is marked chiefly by the expansion of a native population, the rubber area is occupied by a polycultural population involving a majority of non-Malay immigrants, and the Corn Belt is a synthesized population of European ancestry.

7. Crop-and-product yield for the Corn Belt came to depend strongly on sophisticated determinations of cost-price features which controlled

the annual production cycle and the rates of secondary change characterizing the nature of the agricultural region, whereas the product for both the coconut and rubber zones is significantly determined for many of the producers by popular judgments based on different criteria.

8. Crop-and-product yield for the Corn Belt had the benefit of plant and animal breeding programs producing steadily larger yields-per-unit. In the rubber zone a strong plant breeding program now achieves a notably larger yield-per-unit for a portion of the producers only, but the coconut zone has as yet seen little agronomic change improving yield ratios.

9. In farm size the coconut landscape chiefly is an assemblage of very small units, the Corn Belt has been a landscape of moderately sized holdings but has shown a tendency toward increasing size, and the rubber landscape is a mixed assemblage of holdings of many sizes, varying from very small to very large.

Treatment

The dissimilar nature of the three agricultural regions has called for varied treatment. Such varied treatment seems to be required because an agricultural region is the landscape expression of a particular agricultural system. Since much of the operation of cultural processes having to do with the evolution of the Corn Belt complex lay outside the present confines of the Corn Belt it was necessary to present more historic material on the early issues of development. The Corn Belt system was an evolutionary product of a rapidly spreading population over an unfamiliar landscape. The polycultural background of the farm settlers yielded a blended culture creating a distinctive agricultural system. The Philippine case was a more localized affair involving a native plant and a native system in a familiar lansdcape. In this discussion there seems to be little need of tracing the centuries-long evolution of coconut planting in the early Philippines. The origin of the Philippine coconut landscape properly begins with the late nineteenth century and the subsequent stimulus to commercial production. The Malayan example begins with the introduction of the rubber tree into Malaya.

Perspective on Agricultural Regions

It may be asked what generalizations emerge from the considerable volume of diverse data presented in this type of survey? Can a perspective or point of view be gleaned with regard to the processes which create agricultural regions? To begin with a point that seems axiomatic, the processes which create agricultural regions all involve cultural procedures. This is basic, although when agricultural regions mature and are recognized by geographers they appear on our maps as specific entities.

They have been treated as independent phenomena, almost as if they possessed animate powers of determining their own densities, boundaries, and degrees of perpetuity. They have been related to environment, to economic forces, to technology, to agronomic development, and to market demands, but often discussed almost independently of man as a causal force. We have found, in the three examples presented, that agricultural regions, in one sense, are expressions of the subjective choices of man operating in groups, affected by a myriad of cultural influences, all produced by man himself. It is man that creates agricultural landscapes or agricultural regions, since man decides in the end the kinds of crops he will produce. The point that is clear in all three regions examined is that crop-growing traits, in the assemblages we call agricultural regions, originate, take shape, evolve, mature, change, and decline as part of the whole culture of man operating in groups.

The processes of selecting crops to be grown in a given region prior to the maturing of a successful regional assemblage are essentially cultural, subject to many different kinds of stimuli, and affected by a wide variety of historic influences. Among the stimuli are such matters as acquaintance with particular domesticated plants and animals, patterns of ignorance or awareness of the suitability of specific crops in particular ecologic situations, commitment to a particular result in growing crops at all, psychological reactions of people to changing circumstances, and specific formulations for a way of life desired by the people who carry on agriculture. As the selection of crops continues toward the point at which some general uniformity of human decision results, the operation becomes a group procedure in which many different specific cultural processes are joined in the making of collective decisions. Herein lies the determination of a way of life and the patterns of crop combinations which the geographer can recognize as regional expressions.

Cultural Processes Which Create Agricultural Regions

Conceptually, the "whole culture of man operating in groups" is far too broad to be used as an analytical device in the examination of the agricultural region. We have stressed this holistic concept because it has seemed to us that many discussions of agricultural regions have omitted the operation of significant cultural processes. Particularly is this true with regard to discussions of the origins of agricultural regions. Obviously some division of cultural processes is required to permit the formulation and employment of specific analytical devices. We suggest that it is possible to identify six different categories of cultural processes significant to the study of the cultural origin, maturity, and change of the agricultural region. These are: psychological, political, historical,

technologic, economic, and agronomic.[9] We have here used specific
terms to denote processes which clearly distinguish particular sectors
of culture. Perhaps either more or fewer than these six conceivably may
be discernible, and perhaps other words may be deemed preferable for
denoting process categories. Preliminary assessment of any agricultural
region may not achieve recognition of the interplay of the whole series
of processes, and it may not isolate the significance of any one process.
In a zone of highly developed culture the separate operation of the
several processes may be obscure and difficult of assessment.

In our survey of three regional patterns the six processes are not
developed in equal depth for each of the three areas. Since the three
regions are of different kinds, ages, and stages of maturity a strictly con-
formal treatment has been impossible, and we have been concerned
to emphasize aspects which often have not received attention in geographical literature. The following examples identify these processes
and briefly show how they operate.

Psychological process is evident in all three regions, but it operates
quite differently. In the Corn Belt it is seen operating in the way in
which farm populations accept new ideas, in the manner in which
farmers influence one another, and in the way institutions such as
the newspaper and the fair influence practices, these composite elements working to produce a farming "mentality" among settlers new to
the region. The traditional conditioning of the Filipino toward coconut
is in good part psychological, but as a specific operation it differs
markedly from the operation of the process among Corn Belt farmers.
Though our explanation of the process is brief, its common knowledge
and positive assertion by Filipinos makes it both a rational and satisfactory accounting for the acceptance of coconut as a crop. Psychological
process clearly operated among the Malays in their early refusal to accept rubber, and in their later acceptance of it. Their present enthusiasm
for rubber is self-evident to any observer. The striking operation of
psychological process has been clearly evident among the Malays; accounting for its operation is another matter, and we do not find material
easily available for such an accounting. Studies of Malay life and patterns of reaction to alien culture are few and have so far too often been
superficial and satisfied with the unsound generalization that the Malay
is indolent and not interested in basic improvements in his level of living.

[9] Most of these terms have been used in their common definitions. The term psychological has been employed to denote mental, social, and cultural reactions of crop
growers to changing circumstances, with mental itself having specific reference to
habits of thinking, mind-set, mentality, and state of mind. The term agronomic, commonly applied to field crop and soil management, has been extended to include
reference to the management of tree crops for the Philippines and Malaya, normally
included under the term horticulture.

It would be a mistake to expect a really strong operation of psychological process as an important factor in producing change in a mature agricultural region inhabited by people possessing complex and acute cultural equipment for determining the validity of changing crops, and at this level the isolation of the significance of the psychological factor, as independent of other processes, would be particularly difficult. On the other hand, psychological process should be very significant in the early stages of the evolution of an agricultural regionalism when the technologic, economic, and agronomic equipment has not been developed.

Though we have not dealt explicitly with political process in discussing the Corn Belt it should be self-evident that the role of government has been involved from the time of the very initial land survey. In the Philippines the obvious role of political process shows itself in the prohibition of plantation land-holding patterns, and in the free-trade legislation that gave coconut a guaranteed market in the United States. The program of restriction of Malayan production of rubber during the depression crisis of the early 1920's was a clear operation of political process. The government enforcement of a levy against rubber exports, supporting the whole program of upgrading planting stock, and the restriction of alienation of land for rubber planting between 1920 and 1947, exhibit political process. The contemporary program of government settlement projects, in which rubber tree planting so clearly dominates, is another manifestation of political process.

Historical process is evident in the case of the Corn Belt and the coconut landscape, though the pattern differs in the two areas. For the rubber landscape the historic process is a short-run matter only in which international circumstances have been of greater significance than local regional happenings. In the early history of the Corn Belt the technologic process clearly is evident in several different ways. The development of the steel plow which made easier the cultivation of grasslands is an illustration, and the well-known development of other machinery was part of the process. The very simplicity and historic continuity of technology required has been a factor in the growth of the coconut landscape in the Philippines, and changes in technology have not been significant to its expansion. Recent technologic change in rubber production on large estates has taken place in Malaya, but the very simplicity of the technology required has been a significant factor in the rapid spread of rubber among smallholders once they accepted the whole complex.

Basic economic processes have been so strongly at work in all three agricultural zones that we have been at no pains to demonstrate such commonly recognized issues. The economics of the "lazy man's crop," affecting coconut significantly and rubber to a certain extent, is different from that which normally has appealed to Americans. Nevertheless, basic economic processes are responsible for the expansion of coconut and lie behind the appearance of the rubber landscape.

Agronomic processes slowly convinced farmers in the future Corn Belt that corn was a more suitable crop than wheat, though this issue is interlinked with economic processes. Agronomic processes eventually led to the filling in of blank spaces in the early Corn Belt that were at first too wet to yield good corn crops, and agronomic processes have had much to do with recent history of the Corn Belt. Agronomic processes have operated in respect to coconut production also, though these have been relatively minor in importance. Perhaps the failure of agronomic processes to conquer the diseases affecting abacá in the southern Philippines has redounded to the relative continuance of expansion of the coconut landscape. Agronomic processes clearly are behind the recent expansion of the rubber landscape in Malaya, and reliance upon them is interlinked with psychologic and political processes in the very expansion of the rubber landscape despite the evolution of the industrial processes producing synthetic rubber.

We could not devise one all-inclusive format for the examination of the origins of the three agricultural regions. We consider the six categories of cultural processes only tentative and suggestive, to be verified, rejected, or amplified by substantive research on other regions.

The more effective recognition of cultural processes at work among agricultural populations may be of considerable utility to our understanding of the spread, elaboration, differentiation, and change in agriculture the world over. Geographers are concerned with the areal expression of agriculture, and its changing nature, on the face of the earth; and they may properly have equal interest in how and why such areal expressions originate and change.

35. The Mormon Culture Region: Strategies and Patterns in the Geography of the American West, 1847-1964

D. W. Meinig

The Mormons are well known as a distinctive American subculture with a large population in the West. In this selection, Meinig considers the development of this culture region and seeks to delimit its boundary in terms of core, domain, *and* sphere. *It would be useful to compare the idea of* core *in the culture region with the "core-idea" as expressed in the development of the nation-state system (Selection 31).*

The appearance of a "Mormon Region" boldly on the maps of two recent studies on the geography of religion in the United States [1] calls attention to a cultural feature of major significance within our national patterns which has never been adequately recognized by American geographers. The concentration of such a large religious group and its great numerical dominance within a particular area are sufficiently unusual features in America as to be emphasized by both authors. As Zelinsky noted, "the Mormon Region is the most easily mapped and described," and he obviously meant to include it as one of the "only two or possibly three cases of regions whose religious distinctiveness is immediately apparent to the casual observer and is generally apprehended by their inhabitants." [2] The implication is not that Mormons, as persons, are necessarily more religious than others but that, as a

SOURCE: *Annals of the Association of American Geographers*, LV (June, 1965), 191–220. The author is professor of geography, Syracuse University.

[1] W. Zelinsky, "An Approach to the Religious Geography of the United States: Patterns of Church Membership in 1952," *Annals*, Association of American Geographers, Vol. 51 (1961), p. 193; and E. S. Gaustad, *Historical Atlas of Religion in America* (New York: Harper and Row, 1962), map in pocket: "Religion in America: 1950." The official name of this religious group is "The Church of Jesus Christ of Latter-day Saints." I have used "Mormon" throughout this article because it is the most common term used both by members and nonmembers. Mormons also commonly refer to themselves as "Latter-day Saints," "L.D.S.," and "Saints."

[2] Zelinsky, *op. cit.*, footnote 1, pp. 164, 165.

group, they constitute a highly self-conscious subculture whose chief bond is religion and one which has long established its mark upon the life and landscape of a particular area. Either residence within or research upon that area can quickly confirm that fact. This paper is a product of both experiences [3] and is offered as an essay in geographical interpretation which attempts to relate processes and patterns in such a way as to build a refined geographical definition of the Mormon culture region.

Introduction

The existence of the Mormons as a definite, cohesive, readily distinguishable culture within the broader patterns of American national life has been recognized ever since the movement gathered strength and form a century and a quarter ago. Its characteristics have been described and analyzed by a host of scholars in many fields. Theologians and other specialists in religion have of course produced voluminous literature on the subject,[4] while American historians and sociologists have long acknowledged the movement to be of such magnitude and distinction as to merit considerable recognition in even the most general texts. More important for the cultural geographer is the evidence in major research studies focused upon such topics as colonization, settlement patterns, economic organization and development, immigration, and general social patterns which clearly reveals the variant character of Mormon culture.[5] Further confirmation is found in comparative studies

[3] Of the many persons who shared with him some of their intimate understanding of Mormon culture during his years of residence in Utah the author wishes especially to recognize the contributions of H. Bowman Hawkes and William Mulder, although, of course, neither is in any way responsible for the particular statements or interpretations set forth.

[4] Two recent bibliographic articles offer a convenient introduction to the standard and the more recent literature: M. S. Hill, "The Historiography of Mormonism," *Church History*, Vol. XXVIII (1959), pp. 418–26, and P. A. M. Taylor, "Recent Writings on Utah and the Mormons," *Arizona and the West*, Vol. IV (1963), pp. 249–60.

[5] Even though this is not designed to be primarily a bibliographic article, the following works are suggested as a minimum collection of major studies which might be considered as the essential general reading for the cultural geographer interested in the Mormons. T. O'Dea, *The Mormons* (Chicago: Univ. of Chicago Press, 1957), is the most penetrating holistic sociological study, especially good for its discussion of the tensions within Mormon culture today. N. Anderson, *Desert Saints, The Mormon Frontier in Utah* (Chicago: Univ. of Chicago Press, 1942), is probably the best single volume on the Mormons as an historical movement in the Far West during the nineteenth century. L. H. Creer, *The Founding of an Empire; the Exploration and Colonization of Utah, 1776–1856* (Salt Lake City: Bookcraft, 1947), is the best account of the Mormon view of possible refuge areas, their selection of the Great Basin, and their exodus to the Salt Lake Valley. M. R. Hunter, *Brigham Young, the Colonizer* (Salt Lake City: Deseret News Press, 1940), though somewhat laudatory as might be expected from an author who was destined to become one of the General Authorities of the Church, was based upon his doctoral study under Herbert

specifically designed by social scientists to determine whatever differences there may be in values and social behavior between Mormons and other groups. The results of these leave no doubt about the integrity of Mormon culture as a distinctive pattern of life.[6]

If we turn to the works of American geographers we will find that whereas the Mormons have not been ignored they have apparently not been considered to be of major significance. For example, despite their undoubted domination of a large area and their visible imprint upon the land, they have been given far less recognition in textbooks on American geography than in those on American history. In most they receive only incidental if any mention, in none is there any explicit suggestion that a Mormon *region* exists as an important geographical pattern.[7] Reference to textbooks is pertinent because they tend to reflect

Bolton and is a methodical and extremely useful historical geography of Mormon colonization up to 1877. L. Nelson, *The Mormon Village, A Pattern and Technique of Land Settlement* (Salt Lake City: Univ. of Utah Press, 1952), is the definitive study on the origins and character of the distinctive Mormon settlement pattern. L. J. Arrington, *Great Basin Kingdom, An Economic History of the Latter Day Saints 1830–1900* (Cambridge: Harvard Univ. Press, 1958), is a major and meticulous research study which, though emphasizing how most Mo:mon programs drew upon much that was common in American experience, nevertheless describes an economic development which in organization, scale, and character was sharply different from anything around it in the American West. The geographer interested in the Mormons will not only find this book essential reading, but will find its 100 pages of references and chapter notes his most useful bibliographic guide for further study. W. Mulder, *Homeward to Zion, the Mormon Migration from Scandinavia* (Minneapolis: Univ. of Minnesota Press, 1957), is the best study of the nature and role of the "gathering unto Zion" which was such an important part of Mormon development. Mulder's "The Mormons in American History," *Bulletin of the University of Utah*, Vol. XLVIII, No. 11, January 14 (1957) is a fascinating interpretative essay and the volume which he edited together with A. Mortensen, *Among the Mormons, Historic Accounts by Contemporary Observers* (New York: Knopf, 1958), is a collection which offers an unusually orderly, comprehensive, and revealing perspective upon Mormon culture history. Finally, no one interested in the topic should fail to read W. Stegner, *Mormon Country* (New York: Duell, Sloan & Pearce, 1942), one of the fine volumes in the very uneven American Folkways series.
[6] See especially J. L. Landgraf, "Land-Use in the Ramah Area of New Mexico, An Anthropological Approach to Areal Study," *Papers of the Peabody Museum of American Archaelogy and Ethnology, Harvard University*, Vol. XLII (1954), 97 pp., and E. Z. Vogt, "American Subcultural Continua as Exemplied by the Mormons and Texans," *American Anthropologist*, Vol. LVII (1955), pp. 1163–72. Both studies derive from the "Comparative Study of Values in Five Cultures" project of the Laboratory of Social Relations, Harvard University.
[7] C. L. White. E. Foscue, and T. McKnight, *Regional Geography of Anglo-America*, 3rd edition (Englewood Cliffs, N.J.: Prentice-Hall, 1964), gives them considerably more space than any other, including a brief sketch of the Mormon migration, colonization, and mention of cultural differences in settlement patterns, agriculture, and demography. The predominance of Mormons in parts of Idaho, Nevada, and Arizona as well as Utah is also noted but the significance of a definite Mormon region is ignored. Perhaps the opening phrase of the Preface is in itself sufficient explanation of such an omission: "Regions are formed by man as he adjusts himself to his natural environment . . . ," *ibid.*, p. v. The only regional volume relevant to the area is *California and the Southwest*, edited by C. M. Zierer (New York:

the prevailing themes in a field and the character and coverage of its more specialized research. In general, it would not be a gross exaggeration to conclude that the America portrayed therein by American geographers is an area of standardized culture within which economic activities are of singular importance; and these activities, in turn, are largely to be understood as the logical maximization of the opportunities inherent in particular sets of physical conditions and relative locations. A sense of history and a concept of culture are hardly apparent. Predictably, the nontextbook literature shows greater insight into the significance of Mormon regionalism, and geographers who have done fieldwork in the Mormon area are always aware of and usually deal with some of the specific geographical manifestations of the local culture. Nevertheless, in only a few cases have those manifestations been the major focus of study,[8] and in only one is the areal extent of the Mormon domination within the larger frame of the American West a topic of concern.[9] In this latter study Brightman offered a succinct and penetrating analysis, efficiently supported by revealing maps, of the evolution of the political boundaries of Utah toward ever greater concordance with the Mormon-dominated area. It is a theme and an example which deserves greater recognition,[10] but though it offers important evidence

---

Wiley, 1956). Its arbitrary areal limits which include the states of Nevada, Utah, and Arizona would preclude any consideration of the Mormon region as a whole. The Mormons are mentioned briefly in conjunction with several topics but, not surprisingly, are recognized as a separate culture only in the chapter on "rural life," written by the anthropologist W. Goldschmidt (see especially pp. 346–47).

[8] The best example is J. E. Spencer, "The Middle Virgin River Valley: A Study in Culture Growth and Change" (unpub. Ph.D. dissertation, Geography, University of California, Berkeley, 1936); see also by the same author, "The Development of Agricultural Villages in Southern Utah," *Agricultural History*, Vol. XIV (1940), pp. 181–89, and "House Types of Southern Utah," *Geographical Review*, Vol. XXV (1945), pp. 444–57. A short study specifically emphasizing certain Mormon features is A. L. Seeman, "Communities in the Salt Lake Basin," *Economic Geography*, Vol. XIV (1938), pp. 300–08. It is interesting that although Seeman's article is rarely cited by geographers it was reprinted in the recent sociological collection edited by G. A. Theodorson, *Studies in Human Ecology* (Evanston, Ill.: 1961). Two well-known published dissertations by former residents of the area are good examples of works which specifically take into account certain special features of Mormon culture but in which the principal focus is upon more general types of patterns: C. L. White, "The Agricultural Geography of the Salt Lake Oasis." *Journal of the Scientific Laboratories of Denison University*, Vol. XXI (1925–1926), pp. 117–283, and C. D. Harris, "Salt Lake City, a Regional Capital" (Chicago: Univ. of Chicago Press, 1940).

[9] G. F. Brightman, "The Boundaries of Utah," *Economic Geography*, Vol. XVI (1940), pp. 87–95.

[10] Evidently the only text to cite and make even slight use of Brightman's study is R. H. Brown, *Historical Geography of the United States* (New York: Harcourt, Brace, 1948), p. 485. Brown adapted some of Brightman's maps, but his focus throughout the book is upon problems of settlement and physical environment and he was not really concerned with the areal dimensions of Mormon colonization.

and is strongly suggestive of the concept of a Mormon culture region it still does not deal directly with the problem of defining that region.

This general neglect by American geographers is further emphasized by the fact that traveling European geographers have usually been quick to recognize that, when in Utah, they are in the midst of a significantly different culture area. Telling evidence of this is the fact that the only geographical monograph on the subject and the only specific recognition by a geographer of a "Mormonland" as a major component within a set of general regional divisions (rather than purely religious regions, as in Zelinsky) of the United States are the results of German scholarship.[11] Each of these studies includes a map of the Mormon region but it is clear that in neither case was there any intensive research directed toward determining its bounds. The results are obviously offered only as general approximations and in fact the regions depicted in these two works differ very considerably in size and shape and thus offer no certain guide.[12]

Geographers are, of course, not alone in their concern for regional patterns and it is not surprising to find that a Mormon region does appear, if somewhat cryptically, on a map of "Rural Regions of the United States" compiled by American sociologists a quarter of a century ago.[13] Although titled simply "Central Intermountain," the text makes clear that culturally the region is unique because of the large proportion of Mormons in its population.[14] Other features mentioned are the farm-village pattern, commercial farming with relatively little tenancy, and a unique combination of a high average standard of living, and a

[11] H. Lautensach's short monograph "Das Mormonenland, als Beispiel eines sozial-geographischen Raumes," *Bonner Geographische Abhandlungen,* Heft II (1953) was the product of extensive library research following his traverse with the Transcontinental Excursion of the I.G.C. in 1952. Just forty years earlier a French geographer displayed a similar interest in the Mormons as the result of the 1912 Excursion of the I.G.C.; see L. Gallois, "L'Utah," *Annales de Géographie,* Vol. XX (1913), pp. 185–96. B. Hofmeister's recognition of "Mormonenland," as one of thirteen basic regions in his coverage of "Die Vereinigten Staaten Von Amerika" in *Die Grosse Illustrierte Landerkunde,* Band II (Gutersloh: C. Bertelsmann, 1963) pp. 731–915 (Mormonenland, pp. 891–95 and map, p. 830), stemmed from his year of research and teaching at the University of Utah.

[12] Cf. Lautensach, *op. cit.,* footnote 11, p. 10 and Hofmeister, *op. cit.,* footnote 11, pp. 829–30.

[13] A. R. Mangus, *Rural Regions of the United States* (Washington: Work Projects Administration, 1940), Figure 2. This study is an important and typical product of the great interest in regional sociology during the 1930's, an era characterized most clearly by the works of Howard K. Odum and his co-workers on the American South.

[14] Mangus, *op. cit.,* footnote 13, p. 30. It is of interest that the committee which produced "Rural Settlement Patterns in the United States as Illustrated on One Hundred Topographic Quadrangle Maps," *National Academy of Sciences–National Research Council Publication 380* (Washington, D. C.; 1956) used Mangus' regions as their basic framework (smoothing out his county boundaries) but replaced "Central Intermountain" with "Mormon."

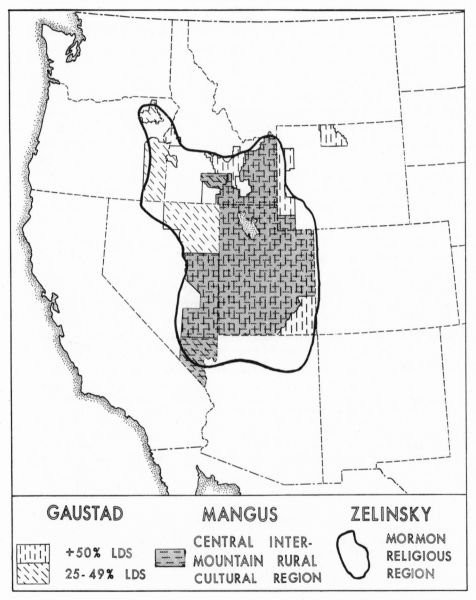

FIGURE 1: The Mormon regions—some recent definitions. The Gaustad and Mangus distributions are by counties. The Gaustad proportions refer to percentages of the total membership in all denominations according to the religious census of 1952. Zelinsky's region was generalized primarily from the data in that same census.

very high birth rate, and large families. Such items are indeed characteristics of Mormon culture, but obviously they describe only a very
limited part of it and their selection merely reflects the purposes and
methods of this particular study. Nevertheless, the determination of the
region on the basis of such specific criteria suggests the possibility of
testing whether Mormon culture is so closely bound to religion that a
map of religious adherents provides a simple key to the bounds of the
culture area. Is the Mormon culture region simply one where Mormons
are a majority of the population, or at least of a majority of those who
profess any religion?[15] An answer can be quickly obtained by the
superimposition of Mangus' "Central Intermountain" region upon the
patterns depicted in the studies by Gaustad and by Zelinsky on the
geography of religion (Fig.1). Since both Mangus and Gaustad worked
with county units their patterns are most easily compared. Although
coincident over a large block of territory there are discordances along
nearly every side as well as with respect to noncontiguous outlying
areas. Zelinsky's Mormon Region, derived from the same statistical
source as Gaustad's,[16] represents a cultural geographer's generalization
based upon his own very considerable knowledge of other relevant patterns.[17] Clearly Mormon numerical preponderance is not a reliable guide
to the Mormon culture area, at least insofar as the latter was established
by Mangus.[18] But there are very good reasons why the cultural geogra-

[15] The use of some key element as a means of delimiting regions of broader significance is, of course, commonplace in geography and it has been a matter of considerable methodological controversy among sociologists and anthropologists. The
use of a master factor for the mapping of a social complex is discussed in C. E.
Lively and C. L. Gregory, "The Rural Sociocultural Area as a Field for Research,"
Rural Sociology, Vol. XIX (1954), pp. 21–31, an article of particular relevance to
cultural geographers. In their discussions of the value of areal studies, techniques of
delimitation, and problems related to the areal dimensions of cultural processes, one
senses much that is parallel with, or relevant to, similar considerations in geography.
[16] Both are based upon the data in the bulletins on *Churches and Church Membership in the United States: an Enumeration and Analysis by Counties, States and
Regions* (New York: National Council of Churches of Christ in the U.S.A., 1956–
1958).
[17] Zelinsky's study also includes a map (*op. cit.*, footnote 1, p. 179) of the distribution of the total membership of the "Churches of Latter-day Saints." This combines
the membership of the Reorganized Church of Jesus Christ of the Latter-day Saints
and two very small splinter groups with a larger body, a logical procedure when
mapping so many denominations at the national scale although the differences between the two are important in any study of Mormon culture. However, because the
Reorganized Mormons are largely in the Midwest the matter has no marked effect
upon the county patterns of concern here.
[18] There is, of course, a difference in date between Mangus' study and the 1952 data
used by Gaustad and by Zelinsky. However, the fact that there were some increases
in the interim in the proportionate Mormon population of certain counties does little
to explain the discordance. Some check on this can be made by reference to Figure 7
in Brightman, *op. cit.*, footnote 9, p. 93, although this shows Mormons as a percentage of the total population, calculated evidently upon the special census of *Religious
Bodies: 1926*, U.S. Bureau of the Census (Washington: Government Printing Office,
1929).

pher should not accept the Mangus delimitation as a definitive regional frame. For one thing, the criteria were too limited to features of interest to rural sociologists concerned with governmental policies to be relied upon for broader definitions of culture areas.[19] For another, the use of counties is much too crude for the scale of the problem, partly because many counties in the Western states are so very large; but more importantly because in the geography of cultures, boundaries may have a special importance for they are likely to be critical zones of contact out of which may develop significant tensions and change. Furthermore, the Mangus map provides only a single uniform area, with no gradation between any possible core and periphery.

In sum, there is ample evidence that a distinctive Mormon culture is recognizable and important and that it is dominant over a large area in the Far West. However, despite several studies which give some suggestion of its location, neither singularly nor together do these offer a sure guide to the geographical dimensions of a Mormon culture region. We need to know more precisely just where the Mormons are and just what is the context of their situation in each locality, which means knowing something about when, why, and how they got there and what is their relationship with reference to other local peoples. Or, to put it more succinctly, even axiomatically, not only must we know the patterns in greater detail but we must know more about the processes which created them. If the culture area concept is to be used by geographers to provide new insights and interpretations rather than merely new compartments for the assemblage of commonplace data, such areas must be viewed not as static uniform patterns but as dynamic areal growths. What follows is an expression of that view, wherein a refined definition of the areal dimensions of Mormon culture is developed out of the perspective of historical geography.

The Search for Zion

It is not essential to that purpose to delve very far into the origins and early development of Mormonism but some perspective is needed. As is well known, historically, it was but one of many experimental, communal, millennial movements of its time; sociologically it was composed largely of elements recognizable in American culture, though singularly combined and at times so exaggerated that some of the specific manifestations would seem startlingly different and discordant. Geographically its New England roots and its persistent involvement with the moving American frontier are features of special interest.

Both Joseph Smith and Brigham Young were born in Vermont, but the New England heritage is more a product of associations in lands of

[19] Mangus, *op. cit.*, footnote 13, p. 1 and Chapter IV.

strong Yankee influence than directly of New England itself. Smith had his early visions, produced his sacred text, the Book of Mormon, and in 1830 formally organized the Church of Jesus Christ of Latter-day Saints, while a resident of western New York.[20] The first temple was built and the first attempt to establish a full society of Latter-day Saints was made at Kirtland in the Western Reserve in Ohio. Both areas were strongholds of New England culture. Such facts do not in themselves explain anything but they begin to give a cultural geography under-pinning to such characterizations as that of Emerson, who succinctly labeled Mormonism as "an afterclap of Puritanism." [21]

The Mormon interest in the frontier began with a concern for Indian missions (for the American Indian has a special importance within Mormon theology), but troubles with their neighbors in New York and Ohio soon caused them to look to the fringes of civilization as a more suitable locale for implanting the ideal society. In 1831 Smith visited Independence, Missouri, then the farthest salient of settlement, and he so liked what he saw that he proclaimed it the new Zion. But as the Saints flocked in, troubles with the Gentiles (the Mormon term for all non-Mormons) became worse than ever. A shift into north-central Missouri brought no improvement, and a further move to the northeast across the Mississippi brought into being the handsome Mormon city of Nauvoo, momentarily the largest in Illinois, but only compounded those animosities which culminated in the murder of Smith by a mob in 1844. Finding it impossible to live within the frontier zone the Mor-mons now prepared to move well beyond it. Actually, Smith had begun to consider the need for a distant refuge some years before. Texas, Oregon, California, and the Great Basin were each given careful con-sideration by the leaders, and a decision in favor of the last came only after diligent study, most especially of Fremont's recent report on that region.[22]

[20] Smith's home was in Palmyra, Wayne County; he claimed to have transcribed the Book of Mormon from "golden plates" unearthed at Hill Cumorah, a few miles south of Palmyra in Ontario County; the Church was first organized at Fayette in Seneca County.

[21] Mulder, "The Mormons in American History," *op. cit.*, footnote 5, p. 14.

[22] The geographical considerations related to this prelude to exodus and to the migra-tion are well covered in Creer, *op. cit.*, footnote 5, and Anderson, *op. cit.*, footnote 5; some useful additional details are presented in B. L. Peterson, "A Geographic Study of the Mormon Migration from Nauvoo, Illinois, to the Great Salt Lake Valley (1846–1947)" (unpublished M.A. thesis, Geography, University of California, Los Angeles, 1941). It was during this confused period immediately following Smith's death that splinter groups formed. The largest of these, the Reorganized Church of Jesus Christ of L.D.S., remained in the Midwest. A small but famous group, led by James J. Strang, settled first in Wisconsin, then moved to Beaver Island in northern Michigan, from which place, after being wracked by internal factions and external persecutions, they were forcibly dispersed in 1856; see M. M. Quaife, *The Kingdom of St. James, A Narrative of the Mormons* (New Haven: Yale University Press, 1930). Another small party emigrated to the Texas Hill country and established a

For the Mormons these years were a search for Zion, for some ground that could be consecrated to the upbuilding of the Kingdom of God. The need to take root was a powerful one, for, as Mulder has noted, "while other millennialists set a time, the Mormons appointed a place," and it was in the process of finding that place that "the Mormons became a genuine people, a covenant folk like ancient Israel with a shared history and at last a homeland." [23]

Deseret

On July 24, 1847, Brigham Young sat in his carriage on a high terrace at the mouth of a mountain canyon, silently soaked up his first view of the Valley of the Great Salt Lake, and said: "This is the place." It became the most famous phrase in Mormon history because it was not simply an opinion but a theocratic pronouncement sufficient in itself to consecrate a new Zion. From it emanated half a century of Mormon colonization in the Far West.

Under the guidance of church leaders, irrigation was begun immediately, as was the allocation of resources, and the survey of the new city, modeled upon Joseph Smith's "Plat of the City of Zion" (which had already been used for those aborted Mormon towns in Missouri and Illinois). It was a rigid gridiron of spacious blocks and streets in which one can discern something of the New England town formalized by the Biblical foursquare and expressing a firm belief in the virtues of social concentration and of a rationally ordered society, a fitting frame for the New Jerusalem.[24]

Once such matters were well under way in Salt Lake Valley, a systematic exploration of other localities was begun. Room was needed not just to accommodate those Mormons already moving across the plains or waiting to flee from the Gentiles in Missouri and Illinois, but for the

colony at Zodiac in Burnet County, *Texas, A Guide to the Lone Star State* (New York: Hastings House, 1940, W.P.A. Writers' Program), pp. 458–59, and C. S. Banks, "The Mormon Immigration into Texas," *Southwestern Historical Quarterly*, Vol. XLIX (1945–1946), pp. 233–44. A group of Mormons who sailed by ship from New York City for the Far West established the village of New Hope in Stanislaus County, California, before they knew for sure where Brigham Young was going to settle. Their leader was so bitter that Young would choose the Salt Lake Valley over the San Joaquin that he left the fold and his followers soon dispersed; see P. Bailey, *Sam Brannan and the California Mormons* (Los Angeles: Westernlore Press, 1959). A group of British converts petitioned, unsuccessfully, for a grant on Vancouver Island, as they wanted to emigrate to the American West but preferred to stay on British soil; see J. B. Munro, "Mormon Colonization Scheme for Vancouver Island," *Washington Historical Quarterly*, Vol. XXV (1934), pp. 278–85. All these cases illustrate further how the Mormon movement was an integral and complex part of the American frontier expansion of the time.

[23] Mulder, "The Mormons in American History," *op. cit.*, footnote 5, pp. 14, 19.
[24] Nelson, *op. cit.*, footnote 5, especially Chapter 11.

"Gathering of the Saints" through all time to come. For, to quote Mulder again,[25]

the gathering, not polygamy, is Mormonism's oldest and most influential doctrine. . . . The invitation and the promise [of Mormonism] involved more than a trip to the sinners bench . . . [it] meant getting out of Babylon and uniting with God's people to build up the Kingdom and await greater spiritual endowments.

As a high Church official told European converts in 1855: [26]

the commandment to gather out to the land of America is just as binding on the Saints so far as it is possible for them to accomplish it, as it was in the first place to be baptized for the remission of sins.

That made it virtually a sacrament and thus the gathering and the general emphasis upon the large family with its doctrinal amplification through polygamy combined to provide a powerful demographic force.

Characteristically not only was a search for sites undertaken methodically, but an orderly means of peopling them was devised. The Church leadership selected the time and the place and many of the specific persons for important new colonizations. The larger body of young persons and newcomers who needed land would be joined to a cadre of experienced pioneers and essential craftsmen carefully selected for the task. The Mormon term for such selection is "called," and it was tantamount to an order, though one usually willingly obeyed as a proper duty whatever the personal sacrifice.

Such features are suggestive of the distinctive character of Mormon colonization, and how it so differed from the general stereotype of the rather chaotic American westward movement. But, again, our main purpose is not to examine these features but to chart the spread of the culture they represent and that too was undertaken according to an orderly plan.[27]

It seems certain that when Brigham Young first stared at that sun-baked desolate valley his vision was not limited by its mountainous margins and great Dead Sea, but reached far beyond to an imagined encompassing empire of which this would be but the nucleus. It did not take long for him to give that dream a more definite shape and name: "Deseret," a word from the Book of Mormon meaning honeybee, symbolizing the productive industriousness of the ideal society. In March, 1849, Congress was petitioned to recognize the State of Deseret,

[25] Mulder, op. cit., footnote 5, pp. 16–17.
[26] Andrew L. Neff, History of Utah, 1847–1869 (Salt Lake City: Deseret News Press, 1940), p. 585.
[27] Colonization of the main localities is well described in the major works previously mentioned, especially in those of Hunter, Anderson, and Arrington, footnote 5, and specific citation will be made only to other studies which add important details or new dimensions to these standard works.

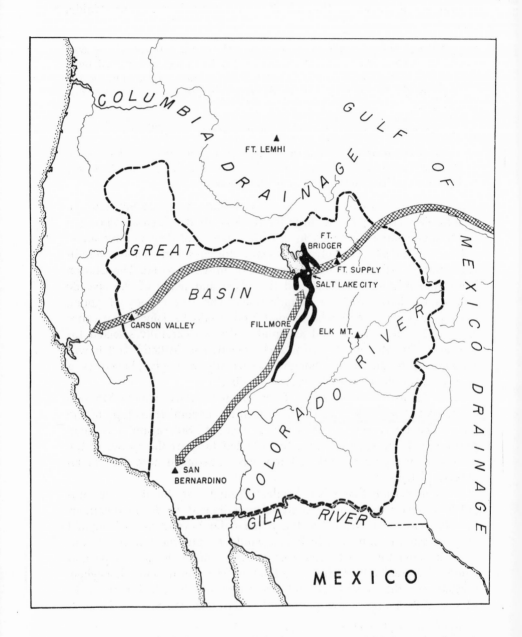

FIGURE 2: Deseret, the proposed Mormon state of 1849, showing the several outposts and missions established near its borders during the years 1850-1857 and principal thoroughfares of that era.

a huge part of the newly acquired Far West, defined largely in hydro-graphic terms: bounded on the north by the Columbian watershed, on the east by the continental divide, on the west by the crest of the Sierra Nevada, and on the south by the course of the Gila River (which was the Mexican border until the Gadsden Purchase four years later) (Fig. 2). Only in the southwest corner were the streams ignored, so as to obtain a frontage on the Pacific. Deseret was thus, in the main, a com-bination of the Great Basin of interior drainage and the watershed of the Colorado River system.

Congress refused to accept Deseret and instead substituted a Utah Territory only half as big and humbly named after the local Indians. But these were not crippling limitations. Brigham Young was appointed governor and Deseret remained real for the Mormons even if unrecog-nized by the nation. The patterns of activities over the next few years make this clear. Salt Lake City was the capital and a rapid filling in of the valleys immediately to the north and south formed an emerging core area. Actually Brigham Young personally selected a new capital at Fillmore, 150 miles south of Salt Lake City, because he gave priority to a rapid occupation of all possible sites in that direction and viewed such a location as more central within the empire he envisioned. Work on a handsome statehouse was begun but after one session the territorial legislature returned to Salt Lake City as a more convenient place.[28] Generically this may be seen as an attempt to force the pattern of core expansion into a particular direction which failed because settlement was as yet too sparse and intermittent and traffic connections too tenuous to support an adequate level of development and spatial inter-action between the Salt Lake Valley and Fillmore.

Around the periphery of Deseret the Mormons soon established a series of outposts which, though not all founded in response to some orderly program of grand strategy, nevertheless clearly indicated their intention to dominate the whole of the area encompassed by that con-cept. The most important and successful of these outlying stations was at San Bernardino in the Los Angeles Basin.[29] Here the Mormons pur-chased a Mexican ranch and soon had a flourishing agricultural com-munity. Its main purpose, however, was to establish a grip upon the Pacific frontage of Deseret, and that position was sought not primarily as an outlet to the sea but as a portal of immigration for the gathering

[28] The federal government failed to provide the expected funds for such territorial buildings, and the accommodations for the legislators and their families were quite inadequate. See Neff, *op. cit.*, footnote 26, E. L. Cooley, "Report of an Expedition to Locate Utah's First Capitol," *Utah Historical Quarterly*, Vol. XXIII (1955), pp. 329–38, and "Utah's Capitols," *Utah Historical Quarterly*, Vol. XXVII (1959), pp. 258–73.
[29] H. F. Raup, "San Bernardino, California, Settlement and Growth of a Pass-Site City," *University of California Publications in Geography*, Vol. VIII (1940).

of the converts from Europe and Atlantic America. The trail between San Bernardino and Great Salt Lake City was to be the main thoroughfare, the Mormon Corridor. Within ten years colonists had occupied most of the small valleys along it within Utah; beyond a single important way station was established at Las Vegas.[30]

Another routeway, the California Trail, crossed Deseret from east to west, and, of course, the great majority of Mormon emigrants came in this way.[31] A trading post built in 1843 by James Bridger in southwestern Wyoming commanded this entryway, but since Brigham Young distrusted Bridger and his fellow mountain men he was anxious to have his own advance base to control this portal and to serve Mormon emigrant parties. In 1853 the Mormons established Fort Supply, a few miles to the south, and two years later got possession of Fort Bridger. At the opposite edge of their realm Mormon settlers arrived in Carson Valley in 1851 lured by the opportunities for trade with California-bound emigrants. But such prospects also attracted Gentile traders, and in 1856 the Church dispatched sixty or seventy families as a reinforcement sufficient to dominate the area and to block local Gentile petitions for annexation to California. Genoa and Franktown were platted as Mormon villages and Carson Valley became regarded as an important outpost guarding the border with turbulent California.

Two Indian missions, though different in specific purpose and soon abandoned under the pressure of Indian attacks, were also part of this pattern. Fort Lemhi, in the Salmon River country, was an attempt to work with the important Bannock tribe; Elk Mountain, on the upper Colorado River, was a mission to local Utes.[32] There were strong theological motives for initiating such work, and more was accomplished with some of the Piute Indians nearer to the Utah settlements, but these two efforts can be regarded in addition as strategic political moves seeking to establish amicable relations with important foreign societies on the borders of Deseret.

Thus within a decade of the entry into the Great Basin, Deseret was transformed from an idea and bold assertion into the developing reality of a Mormon culture region. As yet its substance was far from sufficient to fill the frame. Colonization, expanding as contiguously as nature allowed south from the Salt Lake Valley, was generally confined to a string of lowest and most accessible valleys along the foot of the

[30] G. S. Dumke, "Mission to Mining Town: Early Las Vegas," *Pacific Historical Review*, Vol. XXII (1953), pp. 257–70.
[31] Prior to the Mormon colonization the main California Trail branched from the earlier Oregon Trail in southern Idaho and skirted northwest of the Great Salt Lake. Routes through the Salt Lake Valley had been used, however, in the most famous instance by the ill-fated Donner Party whose delays in crossing the Wasatch and the salt desert doomed it to tragedy in the Sierra snows.
[32] Elk Mountain, at present-day Moab, Utah, was where the old Spanish Trail, a by then little-used route connecting Santa Fe and Los Angeles, crossed the river.

Wasatch Range and Plateau. But though the limits of Deseret lay far beyond, the vast intervening tracts lay open to Mormon expansion, insofar as this was physically possible, for as yet no Gentile colonizations had intruded into that space and the Indians, for the most part, were widely scattered in small bands with only the most tenuous hold upon the land.

Contraction and Contiguous Colonization

Failure of Congress to accept Deseret was a good indication that the nation was not going to shape itself geographically any more than socially to accommodate the Mormons. Even in their Far Western refuge the Mormons could not escape entanglement. Whereas in Missouri and Illinois the Mormons had severe trouble with local and state governments, territorial status enmeshed them with the federal government and with little better results. Problems arose from Indians, emigrants, polygamy, and politics and the great exodus was soon followed by new lamentations. By 1857 Mormonism was a national political issue culminating in the dispatch of a federal army toward Utah to stamp out a supposed rebellion.[33]

The Mormons were determined to resist, and in order to concentrate his people and defenses, Brigham Young called in all settlers from the several exposed outposts. And thus within a few weeks all the Mormons of Carson Valley, San Bernardino, and Las Vegas were headed for Salt Lake City. Fort Bridger and Fort Supply were abandoned and burned and the Saints prepared to resist in the stronghold of the Wasatch. Actually no blood was shed and after weeks of tension a compromise was reached by which a garrison of troops was allowed to exhibit the federal presence and power in Mormondom but without any harsh curbing of the local society.

The whole unfortunate episode solved none of the issues between Mormon and Gentile but it was of major geographical importance; although the idea of a Mormon commonwealth remained, Deseret no longer provided the frame. No attempts were made to reoccupy Carson Valley or San Bernardino. In each area Gentiles were in control either through purchase or occupation of the former Mormon properties. Within two years the discovery of the Comstock Lode brought a swarm of people into the Nevada valley and although it would be a few more years before southern California experienced any real boom it, too, was growing in population. In any case the Mormons could never have simply re-created their former positions and, given their recent experience, they presumably now regarded such locations as too remote and

[33] See N. F. Furniss, *The Mormon Conflict 1850–1859* (New Haven: Yale University Press, 1960).

exposed. Accordingly, in what may conveniently be regarded as a new phase, expansion now became entirely a matter of contiguous colonization, a spreading outward from their early nucleus as compactly as terrain and water allowed.

Most of the new expansion of this phase can be conveniently generalized as being a pattern of movement into successive tiers of valleys, each tier being a segmented series of more or less longitudinal lowlands along the front of or within the Wasatch ranges and high plateaus (Fig. 3). Up to 1858 most of the settlement had taken place within the first tier along the base of the main escarpment, specifically in a discontinuous strip from the lower Bear River Valley north of Ogden, southward through the Salt Lake, Utah, Juab, Pavant, Beaver, and Parowan valleys.

The most famous of the subsequent colonizations was the cotton mission into the Virgin River Valley of extreme southwest Utah, an extension southward within this first tier. Lying 3,000 feet below the settlements just to the north it was hoped that the area would be a producer of subtropical products. Brigham Young suggested olive oil, almonds, figs, grapes, sorghum, tobacco, and cotton as possibilities, and the Civil War soon made cotton the most important. Typically, some Mormon converts from the South were called to supervise production and the Church subsidized a mill which was operated by English converts familiar with textile machinery. Although the venture never fulfilled the initial hope of clothing all Mormondom in its own product, it was a considerable success for many years. This distinctive area became noted for its fruits, vegetables, and sorghum molasses as well, and was soon known as "Utah's Dixie," famous for its mild winter climate. The latter was attractive enough to lure Brigham Young into winter residence, occasionally making St. George in effect the temporary capital of Mormondom.[34]

This southward push of the 1860's reached on farther into the southeast corner of Nevada where several settlements were founded along the Muddy River, a meager tributary of the lower Virgin.[35] With no colony in southern California, Las Vegas was not reestablished. The idea of a link to the Pacific was not entirely forgotten, however. Brigham Young directed that a landing be established on the Colorado River in Boulder Canyon (Callville, very near the site of Hoover Dam), and the navigability of the river be examined. But, as army explorations

---

[34] There is a large literature on this area. General accounts of Mormon colonization usually give considerable space to the Cotton Mission. Spencer, *op. cit.*, footnote 8, 1936, is the most intensive analysis by a geographer. A recent issue of the *Utah Historical Quarterly*, Vol. XXIX (1961), pp. 191–302, devoted entirely to the area, contains some excellent articles and photographs.

[35] Difficulties with the Nevada legislature caused the Mormons to abandon this Muddy River colony in 1871, but it was recolonized in the 1880's.

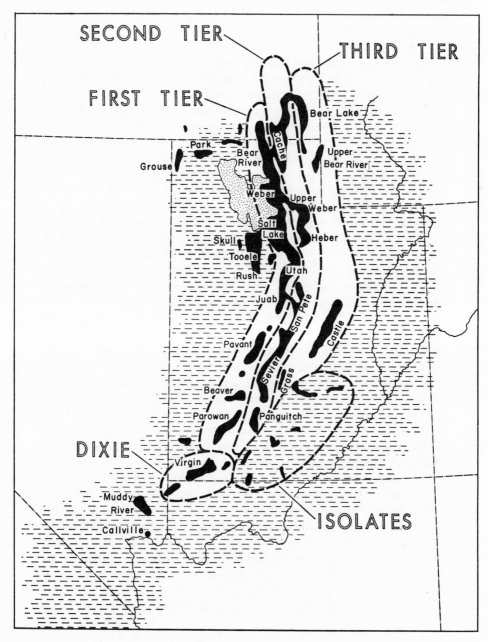

FIGURE 3: "Contiguous" colonizations.

had already demonstrated, the Colorado could not really offer a feasible outlet and the assurance of a transcontinental railroad along the central route soon ended any real interest in the possibility.[36] Faced by the Mohave Desert, Mormon contiguous colonization in this direction was now stalled.

Simultaneous with this southward movement was the expansion into the second tier of valleys, parallel with but elevated above and usually separated by high ridges or narrow canyons from the first. One of the most accessible of these, the San Pete, had been entered even before 1858. Now more settlers poured in and spread through the whole length of the combined San Pete–Sevier and on south into Panguitch and the upper Virgin. In the north they entered the back valleys within the Wasatch, such as Heber, the upper Weber, and the broad Cache Valley. By 1870 the volume and momentum of this expansion led to penetrations farther eastward into a third tier, a more widely spaced scattering of locations including the Bear Lake Valley and the uppermost Bear River in the north to Castle Valley and Grass Valley in the south-central section. The Uinta Basin was an area of considerably greater potential but it was locked in an Indian reservation and unavailable. Farther southward the settlements became so scattered, the size of each valley so small, and the isolation so great that the tier pattern is broken into fragments, a series of isolates, each a tiny, remote, restricted patch of irrigable land within the depths of the intricately sculptured terrain of the high canyonlands. The implantation and the permanence of these little clusters in such difficult country is one of the remarkable achievements of Mormon colonization. But there was a limit even to the most dedicated pioneering; eastward in this section the surface lowers, aridity increases, the few streams are entrenched in narrow boulder-strewn canyons, and the country in general becomes so bleak and broken that for some time it deterred even exploration of the faintly visible highlands beyond.

Thus this eastward movement ran out of land, and westward expansion into the Great Basin was even more severely limited. Here, too, the meridional mountain and bolson terrain formed a succession of tiers, but the irrigation colonist could barely get a foothold within the first set. Tooele and Rush valleys, lying just west of Salt Lake Valley, offered only a few possible sites within their broad expanses, and the next beyond, Skull Valley, was aptly named since extended trials proved existence scarcely possible. Farther west and south large areas were absolutely sterile, salt flat remainders of shrinking Lake Bonneville, and

---

[36] Arrington maintains that Young was never really very serious about this Colorado project and sponsored it primarily as a temporary make-work effort to aid the Dixie mission; L. Arrington, "The Mormon Cotton Mission in Southern Utah," *Pacific Historical Review*, Vol. XXV (1956), pp. 221–38.

only here and there along the base of the massive ranges did a spring-
or snow-fed creek offer a meager ranch site. Northwest of Great Salt
Lake the possibilities were somewhat greater and colonists did occupy
Park and Grouse Creek valleys.

Within thirty years of their entry into the Far West the Mormons
were pressing against the limits of the possibilities for contiguous expansion on the south, east, and west, hemmed in by a girdle of wastelands
which could be gleaned at their margins by herds and flocks but were
barren and impenetrable by the agricultural colonist.

Only in the north, along the linear ranges beyond the margins of
Deseret into the upper Snake River country were there valleys as yet
unoccupied by farmers. But here, too, there were difficulties. One was
an idea, the belief that agriculture in the area would likely be endan-
gered by frost. Like many such preliminary impressions and reasoning
this was largely a misconception and, in fact, the area would prove
much less afflicted than the high valleys within the Wasatch. Usually
such ideas soon gave way in the face of actual farming experiments,
but this one existed strong in the mind of Brigham Young and thus did
not yield so easily. Young made only one extended trip into that country
and returned with a bias against it: [37]

the farther north we go the less good characteristics are connected with the
valleys, except in articles of fish, water, and in some instances, timber; and
when the people are obliged to live in the north country, that will be high
time for them to go there.

His bias was soon reinforced by other problems. The increasing traffic
along the Oregon and California trails, which threaded through this
sector by several alternate routes, lured a number of Gentile ranchers
and traders most of whom had little sympathy for the Mormons. After
Idaho was organized as a territory in 1863 its politics were dominated
by miners and federal officials who shared this antipathy.[38]

It was in this northern sector that the Mormons first encountered any
real competition for the land in the Far West. Now the old Mormon–
Gentile competition for footholds on the frontier reappeared, and thus
in the 1870's we may discern a third phase in Mormon colonization
marked by expansions beyond the broad belt of wastelands and encroachments into Gentile ranching country.

Peripheral Expansions into Alien Lands

Brigham Young's obsession with southward expansion produced the
most remarkable movements during the early years of this era. In 1873

[37] M. D. Beal, *A History of Southeastern Idaho* (Caldwell, Idaho: The Caxton
Printers, 1942), p. 199.
[38] M. Wells, "Origins of Anti-Mormonism in Idaho, 1872–1880," *Pacific Northwest
Quarterly,* Vol. XLVII (1956), pp. 107–16.

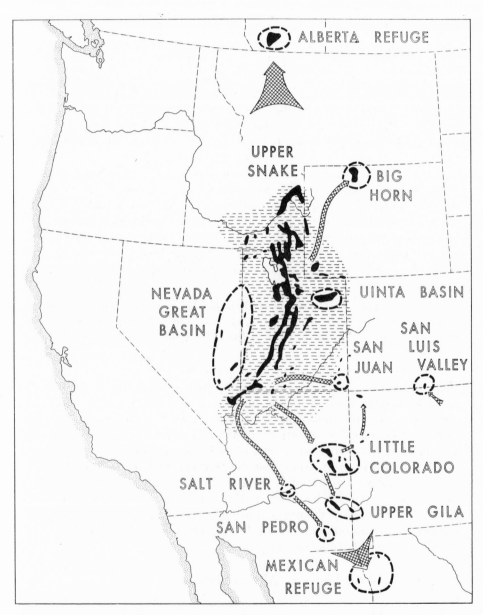

FIGURE 4: Mormon colonization, ca. 1870-1900, showing the expansion to the margins of and beyond the "girdle of wastelands" (indicated by the dashed line pattern).

he sent a scouting party to probe beyond the canyonlands and Navaho country deep into Arizona Territory. That group found little worth reporting, but a second group, two years later, nominated the upper reaches of the Little Colorado as an advantageous locale (Fig. 4). Young immediately "called" a group of colonists and in 1876 an expedition set out from St. George and journeyed 250 miles to establish tiny colonies on scattered patches of irrigable land in this high plateau country. In fact, it proved to be an extremely difficult area to domesticate. At one location the dam washed out seven times before finally secured, several sites were soon abandoned, and the main center of development was shifted farther south around Snowflake and Springerville toward the rim of the plateau.

But before such difficulties were fully apparent (and probably despite them had they been) Young vigorously pushed forward his plans for expansion far beyond. An historian of this movement [39] described how

President Young sat with a large map of America before him, while saying that the company of missionaries called were to push ahead as far as possible toward the Yaqui country in Mexico, which would finally be the objective point; but if they could not reach that country they might locate on the San Pedro or Salt River in Arizona.

In 1877 a Mormon party founded Lehi in the Salt River Valley, just east of the little town of Phoenix; in the following year another group laid out the farm village of Mesa nearby. Brigham Young was now dead (d. August 29, 1877) but the momentum of this southward movement continued, if only briefly. In 1878 a small group from the Salt River colony located at St. David on the San Pedro, less than forty miles from the Mexican border. At the same time difficulties in the Little Colorado settlements prompted a reconnaissance below the rim and beginning in 1879 Mormons from there began to move in upon the valley of the upper Gila.

The critical feature of all these colonizations was not the problem of taming nature, for that was ever an integral part of Mormon expansion, but the fact that in none of these localities were the Mormons the first colonists. Mines and trading posts dotted the map, Anglo- and Spanish-American ranchers and herders held much of the rangeland and riverine pastures, and many of these sites had to be purchased rather than merely occupied. The resultant pattern, therefore, was one of little clusters or strips of Mormon farms and villages hugging a precious and meager stream, enclaved within Gentile rangelands and mining country.[40]

[39] J. H. McClintock, *Mormon Settlement in Arizona* (Phoenix: Manufacturing Stationers, 1921), pp. 201–03.
[40] R. Kay Wyllys, "The Historical Geography of Arizona," *Pacific Historical Review*, XXI (1952), pp. 121–27, provides a brief but useful overview of the spread of the Mormons, Mexicans, Texans, and Californians into the various parts of the territory.

Expansion eastward was similar in type and difficulties. The most famous trek across the wasteland was that of the "Hole-in-the-Rock" mission, a group of more than 200 which pioneered in the San Juan country of Utah's southeastern corner in 1879–1880. Its name and fame came from its almost incredible passage across the Canyon of the Colorado, made possible only by carving footholds in the red sandstone walls and lowering wagons with ropes. It would ever after stand as a symbol of the faith and determination of Mormon pioneers, who, once called to the task, would see it through against enormous odds.[41] But the whole episode had important geographical meaning, too, for the need of such a journey was a mark of desperation and it led to a Promised Land of so little milk and honey that half the colonists were forced to scatter elsewhere after the first year. And there was not much to scatter to even though such potentially rich valleys as the Uncompaghre, Gunnison, and Grand Valley of the Colorado lay just beyond. At the time of this Mormon outreach all of these and much more of western Colorado lay empty, locked up in an Indian reservation. However, in 1881, following the Meeker Massacre, the area was suddenly thrown open to colonists, and two decades of often rather frenzied mining and ranching developments in the Rockies just to the east had built up such pressures that this opening unleashed a flood. Before the Mormons could recruit sufficient strength following their exhausting crossing of the wilderness even to explore on farther, the Gentiles were swarming over this western slope, laying out towns, building railroads, and speculating in mines and real estate.[42]

Thus any hope of contiguous expansion eastward in this sector was gone and, even within their precarious San Juan foothold, the Mormons had to suffer occasional mild harassment from Gentile cattlemen, a good many of whom had brought in herds from Texas and New Mexico some years earlier.[43]

To the south, expansion eastward into New Mexico was only a little more successful than into Colorado. A few missionaries to the Indians were the vanguard and in the early 1880's small groups of families from the Little Colorado colony established a half dozen tiny communities within the broad, bleak, arid zone between the upper San Juan and the upper Gila. None had sufficient potential to support the upbuilding of

[41] D. E. Miller, *Hole-in-the-Rock, an Epic in the Colonization of the Great American West* (Salt Lake City: Univ. of Utah Press, 1959).

[42] For example, Grand Junction, Delta, Montrose, and Durango were all founded in 1881, and within a year had railroad connections to the east.

[43] Cornelia Adams Perkins, Marian Gardner Nielson, and Lenora Butt Jones, *Saga of San Juan* (No place of publication given, Mercury Publishing Company, 1957). The chief settlement offshoots from the initial one at Bluff were Monticello, Verdure, and Blanding in Utah, and Webber, just south of Mancos, in Colorado. On the last see I. S. Freeman, *A History of Montezuma County, Colorado* (Boulder: Johnson Publishing Company, 1958), p. 35.

a major nucleus from which further expansion might be attempted. In every case relations with predecessors, Indians, Anglo-, or Spanish-American ranchers, were often less than amicable and in two or three instances proved a major factor in ultimate withdrawal.[44] Clearly the Mormons were running out of strength in this remote frontier, but even if they had had sufficient numbers and resources to sustain a further push there was nothing open to them beyond, for the middle Rio Grande Valley had been filled with peasant irrigation agriculturalists for centuries.

The Mormon colony in the San Luis Valley of southern Colorado is anomalous in pattern and origin. Situated 200 miles east of the Utah border, it was not a direct outward reach from Mormondom (though it was later reinforced by some Utah migrants). The original nucleus was formed by a group of converts from the Southern states who headed west in 1877 to gather with their fellow Saints in Zion. But there was so little room left within Zion that Brigham Young advised that they seek a location somewhere in Texas or in New Mexico. Through various contacts they were finally encouraged by railroad officials to settle along a new line in the San Luis Valley. Within a few years they had established several communities but they were hemmed in on all sides by ranchers and sheepmen and other agriculturists and never had the resources to buy, nor the strength to expand, successfully.[45]

Nor were conditions more directly east of the Wasatch core much more favorable. The best portions of the Uinta Basin were excluded from grasp by the Indian reservation. The Mormons did obtain a few footholds in the small Ashley Valley section farther east and along the northern margins of the Uinta Range in the southwest corner of Wyoming. But in both areas Gentile ranchers were also well established and when, after the turn of the century, allotments within the Indian reservation were allowed the Mormons obtained a dominant but by no means an exclusive position.

Westward expansion obtained as little as eastward and for the same

[44] Details on these settlements and their problems are well covered in H. M. Foster, "History of Mormon Settlements in Mexico and New Mexico" (unpublished M.A. thesis, History, University of New Mexico, 1937), pp. 66–99. One of them, Ramah, has become well known among social scientists because of the Harvard research project previously mentioned. A useful historical article stemming from that study is I. Telling, "Ramah, New Mexico, 1876–1900: An Historical Episode with Some Value Analysis," *Utah Historical Quarterly*, Vol. XXI (1953), pp. 117–36.

[45] Several attempts were made to colonize various marginal localities, most of which failed because of water and soil deficiencies. A brief account of this colonization is A. Jensen, "The Founding of Mormon Settlements in the San Luis Valley," *The Colorado Magazine*, Vol. XVII (1940), pp. 174–80. An excellent description of the history and character of these Mormon settlements as well as of others in the area is found in David W. Lantis, "The San Luis Valley, Colorado, Sequent Rural Occupance in an Intermontane Basin" (unpublished Ph.D. dissertation, Geography, The Ohio State University, 1950), esp. Vol. 1, pp. 201–27.

general reasons. The barren zone was broad and the footholds beyond were few, isolated, and of very limited potential for farming communities. In the 1860's a small colony was founded in Meadow Valley in Lincoln County, Nevada. But within a year or two silver was discovered at adjacent Pioche and the Gentiles were soon swarming over the whole region. In time the Mormons took root in a few other localities on either side of the Nevada–Utah border but a score of ephemeral mining booms spread a semipermanent population over the whole of Nevada and thus as the Mormons belatedly attempted to move into this western half of old Deseret there was little available to occupy, and their imprint here, as along the Colorado border, was but a small scattering.

Only to the north were the possibilities greater, and, significantly, only after Brigham Young's death was there a strong push in that direction. It was not at first a Church-directed colonization, but once under way Church leaders took a strong interest and gave assistance. It was their decision that the town of Rexburg be founded to serve as principal center in the main district. Mormons spread rapidly northward along most of the tributaries of the upper Snake in the 1880's, including Star Valley in westernmost Wyoming, and also occupied numerous locations somewhat to the west in southernmost Idaho.[46] In every locality Gentile stockmen had preceded them. But though this tardy northward expansion entered a country of much greater possibilities than in any of the other directions here, too, a physical barrier set sharp limits to the irrigation pioneer. The Snake River Plains, a waterless expanse of lava and sagebrush, completed the girdle of wastelands around the main body of Mormondom.

By the late 1880's the Mormons were running out of time as well as land. Over the years the propaganda against polygamy had made it a national issue, as evil as slavery, which had to be stamped out. The federal government, armed with harsh new laws, began to move relentlessly against the Church. It was a terrible crisis, for having been proclaimed by Joseph Smith as a revelation from God, polygamy was first of all a theological doctrine and not a mere social institution. There was no hope of armed resistance this time, but whereas the Church agonized over the problem, there was the need to save the hierarchy from jail. And thus Brigham Young's program for reaching into Mexico took on new meaning. After further reconnaissance and negotiations with the Mexican government, ranchlands in northwestern Chihuahua were purchased and in 1885 Mormon families, chiefly from the Arizona and Dixie colonies, began to move in. Within a few years, six flourishing

[46] Beal, *op. cit.*, footnote 37, gives a detailed coverage of this movement. For the Star Valley settlements see V. Linford, *Wyoming, Frontier State* (Denver: Old West Pub. Co., 1947), pp. 330–31.

settlements had been established, plus two more along the Bavispe River in adjacent (though barely accessible) Sonora.[47] At the same time, others looked northward for a refuge and the Church dispatched an exploration party to seek a location in Canada. In 1887 the town of Cardston was founded and Mormon colonists settled along the St. Mary River in the southwest corner of Alberta. At first they relied on cattle and dry-farmed wheat, but later they turned to irrigation and were the first to establish sugar beet production in the Canadian prairies.[48]

Although the critical feature in each of these refuge-settlements was a location beyond the national border, i.e., beyond the reach of United States marshals, these pressures from the federal government simply gave an added momentum to movements north and south already well under way, and Cardston and Chihuahua were simply the farthest outliers of the Zion-in-the-Mountains whose bounds had been steadfastly stretched outward for forty years (Fig. 4). But time had run out and these foreign refuges would remain as the terminal stations of this elongated, discontinuous spread. In 1890, under the threat of crippling confiscation decrees, the Church yielded to federal power and finally issued a manifesto prohibiting the practice of polygamy. This forced accommodation marked the end of an era for Mormonism. The society entered the twentieth century far from broken but certainly much subdued in the vigor of its leadership and growth. The Gathering had lost its momentum and the concept of a geographically expanding kingdom was no longer feasible. The days of seizing virgin land were long since past and large blocks of land suitable for group colonization were becoming scarce and expensive. One final example of this latter means took place just at this time. In 1893 about fifty families of Mormons settled in various localities of the Greybull area of the Big Horn Basin in Wyoming. It was not a Church-directed movement, there was no designated leader, and there was little advance arrangement for land and water rights. However, this informal infiltration was

[47] The standard published account of the history of these Mexican colonies is T. C. Romney, *The Mormon Colonies in Mexico* (Salt Lake City: Deseret News Press, 1938). Foster, *op. cit.*, footnote 44, gives a description of each settlement, but by far the most satisfactory geographical study is R. A. Schwartzlose, "The Cultural Geography of the Mormon Settlements in Mexico" (unpublished M. A. thesis, Geography, University of California, Berkeley, 1952). A valuable description of these colonies and their wider setting is found in D. D. Brand, "The Historical Geography of Northwestern Chihuahua" (unpublished Ph.D. dissertation, Geography, University of California, Berkeley, 1933). The Mormons were forced to abandon all of these colonies during the Mexican Revolution, beginning in 1912. The two in Sonora and one of the Chihuahua settlements were never reoccupied. Today the Mormons are very largely concentrated in two villages in Chihuahua.
[48] On the Canadian Mormon Colony see Nelson, *op. cit.*, footnote 5, and C. A. Dawson, *Group Settlement: Ethnic Communities in Western Canada*, Vol. VII of *Canadian Frontiers of Settlement*, edited by W. A. Mackintosh and W. L. G. Joerg (Toronto: Macmillan, 1936).

sufficiently successful that when the Church leaders learned in 1899 of an opportunity to obtain the concession of an abortive irrigation scheme nearby along the Shoshone, they negotiated directly with the Wyoming government and sponsored a colonization company. In this manner a typical Mormon nucleus, an organized group colonization centered upon nucleated farm villages, was established in this outlying district.[49] Such Mormon success in irrigation pioneering was by now an old story in the American West, but that, too, would have a new and quite different chapter added in the new century. For the really big irrigation projects had to await the resources of the national government, and though Mormons were often prominent among the colonists of these new federal reclamation areas, they could not move in as a group and proceed to lay out their distinctive villages and organize and allocate the land under the guidance of Church leaders as in the past.

Hence, the capitulation of 1890 to the basic patterns of American society was mirrored in the broad patterns of American geography. Hemmed in on all sides by the manifold strands of Gentile expansion and development, the Mormon colonization region was in final form. The pressure to expand outward would continue but it could not be done on the old terms; now it would mean not just competing with but intermingling with the Gentiles, a new geographical as well as social accommodation.

Gentile Intrusions

Although we have traced the most basic patterns of Mormon colonization, there is another side of the matter which is important to the search for a more precise geographical characterization of their culture region. While the Mormons were seeking to flex out their regional boundaries ever farther, the Gentiles were not only resisting and competing at the edges but were infiltrating directly into its very core (Fig. 5).

It is one of the great fateful ironies of their history that the Mormons selected the Great Salt Lake Valley as an isolated refuge, free from that direct mingling with the Gentiles which had brought such disaster in the states, only to find themselves within two years astride the main transcontinental thoroughfare of America directly in the overland path of those heterogeneous hordes bound for the California gold fields.[50]

---

[49] C. Lindsay, *The Big Horn Basin* (Lincoln: Univ. of Nebraska Press, 1932), a published Ph.D. dissertation from the University of Nebraska, is the authoritative source on this colonization. The three Mormon farm-villages are Byron, Cowley, and Lovell. Burlington and Emblem are also Mormon communities.

[50] The irony is nicely compounded by the fact that the men who first gathered those big flecks of gold from Sutter's millrace were Mormons, members of a disbanded Mexican War battalion who were pausing in California only to work long enough to reequip themselves for the journey east to rejoin their families in Zion.

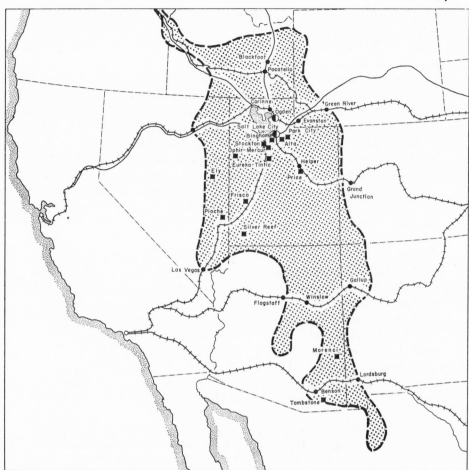

FIGURE 5: Gentile intrusions. The map is designed to be indicative rather than complete, showing the intrusions directly into Mormon centers (split circles), Gentile railroad towns (solid circles), mining camps (squares), and the main railway and wagon routes across the general Mormon sphere of influence (stipple).

The successive commercial strands of the rapidly growing nation crossed the core of Mormonland: the freighting wagons, the overland mail, the pony express, the telegraph, and the railroad. Salt Lake City became the principal way station to the Far West, an attractive site for all who sought to serve the varied needs of transcontinental traffic. Although some of the Mormons themselves were quite ready to engage in such trade, the Church did not encourage it, and their meager local resources allowed them to do little more than barter. Thus the Gentile merchants arrived with money, goods, and connections with Eastern suppliers, and without the restraining influence of a theocracy, and quickly transformed the infant Mormon capital from a farm village into a commercial town. The establishment of the army garrison, the arrival of the railroad, and the development of mines and associated industries fostered a continual expansion of Gentile enterprise. The Mormon leadership vigorously promoted essential industries and tried to monopolize the trade of their flock, but for various reasons they were never wholly successful. In time, the Church as a corporation and individual Mormon entrepreneurs would engage successfully in a wide range of commercial and industrial activities, but the early influence and power of the Gentiles in these realms would never be erased. Salt Lake City became the chief focus of Gentile activity in Mormonland primarily because of its strategic location within the broader patterns of a rapidly developing West.[51] From 1869 on that position was shared with another city forty miles to the north. As the junction of the Central Pacific and Union Pacific, Ogden was quickly changed from an agricultural town into a major railroad center and a growing commercial nucleus. These two cities became the chief examples of Gentile intrusions directly into pre-existing Mormon communities.[52] Elsewhere, some Mormon villages were similarly affected on a much smaller scale, but the more common pattern of intrusion was the development of new Gentile towns within Mormon districts. These were, of course, directly related to new activities which the Gentiles superimposed upon the Mormon rural kingdom. A notorious example of this was Corinne, thirty miles northwest of Ogden. A creation of the railroad, Corinne became the headquarters for the freighting business serving Montana mining districts and was a tumultuous center of strongly anti-Mormon political activity until the

[51] R. J. Dwyer, *The Gentile Comes to Utah: A Study in Religious and Social Conflict, 1862–1890* (Washington, D.C.: The Catholic University of America Press, 1941), is a useful narrative and interpretive history with many incidental references to localities but with no attempt to depict the geography of contact and conflict.
[52] It is quite impossible to present any exact statistical measure of the proportions of Mormon and Gentile for any area. Despite the fine series of religious censuses (1890, 1906, 1916, 1926, 1936) published by the U.S. Bureau of the Census and the 1952 census by the National Council of Churches of Christ (see footnote 16), a host of special problems bedevil the investigator. The principal one involves the definition of membership, which varies among the many different denominations. For example, the Eleventh Census reported a total of 117,640 Mormons in Utah and 9,914 members of other denominations. However, the total population of the state of Utah was 207,905 and there is no way of knowing what proportion of the 80,351 remainder were members of no church and what proportion were children of members or in some way affiliated but not counted as members of particular denominations. The usual statement in such censuses is that Mormons count all those above about eight years of age in Mormon families as members. Such censuses do, of course, give some indication of where the Gentiles are within the Mormon region, even though no exact proportions are calculable. Thus the first detailed census (1890) listed fifteen different non-Mormon church denominations in Salt Lake County, and Salt Lake and Weber (Ogden) counties accounted for fifty-six per cent of the total state membership in non-Mormon churches. See Belinksy, *op. cit.*, footnote 1, for a good succinct coverage of the literature and problems associated with using religious censuses.

completion of railroads northward reduced it to a local trade center. In time, other railroads cut into or through the Mormon region, such as the Oregon Short Line (Union Pacific) across southern Idaho; the Denver & Rio Grande from Colorado across the Wasatch into Salt Lake City and Ogden; the Los Angeles & Salt Lake (Union Pacific) through the southwestern Utah deserts, reestablishing Las Vegas as an important way station to California; the Santa Fe across the Colorado Plateau in northern Arizona; and the Southern Pacific through the border desert county. Each of these passed through or near established Mormon communities. In a few cases the railroad's own needs added new people and activities and thereby altered the old towns, but for the most part, each railroad prompted a whole new string of settlements, varied in size and importance from the livestock loading stations and whistlestop track-crew hamlets spaced every few miles along the way to major division points, such as Pocatello, Helper, and Winslow. Whatever their size, such places were wholly different in character from the Mormon villages and towns, and thus each of these major rail lines became a Gentile swath cutting through the Mormon region.

Even before the first railroad, though mainly just after, another kind of alien community, the mining town, appeared in the midst of Mormon country. Stockton, where gold was discovered by federal troops just over the range west of Salt Lake City, was the first mining town, but soon there were many more, and some much larger and longer lived. Among the most important ones were the mining camps and smaller towns that developed in several districts around the fringes of the Mormon core: Bingham, Alta, Park City, Ophir-Mercur, and Eureca-Tintic. Others, such as Frisco, Silver Reef, Pioche, Ely, Morenci, and Tombstone, sprang up suddenly in outlying districts near Mormon communities. Coal mines, to serve the railroads, and smelters were also developed in several localities and especially in Carbon County, eastern Utah, where coal and railroad towns grew up directly adjacent to the farm villages of Castle Valley.[53]

By their nature usually located on the mountainsides but very often directly visible from the valley floors, these sprawling, bustling, smoking camps were a startling discordant imprint upon the bucolic Mormon landscape and their mark upon the regional society was no less vivid. It was the activities within and related to these towns, the mining and transportation centers, that injected cultural variety into Mormonland. They provided the entry for Roman Catholics, Protestants, Anglicans, Eastern Orthodox, and Jews. They were peopled not as the Mormon towns with just a narrow range of Anglo-Americans and converts from

[53] Details on the history of the various mining camps are scattered in many sources. One of the most convenient and satisfactory introductions to the various mining activities in Utah is to be found in the *Utah Historical Quarterly*, Vol. XXXI (Summer, 1963), an issue entirely devoted to the history of the Utah mining industry.

Protestant Europe, but with Irish and Italians, Greeks and Slavs, Syrians and Portuguese, Chinese and Mexicans, and they displayed all the social variety that these imply. Whereas Mormon society tended toward uniformity, stability, cohesiveness, and a self-conscious circumscription of its attitudes and activities, the Gentile society of such towns was heterogeneous, mobile, volatile, splintered into a mosaic of sects and parties, and as a whole operated with few curbs upon its activities. In time some convergence of these two would be quite apparent; yet they remain today recognizably distinct wherever they exist side by side.

Added to the initial impetus from their transportation functions, servicing these industrial centers was a great stimulus to the growth and cosmopolitan character of Salt Lake City and Ogden. Their manufacturing, wholesaling, retailing, and financial activities were long more a reflection of their ties to these intrusive or immediately peripheral Gentile centers than to the vast but rural and relatively poor Mormon tributary area. The Salt Lake Valley became one of the world's major smelting districts, and the shadows of the towering smelter stacks striped across the adjacent alfalfa and sugar beet fields became a landscape symbol of the close juxtaposition of Mormon and Gentile, yet for many years the farmer and the smelter worker moved in almost entirely separate social circles.[54]

Within Salt Lake City itself, the central business district developed along a dualistic spatial pattern which was a vivid reflection of this social and economic dichotomy. The Hotel Utah on the north and the Hotel Newhouse four blocks on the south (long Mormon blocks, each the size of a ten-acre square) have long formed the terminals of the main retail shopping district. The prominent Mormon establishments are clustered around one shopping district, whereas the Gentile establishments are clustered around the other. The principal Mormon focus is, of course, upon Temple Square directly across from the Hotel Utah with the temple and more widely known tabernacle, and within a block of it, the Church headquarters and offices and the principal Mormon hotel, department store, bank, insurance company, publishing house, and radio station.[55] The Hotel Newhouse, on the other hand, was built with money from the silver mines of southwest Utah, and within two

[54] The smelters are nearly all gone, but a modern counterpart is the Geneva steel plant in Utah Valley which is often photographed with dairy cows in the foreground and expressly presented not only as an intrusion of modern industry into an older rural setting, but sometimes as a symbol of a national industry implanted abruptly in a Mormon locality, though usually, and with some justification, as a symbol of the accommodation between the two rather than a persisting dichotomy.

[55] To speak of these as Mormon does not necessarily mean that each one is owned, or was begun, directly by the Church as a corporation, although some were, but that at least they were founded by individual Mormons who were also prominent within the Church hierarchy. The internal structure and cohesiveness of the society gives ample justification for the label.

blocks of it are large department stores, several banks, office buildings and the stock exchange, all established by non-Mormons, chiefly from the wealth of the region's mining districts.[56] Added to these, across the street from the Hotel Newhouse and thus in a sense counterbalancing Temple Square, is the large building housing the post office and other agencies of the federal government which was, of course, among the earliest instruments of Gentile intrusion. This pattern should not be exaggerated into an absolute cleavage. There has always been considerable interfingering in the blocks between, and certainly it has been a long time since retail shopping patterns were in any important degree socially segregated; yet these clusters are clearly there and they are representative of a feature of profound significance in the heritage of the city and region.[57]

The Mormon Culture Region

It should be evident from the foregoing material that defining the Mormon region is not a simple task. The context of the Mormon situation is sufficiently varied from place to place to make any single perimeter deceptive; whatever the criteria, the resultant areal compartment cannot possibly reflect adequately those variations. This is, of course, commonly true of cultures; it is one of the most serious difficulties in mapping them, and has been one of the important bases for criticism of the whole culture area concept. But the problem is easily exaggerated. The most obvious improvement is to make use of some generic concepts which can express the areal dimensions of significant gradations in the content and situation of the culture under study. In the following section the terms *core, domain,* and *sphere* will be defined and used for that purpose. Because cultures are areal growths such gradations are also likely to represent a sequential spread from a locality of origin, or *hearth.* Thus these terms will be at least suggestive of patterns in both time and space.

[56] Such matters are common knowledge locally, and there is plenty of biographical data on the men who were involved and their sources of wealth. For example, W. M. McPhee in a recent article "Vignettes of Park City," *Utah Historical Quarterly,* Vol. XXVIII (1960), pp. 136–53, noted that the Kearns, Keith, Tribune, and Judge buildings, the Keith O'Brien Department Store, and the Moxum Hotel, all of which are clustered on the south end of the CBD, were constructed by men who made their fortunes in the Park City mining district. McPhee also gave a succinct account of the character of the local society and its anti-Mormon attitudes during the early mining era.

[57] The separation of Mormon and Gentile clusters was apparent from the first; this specific pattern between the two main hotels began to take shape ca. 1905–1915. For a somewhat more detailed examination of these patterns and their broader context see R. R. Boyce, "An Historical Geography of Greater Salt Lake City, Utah" (unpublished M. A. thesis, Geography, University of Utah, 1957). The new large federal building just completed is a departure from this pattern and may be taken as a symbol of the much more relaxed relationship between the two.

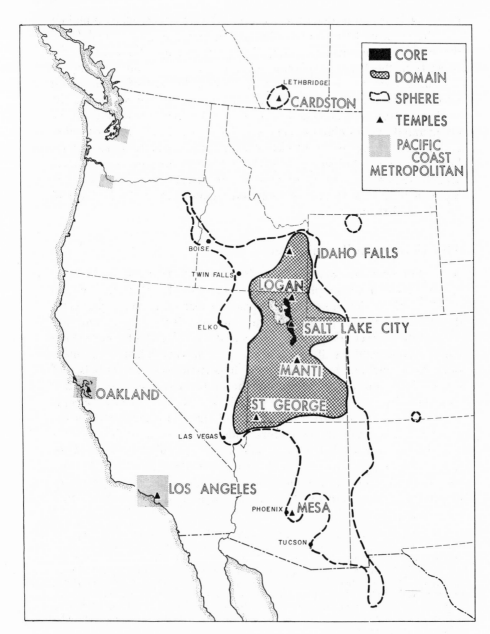

FIGURE 6: The Mormon culture region.

A *core* area, as a generic term, is taken to mean a centralized zone of concentration, displaying the greatest density of occupance intensity of organization, strength, and homogeneity of the particular features characteristic of the culture under study. It is the most vital center, the seat of power, the focus of circulation. The *core* of the Mormon region is clearly the Wasatch Oasis, that densely occupied strip along the base of the mountain wall, pivoted upon Salt Lake City and extending about sixty-five miles to the north and to the south (Fig. 6). It qualifies by all the obvious measures of density, intensity, and nodality. It contains the main cluster of cities which have been growing so rapidly in recent years that what was once a string of discrete centers spaced along the north-south routeways has become an increasingly dense and continuous urban strip, the megalopolis of Mormonland. Herein also lies the majority of the industrial plants and output of the region; yet the region remains one of the most productive of the many agricultural districts as well. And the intimate juxtaposition of the two, the sustained encounter between the rural, provincial, tradition-laden sector and the dynamic, national, industrial sector, is one of the important distinguishing features of this core area.

Together, Salt Lake City and Ogden are the focus of all the major strands of communication in the central Far West. Salt Lake City is one of the nation's major regional commercial capitals, serving all of the main Mormon area and beyond.[58] Mormons as far distant as Cardston, California, and southern Arizona are likely to turn to its firms for various needs and services. Its role as a religious capital is perhaps even greater than commonly realized, for the Mormon Church is a rigidly hierarchical theocracy, with power emanating from a pinnacle, and there is an unusually dense traffic of orders, materials, and persons moving within its functional structure. Church members even in the most remote districts are periodically visited by leaders from Salt Lake City. And twice a year, every April and October, representatives from nearly every Mormon community journey to Temple Square for the semi-annual Conference to be informed, directed, exhorted, and inspired by their leaders. Such journeys and gatherings can take on the air of pilgrimages for the faithful from the far corners of Zion. In such ways the Mormon region is a nodal region culturally as well as commercially.

It may seem contradictory that this core is not the most Mormon in the sense of numerical or relative dominance; indeed, it has always contained the majority of the Gentiles within the main Mormon area. But the fact that this has been the main focus of sustained Mormon–Gentile contact is another of the important definitive attributes of this core. For that contact has been a creative tension, a source of innovation, both as a stimulus to the definition and defense of differences and

58 Harris, *op. cit.*, footnote 8.

to the pressure for adaptation and accommodation. Mormonism today owes much of its character to a century of that tension in this same area, and whatever Mormonism becomes, it will be strongly influenced by this same geographical intimacy between Mormon and Gentile. However, the most single compelling reason for the recognition of a Mormon region is the simple fact that its residents are aware that such a tension still exists, now wholly peacefully, usually amicably, but always consciously.

In recent years the contact between the two has been somewhat broadened in extent and altered in character. The mining and smelting industries are now much less important proportionately and no longer represent the cleavage between the two groups so clearly. In the one major district remaining, Bingham Canyon, the old mining and smelting towns are virtually gone and the workers, now Mormon as well as Gentile, commute from Salt Lake City and its suburbs. The federal government is by far the most potent instrument, directly and indirectly, of the Gentile presence. There is the usual array of agencies, but also a cluster of major military installations and many new defense industries. Such was the case of the large Geneva steel mill in 1942 and such is the case of numerous chemical and electronic plants of the last decade. Concentrated in this core between Provo and Brigham City, these facilities employ thousands of Mormons; yet they are national in scope, alien in control, and are responsible for steady injections of Gentile people and influences into Mormondom.

The *domain* refers to those areas in which the particular culture under study is *dominant,* but with markedly less intensity and complexity of development than in the core, where the bonds of connection are fewer and more tenuous and where regional peculiarities are clearly evident. The *domain* of the Mormon region extends from the upper Snake River country of southeastern Idaho to the lower Virgin in southeastern Nevada. The generalized pattern on the map includes some mountain and desert areas with no population at all but is drawn so as to enclose all of the areas of contiguous colonization in which Mormon settlers became and remained dominant.[59] In a numerical and narrow sense, this is the most thoroughly Mormon area. Indeed, in the most recent religious census there were eight counties within it which reported no adherents whatsoever of any other denomination, an

[59] The pattern of the *domain* should be generally clear when related to previous maps. The indentation in eastern Utah reflects the coal and railroad towns of Carbon County and the fact that the country east of these is nearly uninhabited except for a few, mainly Gentile hamlets along the railroad. The indentation along the western border is produced by drawing the boundary arbitrarily through the middle of the broad salt desert.

astonishing homogeneity for any American region.[60] Older Gentile intrusions were almost entirely focused upon mining and railroad towns; all of the former and many of the latter are now reduced in size and significance. New intrusions are noticeable only in southeastern Utah where oil, natural gas, uranium, and potash developments have attracted a considerable influx of outsiders and here and there in towns along the main highways where the continued growth of tourist and commercial traffic has created new opportunities and lured a few new persons. But no new Gentile communities have arisen and, even though the stereotyped rectangularity of some of the old Mormon towns has been deformed by the highway strip developments common to all America, the Mormon towns and this whole domain remain strongly rural and provincial. Much of it is still back country, remote from the metropolitan touch, and the distinctive Mormon landscape with its patterns of nucleated villages and fields and its prominent ward chapels is everywhere still visible.

The *sphere* of a culture may be defined as the zone of outer influence and, often, peripheral acculturation, wherein that culture is represented only by certain of its elements or where its peoples reside as minorities among those of a different culture. Sphere boundaries are often less easy to define because there may be fine gradations of culture differences and the limits of influences may be rapidly changing. The *Mormon Culture Sphere* is defined as including those areas where Mormons live as nucleated groups enclaved within Gentile country or where they are of long-standing major local numerical significance.

Geographically the Mormon sphere is composed of a fringe, greatly elongated in the south, encompassing the domain, and of a long salient and some outliers on the north and east, each with a special history. For the most part, the circumferential sphere merely encloses those little clusters of rural Mormons which represent the outer ripple of the last wave of expansion late in the last century. The origins of the three noncontiguous areas have already been described. The narrow extension across southern Idaho and penetration into eastern Oregon represents a strong infiltration reinforced by local conversions. It was not a group movement but a gradual and diffuse migration developing after 1890 in response to various local opportunities. The Oregon position is not the most recent foothold of a contiguous advance but rather an early outlier belatedly joined to the rest of the sphere by more recent migrants to intervening districts. It was initiated by a Mormon entrepreneur who

[60] *Churches and Church Membership in the United States*, op. cit., footnote 16. The counties were Franklin and Teton in Idaho, Garfield, Kane, Morgan, Rich, Washington, and Wayne in Utah. In addition, Emery, Millard, Piute, Sevier, and Wasatch counties in Utah each reported fewer than a total of fifty members of all other denominations.

recruited Mormon laborers for his lumber operations in Baker County. Gradually farms in the Grande Ronde Valley were obtained and a growing nucleus established.[61] To the east, new government-sponsored irrigation projects were principally responsible for a steady influx of Mormons into the Minidoka, Payette, Malheur, and Weiser districts. In these areas the Mormons are mostly scattered among the Gentiles in farm and town alike rather than strongly clustered in villages of their own creation. Yet they have become dominant in some localities and are the largest single religious group in most of the counties involved.

Actually, the majority of the Mormons within this sphere today live in urban areas, such as Phoenix, Tucson, Las Vegas, Elko, Twin Falls, Boise, and Lethbridge. In none of these areas are they dominant as they are in the cities of their domain; but in every case they are recognized as a very important social and religious group; in some cities and towns they tend to be clustered in certain residential areas, and in each they have close kinship ties with adjacent rural areas. These urban Mormon groups were originally formed and continue to be sustained in part by local rural migrants.

Thus, although this Mormon sphere encompasses considerable variety in local contexts, everywhere the Mormons have some deep roots in the general locality; are usually in some degree clustered; are recognized by other people as a separate cohesive body who impress a distinctive mark upon the local economy, politics, and society; and are highly self-conscious of themselves in the same way.[62] Such in-group solidarity may stem from a view of themselves as being a handful of stalwarts manning a beleaguered outpost against a surrounding hostile world, as in some of the remote rural villages,[63] or the solidarity may reflect, as in the courteous but evangelically aggressive behavior in urban centers, a vigorous and optimistic self-confidence. In either case, it is just such self-awareness and patterned behavior that makes Mormon culture a recognizable and viable thing, and thus makes the definition of its area important.

These three generic categories, *core, domain,* and *sphere,* complete our refined definition of the Mormon culture region, yet they leave tens of thousands of Mormons in the American West beyond its bounds. There is, therefore, a fourth category but it is not of the same kind, that is, it does not represent simply a gradation outward from the other

[61] I am grateful to Professor L. C. Johnson of Eastern Oregon College for supplying me with copies of local manuscript materials on the Mormons in this area.

[62] See W. C. Bailey, "A Typology of Arizona Communities," *Economic Geography,* Vol. XXVI (1950), pp. 94–104, on the need to recognize the Mormons as a distinctive group.

[63] See T. F. O'Dea, "The Effects of Geographical Position on Belief and Behavior in a Rural Mormon Village," *Rural Sociology,* Vol. XIX (1954), pp. 358–64, for an incisive commentary on Ramah as an example.

three. Reference here is to the Mormons living in the Pacific Coast states, and within these very largely in the main metropolitan areas of Los Angeles, the San Francisco Bay region, Portland, and Puget Sound. Altogether these Pacific Coast Mormons represent nearly a fifth of the total national membership and they have organized their religious and social life into wards and stakes with an intensity quite the equal of those in Utah itself. Yet despite these numbers and this zeal there remain critical differences between these Mormons and those within the *sphere*. For these metropolitan groups are not simply farther outliers of an expanding Zion. Here they are but one small ingredient in a movement shared by Americans of all faiths, and although their total numbers are impressive as Mormon proportions, they are but a small minority of these Pacific Coast populations. Furthermore, here they are intermingled as individuals in residence and in work with Americans of every sect; their ward chapels stand among those of a dozen denominations in the same general neighborhoods. Here there can be no nucleation, no spatial insularity as a group against the encompassing Gentile world. The Mormons of Seattle, or Oakland, or Los Angeles, unlike those of Phoenix or Las Vegas, have no deep local roots, their families have not importantly shaped the history of the area, they have no ties with a sector of old rural Mormondom nearby. The local society in these coastal communities is not characterized by them nor in any special "Mormon way" importantly influenced by them, and thus, despite their undoubted significance in other ways, because they have not impressed a distinctive mark upon these metropolitan regions as a whole, these Pacific Coast areas are simply not part of the Mormon region as defined in terms of historical cultural geography. We are dealing here not with an expansion of Zion but with a dispersion into Babylon.

Thus, in building their Zion in the mountains, the Mormons have left their stamp upon districts within and along the North American cordillera from a corner of Alberta to a corner of Chihuahua. Such limits represent a lengthy outreach, but viewed as a whole the resulting Mormon religion is asymmetrical, discontinuous, and uneven in character. Its elongation southward from its core and capital and the discontinuities in the north are largely the results of the bias of Brigham Young. His obsession with the need for a thrust toward Mexico put the Mormon pioneer only a little behind the first wave of stockmen and ahead of most other farmers in Arizona, whereas his prejudice against the north allowed the whole breadth of Montana to intervene as a Gentile stronghold between the Mormon domain and its belated foothold in Alberta. On the other hand, the slow steady spread of Mormon influence westward along the old, once-shunned routeway to Oregon shows that the ability to penetrate the Gentile periphery did not end with the close

of the great colonization era at the turn of the century; and the sheer
demographic power, the cohesiveness of the society, and a still strong
predilection for the rural life suggests that such penetration may well
continue for many years.[64]

If the shape of the Mormon region is discordant with that of Deseret
the failure of that original strategy was not an entire loss. For an agricultural people the gain of southeastern Idaho surely more than offsets
the loss of most of Nevada. Within the bounds of Deseret, penetration
of western Colorado might have yielded more than the penetration of
the plateaulands of Arizona, though such a thrust would almost certainly have been just as gravely weakened by the difficulties of distance
and isolation. The major loss in the contraction of 1857 was, of course,
the withdrawal from San Bernardino. Even though it seems clear that
the Mormons simply would never have been able to hold firm control
of such an attractive and accessible locale, it does seem possible that if
the zeal and determination that went into the Arizona and San Juan
colonizations had been focused upon the Los Angeles Basin, a foothold
might have been established with sufficient strength to have sustained
Mormon control of a specific and significant district amid the swirling
patterns of Gentile development. But the main purpose of an historical
geography analysis is not to suggest what might have been but to reveal
what has been, what is, and what probably will be. Having identified
the basic components of the Mormon region and offered some explanation of the processes which created them, we may usefully conclude
with a summation of how they are proportioned to the whole and how
current trends seem destined to affect them.

Conclusion

The *core* of the Mormon region appears to be well stabilized in area,
character, and significance. About 40 per cent of the total Mormon population [65] in the United States is concentrated within its bounds, a proportion which has not changed greatly for more than fifty years.[66]
Whereas instabilities in defense industries may well affect the short-term

[64] For example, a sample survey in the new Columbia River irrigation project found
that the Mormons were the largest single denomination represented, although they
comprised only fifteen per cent of the total; M. A. Straus and B. D. Parrish, "The
Columbia River Settler, a Study of Social and Economic Resources in New Land
Settlement," *Washington Agricultural Experiment Station Bulletin 566* (Pullman:
State College of Washington, May, 1956), pp. 10–11.
[65]The proportions in this summary were calculated on the basis of the 1952 religious
census (footnote 16). They can be no more than approximations, but when put in
context with other fragmentary evidence, they appear to be sufficiently accurate for
their time to warrant their use for such a general view. More serious is the fact that
this source is now more than a decade old.
[66] In 1916 about thirty-five per cent of the Mormons were in this *core* area.

rate of growth, the basic economy is so well established and the location so strategic with reference to so many developments elsewhere in the whole Far West that there is no reason to believe that this area cannot continue to support something near that proportion despite the Mormons' vigorous rate of natural increase. That same rate of growth will also likely keep the Mormon–Gentile ratio fairly stable despite the certain continued influx of outsiders. Furthermore, there is ample room within the Wasatch Oasis for such industrial and population growth and little indication of any incipient expansion of the *core* into bordering areas.[67]

In 1952 the *domain* contained about 28 per cent of the total Mormon population. It is almost certain that the proportion is now less and that it will continue to decline gradually. For it is so heavily rural, and so readily served by the core, that there is little basis for growth. A few small cities may expand but in general this sector will continue to be a net exporter of people, sending them to the *core*, to peripheral cities in the *sphere*, and to the Pacific Coast. The *domain* is more than 90 per cent Mormon and its known resources offer little reason to expect any major Gentile intrusions. However, it is possible that mineral developments along its eastern edge could draw a sufficient influx to submerge the Mormon population there to a minority position. In our geographical terms such a change would mean a change in category and necessitate a redrawing of the boundary to shift such areas from the *domain* into the *sphere*. Though the stamp of the Mormon culture is indelibly upon this domain, by any quantitative measure it is of declining significance.

The *sphere*, containing about 13 per cent of the Mormons, is as questionable in its prospects as variable in its past. In general, Mormons constitute about 25 per cent of the total religious adherents, but proportions and trends differ from place to place. In southern Idaho and eastern Oregon their position will probably strengthen gradually, though steadily; however, in general the rural areas will surely stagnate. Nevertheless, because of the strong Mormon foothold in such thriving centers as Phoenix, Las Vegas, Boise, and Lethbridge the *sphere* is in a better position to sustain and even increase its proportionate position than is the *domain*. Yet such growth at the edges necessarily requires an ever-greater integration with the Gentile world.

In 1952 about 17 per cent of the Mormons lived in or near the met-

[67] The establishment of defense industries in Tooele Valley and the growth of some commuter traffic between it and Salt Lake Valley may suggest an incipient expansion of the *core* westward but this appears to be a stagnant situation and Tooele Valley is unlikely to have sufficient attractions to compete for industries and residents. It is conceivable that vigorous growth at the northern end of the *core* could lead toward an integration of Cache Valley into the *core* complex, but there is little reason at present to expect this.

ropolitan regions along the Pacific Coast. That proportion was then threefold greater than fifteen years before and it has been increasing steadily since. Such a growth has been supported by migrations from all the other Mormon areas, from the *core* as well as from the periphery, from the capital as well as from the black valley farms, and it has not only been lured by the great range of economic opportunity and the amenities of life in these coastal districts, but has been driven by the most powerful demographic pressures in America. For the Mormon region has long been a distinct demographic region within the nation, in which an unusually high birthrate combined with an unusually low death rate to produce a remarkable rate of natural increase. In recent years that increase has ranged from twenty-seven to thirty-two per thousand, well more than double the American average.[68] To try to contain such growth within the historic Zion under the conditions of modern America would almost certainly result in the gradual impoverishment of the whole. Thus the idea of a Mormon commonwealth self-contained and sufficient unto its own future is no longer tenable; not only is the day of the Gathering essentially over but even some portion of those born in Zion must disperse into the world.

The Church leadership has, of course, been well aware of this fundamental change and it has responded with a new strategy. If the Saints cannot all be gathered into Zion, then insofar as possible Zion will have to be taken to the Saints. One of the great reasons for gathering to Zion was to be near a temple, for a Mormon temple is not a place of congregational worship analogous with a cathedral, but a place for the performance of certain sacred ordinances peculiar to their faith.[69] The theological importance of these ceremonies is so great that the religious life of those who do not have at least occasional access to them is considered seriously impoverished. Over the years seven temples were built, spaced out to serve the population of the whole Mormon region. Members beyond those bounds simply had to journey to Zion or suffer a spiritual deficiency. The dedication of the Los Angeles temple in 1956 was, therefore, a cause for great rejoicing among the Mormons of California, but it was also a geographical fact of profound theological and sociological significance. It was a tangible, irrefutable, recognition that:[70]

[68] The Church periodically publishes such vital statistics for their membership as a whole: e.g., 1956, birthrate 37.64, death rate 5.53, net increase per thousand 32.11; 1962, birthrate 33.16, death rate 5.42, net increase per thousand 27.74. In 1962 the national figures were: birthrate 22.4, death rate 9.5, net increase per thousand 12.9.
[69] Baptism by proxy for the dead and "celestial marriage" are the chief temple ordinances.
[70] O'Dea, *op. cit.*, footnote 5, p. 261.

there is a way of life, Mormon in its spirit, that does not require literal removal to Utah and concrete participation in a sociogeographical entity. The gathered may now be gathered in spirit, and Zion need not be literally in the mountain tops of Deseret.

Similarly, the erection of temples in England, in Switzerland, and in New Zealand in the last decade was an admission that this spiritual Zion could even be extended to those rooted beyond the bounds of God's chosen continent of America.[71]

It is tempting to conclude with the reminder that the original frame of their western Zion included a seashore as well as the mountaintops and that the Los Angeles temple is simply a belated reassertion of the Mormon hold upon a far corner of Deseret. But that would distort the situation. Los Angeles is of enormous importance in the changing patterns of Mormonism, but it is so precisely because the Mormon presence there is not an extension of the Mormon region but a foothold in the outer world. Geographically, the most significant trend in Mormon culture is the fact that the greatest growth in membership is taking place beyond the limits of the historic Mormon culture region, that is, in areas which it cannot hope to dominate. It does not take much foresight to realize that California will someday have more Mormons than Utah (in November, 1964, a temple was dedicated at Oakland to serve the rapidly growing nucleus in the Bay region), but it is essential also to realize that California cannot be captured, for it can only be adjusted to. It is quite reasonable, therefore, to see emerging in Mormon culture a new geographical pattern which can be symbolized as a Salt Lake City-Los Angeles axis. It is a linkage of the old nodal culture region rigorously focused upon Temple Square with the new expanding, relatively wealthy *diaspora* intimately enmeshed in the larger world. It is a link between the old *core* and the new frontier, between the old Zion and a newly appreciated Babylon. Such an axis is already discernible; the Mormon traffic between the two is ever greater, with Las Vegas once more a convenient if somewhat altered refreshment stop along a new-style Mormon Corridor. Mormon and Gentile live together in each terminal. In the one the Mormons set the pattern and the Gentiles intruded, in the other the situations are reversed. Modern Mormonism emerged from that first encounter and the Mormonism of the future will surely

[71] The Hawaiian temple on Oahu, dedicated in 1919, was actually the first outside of Zion. This was built to serve the converts made in Hawaii and various other Polynesian islands in recognition that it was quite impractical for them to emigrate or even visit the mainland. In earlier years, however, the gathering even of Saints so far removed in culture and distance was encouraged; see Stegner, *op. cit.*, footnote, 5, pp. 136–41, for the account of the pathetic attempt of a small group of Hawaiians to colonize the desolate wastes of Skull Valley, Utah.

reflect this sustained culture contact at both ends of this new geographical axis.

The Mormon region will long endure as a major pattern within the American West and, thereby, will continue to warrant far greater attention from American geographers than it has yet received, but Mormon culture will be ever less completely encompassed within that region and will perhaps be shaped as much by what happens to it outside those bounds as by the happenings inside.

IX. THE FUTURE OF MAN ON THE EARTH

36. Bombs, Babies, Bulldozers

Stuart Chase

After examination of the variety of man's activities on the earth, it appears that never before have the opportunities for the abundant life been greater. But at the same time, the threats to this life, indeed, to life itself, are constantly increasing, and any prolonged period of stability appears to be more and more unlikely. If there is to be any prospect at all of a reasonable—or of any—world, it must come through greater understanding everywhere of the great differences which separate, but need not divide, men. Geography and geographic knowledge can contribute to this understanding. If we can manage some measure of accommodation in three major problems confronting us—Stuart Chase labels them "Bombs, Babies, and Bulldozers" in this concluding selection—there will be possibilities of achieving a better future for all men on the earth.

Every day in the headlines and over the airwaves the problems come crowding in—civil liberties, political corruption, juvenile delinquency, taxes, crime, unbalanced budgets, medical care, death on the highways. . . . an endless list. Most are important; all require attention. But looming over them, like Everest above its foothills, are three transcendent issues: nuclear war, the population explosion, and the destruction of living space. We can label them bombs, babies, and bulldozers, the last as a symbol for those activities of modern technology which lead to massive corruption of the environment.

The careful observer never loses sight of these three peaks with their connecting ridges. His excitement is restrained about the Common Market, the state of the federal budget, even a trip to the moon. The big three make all other problems relatively minor. He is convinced

SOURCE: *Saturday Review*, January 26, 1963, p. 21. The author is an economist and writer.

that they must be met and composed if civilization is to continue. We can struggle along somehow, he thinks, plagued by the race question, the crime question, the money question, the form-of-government question. All have been with us for centuries. But the careful observer doubts if we can muddle through the three B's. He does not abandon his daily tasks and indulge in perpetual lamentation like Jeremiah, but he is inclined to husband his reforming zeal for these issues, and to measure all headlines in relation to them.

Bombs come first in priority. They could fall at literally any moment, as a result of mechanical failure or man failure. A recent breakdown in electronic signals almost triggered a shower of them. So did a flight of geese across an Arctic radar screen—which triggers an ironic thought.

Babies come second. At present rates of increase, they promise to double the population of the world by the end of the century—from three billion to six billion. This can hardly fail, the demographers predict, to leave the hungry world—two-thirds of mankind—hungrier than ever. Some observers call population the world's number one problem, and it may be for the long run. It is not, however, so immediate as nuclear extinction by accident, or by extension of the so-called nuclear club. Red China, Israel, Egypt are standing in line.

Bulldozers, representing the assault on living space, are also not immediately catastrophic. This problem is well along the road, however, to complicating existence unendurably—with the traffic jams and smog of Los Angeles as an indication of what the future may hold. This issue, the third in priority, affects high-energy societies more than underdeveloped areas. In fact, the more developed we are, the worse it becomes.

All three result directly from the fact that technology is advancing at an exponential rate, and they thus represent something unprecedented in human affairs. Without modern science they would not exist. History, accordingly, offers almost no lessons to guide us. As invention cannot be halted—at least short of nuclear war—it looks as if we must use the scientific method to control the calamitous effects of science, or retire defeated from the human drama.

These menaces are strictly man-made, the result of activity in the human cortex. They bear no causal relation to natural calamities like earthquakes and hurricanes and other so-called Acts of God. The unfortunate fact that most of us regard them as beyond human intervention does not remove the obligation to control the effects of our ingenuity. Nuclear weapons are based on the work of atomic physicists, especially Einstein. The population upsurge is based on the work of medical scientists, dramatically reducing the death rate in the past few decades while birth rates remain static. The assault on living space is primarily the work of the internal combustion engine.

The genie is out of the bottle and there is no hope of stuffing him back. There are, however, some possibilities of taming him, despite the current apathy. Let us examine the challenges in a little more detail.

Bombs

Two schools of thought seek to mitigate the thermonuclear threat. One says that War III will not come; the other that it will come but can be made "acceptable" by shelters and civil defense. Opposed to these views are most of the world's scientists, a substantial number of military men, and intelligent laymen in every country. Even a politician, here and there, shows some uneasiness about Doomsday.

Scientists have an articulate spokesman in C. P. Snow. They calculate that if the arms race continues, while more nations join the nuclear club, the probability of war approaches 100 per cent. Said Snow, in 1961, in a statement quoted around the world:

> Within at the most ten years, some of these bombs are going off. I am saying this as responsibly as I can. That is a certainty. On the one side, therefore, we have a finite risk [in negotiated agreements]. On the other side we have a certainty of disaster. Between a risk and a certainty a sane man does not hesitate.

General Douglas MacArthur was also speaking responsibly when he told the Philippine Assembly in 1961 that war in the nuclear age had lost its meaning. It could settle nothing. "If you lose you are annihilated. If you win, you stand only to lose. . . . It contains now only the germs of double suicide."

There is an ironic corollary to the general's statement. However mighty a nation's military power today, it cannot use that power without inviting its own destruction. Proposed agreements to employ only conventional weapons disregard two vital points: First, there is no referee to enforce such agreements; second, in battle, war psychology takes over. We hardly need expert testimony to assure us that the battle will escalate to nuclear weapons, especially if the possessor of them faces defeat. In September, 1962, Secretary of Defense McNamara threatened to use nuclear weapons if superior Russian tanks and artillery were to drive us out of Berlin.

Military experts can discuss "first strike," "second strike," and "counter-strike-with-bonus"; but beyond these semantic exercises, it is obvious to the careful inquirer that both the U.S. and the USSR are now equipped to eliminate each other as viable societies by exploding a few large hydrogen bombs high in the stratosphere, generating firestorms of meteorological dimensions. These can incinerate every combustible object, natural or man-made, over vast areas, including occupants of all but the deepest oxygen-equipped shelters.

A point seldom mentioned about such an attack, but one that interests me as an economist, is the destruction of the records essential to a civilization—title deeds, mortgages, contracts, bank ledgers, accounts receivable, loans, bonds, notes, and securities. The loss of legal titles alone might be more serious than the loss of power grids. "It takes fewer megatons," says Gerald Piel, "to kill the corporate body of the state than to destroy the forces that are supposed to defend it."

Unimaginative people will dream on, taking refuge in what psychologists call "denial," and hoping for the best. People with reflective minds know that when the button is pushed, accidentally or otherwise, the country they love will, in a matter of minutes, cease to exist as a going concern. The fact that the enemy also ceases to exist is scant consolation. Our freedoms will be buried in the same trench with his tyrannies.

Reflective citizens are as sure of this as they are of $E=mc^2$, the equation upon which the nuclear age is founded. Yet they hesitate to move in the circumstances, while their political leaders act as if a twenty-megaton bomb were on a par with a Sherman tank. Are we mad, then, leaders and citizens together? Yes, we are mad in a cosmic sense, but sane enough in terms of cultural lag. Our leaders are playing power politics in the formal patterns appropriate to pre-nuclear times. They engage in a spirited arms race, exchange picturesque insults, rattle rockets as if they were sabers, refuse to trust their rivals in any military agreement, announce that their only concern is national security, which, they insist, is tantamount to the well-being of mankind, and assure us that they can protect their nation's security.

In the light of thermonuclear weapons, now poised in their silos, all this is preposterous and nonsense, and will be so regarded by the historians of 1980—if there are any historians in 1980. But in the light of traditional power politics it is business as usual, in direct line from Napoleon and Metternich through Disraeli to Kaiser Wilhelm II.

Sometimes one wonders if the cultural lag can be corrected, in the ten years that Snow gives us, without a violent physical lesson. Remember, for instance, how unemployment dragged on through the 1930s because of cultural lag in fiscal traditions. We did not dare release enough purchasing power to put idle men to work. The violence at Pearl Harbor ended this mental block. The country awoke to the realization that a great nation can afford anything it can produce. Congress appropriated the money and within a few months there was a labor shortage. The bankruptcy so freely predicted in the earlier period never came.

Suppose a big plane on a practice flight dropped a large hydrogen bomb by accident while flying over the unpopulated part of the Florida Everglades. Suppose its safety devices failed and it exploded at ground zero. No serious firestorm was generated, but rather a huge, volcanic chasm, miles in diameter and hundreds of feet deep.

Suppose, when geiger counters declared the area free of radiation, Congress went down in a body to view the holocaust. With it came top Administrative officials and the staffs of all the embassies. Hundreds of thousands of motorists meanwhile took a guided tour along the Tamiami Trail. Suppose these viewers were emotionally gripped by the horror of the wounded earth, and, by means of television, Telstar, and the press, the effect reached every person with a spark of imagination, here and abroad. If this is what one bomb can do, what would fifty do?

Would such a lesson help to free us from the bondage to the past? One must leave the question to the social psychologists.

Babies

In 1961 I attended a cultural exchange conference in the Crimea, where American writers, scientists, and artists met with their Russian counterparts. When the American delegation raised the population question, the Russians denied there was such a problem—obviously following the party line. The Malthusian idea that population tends to outrun subsistence was, they said, "completely unacceptable." (The MacArthur point about mutual suicide, on the contrary, was quite acceptable.) The reason seems to be that Russia lost 20,000,000 dead in World War II, most of them potential fathers. The birth rate was cut way back. There is no population explosion now behind the Iron Curtain, and there will be none for some years to come. (There is none in Western Europe either.) Unfortunately, we cannot say the same for Asia, Africa, or Latin America. The Russians will soon begin to feel its impact, as they try to underwrite ex-colonial countries where people increase faster than food.

Population in the emerging nations is now growing at the rate of almost 3 per cent a year. For every 1,000 persons in January, there will be 1,030 next January. In twenty-three years there will be 2,000 persons; population will have doubled. The hungry world is characterized by a per capita income of $100 or less per year, and an illiteracy rate of 50 per cent or more. It comprises two-thirds of humanity, and is growing twice as fast as the affluent one-third. The U.S. rate is higher than that of Europe, but far below that of Latin America, Asia, and Africa.

The Population Reference Bureau cites the island of Mauritius in the Indian Ocean as "a symbol and a warning." Its population in 1946 was 428,000, on an area about half the size of Long Island. Then modern science arrived, with DDT to control malaria, and other public health measures. In five years the death rate fell from thirty-six per 1,000 to fourteen, while the birth rate rose a little. By 1961 there were 656,000 people on the island, a 50 per cent increase in fifteen years, due almost entirely to excess of births over deaths. If this continues Mauritius will be swamped by 2,000,000 persons by the end of the century, and the island "reduced to indescribable misery."

A similar crisis is developing all over the underdeveloped areas, says the Bureau. High birth rates combine with falling death rates "to produce such a rapid rise that efforts to improve conditions are completely thwarted." There are now more poor people, more illiterate people, and more unskilled people on the planet than ever before, and year by year their numbers climb.

More food can certainly be grown or synthesized, but this demands huge blocks of capital for dams, irrigation systems, erosion control, fertilizer and chemical plants, tractors, agricultural schools. If the food supply can be increased by 1 per cent a year—an optimistic estimate—and population continues at 3 per cent, sooner or later the time-honored adjusters may be expected to move in—mass famine, infant mortality, new varieties of contagion, perhaps exposure of the aged.

There appears to be only one reasonable answer—the control of the birth rate to a point where people expand no faster than subsistence. Japan has shown the way, reducing her birth rate from thirty-four per 1,000 to eighteen in recent years. Population, which threatened to overwhelm the islands, is now growing at 1 per cent a year, and Japan expects an actual labor shortage in the 1970s. Demographers calculate that to maintain a stationary population, the birth rate and the death rate must balance at about fourteen per 1,000.

In introducing the Alliance for Progress, President Kennedy warned that South America's population explosion imposed a limit on economic development. Since then, however, a curtain has fallen. Says D. S. Greenberg in *Sciences:*

> It appears that the administration has no inclination to incur the enormous political hazards involved in promoting birth control. The field is left to a few American foundations, which, with limited resources, have been assisting the Indian and Pakistan governments; and to Sweden, which appears likely to become the most significant force for attempting to reverse the population explosion.

The United States Government seems to suffer from a cultural lag in this department almost as severe as that in the military establishment.

Bulldozers

The more goods we have the more goods and services we seem to need to offset the complexities of affluence. Consider the motor car. It cannot operate in quantity without remaking both the landscape and the institutions of the society which accepts it. The United States and Canada have been subjugated; Europe is on the way. Russian planners told me in Moscow that they do not propose to be overwhelmed—little do they know! Accessory services include oil fields, refineries, superhighways, vast plains of black-top, motels, garages, filling stations, traffic police, signal systems, huge industrial establishments, and fleets of ambulances.

A collateral paradox is that the faster technology permits us to go at one point, the slower we often go at another. Surging chariots, capable of 120 miles an hour, crawl along at two miles an hour in traffic jams. It often takes longer to taxi from Times Square to a New York airport than to fly from the airport to Washington.

The bulldozer shears off the sides of mountains to blast a path for a six-lane highway, and shatters woodland and meadow for a 500-lot subdivision. It is not responsible, of course, for all our environmental lesions, but for enough to serve as a symbol. It also looks the part of a devouring monster from the Silurian age. The plow, drawn by its brother the tractor, uproots the native cover of the plains and promotes deserts. Its small brother, the outboard motor, increasingly jams the waterways.

Bulldozers are the chief architects of a condition which students of regional planning are coming to call "spread-city." A typical pattern shows lots for single dwellings, interspersed with scattered factories, stores, shopping centers, parking lots, tied together with a network of freeways. Little natural open space remains; brooks go underground.

California Tomorrow, a conservation agency, labels this pattern "slurbs—our sloppy, sleezy, slovenly, slipshod semicities." Slurbs convert good cropland into a dismal mixture of used-car lots, pizza parlors, drive-in movies, and trailer parks, scattered helter-skelter on a wallpaper background of subdivisions. Over it all rises an ever-thickening blanket of smog.

Business in the core city is declining while its residents slip down the income scale. The unskilled, the less educated, the high school dropouts remain, while the middle class moves outward to find space for children, only perhaps to encounter a black-top wasteland. Working hours at office and shop have declined, but not when measured from portal to portal, as the breadwinner creeps along the freeway in a cloud of carbon monoxide.

Spread-city, now standard in the United States and expanding in Europe, tends to be a rootless place, lacking community life and offering forms of discomfort and dislocation hitherto unknown, with juvenile delinquency as an alarming symptom. It is the creation of the internal combustion engine, which proceeds on a life of its own, leaving human beings increasingly out of place amid its fumes and disorder. Technical details are often excellent—sports cars, cabin cruisers, refrigerators, washing machines, bathrooms, Dorado Beach, a concert hall and art museum here, a research laboratory there; but the over-all structure is chaotic. With nearly twice our present population due by the end of the century, spread-city does not bear thinking of.

We live in a thin lamination on the surface of our small planet, between an ocean of air above, and the rocky crust beneath. Up in a rocket it grows steadily colder, down in a mine it grows steadily hotter. The air must be pure if we are able to breathe; the soil must be arable if we are to eat; the water must be clean if we are to drink. Two-thirds of the globe is covered with salt water, while polar ice, tundra, mountains, swamps, deserts, and rain forest reduce living space to not more than one-eighth of the globe's surface.

Light, air, water, soil, plants, animals, man are linked in an ecological unity. Any damage to one has immediate and serious repercussions on the others. Man has created deserts by overgrazing in the past, but these are minor compared to the massed assaults on living space now in process. Not only spread-city, but pollution of air and water, stripmining, dust storms, the effects of pesticides as argued by Rachel Carson, fallout, sonic boom, radioactive wastes from atomic power plants dumped into rivers and the sea, the disruption of the Van Allen belt by nuclear explosions in outer space—all are hacking away at our thin lamination.

"Man," says Raymond Bouillenne, writing in *Science*, "is reluctant to accept his place in nature." Indeed, he often seems determined to wreck that balance of nature in which he lives and has his being.

James Thurber in one of his fables describes a conference of ostriches, depressed because they cannot fly. One, named Oliver, complains that men can fly sitting down while ostriches cannot fly at all. "The old ostrich looked at Oliver severely, first with one eye, then with the other. 'Man is flying too fast for a world that is round,' he said. 'Soon he will catch up with himself in a great rear-end collision, and Man will never know that what hit Man from behind was Man.'"

There is of course no entity "man"—just men and women, grouped in the normal frequency distribution curve, with geniuses at one end and dullards at the other. Somewhere in between is a group with intelligence and imagination in every country who are becoming aware of what "man" must do if he is to avoid that rear-end collision.

Absolute sovereignty must be abandoned, the arms race reversed, institutions for the peaceful settlement of national disputes set up. The rate of population increase must be kept in phase with the food supply. Living space must be defended for living. Above the normal run of problems in the headlines tower these three. Applied science created them all, and a combined scientific and humane effort could solve them. But, as the clock on the *Bulletin of the Atomic Scientists* indicates each month, it is close to high noon.

Correlation of This Book with Representative Texts

	JAMES A Geography of Man, 3d ed. Blaisdell, 1966	KENDALL, GLENDINNING, AND MAC FADDEN Introduction to Geography, 2d ed. Harcourt, Brace, & World, 1962	MURPHEY An Introduction to Geography 2d ed. Rand McNally, 1966
Text chs.	Related Selections in *Cultural Geography*		
1	5-8	1-4	1, 2, 6
2	1-5, 23-31		10, 11, 28, 29, 33
3	7, 12, 22, 25		5-8
4	13	36	15, 17, 37, 38, 39
5			
6	19		
7	14, 35, 31	27, 30	5, 7, 8
8	25		
9	10		
10		7, 12, 22	
11	27	25	23, 24, 30
12	9-16, 37-39		16, 33
13		5-8	
14		37-39	
15		9	10
16		10-16	
17		7, 12, 13, 26	
18			
19		36	35
20		24, 30	
21			19
22			
23		23, 30	37
24		31	
25		17-22, 40	
26			
27			16, 30
28			
29			
30			7, 12, 22, 25
31			12, 22, 25
32			31
33			
34			17
35			
36			14, 15, 21, 27, 38

	PHILBRICK *This Human World* Wiley, 1963	TREWARTHA, ROBINSON, AND HAMMOND *Elements of Geography: Physical and Cultural* 5th ed. McGraw-Hill, 1967
Text chs.	Related Selections in *Cultural Geography*	
1	*1-4, 37*	
2	*9, 11, 28*	
3		
4	*5-8*	
5	*21, 22, 37-39*	
6		
7	*23, 24*	*13, 17, 30, 37*
8	*33*	*7, 12, 22, 25*
9	*10, 23, 33, 35*	*19*
10	*31*	*14, 30*
11	*17, 24*	
12		
13	*14, 15, 21*	
14	*14, 38*	
15	*12, 22*	*25*
16	*37*	*27*
17	*25, 30*	*38*
18		
19		*36*
20	*32-36*	*5, 7, 8*
21		
22		
23		
24		*23, 24*
25		*9-16, 28, 40*
26		*9-16, 28, 40*
27		*7, 13, 19, 25, 26*
28		*23, 24, 27, 29, 30*
29		*31*
30		
31		
32		
33		
34		
35		
36